Blackboard Systems

The Insight Series in Artificial Intelligence

Series Editor: Tony Morgan, Systems Designers plc.

Associate Editor: Bob Muller, Digital Equipment Corporation.

The series derives its name from the Insight study group sponsored by Systems Designers plc, whose workshops, conferences and study visits promoted international collaboration between companies and other institutions toward the common goal of applying advanced AI technology.

Other titles in the series:

Management Expert Systems, *edited by C.J. Ernst*

Blackboard Systems

Edited by
Robert Engelmore
Stanford University

Tony Morgan
Systems Designers plc

 ADDISON-WESLEY PUBLISHING COMPANY
Wokingham, England · Reading, Massachusetts · Menlo Park, California
New York · Don Mills, Ontario · Amsterdam · Bonn · Sydney
Singapore · Tokyo · Madrid · San Juan

The programs presented in this book have been included for their instructional value. They have been tested with care but are not guaranteed for any particular purpose. The publisher does not offer any warranties or representations, nor does it accept any liabilities with respect to the programs.

Many of the designations used by manufacturers and sellers to distinguish their products are claimed as trademarks. Addison-Wesley has made every attempt to supply trademark information about manufacturers and their products mentioned in this book. A list of the trademark designations and their owners appears on p. xviii.

Jacket designed by John Gibbs (from plates taken from Chapter 8 of this book) and printed by The Riverside Printing Co. (Reading) Ltd.
Text design by Lesley Stewart.
Typeset by Columns, Reading.
Printed in Great Britain by T.J. Press (Padstow), Cornwall.

First printed 1988.

British Library Cataloguing in Publication Data
Blackboard systems.—(Insight series in
   artificial intelligence).
   1. Computer systems. Programs. Blackboard
systems
   I. Engelmore, R.S. (Robert S.)   II. Morgan,
A.J. (Antony J.)   III. Series
004.1'25

   ISBN 0–201–17431–6

Library of Congress Cataloging in Publication Data
Blackboard systems.

   (The Insight series in artificial intelligence)
   Bibliography: p.
   Includes index.
   1. Blackboard systems (Computer programs)
   2. Artificial intelligence—Computer programs.
   3. Problem solving—Computer programs.   I. Engelmore,
R.S. (Robert S.)   II. Morgan, A.J. (Antony J.)
III. Series.
   Q336.B42   1988   006.3'3   88–16764
   ISBN 0–201–17431–6

Foreword

The science of artificial intelligence has provided its system builders with only a small number of different frameworks for building the reasoning subsystem – the 'inference engine'. Of these, only a few have achieved any practical use, and among these the obvious chaining methods (as old as the ancient Greeks) predominate. In designing the system, the builder decides whether to commit to forward chaining or backward chaining. This is a strong commitment since the chaining procedures are largely black boxes. Their behaviour, step by step as the line of reasoning unfolds, is not easily modifiable. Back chainers will back-chain; forward chainers will forward-chain. But the challenge of real problems may require more flexibility than this. To provide this flexibility and other advantages (discussed below), the blackboard framework was invented.

In my opinion, for building expert systems, the blackboard framework is the most general and flexible knowledge system architecture.

- Using this framework, many and varied sources of knowledge can participate in forming and modifying the emerging solution or hypothesis.

- Each knowledge source can contribute opportunistically since each has continual access to the current state of the solution. Thus the right knowledge can be applied at the right time.

- As steps are taken toward the solution, the processing commitments are minimized since the solution is built incrementally, piece by piece, as knowledge sources are activated.

- Steps of forward chaining can be arbitrarily interleaved with steps of backward chaining. And in contrast with most generate-and-test procedures, a complete test solution does not have to be built before making a decision to modify or abandon it.　　v

In the blackboard model, the knowledge sources and the solution space are usually structured hierarchically, as they would be in a human expert. This factoring of the space into predefined conceptual classes is a powerful engineering tool, for a reason that is often overlooked. The language of each individual knowledge source can be specialized to the language of the conceptual objects at its input and output levels. In earlier systems, such as DENDRAL, the many sources of knowledge had to use the same conceptual language. Indeed, to bring this about was one of the major knowledge engineering feats of the DENDRAL project. The emerging solution was a chemical graph and all the knowledge sources had to speak the language of chemical subgraphs. With the blackboard model, such engineering feats are no longer necessary.

Knowledge system building in a blackboard framework is simplified, because global effects of applying knowledge are minimized to highly structured and disciplined changes to the current best hypothesis. Otherwise, the knowledge sources are autonomous – each is an expert system in its own right.

The blackboard framework introduces some dimensions of expert system programming techniques that are difficult to achieve in other frameworks:

Dynamic control   At each step in the formation of the solution, a decision can be made as to how best to make inferences related to that step. Is there some interesting/important new data? Then a little data-directed forward chaining is called for. Has some concept at one of the higher levels of abstraction just been inferred? Then perhaps some model-based reasoning is called for to generate expectations for the lower levels. Or perhaps, at times when certain key events have occurred, some numeric computation is necessary. In the blackboard framework, *incremental* formation of the solution is the norm. The method for taking the incremental step can be decided anew at each step.

Focus of attention   Similarly, there is no rigidity with respect to what part of the emerging solution should be attended to next; for example, whether attention should go to an element at a low level of abstraction or at a high conceptual level. It all depends on the current state of the problem solving process. This is in stark contrast to the data reduction pipelines of the traditional engineering approach, where the flow is entirely from data to hypothesis, with no feedback. In the blackboard model the bidirectionality is part of the basic idea.

Flexibility of programming the control   If one has a great deal of knowledge about how human experts apply varied sources of knowledge in one's domain, then this knowledge can be codified either in control rules (fairly simple to do), or in complex control regimes. BB1 even uses a separate blackboard to solve the problem of 'what next?'

Island driving   Because the entire current best hypothesis is visible to the knowledge source, a particularly interesting and effective 'what next?' strategy is readily available. If some pieces of the solution/hypothesis seem to be complete, or well-developed with a high degree of certainty, these pieces can be treated as well-formed 'islands'. The strategy then focuses attention on building inferential 'bridges' between these islands. The emergence of islands redefines the solution space. Islands aggregate smaller solution elements; there are fewer islands than solution elements. In addition, island driving focuses problem solving attention on important tasks, namely those reasoning steps that will link the islands together into a larger solution.

The use of multiple, independent sources of knowledge raises the possibility of exploiting parallel programming techniques. The knowledge engineering activity in building blackboard systems is an activity of 'dividing things up': knowledge into knowledge sources, a knowledge source into rules or frames, solution objects into levels of abstraction, each level into solution elements at that level, and so on. The various entities created by the 'dividing up' can operate relatively autonomously, for example the knowledge sources operating on their respective levels of abstraction, or the rules of a knowledge source operating independently, or the solution elements on the blackboard (i.e. the nodes) independently activating knowledge relevant to them. The latter, which is the contribution of the POLIGON system, is particularly novel and interesting.

Thus the opportunity for parallel processing is considerable. The problem of distributing the computation and the problem of expressing the intrinsic parallelism are both problems that are under serious study right now. The amount of control knowledge that is optimal for solution formation in parallel implementations is a serious and difficult question. Too much control 'serializes' the computation excessively; too little control usually leads to very inefficient and ineffective problem solving.

Knowledge assembly

AI students in their first course are often indoctrinated with the view that 'problem solving is search'. This was indeed the founding paradigm of the AI science. As a consequence of the knowledge-is-power hypothesis (which I have recently been calling the Knowledge Principle), they are also taught that 'knowledge prunes and directs search'.

Though search methods can be used with the blackboard framework, the usual solution formation seen in blackboard systems is *not* best viewed as 'search for solutions'. The activity is best viewed as 'knowledge assembly' – finding the right piece of knowledge to build into the right place in the emerging solution structure.

An interesting analogy is the construction of a building. It is pieced together by expert crafts-specialists, such as carpenters, plumbers, and electricians. Their activity is guided 'from above' by specialists such as kitchen-designers, elevator-designers, and bathroom designers. At other levels, there are floor-designers, and supervising architects. With each specialist contributing at his own level, the building – the 'metaphorical solution' – is assembled.

The power and utility of the blackboard model for problem solving is only just beginning to be appreciated outside the walls of academic research. That may be due in part to a lack of conveniently available literature on the subject. The editors of this book have performed a valuable service to the community at large by selecting and assembling this collection of historically as well as technically important articles on blackboard systems.

Edward A. Feigenbaum
Stanford University
Stanford, California, USA

Preface

The subject of this book was originally due to a side-effect in the history of artificial intelligence. In the early 1970s, the United States Department of Defense launched a national effort to produce a computer system that could understand natural speech. The speech-understanding program met its limited goals after five years, and gave a major push to the technology of speech and language understanding. But there was a spinoff from that effort that may well turn out to have an ever more important impact on the course of technology. That spinoff was the blackboard model of problem solving. As we hope to illustrate in this book, the blackboard model is a very simple yet powerful idea for coping with problems characterized by the need to deal with uncertain data, make use of uncertain knowledge, and apply a non-deterministic solution strategy. The generality of the model has since been demonstrated many times over in the domains of signal understanding, vision, planning, protein structure determination, and data fusion to name a few. Moreover, the model has been used as the basis for exploring the areas of distributed and parallel problem solving. Examples of blackboard systems in all of these domains can be found in the later chapters of the book.

In assembling this book, we had several objectives in mind. One is to explain the meaning of the term 'blackboard system', as well as related terms such as 'blackboard model', 'blackboard framework', and 'blackboard shell'. A second objective is to provide a historical perspective of blackboard systems by tracing the development of the key ideas. A third is to identify and evaluate the contributions made by different systems. Fourth, to illustrate by example, the range of blackboard applications and implementations. Fifth, to collect, in one volume, what we believe to be the most important papers in the field, including some that are no longer easily available and others that have not appeared before. Finally, by carrying out this task, we hope to provide a snapshot of the current state of the art (as of late 1987). It is not our objective to explain in detail how one implements a blackboard system; that is an appropriate subject for a separate treatise. We intend this volume to be a source book of ideas for system designers as well as a reference work for teachers and graduate students in computer science or engineering.

Organization of the book

Parts I through V contain 28 chapters on various blackboard systems, organized according to the evolutionary development shown in Figure 1.8. After Hearsay-II, chronicled in Part I, there were a number of 'early' applications, the most significant of which are described in Part II. Many of the applications inspired the design and implementation of the first generation of blackboard frameworks, which are covered in Part III. The frameworks facilitated the development of another wave of applications, presented in Part IV, which in turn have pointed to the need for more advanced programming environments, such as those reported in Part V. The contents of the five parts, as well as the chapters themselves, are only roughly chronologically ordered, as each development phase has a large overlap with its neighbors, particularly in the last decade. Finally, in Chapter 30, we attempt to summarize what we've learned about blackboard systems, and to indicate directions for further research.

In the first section of each of the five parts we give an overview of the systems discussed therein, plus some pointers to other relevant papers and/or systems. In some cases, the papers presented are edited versions of the originals or may even be composed from more than one paper by the same authors. Our guidelines in making such ligations and excisions were to avoid unnecessary exposition given the context of the book as a whole (for example, we didn't feel it was necessary to include every author's definition of a blackboard system), to keep the discussion of the application domains down to a reasonable length, to keep the scope of the chapters within reasonable boundaries, and to try to keep the narrative as clear as possible within the constraints of editorial time and publication space. Where chapters have been amended, we have so indicated in the introductory sections.

We are especially pleased that some papers were written (or rewritten) specifically for this book; in particular, Chapters 7, 14, 15, 16, 22, 27 and 29, and we thank the respective authors for their considerable efforts.

Acknowledgments

The completion of this book took considerably longer than we first estimated (we started in the Autumn of 1985), and we would still be working on it if it were not for the considerable talents and generous amounts of time of many colleagues and friends. First and foremost we owe a great debt to Penny Nii, who wrote an excellent overview of blackboard systems for *AI Magazine* in 1986 and allowed us to borrow freely from that article, thus sparing us a lot of the work we would have had to do ourselves. Moreover, she provided much constructive criticism, and served both as a co-author with us for several of the introductory chapters and as a direct contributor of three articles (Chapters 6, 12 and 25). We are also indebted to Barbara Hayes-Roth, who contributed four articles (Chapters 10, 14, 20 and 29), two of which she kindly agreed to prepare specifically for this book. Other colleagues who supported and encouraged us by contributing new material were Dolores Byrne, Alan Garvey, Micheal Hewett, Vaughan Johnson, Bill Lakin, John Miles, Dave Reynolds, Anita Tailor, Allan Terry and Roberto Zancanato, and we thank them all for their special efforts. We had many helpful discussions with Harold Brown, who also prepared (with Penny Nii) an excellent tutorial on blackboard systems, from which we gained much useful information. Many thanks also to David Braunstein, who wrote an earlier overview of blackboard systems which contained an extensive bibliography that we could build upon. Finally, we thank Ellie Engelmore and Polly Rogers, who wrote many letters requesting copyright permissions, entered many chapters on-line, and tried their best to keep one of us organized and moving forward; Kath Ledger for her tireless pursuit of references; and Gwen Morgan for long-term support.

    Special thanks must go to Bob Muller, who was the start of it all.

October, 1987

R.S. Engelmore
Stanford University
Stanford, California, USA

A.J. Morgan
Systems Designers plc
Camberley, Surrey, UK

Publisher's Acknowledgments

We are indebted to the authors and publishers for giving their permission to reproduce their material. The individual credits are listed below, arranged in order of Chapter:

1. Nii, H.P. (1986) Blackboard Systems: The Blackboard Model of Problem Solving and the Evolution of Blackboard Architectures. *AI Magazine* **7** (2). Copyright American Association for Artificial Intelligence

3. Erman, L.D., Hayes-Roth, F., Lesser, V.R. and Reddy, D.R. (1980) The Hearsay-II Speech-Understanding System: Integrating Knowledge to Resolve Uncertainty. *ACM Computing Surveys* **12** (2), pp. 213–53. Copyright 1980, Association for Computing Machinery, Inc., reprinted by permission

4. Lesser, V.R. and Erman, L.D. (1977) A Retrospective View of the Hearsay-II Architecture. In *Proceedings of IJCAI–77*, pp. 790–800; and Erman, L.D. and Lesser, V.R. (1978) Hearsay-II: Tutorial Introduction and Retrospective View. Tech. report CMU–CS–78–117, Department of Computer Science, Carnegie-Mellon University; and (1986) The Hearsay-II System: A Tutorial. Speech Science Publications. Copyright Wayne A. Lea

6. Nii, H.P., Feigenbaum, E.A., Anton, J.J. and Rockmore, A.J. (1982) Signal-to-Symbol Transformation: HASP/SIAP Case Study. *AI Magazine* **3**, 23–35. Copyright American Association for Artificial Intelligence

7. Terry, A. (1985) Using Explicit Strategic Knowledge to Control Expert Systems

8. Draper, B.A., Collins, R.T., Brolio, J., Hanson, A.R. and Riseman, E.M. (1988). Issues in the Development of a Blackboard-Based Schema System for Image Understanding. *International Journal of Computer Vision* **2**. (Plates 1–3)

9. Nagao, M., Matsuyama, T. and Mori, H. (1979) Structural Analysis of Complex Aerial Photographs. In *Proceedings IJCAI–79*, pp. 610–16. Morgan Kaufmann Publishers

10. Hayes-Roth, B., Hayes-Roth, F., Rosenschein, S. and Cammarata, S. (1979) Modeling Planning as an Incremental, Opportunistic Process. In *Proceedings IJCAI–79*, pp. 375–83. Morgan Kaufmann Publishers

12. Nii, H.P. and Aiello, N. (1979) AGE (Attempt to GEneralize): a Knowledge-Based Program for Building Knowledge-Based Programs. In *Proceedings IJCAI-79*, pp. 645–55. Morgan Kaufmann Publishers

13. Erman, L.D., London, P.E. and Fickas, S.F. (1981) The Design and an Example Use of Hearsay-III. In *Proceedings IJCAI–81*, pp. 409–15. Morgan Kaufmann Publishers

14. Hayes-Roth, B. (1985) A Blackboard Architecture for Control. *Artificial Intelligence* **26** (3), pp. 251–321. North-Holland/Elsevier; and Hewett, M. and Hayes-Roth, B. (1987) The BB1 Architecture: a Software Engineering View. Tech. report KSL–87–10, Stanford University

15. Tailor, A. MXA – a Blackboard Expert System Shell. Copyright Systems Designers plc

16. Zanconato, R. BLOBS – an Object-Oriented Blackboard System Framework for Reasoning in Time. Copyright Cambridge Consultants Ltd

18. Lesser, V.R. and Corkhill, D.D. (1983) The Distributed Vehicle Monitoring Testbed: a Tool for Investigating Distributed Problem Solving Networks. *AI Magazine* **4**, (3), pp. 15–33. Copyright American Association for Artificial Intelligence

19. Williams, M.A. (1984) Hierarchical Multi-expert Signal Understanding. Tech. report ESL–IR201. ESL, Inc; and Nii, H.P. (1986) Blackboard Systems (Part 2). *AI Magazine*, **7** (3), pp. 82–106. Copyright American Association for Artificial Intelligence

20. Hayes-Roth, B., Buchanan, B., Lichtarge, O., Hewett, M., Altman, R., Brinkley, J., Cornelius, C., Duncan, B. and Jardetzky, O. (1985) PROTEAN: Deriving Protein Structure from Constraints. (Plates 8–9)

21. Pearson, G. Mission Planning within the Framework of the Blackboard Model. © 1985 IEEE. Reprinted, with permission, from *Expert Systems in Government Symposium*, edited by Kamal N. Karna

22. Lakin, W.L., Miles, J.A. and Byrne, C.D. Intelligent Data Fusion for Naval Command and Control. Copyright © Controller, HMSO, London, 1986. (Plates 4–7)

24. Ensor, J.R. and Gabbe, J.D. Transactional Blackboards. *The International Journal for Artificial Intelligence in Engineering*, **1** (2), pp. 80–84. Copyright 1986, Bell Telephone Laboratories, Inc., reprinted by permission

25. Nii, H.P. (1986) CAGE and POLIGON: two Frameworks for Blackboard-Based Concurrent Problem Solving. Tech. report KSL–86–41. Stanford University

26. Corkhill, D.D., Gallagher, K.Q. and Murray, K.E. (1986) GBB: a Generic Blackboard Development System. In *Proceedings AAAI–86*, pp. 1008–14. Morgan Kaufmann Publishers

27. Reynolds, D. MUSE: a Toolkit for Embedded, Real-time AI. Copyright Cambridge Consultants Ltd

28. Jones, J., Millington, M. and Ross, P. (1986) A Blackboard Shell in PROLOG. In *Proceedings ECAI–86*, pp. 428–36. Also in Du Boulay *et al.* (1987) *Advances in Artificial Intelligence II*. Elsevier/North-Holland

29. Hayes-Roth, B., Vaughan Johnson, M., Garvey, A. and Hewett, M. (1986) Application of the BB1 Blackboard Control Architecture to Arrangement Assembly Tasks. *The International Journal for Artificial Intelligence in Engineering*, **1** (2), pp. 85–94

Contents

Part III

Part IV

Part V

1

Introduction

R.S. Engelmore, A.J. Morgan and H.P. Nii

1.1 What are blackboard systems? Some definitions

The reader will note that different authors will give different meanings to various technical terms, an unfortunate but probably unavoidable phenomenon in a young and expanding line of research. Thus, terms such as blackboard system, blackboard model, blackboard architecture, blackboard framework, and blackboard shell have all been used in one way or another in the papers contained here. To maintain the confusion, one author's use of the term 'architecture' may be synonymous with another author's use of the term 'framework'. Since there is no agreement on definitions, we will adopt the following:

- A **blackboard system** is a generic term which covers applications and frameworks, as defined below.
- A **blackboard model** is a particular kind of problem-solving model, defined at some length in Section 1.2.
- A **blackboard framework** is either a specification of the components of a blackboard model or an implementation of the specification. Thus, AGE is an implementation of a particular set of choices within the blackboard model. (AGE is discussed in Chapter 12.) By adding domain knowledge (including knowledge about the problem-solving strategy to be used), a scientist/engineer/programmer can build a blackboard application. Frameworks are discussed further in Section 1.4.
- A **blackboard application** is a system that solves a particular kind of problem, such as speech understanding, mission planning, or the interpretation of a visual scene. Early applications were developed directly in some programming languages, such as LISP. In recent

times, however, it has become more common for a blackboard application to be developed on top of a blackboard framework.

- A **blackboard architecture** is another generic term which refers to the design of a blackboard system (or to part of a system, as in Hayes-Roth's term, 'blackboard architecture of control', in Chapter 14).

- A **blackboard shell** is synonymous with a blackboard framework.

For the purpose of this introduction we need only define blackboard systems at three levels of abstraction. The lowest level of abstraction is, of course, the blackboard application, i.e. a program that actually solves a real problem. Ten such applications are included in Parts I, II and IV of this book. The blackboard framework, of which the systems in Parts III and V are examples, represents an intermediate level of abstraction, and the blackboard model is the most abstract and general description.

The following two sections, which define the blackboard model and blackboard framework, are edited excerpts from Nii (1986b). The editors wish to express our thanks to Penny Nii for permission to edit and use her article (thereby sparing us considerable expository writing!).

1.2 The blackboard model

A problem-solving model is a scheme for organizing reasoning steps and domain knowledge to construct a solution to a problem. For example, in a backward-reasoning model, problem solving begins by reasoning backwards from a goal to be achieved towards an initial state (data). More specifically, in a rule-based backward-reasoning model, knowledge is organized as 'if–then' rules and modus ponens inference steps are applied to the rules from a goal rule back to an 'initial-state rule' (a rule that looks at the input data). An excellent example of this approach to problem solving is the MYCIN program (Shortliffe, 1976). In a forward-reasoning model, however, the inference steps are applied from an initial state toward a goal. The R1/XCON system exemplifies such a system (J. McDermott, 1982). In an opportunistic-reasoning model, pieces of knowledge are applied either backward or forward at the most 'opportune' time. Put another way, the central issue of problem solving deals with the question: What pieces of knowledge should be applied when and how? A problem-solving model provides a conceptual framework for organizing knowledge and a strategy for applying that knowledge.

The blackboard model is a relatively complex problem-solving model prescribing the organization of knowledge and data and the problem-solving behavior within the overall organization. Its character-

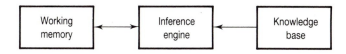

Figure 1.1 Example of the classical expert system structure.

istics can be best appreciated by contrasting it with more familiar computational models. The standard model of computation, for example, consists of a program acting upon a database. The program itself consists of a set of procedures and some control mechanism for ordering their application. The problem-solving knowledge is embedded in the procedures and the control structure. Most programs employing algorithmic methods use this standard model.

A second model is the 'classical' expert system structure, exemplified by MYCIN, and shown in Figure 1.1. The input to the system and the results of computations are kept in a working memory. The contents of the working memory are used by the inference engine in conjunction with knowledge in the knowledge base to infer new hypotheses that are placed in the working memory. The inference engine continues to access the working memory (read/write) and the knowledge base (read only) until a completion condition is detected. An important characteristic of this model is the separation of the knowledge from the inference engine (i.e. the program) which uses it. However, the model has two weaknesses:

(1)   The control of the application of the knowledge is implicit in the structure of the knowledge base, e.g. in the ordering of the rules for a rule-based system.

(2)   The representation of the knowledge is dependent on the nature of the inference engine (a rule interpreter, for example, can only work with knowledge expressed as rules).

We can view the blackboard model as a natural evolution which seeks to eliminate the inherent weaknesses of the classical expert system structure. First we segment the knowledge into modules (each module containing related entities) and provide a separate inference engine for each module. Now there is no requirement for the separate parts of the knowledge base to use the same representation method, nor for the separate inference engines to operate in the same way. The communication between the modules is now limited to reading and writing in the working memory; each module must read/write in a format acceptable to other modules. We can take the argument further, and subdivide the working memory so that it contains regions with differing data structures. What we have now defined is, essentially, a rudimentary blackboard

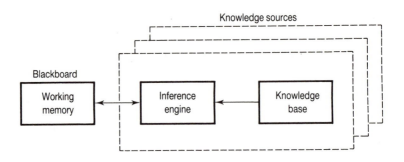

Figure 1.2   Example of a rudimentary blackboard model.

model, as summarized in Figure 1.2. The structured working memory is the blackboard; the modular inference engine/knowledge base pairs are the knowledge sources.

The blackboard model thus consists of two basic components as shown in Figure 1.3:

(1) *The knowledge sources*   The knowledge needed to solve the problem is partitioned into knowledge sources, which are kept separate and independent.

(2) *The blackboard data structure*   The problem-solving state data are kept in a global database, the blackboard. Knowledge sources produce changes to the blackboard which lead incrementally to a solution to the problem. Communication and interaction among the knowledge sources take place solely through the blackboard.

There is no control component specified in the blackboard model. The model merely specifies a general problem-solving behavior. The actual locus of control can be in the knowledge sources, on the blackboard, in a separate module, or in some combination of the three. The need for a control component in blackboard frameworks is discussed later.

The blackboard model of problem solving is a highly structured, special case of opportunistic problem solving. In addition to opportunistic reasoning as a knowledge-application strategy, the blackboard model prescribes the organization of the domain knowledge and all the input and intermediate and partial solutions needed to solve the problem. We refer to all possible partial and full solutions to a problem as its solution space.

In the blackboard model the solution space is organized into one or more application-dependent hierarchies. The hierarchy may be an abstraction hierarchy, a part-of hierarchy, or any other type of hierarchy appropriate for solving the problem. Information at each level in the hierarchy represents partial solutions and is associated with a unique

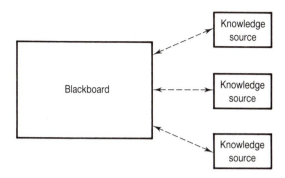

Figure 1.3 The blackboard model. There is a global database called the blackboard, and there are logically independent sources of knowledge called the knowledge sources. The knowledge sources respond to changes on the blackboard. Note that there is no control flow; the knowledge sources are self-activating. (---, data flow.)

vocabulary that describes the information. The domain knowledge is partitioned into independent modules of knowledge that transform information on one level, possibly using information at other levels, of the hierarchy into information on the same or other levels. The knowledge modules perform the transformation using algorithmic procedures or heuristic rules that generate actual or hypothetical transformations. Opportunistic reasoning is applied within this overall organization of the solution space and task-specific knowledge; that is, which module of knowledge to apply is determined dynamically, one step at a time, resulting in the incremental generation of partial solutions. The choice of a knowledge module is based on the solution state (particularly, the latest additions and modifications to the data structure containing pieces of the solution) and on the existence of knowledge modules capable of improving the current state of the solution. At each step of knowledge application, either forward- or backward-reasoning methods may be applied. There are various other ways of categorizing reasoning methods; for example, event driven, goal driven, model driven, expectation driven, and so forth. Without getting into the subtle differences between these methods, it is safe to say that any one of these methods can be applied at each step in the reasoning process.

The difficulty with this description of the blackboard model is that it only outlines the organizational principles. For those who want to build a blackboard system, the model does not specify how it is to be realized as a computational entity. That is, the blackboard model is a conceptual entity, not a computational specification. Given a problem to be solved, the blackboard model provides enough guidelines for sketching a solution, but a sketch is a long way from a working system. To design and

Figure 1.4   Solving jigsaw puzzles.

build a system, a detailed model is needed. Before moving on to adding details to the blackboard model, we explore the implied behavior of this abstract model.

Let us consider a hypothetical problem of a group of men trying to put together a jigsaw puzzle. Imagine a room with a large blackboard and around it a group of people each holding over-size jigsaw pieces. We start with volunteers who put on the blackboard (assume it's sticky) their most 'promising' pieces. Each member of the group looks at his pieces and sees if any of them fit into the pieces already on the blackboard. Those with the appropriate pieces go up to the blackboard and update the evolving solution. The new updates cause other pieces to fall into place, and other people go to the blackboard to add their pieces (see Figure 1.4). It does not matter whether one person holds more pieces than another. The whole puzzle can be solved in complete silence; that is, there need be no direct communication among the group. Each person is self-activating, knowing when his pieces will contribute to the solution. No *a priori* established order exists for people to go up to the blackboard. The apparent cooperative behavior is mediated by the state of the solution on the blackboard. If one watches the task being performed, the solution is built incrementally (one piece at a time) and opportunistically (as an opportunity for adding a piece arises), as opposed to starting, say, systematically from the left top corner and trying each piece.

This analogy illustrates quite well the blackboard problem-solving behavior implied in the model and is fine for a starter. Now, let's change the layout of the room in such a way that there is only one center aisle wide enough for one person to get through to the blackboard. Now, no more than one person can go up to the blackboard at one time, and a monitor is needed, someone who can see the group and can choose the order in which a person is to go up to the blackboard. The monitor can ask all people who have pieces to add to raise their hands. The monitor can then choose one person from those with their hands raised. To select one person, criteria for making the choice is needed; for example, the person who raises his hand first, the person with a piece that bridges two solution islands (that is, two clusters of completed pieces) and so forth. The monitor needs a strategy or a set of strategies for solving the puzzle. The monitor can choose a strategy before the puzzle solving begins or can develop strategies as the solution begins to unfold. In any case, it should be noted that the monitor has a broad executive power. The monitor has so much power that the monitor could, for example, force the puzzle to be solved systematically from left to right; that is, the monitor has the power to violate one essential characteristic of the original blackboard model, that of opportunistic problem solving.

The last analogy, though slightly removed from the original model, is a useful one for computer programmers interested in building blackboard systems. Given the serial nature of most current computers, the conceptual distance between the model and a running blackboard system is a bit far, and the mapping from the model to a system is prone to misinterpretation. By adding the constraint that solution building physically occur one step at a time in some order determined by the monitor (when multiple steps are possible and desirable), the blackboard model is brought closer to the realities inherent in serial computing environments. The serialization of the blackboard model is useful only because we tend to work on uniprocessor computers. There is considerable research interest in concurrent problem-solving methods. One starting point for this work is the pure blackboard model. One can see, at least conceptually, much parallelism inherent in the model. The problem is how to convert the model into an operational system that can take advantage of many (100s to 1000s) processor–memory pairs. Some of these issues are discussed in more detail in Part V (Chapters 24 and 25).

Although the elaborate analogy to jigsaw puzzle solving gives us additional clues to the nature of the behavior of blackboard systems, it is not a very good example for illustrating the organization of the blackboard or for the partitioning of appropriate knowledge into knowledge sources. To illustrate these aspects of the model, we need another example. This time let us consider another hypothetical problem, that of finding koalas in a eucalyptus forest (see Figure 1.5).

This koala problem has a long history. It was invented by Ed Feigenbaum (after a trip to Australia) and Penny Nii in 1974, during the time when they were not allowed to write about the HASP project (Chapter 6). The primary objective of this example was to illustrate the power of model-directed reasoning in interpreting noisy data. It is resurrected here as an example that does not require specialized domain knowledge.

Imagine yourself in Australia. One of the musts if you are a tourist

Figure 1.5   Finding koalas.

is to go and look for koalas in their natural habitat. So you go to a koala preserve and start looking for them among the branches of the eucalyptus trees. You find none. You know that they are rather small, grayish creatures that look like bears (more details at this descriptive level would be considered factual knowledge and can be used as a part of a prototypical model of koalas). The forest is dense, however, and the combination of rustling leaves and the sunlight reflecting on the leaves adds to the difficulty of finding these creatures, whose coloring is similar to that of their environment (in other words, the signal-to-noise ratio is low). You finally give up and ask a ranger how you can find them. He gives you the following story about koalas: 'Koalas usually live in groups and seasonally migrate to different parts of the forest, but they should be around the northwest area of the preserve now. They usually sit on the crook of branches and move up and down the tree during the day to get just the right amount of sun.' (This is knowledge about the prototypical behavior pattern of koalas. The ranger suggests a highly model-driven approach to finding them.) 'If you are not sure whether you have spotted one, watch it for a while; it will move around, though slowly.' (This is a method of detection as well as confirmation.) Armed with the new knowledge, you go back to the forest with a visual image of exactly where and what to look for. You focus your eyes at about 30 feet with no luck, but you try again, and this time focus your eyes at 50 feet, and suddenly you do find one. Not only one, but a whole colony of them.

Let's consider one way of formulating this problem along the lines of the blackboard model. Many kinds of knowledge can be brought to bear on the problem: the color and shape of koalas, the general color and texture of the environment (the noise characteristics), the behavior of the koalas, effects of season and time of the day, and so on. Some of the knowledge can be found in books, such as a *Handbook of Koala Sizes and Color* or *Geography of the Forest*. Some knowledge is informal – the most likely places to find koalas at any given time, or their favorite resting places. How can these diverse sources of knowledge be used effectively? First, we need to decide what constitutes a solution to the problem. Then we can consider what kinds of information are in the data, what can be inferred from them, and what knowledge might be brought to bear to achieve the goal of finding the koalas.

Think of the solution to this problem as a set of markings on a series of snapshots of the forest. The markings might say 'This is certainly a koala because it has a head, body and limbs, and because it has changed its position since the last snapshot'; or 'This might be a koala, because it has a blob that looks like a head'; or 'These might be koalas because they are close to the one we know is a koala and the blobs could be heads, legs or torsos'. The important characteristics of the solution are that the solution consists of bits and pieces of information, and it is a reasoned solution with supporting evidence and supporting lines of reasoning.

Having decided that the solution would consist of partial and hypothetical identifications, as well as complete identifications constructed from partial ones, we need a solution-space organization that can hold descriptions of bits and pieces of the koalas. One such descriptive framework is a part-of hierarchy. For each koala, the highest level of description is the koala itself, which is described on the next level by head and body; the head is described on the next level by ears, nose and eyes; the body is described by torso, legs and arms; and so on. At each level, there are descriptors appropriate for that level; size, gender and height on the koala level, for example. Each primitive body part is described on the lower levels in terms of geometric features, such as shapes and line segments. Each shape has color and texture associated with it as well as its geometric descriptions (see Figure 1.6). In order to identify a part of the snapshot as a koala, we need to mark the picture with line segments and regions. The regions and pieces of lines must eventually be combined, or synthesized, in such a way that the description of the constructed object can be construed as some of the parts of a koala or a koala itself. For example, a small, black circular blob could be an eye, but it must be surrounded by a bigger, lighter blob that might be a head. The more pieces of information one can find that fit the koala description, the more confident we can be. In addition to the body parts that support the existence of a koala, if the hypothesized koala is at about 30–50 feet above ground, we would be more confident than if we found the same object at 5 feet.

The knowledge needed to fill in the koala descriptions falls into place with the decision to organize the solution space as a part-of

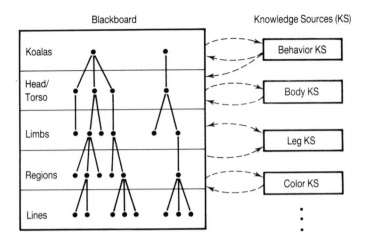

Figure 1.6   Koalas: blackboard structure and knowledge sources. The koalas in the scene are described as a part-of hierarchy. Specialist knowledge modules contribute information about what they 'see' to help in the search for koalas.

abstraction hierarchy. We would need a color specialist, a shape specialist, a body-part specialist, a habitat specialist, and so forth. No one source of knowledge can solve the problem; the solution to the problem depends on the combined contributions of many specialists. The knowledge held by these specialists is logically independent. Thus, a color specialist can determine the color of a region without knowing how the shape specialist determined the shape of the region. However, the solution of the problem is dependent on both of them. The torso specialist does not have to know whether the arm specialist checked if an arm had paws or not (the torso specialist probably doesn't even know about paws), but each specialist must rely on the other specialists to supply the information each needs. Cooperation is achieved by assuming that whatever information is needed is supplied by someone else.

The jigsaw puzzle and the koala problems illustrate the organization of information on the blackboard database, the partitioning of domain knowledge into specialized sources of knowledge, and some of the characteristic problem-solving behavior associated with the blackboard model. As in the jigsaw problem, the problem-solving behavior in the koala problem would be opportunistic. As new pieces of evidence are found and new hypotheses generated, appropriate knowledge sources analyze them and create new hypotheses. Neither of these examples, however, answers the questions of how the knowledge is to be represented, or of what the mechanisms are for determining and activating appropriate knowledge. As mentioned earlier, problem-solving models are conceptual frameworks for formulating solutions to problems.

The models do not address the details of designing and building operational systems. How a piece of knowledge is represented, as rules, objects or procedures, is an engineering decision. It involves such pragmatic considerations as 'naturalness', availability of a knowledge representation language, and the skill of the implementers, to name but a few. What control mechanisms are needed depends on the complexity and the nature of the application task. We can, however, attempt to narrow the gap between the model and operational systems. Now, the blackboard model is extended by adding more details to the three primary components in terms of their structures, functions and behaviors.

1.3 The blackboard framework

Applications are implemented with different combinations of knowledge representations, reasoning schemes and control mechanisms. The variability in the design of blackboard systems is due to many factors, the most influential being the nature of the application problem itself. It can be seen, however, that blackboard architectures that underlie application programs have many similar features and constructs. (Some of the better known applications are discussed in Parts II and IV.) The blackboard framework is created by abstracting these constructs. There is an implicit assumption that systems can be described at various levels of abstraction. Thus, the description of the framework is more detailed than the model and less detailed than a specification of an application. The blackboard framework, therefore, contains descriptions of the blackboard system components that are grounded in actual computational constructs. The purpose of the framework is to provide design guidelines appropriate for blackboard systems in a serial-computing environment. One can view the blackboard framework as a prescriptive model; that is, it prescribes what must be in a blackboard system. However, it must be kept in mind that application problems often demand extensions to the framework, as can be seen in the examples in later chapters. Figure 1.7 shows some modifications to Figure 1.3 to reflect the addition of system-oriented details.

The knowledge sources

The domain knowledge needed to solve a problem is partitioned into **knowledge sources** (KSs) that are kept separate and independent.

The objective of each knowledge source is to contribute information that will lead to a solution to the problem. A knowledge source takes a set of current information on the blackboard and updates it as encoded in its specialized knowledge.

The knowledge sources are represented as procedures, sets of rules,

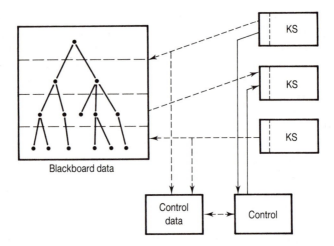

Figure 1.7 A blackboard framework. The data on the blackboard are hierarchically organized. The knowledge sources are logically independent, self-selecting modules. Only the knowledge sources are allowed to make changes to the blackboard. Based on the latest changes to the information on the blackboard, a control module selects and executes the next knowledge source (KS). (—, control flow; ---, data flow.)

or logic assertions. To date most of the knowledge sources have been represented as either procedures or as sets of rules. However, systems that deal with signal processing either make liberal use of procedures in their rules, or use both rule sets and procedurally encoded knowledge sources.

The knowledge sources modify only the blackboard or control data structures (that might also be on the blackboard), and only the knowledge sources modify the blackboard. All modifications to the solution state are explicit and visible.

Each knowledge source is responsible for knowing the conditions under which it can contribute to a solution. Each knowledge source has preconditions that indicate the condition on the blackboard that must exist before the body of the knowledge source is activated. One can view a knowledge source as a large rule. The major difference between a rule and a knowledge source is the grain size of the knowledge each holds. The condition part of this large rule is called the knowledge source precondition, and the action part is called the knowledge source body.

The blackboard data structure

The problem-solving state data are kept in a global database, the blackboard. Knowledge sources produce changes to the blackboard that lead incrementally to a solution, or a set of acceptable solutions, to the problem. Interaction among the knowledge sources takes place solely through changes on the blackboard.

The purpose of the blackboard is to hold computational and solution-state data needed by and produced by the knowledge sources. The knowledge sources use the blackboard data to interact with each other indirectly.

The blackboard consists of objects from the solution space. These objects can be input data, partial solutions, alternatives, and final solutions (and, possibly, control data).

The objects on the blackboard are hierarchically organized into levels of analysis. Information associated with objects (that is, their properties) on one level serves as input to a set of knowledge sources, which, in turn, place new information on the same or other levels.

The objects and their properties define the vocabulary of the solution space. The properties are represented as attribute–value pairs. Each level uses a distinct subset of the vocabulary. Many times, the names of the attributes on different levels are the same, for example 'type'. Often these are shorthand notations for 'type-of-x-object' or 'type-of-y-object'. Sometimes they are duplications of the same attribute for convenience sake.

The relationships between the objects are denoted by named links. The relationship can be between objects on different levels, such as 'part-of' or 'in-support-of', or between objects on the same level, such as 'next-to' or 'follows'.

The blackboard can have multiple blackboard panels; that is, a solution space can be partitioned into multiple hierarchies. This feature was first used in the CRYSALIS system discussed in Chapter 7.

Control

The knowledge sources respond opportunistically to changes on the blackboard. There is a set of control modules that monitor the changes on the blackboard and decide what actions to take next. Various kinds of information are made globally available to the control modules. The information can be on the blackboard or kept separately. The control information is used by the control modules to determine the focus of attention.

The focus of attention indicates the next thing to be processed. The focus of attention can be either the knowledge sources (that is, which knowledge sources to activate next) or the blackboard objects (i.e. which solution islands to pursue next), or a combination of both (i.e. which knowledge sources to apply to which objects). Any given system usually employs one of the three approaches, not all.

The solution is built one step at a time. Any type of reasoning step (data driven, goal driven, model driven, and so on) can be applied at each stage of solution formation. As a result, the sequence of knowledge source invocation is dynamic and opportunistic rather than fixed and preprogrammed.

Pieces of problem-solving activity occur in the following iterative sequence:

(1)   A knowledge source makes change(s) to blackboard object(s). As these changes are made, a record is kept in a data structure that holds the control information.

(2)   Each knowledge source indicates the contribution it can make to the new solution state. (This can be defined *a priori* for an application, or dynamically determined.)

(3)   Using the information from points 1 and 2, a control module selects a focus of attention.

(4)   Depending on the information contained in the focus of attention, an appropriate control module prepares it for execution as follows:

  (a)   If the focus of attention is a knowledge source, a blackboard object (or sometimes a set of blackboard objects) is chosen to serve as the context of its invocation (knowledge-scheduling approach).

  (b)   If the focus of attention is a blackboard object, a knowledge source is chosen which will process that object (event-scheduling approach).

  (c)   If the focus of attention is a knowledge source and an object, that knowledge source is ready for execution. The knowledge source is executed together with the context thus described.

Criteria are provided to determine when to terminate the process. Usually, one of the knowledge sources indicates when the problem-solving process is terminated, either because an acceptable solution has been found or because the system cannot continue further for lack of knowledge or data.

Problem-solving behavior and knowledge application

The problem-solving behavior of a system is determined by the knowledge-application strategy encoded in the control modules. The choice of the most appropriate knowledge-application strategy is dependent on the characteristics of the application task and on the quality and quantity of domain knowledge relevant to the task. It might be said that this is a hedge, that there should be a knowledge-application strategy or a set of strategies built into the framework to reflect different problem-solving behaviors. It is precisely this lack of doctrine that makes the blackboard framework powerful and useful. If an application task calls for two forward-reasoning steps followed by three backward-reasoning steps at some particular point, the framework allows for this. This is not to say that a system with built-in strategies cannot be designed and built. If there is a knowledge-application strategy 'generic' to a class of applications, it might be worthwhile to build this particular strategy into the framework. Basically, the acts of choosing a particular blackboard region and choosing a particular knowledge source to operate on that region determine the problem-solving behavior. Generally, a knowledge source uses information on one level as its input and produces output information on another level. Thus, if the input level of a particular knowledge source is on a level lower (closer to data) than its output level, then the application of this knowledge source is an application of bottom-up, forward reasoning.

Conversely, a commitment to a particular type of reasoning step is a commitment to a particular knowledge-application method. For example, if we are interested in applying a data-directed, forward-reasoning step, we would select a knowledge source whose input level is lower than its output level. If we are interested in goal-directed reasoning, we would select a knowledge source that put information needed to satisfy a goal on a lower level. Using the constructs in the control component one can make any type of reasoning step happen at each step of knowledge application. The control component of the framework is extensible in many directions. In the BB1 system, discussed in Chapter 14, the control problem is viewed as a planning problem. Knowledge sources are applied according to a problem-solving plan in effect. The creation of a problem-solving plan is treated as another problem to be solved using the blackboard approach.

How a piece of knowledge is stated often presupposes how it is to be used. Given a piece of knowledge about a relationship between information on two levels, that knowledge can be expressed in top-down or bottom-up application forms. These can further be refined. The top-down form can be written as a goal, an expectation, or as an abstract model of the lower-level information. For example, a piece of knowledge can be expressed as a conjunction of information on a lower level needed to generate a hypothesis at a higher level (a goal), or it can be expressed as information on a lower level needed to confirm a hypothesis at a higher level (an expectation), and so on. The framework does not presuppose nor does it prescribe the knowledge-application, or reasoning, methods. It merely provides constructs within which any reasoning methods can be used. Many interesting problem-solving behaviors have been implemented using these constructs; some of them are discussed in later chapters.

1.4 Some history

The rest of this book is organized along broadly chronological lines. Part I covers the original development of the blackboard concepts in the Hearsay-II project. In Part II we examine the early application systems that were triggered by Hearsay-II. Experience with early applications led to attempts to produce generalized systems, which are described in Part III. The more recent applications, covered in Part IV, were able to make use of the earlier tools and experiences to develop more complex systems. In Part V, we illustrate the extensions and refinements that typify the current state of development. Finally, in Chapter 30 we attempt to summarize the field and to draw some conclusions from the first ten years of blackboard systems.

In order to discuss the details of various blackboard systems, it is helpful to trace the intellectual history of the blackboard concepts. Aside from being interesting in itself, it explains the origins of ideas and reasons for some of the differences between blackboard system designs. The reasons often have no rational basis but have roots in the 'cultural' differences between the research laboratories that were involved in the early history of blackboard systems.

1.4.1 Early history (from Nii, 1986b)

The blackboard model (and, subsequently, the frameworks) discussed in this book arose from abstracting features from the Hearsay-II speech understanding system (see Part I). However, we can trace the basic blackboard concepts back to 1962, when Allen Newell wrote:

> Metaphorically we can think of a set of workers, all looking at the same blackboard: each is able to read everything that is on it, and to judge when he has something worthwhile to add to it. This conception is just that of Selfridge's Pandemonium (Selfridge, 1959): a set of demons, each independently looking at the total situation and shrieking in proportion to what they see that fits their natures. . . . [Newell, 1962]

The above quotation is the first reference to the term 'blackboard' in the AI literature. Newell was concerned with the organizational problems of programs that existed at the time (for example, checker-playing programs, chess-playing programs, theorem-proving programs), most of which were organized along a generate-and-test search model (Newell, 1969). (See Feigenbaum and Feldman (1963) for a collection of articles describing some of these programs.) The major difficulty in these programs was rigidity. Newell notes:

. . . a program can operate only in terms of what it knows. This knowledge can come from only two sources. It can come from assumptions [or] it can come from executing processes . . . either by direct modification of the data structure or by testing . . . but executing processes takes time and space [whereas] assumed information does not have to be stored or generated. Therefore the temptation in creating efficient programs is always to minimize the amount of generated information, and hence to maximize the amount of stipulated information. It is the latter that underlies most of the rigidities.

In one example, Newell discusses an organization to synthesize complex processes by means of sequential flow of control and hierarchically organized, closed subroutines. Even though this organization had many advantages (isolation of tasks, saving space by coding nearly identical tasks once, and so on), it also had difficulties. First, conventions required for communication among the subroutines often forced the subroutines to work with impoverished information. Second, the ordered subroutine calls fostered the need for doing things sequentially. Third, and most importantly, it encouraged programmers to think of the total program in terms of only one thing going on at a time. However, in problem solving there are often many possible things to be processed at any given time (for example, exploring various branches of a search tree), and relatively weak and scattered information is necessary to guide the exploration for a solution (for example, observations noticed while going down one branch of a search tree could be used when going down another branch). The primary difficulties with this organization, then, were inflexible control and restricted data accessibility. It is within this context that Newell notes that the difficulties 'might be alleviated by maintaining the isolation of routines, but allowing all the subroutines to make use of a common data structure'. He uses the blackboard metaphor to describe such a system.

The blackboard solution proposed by Newell eventually became the production system (Newell and Simon, 1972), which in turn led to the development of the OPS system (Forgy and McDermott, 1977). An overview of production systems is given in Davis and King (1977). In OPS, the 'subroutines' are represented as condition–action rules, and the data are globally available in the working memory. One of the many 'shrieking demons' (those rules whose 'condition sides' are satisfied) is selected through a conflict-resolution process. The conflict-resolution process emulates the selection of one of the loudest demons; for example, one that addresses the most specific situation. OPS does reflect the blackboard concept as stated by Newell and provides for flexibility of control and global accessibility to data. However, the blackboard systems as we know them today took a slightly more circuitous route before coming into being.

In a paper first published in 1966 (later published as Simon (1977)), Simon mentions the term blackboard in a slightly different context from Newell. The discussion is within the framework of an information processing theory about discovery and incubation of ideas:

> In the typical organization of a problem-solving program, the solution efforts are guided and controlled by a hierarchy or tree of goals and subgoals. Thus, the subject starts out with the goal of solving the original problem. In trying to reach this goal, he generates a subgoal. If the subgoal is achieved, he may then turn to the now-modified original goal. If difficulties arise in achieving the subgoal, sub-subgoals may be created to deal with them . . . we would specify that the goal tree be held in some kind of temporary memory, since it is a dynamic structure, whose function is to guide search, and it is not needed when the problem solution has been found. . . . In addition, the problem solver is noticing various features of the problem environment and is storing some of these in memory. . . . What use is made of [a feature] at the time it is noted depends on what subgoal is directing attention at that moment . . . over the longer run, this information influences the growth of the subgoal tree. . . . I will call the information about the task environment that is noticed in the course of problem solution and fixated in permanent (or relatively long-term) memory the 'blackboard' . . . .

Although Newell's and Simon's concerns appear within different contexts, the problem-solving method they were using was the goal-directed, generate-and-test search method. They encountered two common difficulties: the need for previously generated information during problem solving and for flexible control. It was Simon who proposed the blackboard ideas to Raj Reddy and Lee Erman for the Hearsay project. These historical notes are taken from personal communications between Herbert Simon and Penny Nii.

Although the blackboard metaphor was suggested by Simon to the Hearsay designers, the final design of the system, as might be expected, evolved out of the needs of the speech-understanding task. Such system characteristics as hierarchically organized analysis levels on the blackboard and opportunistic reasoning, which we now accept as integral parts of blackboard systems, were derived from needs and constraints that were different from Newell's and Simon's. One of the key notions attributable to the speech-understanding problem was the notion of the blackboard partitioned into analysis levels. This is a method of using and integrating different 'vocabularies', as mentioned earlier, in problem solving. In most problem-solving programs of the time, such as game-playing and theorem-proving programs, the problem space had a homogeneous vocabulary. In the speech-understanding problem, there was a need to integrate concepts and vocabularies used in describing grammars, words, phones, and so on.

There are two interesting observations to be made from early history. First, the early allusions to a blackboard are closely tied to search methodologies, and, not surprisingly, the use of generate-and-test search is evident in Hearsay-II. Second, although the Hearsay-II blackboard system was designed independently from the OPS system, there are, as we might expect, some conceptual similarities. For example, the scheduler in Hearsay-II is philosophically and functionally very similar to the conflict-resolution module in OPS, which, in turn, is a way of selecting one of the shrieking demons. Part I of this book contains a full description of Hearsay-II.

1.4.2 After Hearsay-II

Figure 1.8 summarizes the chronological development of ideas and systems since the Hearsay-II project. From the initial experimental work in the early 1970s, it is possible to identify several broadly chronological waves of development, although because of the differences in aims and resources between the different groups there is considerable overlap between waves. The blackboard model developed for Hearsay-II inspired other groups to adopt it for other applications such as signal interpretation (Chapter 6), three-dimensional molecular structure modeling (Chapter 7), image understanding (Chapters 8, 9) and planning (Chapter 10). Following the earlier applications, several workers recognized the need to abstract the essential features of the approach and produced generalizations such as AGE (Chapter 12), Hearsay-III (Chapter 13) and BB1 (Chapter 14).

Victor Lesser, one of the architects of Hearsay-II, and his colleagues at the University of Massachusetts continued to explore the blackboard model as a basis for cooperative, distributed problem solving. They used networks of blackboard systems that shared the results of their individual efforts to arrive at a globally consistent solution (Chapter 18).

An interesting follow-up to the Hearsay-II work was the PhD thesis by Donald McCracken (1979) in which he implemented 12 Hearsay-II knowledge sources in a pure production system architecture. Among other conclusions, McCracken noted the superiority of the blackboard architecture with respect to representing declarative knowledge and with respect to overall space and time efficiency.

Since 1980 the number of blackboard systems has proliferated significantly. In Great Britain, a company called SPL developed a signal understanding system (SUS) for the Admiralty Research Establishment using a blackboard architecture that was later generalized into the MXA framework (Chapter 15). The SUS and MXA designers were aware of the

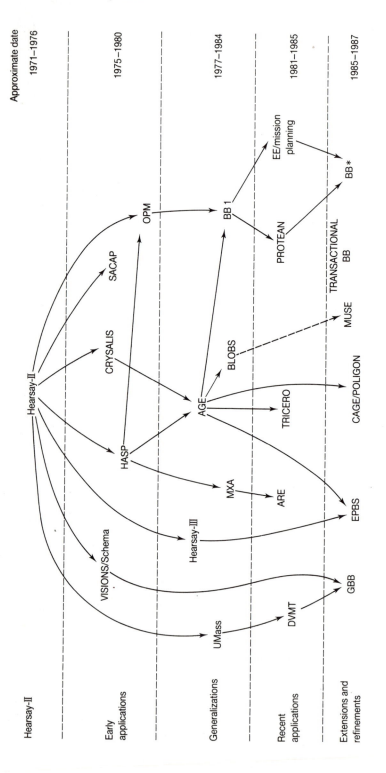

Figure 1.8   Evolution of blackboard systems.

related systems, HASP and AGE, although it was necessary to implement their system 'from scratch' due to lack of adequate documentation of the American systems. (This is a typical and valid complaint of all newcomers to the field.) A more recent incarnation of SUS is the system for data fusion reported in Chapter 22. The documentation of the AGE blackboard framework provided the basis for the development of at least two other frameworks: an object-oriented system called BLOBS (Chapter 16) and a PROLOG-based system developed at the University of Edinburgh (Chapter 28). The BLOBS system, which was concerned with the problem of reasoning about time-dependent data, influenced the development of a recent system caled MUSE (Chapter 27) for solving certain classes of real-time problems.

In Japan, Fujitsu has developed a commercial blackboard frame-work (one of the first to our knowledge), called ESHELL, which is based strongly on AGE. As of this writing, there has been nothing written in English about ESHELL, except for some promotional literature from Fujitsu. ESHELL provides two forms of knowledge representation (production rules and frames), a 'tailorable inference engine' (depth first, breadth first or user-defined best first sequencing of the knowledge sources), and utilities to represent and modify knowledge. The company has used ESHELL for several applications, including an expert system for diagnosing problems with stacker cranes used in automated warehouses, and an expert system for dispatching ships that carry raw materials to factories.

In the United States, three of the developers of Hearsay-II left Carnegie-Mellon University and pursued related work at other institutions. Victor Lesser moved to the University of Massachusetts where he devoted his efforts to distributed problem solving using the blackboard model. He and his colleagues, notably Daniel Corkill, developed a distributed blackboard application for monitoring moving vehicles (Chapter 18); and more recently have generalized the concepts learned in that project in a framework called GBB (Chapter 26).

The Hayes-Roths moved to the Rand Corporation where they jointly worked on the OPM planning system (Chapter 10). In 1982 Barbara Hayes-Roth joined the Heuristic Programming Project (HPP, later to be incorporated into the Knowledge Systems Laboratory) at Stanford and began development of BB1 (Chapter 14). The control architecture of BB1 is a development of the ideas first presented in OPM. Many of these ideas were further sharpened by applying the framework to several application areas, including protein structure determination (Chapter 20), mission planning (Chapter 21), and a civil engineering task of arranging objects at a construction site (discussed in Chapter 29). The applications spurred the further development of BB1 into a layered programming environment called BB* (Chapter 29).

The third Hearsay-II principal, Lee Erman, moved to the Information Science Institute (ISI) of the University of Southern California and started a project to generalize Hearsay-II into a framework, called Hearsay-III, that embodied and generalized the control concepts developed in the earlier speech-understanding system (Chapter 13). The name of the system is a misnomer: Hearsay-III is a blackboard framework and contains no specialized knowledge about speech understanding.

The AGE system (Chapter 12), developed by Nii *et al.* at the HPP, was distributed widely and several notable applications were developed on top of it. A particularly interesting one was TRICERO (Chapter 19), a multisensor data-fusion system using separate blackboard subsystems. Since 1985, Nii and co-workers have been investigating parallel problem solving using the blackboard model. Two frameworks have been developed with two radically different concepts of control: CAGE and POLIGON (Chapter 25). The extension of the blackboard architecture to a multiprocessor environment has also been investigated at Bell Laboratories (Chapter 24).

Part I

2

Hearsay-II

R.S. Engelmore, A.J. Morgan and H.P. Nii

In 1971, the Defense Advanced Research Projects Agency (DARPA) began an ambitious five-year experiment in speech understanding. The goals of the project were to provide recognition of utterances from a limited vocabulary in near-real time. Three organizations finally demonstrated systems at the conclusion of the project in 1976. These were Carnegie-Mellon University (CMU), who actually demonstrated two systems; Bolt, Beranek and Newman (BBN); and System Development Corporation with Stanford Research Institute (SDC/SRI). A review of progress in speech understanding at the end of the DARPA project is given in Reddy (1976).

The system that came closest to satisfying the original project goals was the CMU HARPY system. The relatively high performance of the HARPY system was largely achieved through 'hard-wiring' information about possible utterances into the system's knowledge base. Although HARPY made some interesting contributions, its dependence on extensive pre-knowledge limited the applicability of the approach to other signal-understanding tasks.

The other system developed at CMU was Hearsay-II. Although less successful than HARPY in pure performance terms, it included a number of novel ideas which were to prove fruitful in application to a variety of problems. In all, some 30–40 man-years were spent developing Hearsay-II (Davis, 1982) over a number of design iterations.

The first description of the Hearsay system appeared in Reddy et al. (1973a). The authors described the limitations of extant speech-recognition systems and proposed a model that would overcome the limitations. The system architecture, described presently, came to be known as the Hearsay-I architecture. To summarize, the article stated that, although the importance of context, syntax, semantics and phonological rules in the recognition of speech was accepted, no system had been built that incorporated these ill-defined sources of knowledge. At the same time, the authors' previous work indicated that:

(1)   the limitation of syntax-directed methods of parsing from left to right had to be overcome;

(2)   parsing should proceed both forward and backward from anchor points;

(3)   because of the lack of feedback in a simple part-of hierarchical structure, the magnitude of errors on the lower level propagated multiplicatively up the hierarchy; that is, minor errors in the signal level, for example, became major errors on the sentence level.

The organizational model of Hearsay-I addressed the following requirements:

(1)   the contribution of each source of knowledge (syntax, semantics, context, and so on) to the recognition of speech had to be measurable;

(2)   the absence of one or more knowledge sources should not have a crippling effect on the overall performance;

(3)   more knowledge sources should improve the performance;

(4)   the system must permit graceful error recovery;

(5)   changes in performance requirements, such as increased vocabulary size or modifications to the syntax or semantics, should not require major modifications to the model.

The functional diagram of the Hearsay-I architecture is shown in Figure 2.1, and its behavior is summarized as follows:

> The EAR module accepts speech input, extracts parameters, and performs some preliminary segmentation, feature extraction, and labeling, generating a 'partial symbolic utterance description'. The recognition overlord (ROVER) controls the recognition process and coordinates the hypothesis generation and verification phases of various cooperating parallel processes. The TASK provides the interface between the task being performed and the speech recognition and generation (SPEAK-EASY) parts of the system. The system overlord (SOL) provides the overall control for the system. [Reddy et al., 1973a]

From Figure 2.2, which illustrates the recognition process, one can glean the beginnings of an organization of a blackboard system. Note how the

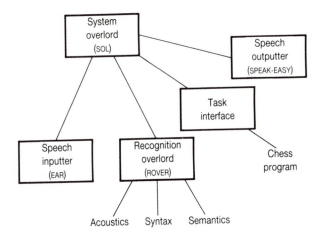

Figure 2.1   Overview of the Hearsay-I system (Reddy *et al.*, 1973a).

overlord (ROVER) controlled the invocation of activities. The beginnings of the scheduler as well as the knowledge sources are apparent as they became incorporated in Hearsay-II.

> Since the different recognizers are independent, the recognition overlord needs to synchronize the hypothesis generation and verification phases of various processes. . . . Several strategies are available for deciding which subset of the processes generates the hypotheses and which verify. At present, this is done by polling the processes to decide which process is most confident about generating the correct hypothesis. In voice chess (the task domain for Hearsay-I was chess moves), where the semantic source of knowledge is dominant, that module usually generates the hypotheses. These are then verified by the syntactic and acoustic recognizers. However, when robust acoustic cues are present in the incoming utterance, the roles are reversed with the acoustic recognizer generating the hypotheses. [Reddy *et al.*, 1973b]

Knowledge sources are activated in a lock-step sequence consisting of three phases: poll, hypothesize and test. During the polling phase, the overlord queries the knowledge sources to determine which ones have something to contribute to that region of the sentence hypothesis which is 'in focus' and with what level of 'confidence'. The poll portion of the poll, hypothesize and test sequence is also very characteristic of OPS and Hearsay-II. This construct takes on a totally different form in HASP and other subsequent systems, as we shall discuss later. In the hypothesizing phase, the most promising knowledge source is activated to make its

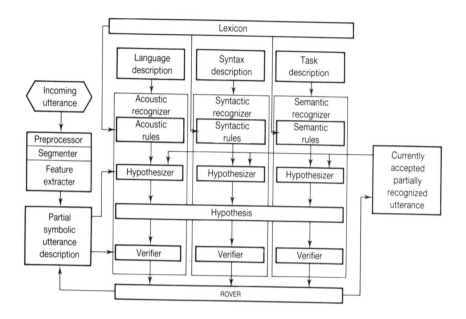

Figure 2.2 Details of the recognition process (Reddy *et al.*, 1973b).

contribution. Finally, in the testing phase, knowledge sources evaluate the new hypotheses.

Some of the difficulties encountered in Hearsay-I can be attributed to the way in which the solution to the application task was formulated, and other difficulties arose from the design of the system. The problem was formulated to use the hypothesize-and-test paradigm only on the word level, that is, the blackboard only contained a description at the word level. This meant that all communication among the knowledge sources was limited to sharing information at the word level. This formulation caused two major difficulties. First, it became difficult to add non-word knowledge sources and to evaluate their contributions. Second, the inability to share information contributed by non-word knowledge sources caused the information to be recomputed by each knowledge source that needed it. In other words, the difficulty lay in trying to force the use of a single vocabulary (that is, from the word level) when multiple vocabularies (for example, on the acoustic level) were needed.

The architectural weaknesses of Hearsay-I, as stated by its designers (Lesser *et al.*, 1975), lay in:

(1)   the lock-step control sequence that limited 'parallelism',

(2)   the lack of provision to express relationships among alternative sentence hypotheses, and

(3) the built-in problem-solving strategy that made modifications awkward and comparisons of different strategies impossible.

To overcome these difficulties, information (in the multiple vocabularies needed to understand utterances) used by all the knowledge sources was uniformly represented and made globally accessible on the blackboard in Hearsay-II. In addition, a scheduler dynamically selected and activated the appropriate knowledge sources.

We have chosen two papers to illustrate Hearsay-II. Chapter 3 describes the organization of the system in its final form, and is the most frequently cited description of Hearsay-II. The operation of the system is illustrated by an extended description of the processing of a single utterance. The paper also includes a review of the performance of Hearsay-II and a comparison with other DARPA speech projects.

Chapter 4 gives more detail on the system components, particularly the knowledge sources. Most of the development of Hearsay-II was concentrated in a three-year period, and the article illustrates how the design of the system changed during the final year of development. Issues relating to parallel processing in blackboard frameworks are also discussed. Parallelism was one of the original design goals of Hearsay-II and has remained a long-term aim in subsequent blackboard systems work. However, to the present, experiments have been confined to simulations of parallel operation. The material in Chapter 4 was derived from two papers. Most of the material is taken from Lesser and Erman (1977). We have augmented that text with a description of some of the principal knowledge sources, taken from a companion paper (Erman and Lesser, 1978a). Both papers were originally published as CMU technical reports.

3

The Hearsay-II Speech-Understanding System: Integrating Knowledge to Resolve Uncertainty

Lee D. Erman, Frederick Hayes-Roth, Victor R. Lesser and D. Raj Reddy

3.1 Introduction

The Hearsay-II speech-understanding system developed at Carnegie-Mellon University recognizes connected speech in a 1000-word vocabulary with correct interpretations for 90% of test sentences. Its basic methodology involves the application of symbolic reasoning as an aid to signal processing. A marriage of general artificial intelligence techniques with specific acoustic and linguistic knowledge was needed to accomplish satisfactory speech-understanding performance. Because the various techniques and heuristics employed were embedded within a general problem-solving framework, the Hearsay-II system embodies several design characteristics that are adaptable to other domains as well. Its structure has been applied to such tasks as multisensor interpretation (Nii and Feigenbaum, 1978), protein-crystallographic analysis (Engelmore and Nii, 1977), image understanding (Hanson and Riseman, 1978b), a model of human reading (Rumelhart, 1976) and dialogue comprehension (Mann, 1979). This paper discusses the characteristics of the speech problem in particular, the special kinds of problem-solving uncertainty in that domain, the structure of the Hearsay-II system developed to cope with that uncertainty, and the relationship between Hearsay-II's structure and the structures of other speech systems.

Uncertainty arises in a problem-solving system if the system's knowledge is inadequate to produce a solution directly. The fundamental method for handling uncertainty is to create a space of candidate solutions and search that space for a solution. 'Almost all the basic methods used by intelligent systems can be seen as some variation of search, responsive to the particular knowledge available' (Newell *et al.*, 1977, p. 17). In a difficult problem, i.e. one with a large search space, a problem solver can be effective only if it can search efficiently. To do so, it must apply knowledge to guide the search so that relatively few points in the space need be examined before a solution is found. A key way of accomplishing this is by augmenting the space of candidate solutions with candidate *partial* solutions and then constructing a complete solution by extending and combining partial candidates. A candidate partial solution represents all complete candidates that contain it. By considering partial solution candidates, we can often eliminate whole subspaces from further consideration and simultaneously focus the search on more promising subspaces.

To solve a problem as difficult as speech understanding, a problem solver requires several kinds of capabilities in order to search effectively: it must collect and analyze data, set goals to guide the inferential search processes, produce and retain appropriate inferences, and decide when to stop working for a possibly better solution. Years ago, when AI problem solvers first emerged, they attempted to provide these capabilities through quite general domain-independent methods, the so-called *weak* methods (Newell, 1969). A prime example of such a problem solver is GPS (Ernst and Newell, 1969). More recently, several major problem-solving accomplishments, such as DENDRAL (Feigenbaum *et al.*, 1971) and MYCIN (Shortliffe, 1976), have reflected a different philosophy: powerful problem solvers depend on extensive amounts of knowledge about both the problem domain and the problem-solving strategies effective in that domain (Feigenbaum, 1977). Much of what we view as expertise consists of these two types of knowledge; without capturing and implementing this knowledge, we could not create effective computer problem solvers. Because knowledge plays a crucial role in these kinds of tasks, many people call the corresponding problem solvers *knowledge-based systems* (Barnett and Bernstein, 1977). The design of Hearsay-II is responsive to both concerns. While formulated as a general system-building framework that would structure and control problem-solving behavior involving multiple, diverse and error-full sources of knowledge, the current Hearsay-II system consists of a particular collection of programs embedding speech knowledge that are capable of solving the understanding problem.

The problem of speech understanding has been actively pursued recently (Reddy, 1975; 1976; CMU, 1977; Bernstein, 1976; Walker, 1978; Woods *et al.*, 1976; Klatt, 1977; Medress *et al.*, 1978; Lea, 1980). With the exception of HARPY (Lowerre and Reddy, 1980), however, none of the other efforts has been presented as a structure for problem solving in other domains.

The difficulty of the speech-understanding problem, and hence the need for powerful problem-solving methods, derives from two inherent sources of uncertainty or error. The first includes ordinary variability and noise in the speech waveform, and the second includes the ambiguous and inaccurate judgments arising from an application of incomplete and imprecise theories of speech. Because we cannot resolve these uncertainties directly, we structure the speech-understanding problem as a space in which our problem solver searches for a solution. The space is the set of (partial and complete) *interpretations* of the input acoustic signal, i.e. the (partial and complete) mappings from the signal to the possible messages. The goal of our problem-solving system is to find a complete interpretation (i.e. a message and mapping) which maximizes some evaluation function based on knowledge about such things as acoustic-phonetics, vocabulary, grammar, semantics and discourse. This resolution of the combined sources of uncertainty requires the generation, evaluation and integration of numerous partial interpretations. The need to consider many alternative interpretations without spawning an explosive combinatorial search thus becomes a principal design objective. Each of these issues is discussed in more detail in the following section.

3.1.1 Dimensions of the problem: uncertainty and hypothetical interpretations

The first source of difficulty in the speech problem arises from the speaking process itself. In the translation from intention to sound, a speaker transforms concepts into speech through processes that introduce variability and noise (see Figure 3.1). If, for example, we consider the semantic, syntactic, lexical and phonemic stages, the types of variance introduced from one level to the next would correspond to errors or peculiarities of conceptualization, grammar, word choice and articulation. In addition to these sources of variability, speech is often affected by

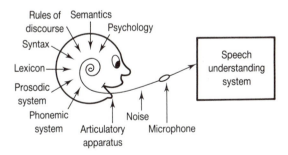

Figure 3.1 Some of the mechanisms that affect the message: psychology of the speaker, semantics, rules of discourse, syntax, lexicon, prosodic system, phonemic system, speaker's articulatory apparatus, ambient environmental noise and microphone and system. (After Newell (1975).)

pauses, extraneous sounds, or unnecessary phrase repetitions. The effect of these factors upon the physical sound signal is to distort it significantly from the *ideal message*, that is, from the message that would be produced if the production mechanisms did not introduce variability and noise. Accordingly, we speak of the disparity between the ideal and actual signals as **error**, and of the variety of factors that contribute to such distortion as **souces of error**. Thus the first source of error is inherent in the speaker and his environment.

The second source of error in the understanding process is intrinsic to the listener. Just as the speaker must transform his intention through successive intermediate levels of representation, so we presume the listener must accomplish the inverse of those transformations; from the physical signal the listener must detect acoustic-phonetic elements, syllables, words, and syntactic and conceptual structures corresponding to the speaker's intentions. At each step in this reconstruction the listener may introduce new errors corresponding to incorrect perceptual or interpretive judgments. Though the levels of representation appear to be linearly ordered, the encoding and decoding processes do not necessarily operate sequentially through this ordering. Because a machine speech-understanding system must also develop interpretations of what was spoken and what was intended, it is likely to commit similar mistakes in judgment. These judgmental errors can be viewed as the result of applying inadequate or inaccurate theoretical models to the speech-analysis task. If the first source of error is deviation between ideal and spoken messages due to inexact production, the second source of error is deviation between spoken and interpreted messages due to imprecise rules of comprehension.

To comprehend an utterance in the context of such errors, a speech-understanding system must formulate and evaluate numerous candidate interpretations of speech fragments. Understanding a message requires us to isolate and recognize its individual words and parse their syntactic and conceptual relationships. Each intermediate state of this process can be viewed as either the generation or evaluation of symbolic interpretations for portions of the spoken utterance. We use the term **hypothesis** to refer to a partial interpretation actually constructed. During the process of speech interpretation, hypotheses may vary from highly confident identification of particular words to great confusion concerning particular portions of the utterance. Between these two extremes, the listener may entertain simultaneously several competing hypotheses for what was said. Competing alternatives might occur at any of several levels of abstraction. For example, at the word level the listener may struggle to distinguish whether 'till' or 'tell' was spoken in one portion of the utterance while simultaneously attempting to differentiate the words 'brings' and 'rings' in another interval. These uncertainties derive from comparable uncertainties at lower levels of interpretation, such as syllabic and acoustic, where multiple competing hypotheses can also exist simultaneously. Similarly, uncertainty among word hypotheses at the lexical level engenders uncertainty at higher levels of interpretation. Thus the previously discussed inability to distinguish between alternative words may be the underlying cause of an inability to distinguish between the four hypothetical phrase interpretations:

till Bob rings
tell Bob rings
till Bob brings
tell Bob brings

Just as this example suggests, higher-level interpretations incorporate lower-level ones. A phrase-level hypothesis consists of a selection of word hypotheses from each interval of time spanned by the higher level hypothesis. Only one lower level hypothesis in any time interval can be incorporated into the higher-level interpretation. Thus a phrase consists of a sequence of words, a word consists of a sequence of syllables, a syllable consists of a sequence of acoustic-phonetic segments, and so on. An overall interpretation of an entire utterance would consist of a syntactic or semantic analysis that recursively incorporated one hypothesis from each level of interpretation for each temporal interval of the utterance.

A fundamental assumption underlying the understanding problem is that a correct interpretation of an utterance should minimize the difference between those properties of the speech that the hypothetical interpretation would predict and those that are observed. This gives rise to the notion of the **consistency** between an interpretation and its supporting data. Thus certain parameter values derived from an acoustic waveform are more or less consistent with various phonetic classifications, particular sequences of phones are more or less consistent with various monosyllabic categorizations, and various syllable sequences are more or less consistent with particular lexical and phrase interpretations. The concept of consistency between two adjacent levels of interpretation can be generalized to permit consideration of the consistency between hypotheses at any two levels and, in particular, the consistency between an overall interpretation of the utterance and its supporting hypotheses at the lowest acoustic-parametric level. A central assumption is that the greater the consistency between the overall interpretation and the acoustic data, the more likely the interpretation is to be correct.

We refer to the likelihood that some hypothesis is correct as its **credibility**. As the preceding suggests, the credibility of each hypothesis is a measure of consistency between the data generating the hypothesis and the expectations it engenders. A credibility calculation involves a judgment about the knowledge used in creating the hypothesis and therefore is itself subject to uncertainty.

To assess the credibility of a hypothesis, we need basically to evaluate two things: all plausible alternatives to this hypothesis and the degree of support each receives from data. Consider, for example, the evaluation of word hypotheses. Initially, nearly all words in the language are plausible candidates for occurring within any time interval. As a consequence, our uncertainty at the outset, as approximated by the number of equally plausible alternatives, is maximal. Over time we accrue evidence to eliminate some of these alternatives. Moreover, by eliminating one particular hypothesis, we may logically exclude others that are in temporally adjacent regions and that depend directly on that hypothesis. For example, if we have ruled out all possible adjectives and nouns in a particular location, we can also rule out adjectives in the preceding interval. Conversely, if we can identify a particular word as an adjective, we can increase our belief that the following word will be an adjective or noun. In general, each individual hypothesis is strengthened by its apparent combinability with others. Thus we say uncertainty is reduced by detecting mutually supporting hypotheses that are consistent with the acoustic data. Equivalently, the credibility of hypotheses increases as a function of their involvement in such mutually supportive clusters.

This technique for reducing uncertainty leads to the following incremental problem-solving method. The goal of the problem solver is to construct the most credible overall interpretation. The fundamental operations in the construction are hypothesis generation, hypothesis combination, and hypothesis evaluation. At each step in the construction, sources of knowledge use these operations to build larger partial interpretations, adding their constraints to the interpretation. The accrual of constraints reduces the uncertainty inherent in the data and in the knowledge sources themselves.

Three requirements must be met for such a problem solver to be effective:

(1)   At least one possible sequence of knowledge-based operations must lead to a correct overall interpretation.

(2)   The evaluation procedure should assess the correct overall interpretation as maximally credible among all overall interpretations generated.

(3)   The cost of problem solving must satsify some externally specified limit. Usually this limit restricts the time or space available for computing. As a consequence, it leads to restrictions on the number of alternative partial interpretations that can be considered. Alternative partial solutions must be considered in order to ensure

that a correct one is included. The greater the uncertainty in the knowledge used to generate and evaluate hypotheses, the greater the number of alternatives that must be considered, leading to a possible combinatorial explosion.

As we have seen, the speech-understanding problem is characterized by the need for highly diverse kinds of knowledge for its solution and by large amounts of uncertainty and variability in input data and knowledge. The diversity of knowledge leads to a search space of multilevel partial solutions. The uncertainty and variability mean that the operators used for searching the space are themselves error-prone; therefore many competing alternative hypotheses must be generated. To avoid a combinatorial explosion, a powerful control scheme is needed to exploit selectively the most promising combinations of alternatives. As systems tackle more such difficult real-world problems, such multilevel representations and powerful control schemes will become increasingly important (Hayes-Roth et al., 1978a). The next section discusses how the Hearsay-II system copes with these representation and control problems.

3.1.2 Hearsay-II problem-solving model

The key functions of generating, combining and evaluating hypothetical interpretations are performed by diverse and independent programs called **knowledge sources** (KSs). The necessity for diverse KSs derives from the diversity of transformations used by the speaker in creating the acoustic signal and the corresponding inverse transformations needed by the listener for interpreting it. Each KS can be schematized as a condition–action pair. The condition component prescribes the situations in which the KS may contribute to the problem-solving activity, and the action component specifies what that contribution is and how to integrate it into the current situation. The condition and action components of a KS are realized as arbitrary programs. To minimize reevaluating the condition programs continuously, each condition program declares to the system the primitive kinds of situations in which it is interested. The condition program is triggered only when there occur changes that create such situations (and is then given pointers to all of them). This changes a polling action into an interrupt-driven one and is more efficient, especially for a large number of KSs. When executed, the condition program can search among the set of existing hypothetical interpretations for arbitrarily complex configurations of interest to its KS. According to the original conception of the diverse stages and processes involved in speech understanding, KSs have been developed to perform a variety of functions. These include extracting acoustic parameters, classifying acoustic segments into phonetic classes, recognizing words, parsing

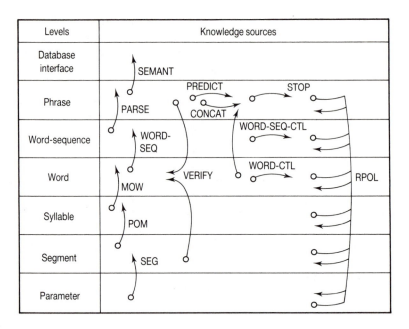

Figure 3.2 The levels and knowledge sources of September 1976. KSs are indicated by vertical arcs with the circled ends indicating the input level and the pointed ends indicating output level.

phrases, and generating and evaluating predictions for undetected words or syllables. Figure 3.2 presents a schematic view of the KSs in the September 1976 configuration of the Hearsay-II speech-understanding system. Table 3.1 gives a brief functional description of these KSs.

Because each KS is an *independent* condition–action module, KSs communicate through a global database called the **blackboard**. The blackboard records the hypotheses generated by KSs. Any KS can generate a hypothesis (record it on the blackboard) or modify an existing one. These actions in turn may produce structures that satisfy the applicability conditions of other KSs. In this framework the blackboard serves in two roles: it represents intermediate states of problem-solving activity, and it communicates messages (hypotheses) from one KS that activate other KSs.

The blackboard is subdivided into a set of information levels corresponding to the intermediate representation levels of the decoding processes (phrase, word, syllable, etc.). Each hypothesis resides on the blackboard at one of the levels and bears a defining label chosen from a set appropriate to that level (e.g. the word FLYING, the syllable ING, or the phone NG). The hypothesis contains additional information, including its time coordinates within the spoken utterance and a crediblity

Table 3.1 Functional description of the speech-understanding KSs.

Signal acquisition, parameter extraction, segmentation and labeling
- SEG: digitizes the signal, measures parameters and produces a labeled segmentation

Word spotting
- POM: creates syllable-class hypotheses from segments
- MOW: creates word hypotheses from syllable classes
- WORD-CTL: controls the number of word hypotheses that MOW creates

Phrase-island generation
- WORD-SEQ: creates word-sequence hypotheses that represent potential phrases from word hypotheses and weak grammatical knowledge
- WORD-SEQ-CTL: controls the number of hypotheses that WORD-SEQ creates
- PARSE: attempts to parse a word sequence and, if successful, creates a phrase hypothesis from it

Phrase extending
- PREDICT: predicts all possible words that might syntactically precede or follow a given phrase
- VERIFY: rates the consistency between segment hypotheses and a contiguous word-phrase pair
- CONCAT: creates a phrase hypothesis from a verified contiguous word–phrase pair

Rating, halting and interpretation
- RPOL: rates the credibility of each new or modified hypothesis, using information placed on the hypothesis by other KSs
- STOP: decides to halt processing (detects a complete sentence with a sufficiently high rating, or notes the system has exhausted its available resources) and selects the best phrase hypothesis or set of complementary phrase hypotheses as the output
- SEMANT: generates an unambiguous interpretation for the information-retrieval system which the user has queried

---

rating. The sequence of levels on the blackboard forms a loose hierarchical structure: hypotheses at each level aggregate or abstract elements at the adjacent lower level. The possible hypotheses at a level form a search space for KSs operating at that level. A partial interpretation at one level can constrain the search at another level.

Within this framework we consider two general types of problem-solving behaviors. The first type, associated with means–ends analysis and problem-reduction strategies (Ernst & Newell, 1969; Nilsson, 1971; Sacerdoti, 1974), attempts to reach a goal by dividing it into a set of simpler subgoals and reducing these recursively until only primitive or immediately solvable subgoals remain. Such a strategy is called **top-down** or **analysis-by-synthesis**. In speech understanding, where the goal is to find the most credible high-level interpretation of the utterance, a top-down approach would recursively reduce the general sentential concept goal into alternative sentence forms, each sentence form into specific alternative word sequences, specific words into alternative phone sequences, and so forth, until the one alternative overall interpretation most consistent with the observed acoustic parameters is identified. The second, or **bottom-up**, method attempts to synthesize interpretations directly from characteristics of the data provided. One type of bottom-up method would employ procedures to classify acoustic segments within phonetic categories by comparing their observed parameters with the ideal parameter values of each phonetic category. Other bottom-up procedures might generate syllable or word hypotheses directly from sequences of phone hypotheses, or might combine temporally adjacent word hypotheses into syntactic or conceptual units. For a hypothesis generated in either the top-down or bottom-up mode, we would like to represent explicitly its relationship to the preexisting hypotheses that suggested it. *Links* are constructed between hypotheses for this purpose.

Both types of problem-solving behaviors can be accommodated simultaneously by the condition–action schema of a Hearsay-II KS. Top-down behaviors represent the reduction of the higher-level goal as the condition to be satisfied and the generation of appropriate subgoals as the associated action. Bottom-up behaviors employ the condition component to represent the lower-level hypothesis configurations justifying higher-level interpretations, and employ the action component to represent and generate such hypotheses. In both cases the condition component performs a test to determine if there exists an appropriate configuration of hypotheses that would justify the generation of additional hypotheses prescribed by the corresponding action component. Whenever such conditions are satisfied, the action component of the KS is *invoked* to perform the appropriate hypothesis generation or modification operations. For example, the action of the POM KS (see Figures 3.2 and 3.3) is to create hypotheses at the syllable level. The condition for invoking the MOW KS is the creation of a syllable hypothesis. Thus the action of POM triggers MOW. The invocation condition of RPOL, the rating KS, is the creation or modification of a hypothesis at any level; thus POM's actions also trigger RPOL. In short, control of KS activation is determined by the blackboard actions of other KSs, rather than explicit calls from other KSs or some central sequencing mechanism. This *data-directed* control regime permits a more flexible scheduling of KS actions in response to changing conditions on the blackboard. We refer to such an ability of a system to exploit its best data and most promising methods as *opportunistic* problem solving (Nii and Feigenbaum, 1978; Hayes-Roth and Hayes-Roth, 1979a).

While it is true that each condition–action knowledge source is logically independent of the others, effective problem-solving activity depends ultimately on the capability of the individual KS actions to construct cooperatively an overall interpretation of the utterance. This high-level hypothesis and its recursive supports represent the *solution* to the understanding *problem*. Since each KS action simply generates or modifies hypotheses and links based on related information, a large number of individual KS invocations may be needed to construct an overall interpretation.

Any hypothesis that is included in the solution is *cooperative* with the others. Conversely, any hypothesis that is unincorporated into the solution is *competitive*. In a similar way, KS invocations can be considered cooperative or competitive depending on whether their potential actions would or would not contribute to the same solution. Because of the inherent uncertainty in the speech-understanding task, there are inevitably large numbers of plausible alternative actions in each time interval of the utterance. Before the correct interpretation has been found, we cannot evaluate with certainty the prospective value of any potential action. Actions appear cooperative to the extent to which they contribute to the formation and support of increasingly comprehensive interpretations. Conversely, any hypothesis occupying the same time interval as another hypothesis but not part of its support set must be considered competitive. That is, two hypotheses compete if they represent incompatible interpretations of the same portion of the utterance. As a result, KS invocations can be viewed as competitive if their likely actions would generate inconsistent hypotheses, and they can be viewed as cooperative if their actions would combine to form more comprehensive or more strongly supported hypotheses.

The major impediment to discovery of the best overall interpretation in this scheme is the combinatorial explosion of KS invocations that can occur. From the outset, numerous alternative actions are warranted. A purely top-down approach would generate a vast number of possible actions, if unrestrained. Because certainty of recognition is practically never possible and substantial numbers of competing hypotheses must be entertained at each time interval of analysis, any bottom-up approach generates a similarly huge number of competing possible actions. Thus additional constraints on the problem-solving activity must be enforced. This is accomplished by selecting for execution only a limited subset of the invoked KSs.

The objective of *selective attention* is to allocate limited computing resources (processing cycles) to the most important and most promising actions. This selectivity involves three components. First, the probable effects of a potential KS action must be estimated before it is performed. Second, the global significance of an isolated action must be deduced from analysis of its cooperative and competitive relationships with existing hypotheses; *globally significant actions* are those that contribute to the detection, formation or extension of combinations of redundant hypotheses. Third, the desirablity of an action must be assessed in comparison with other potential actions. While the inherent uncertainty of the speech task precludes error-free performance of these component tasks, there have been devised some approximate methods that effectively control the combinatorics and make the speech-understanding problem tractable.

Selective attention is accomplished in the Hearsay-II system by a heuristic scheduler which calculates a priority for each action and executes, at each time, the waiting action with the highest priority (Hayes-Roth and Lesser, 1977). The priority calculation attempts to estimate the usefulness of the action in fulfilling the overall system goal of recognizing the utterance. The calculation is based on information provided when the condition part of a KS is satisfied. This information includes the *stimulus frame*, which is the set of hypotheses that satisfied the condition, and the *response frame*, a stylized description of the blackboard modifications that the KS action is likely to perform. For example, consider a syllable-based word hypothesizer KS (such as MOW); its stimulus frame would include the specific syllable hypothesis that matched its condition, and its response frame would specify the expected action of generating word hypotheses in a time interval spanning that of the stimulus frame. In addition to this action-specific information, the

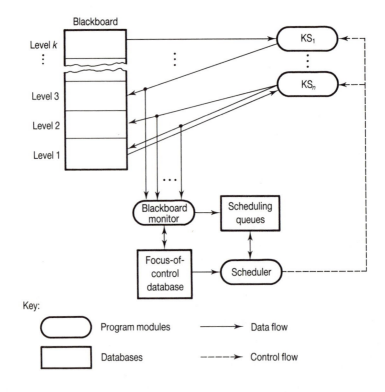

Figure 3.3   Schematic of the Hearsay-II architecture.

scheduler uses global state information in its calculations and considers especially the credibility and duration of the best hypotheses in each level and time region and the amount of processing required from the time the current best hypotheses were generated. The latter information allows the system to reappraise its confidence in its current best hypotheses if they are not quickly incorporated into more comprehensive hypotheses.

3.1.3 Hearsay-II architecture

Figure 3.3 illustrates the primary architectural features of the Hearsay-II system. At the start of each cycle, the scheduler, in accordance with the global state information, calculates a priority for each activity (KS condition program or action program) in the scheduling queues. The highest priority activity is removed from the queues and executed. If the activity is a KS condition program, it may insert new instances of KS action programs into the scheduling queues. If the activity is a KS action program, the blackboard monitor notices the blackboard changes it makes. Whenever a change occurs that would be of interest to a KS condition program, the monitor creates an activity in the scheduling queues for that program. The monitor also updates the global state information to reflect the blackboard modifications.

3.2 An example of recognition

In this section we present a detailed description of the Hearsay-II speech system understanding one utterance. The task for the system is to answer questions about and retrieve documents from a collection of computer science abstracts (in the area of artificial intelligence). Example sentences:

> 'Which abstracts refer to theory of computation?'
> 'List those articles.'
> 'What has McCarthy written since nineteen seventy-four?'

The vocabulary contains 1011 words (in which each extended form of a root, e.g. the plural of a noun, is counted separately if it appears). The grammar defining the legal sentences is context-free and includes recursion. The style of the grammar is such that there are many more nonterminals than in conventional syntactic grammars; the information contained in the greater number of nodes imbeds semantic and pragmatic constraint directly within the grammatical structure. For example, in place of 'Noun' in a conventional grammar, this grammar includes such nonterminals as 'Topic', 'Author', 'Year' and 'Publisher'. Because of its emphasis on semantic categories, this type of grammar is called a *semantic template grammar* or simply a *semantic grammar* (Hayes-Roth and Mostow, 1975; Burton, 1976; Hayes-Roth, 1980). The grammar allows each word to be followed, on the average, by 17 other words of the vocabulary. (Actually, a family of grammars, varying in the number of words (terminals) and in the number and complexity of sentences allowed, was generated. The grammar described here and used in most of the testing is called X05.) The standard deviation of this measure is very high (about 51), since some words (e.g. 'about' or 'on') can be followed by many others (up to 300 in several cases).

3.2.1 Introduction to the example

We will describe how Hearsay-II understood the utterance 'Are any by Feigenbaum and Feldman?' To improve clarity, the description differs from the actual computer execution of Hearsay-II in a few minor details. Each major *step* of the processing is shown; a step usually corresponds to the action of a knowledge source. Executions of the condition programs

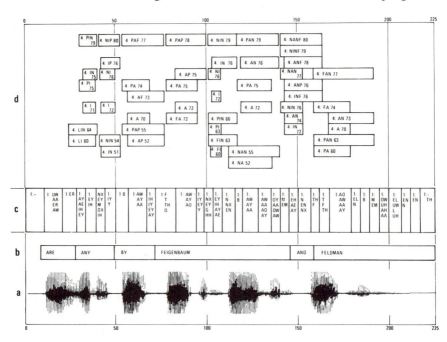

Figure 3.4 The example utterance: (a) the waveform of 'Are any by Feigenbaum and Feldman?'; (b) the correct words (for reference); (c) segments; (d) syllable classes; (e) words (created by **MOW**); (f) words (created by **VERIFY**); (g) word sequences; (h) phrases.

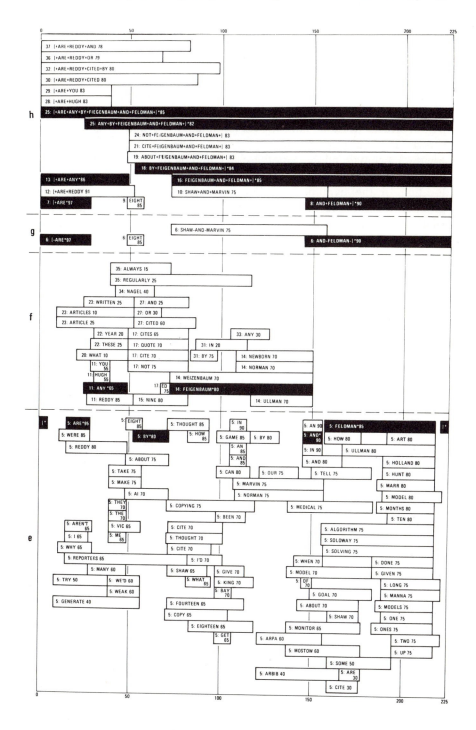

Figure 3.4   (cont.)

of the KSs are not shown explicitly, nor do we list those potential knowledge-source actions which are never chosen by the scheduler for execution. Executions of RPOL are also omitted; in order to calculate credibility ratings for hypotheses, RPOL runs in high-priority immediately after any KS action that creates or modifies a hypothesis.

The waveform of the spoken utterance is shown in Figure 3.4(a). The 'correct' word boundaries (determined by human inspection) are shown in Figure 3.4(b) for reference. The remaining sections of Figure 3.4 contain all the hypotheses created by the KSs. Each hypothesis is represented by a box; the box's horizontal position indicates the location of the hypothesis within the utterance. The hypotheses are grouped by level: segment, syllable, word, word sequence and phrase. Links between hypotheses are not shown. The processing will be described in terms of a sequence of *time steps*, where each step corresponds approximately to KS execution governed by one scheduling decision. Within each hypothesis, the number preceding the colon indicates the time step during which the hypothesis was created. The symbol following the colon names the hypothesis. At the word level and above, an asterisk (*) following the symbol indicates that the hypothesis is correct. The trailing number within each hypothesis is the credibility rating on an arbitrary scale ranging from 0 to 100.

In the step-by-step description, the name of the KS executed at each step follows the step number. An asterisk following the KS name indicates that the hypotheses in the stimulus frame of this KS instantiation are all correct. Single numbers in parentheses after hypotheses are their credibility ratings. All times given are in centi-second units; thus the duration of the whole utterance, which was 2.25 s, is marked as 225. When begin- and end-times of hypotheses are given, they appear as two numbers separated by a colon (e.g. 52 : 82). As in the figure, correct hypotheses are marked with an asterisk.

3.2.2 The example

The utterance is recorded by a medium-quality Electro-Voice RE-51 close-speaking headset microphone in a moderately noisy environment (>65 dB). The audio signal is low-pass filtered and 9-bit sampled at 10 kHz. All subsequent processing, including the control of the A/D converter, is performed digitally on a time-shared PDP-10 computer. Four acoustic parameters (called ZAPDASH) are derived by simple algorithms operating directly on the sampled signal (Goldberg *et al.*, 1977). These parameters are extracted in real time and are used initially to detect the beginning and end of the utterance.

Step 1   KS: SEG
> Stimulus: Creation of ZAPDASH parameters for the utterance.
> Action: Create segment hypotheses.

The ZAPDASH parameters are used by the SEG knowledge source as the basis for an acoustic segmentation and classification of the utterance (Gill *et al.*, 1978). This segmentation is accomplished by an iterative refinement technique: first, silence is separated from nonsilence; then the nonsilence is broken down into the sonorant and nonsonorant regions, and so on. Eventually five classes of segments are produced: silence, sonorant peak, sonorant nonpeak, fricative and flap. Associated with each classified segment is its duration, absolute amplitude and amplitude relative to its neighboring segments (i.e. local peak, local valley or plateau). The segments are contiguous and nonoverlapping, with one class designation for each.

SEG also does a finer labeling of each segment, using a repertory of 98 phonelike labels. Each of the labels is characterized by a vector of autocorrelation coefficients (Itakura, 1975). These template vectors were generalized from manually labeled speaker-specific training data. The labeling process matches the central portion of each segment against each of the templates using the Itakura metric and produces a vector of 98 numbers. The *i*th number is an estimate of the (negative log) probability that the segment represents an occurrence of the *i*th allophone in the label set. For each segment, SEG creates a hypothesis at the segment level and associates with it the vector of estimated allophone probabilities. The several highest rated labels of each segment are shown in Figure 3.4(c).

Step 2   KS: WORD-CTL
> Stimulus: Start of processing.
> Action: Create goal hypotheses at the word level. These will control the amount of hypothesization that MOW will do. (The goal hypotheses are not shown in Figure 3.4).

Step 3   KS: WORD-SEQ-CTL
> Stimulus: Start of processing.
> Action: Create goal hypotheses at the word-sequence level. These will control the amount of hypothesization that WORD-SEQ will do.

Step 4   KS: POM
> Stimulus: New segment hypotheses.
> Action: Create syllable-class hypotheses.

Using the labeled segments as input, the POM knowledge source (Smith, 1976) generates hypotheses for likely syllable classes. This is done by first identifying syllable nuclei and then parsing outward from each nucleus, using a probabilistic grammar with production rules of the form:

Table 3.2 Phone classes used to define the syllable classes.

Code	Phone class	Phones in class
A	A-like	AE, AA, AH, AO, AX
I	I-like	IY, IH, EY, EH, IX, AY
U	U-like	OW, UH, U, UW, ER, AW, OY, EL, EM, EN
L	Liquid	Y, W, R, L
N	Nasal	M, N, NX
P	Stop	P, T, K, B, D, G, DX
F	Fricative	HH, F, TH, S, SH, V, DH, Z, ZH, CH, JH, WH

syllable-class → segment-sequence

The rules and their probabilities are induced by an off-line program that trains on manually segmented and labeled utterances. For each nucleus position, several (typically three to eight) competing syllable-class hypotheses may be generated.

Figure 3.4(d) shows the syllable-class hypotheses created. Each class name is made up of single-letter codes representing classes of phones, as given in Table 3.2.

> *Step 5* KS: MOW
> Stimulus: New syllable hypotheses.
> Action: Create word hypotheses.

The syllable classes are used by MOW in step 5 to hypothesize words. (MOW will also be reinvoked upon a modification to the word goal hypotheses by WORD-CTL.) Each of the 1011 words in the vocabulary is specified by a pronunciation description. For word hypothesization purposes, an inverted form of the dictionary is kept; this associates each syllable class with all words whose pronunciation contains it. The MOW KS (Smith, 1976) looks up each hypothesized syllable class in the dictionary and generates word candidates from among those words containing that syllable class. For each word that is multisyllabic, all of the syllables in one of the pronunciations must match with a rating above a specified threshold. Typically, about 50 words of the 1011-word vocabulary are generated at each syllable nucleus position.

Finally, the generated word candidates are rated and their begin- and end-times adjusted by the WIZARD procedure (McKeown, 1977). For each word in the vocabulary, WIZARD has a network description of its possible pronunciations. A word rating is calculated by finding the one path through the network which most closely matches the labeled segments, using the probabilities associated with the segment for each label; the resultant rating reflects the difference between this optimal path and the segment labels. WIZARD is, in effect, a miniature version of the HARPY speech-recognition system (see Section 3.3.3), except that it has a network for each word, rather than one network containing all sentences.

Processing to this point has resulted in a set of bottom-up word candidates. Each word includes a begin-time, an end-time, and a credibility rating. MOW selects a subset of these words, based on their times and ratings, to be hypothesized; these selected word hypotheses form the base for the top-end processing. Words not immediately hypothesized are retained internally by MOW for possible later hypothesization.

Since the September 1976 version, the POM and MOW KSs have been replaced by NOAH (Smith, 1977; Smith and Erman, 1981). This KS outperforms, in both speed and accuracy, POM and MOW (with WIZARD) on the 1011-word vocabulary and is able to handle much larger vocabularies; its performance degradation is only logarithmic in vocabulary size, in the range of 500 to 19 000 words.

The amount of hypothesization that MOW does is controlled by the WORD-CTL (Word Control) KS. At step 2, WORD-CTL created initial goal hypotheses at the word level; these are interpreted by MOW as indicating how many word hypotheses to attempt to create in each time area. Subsequently, WORD-CTL may retrigger and modify the goal hypotheses (and thus retrigger MOW) if the overall search process stagnates; this condition is recognized when there are no waiting KS instantiations above a threshold priority or when the global measures of current state of the problem solution have not improved in the last several KS executions.

WORD-CTL (and WORD-SEQ-CTL) are examples of KSs not directly involved in the hypothesizing and testing of partial solutions. Instead, these KSs control the search by influencing the activations of other KSs. These *policy* KSs impose global search stategies on the basic priority scheduling mechanism. For example, MOW is a generator of word hypotheses (from the candidates it creates internally) and WORD-CTL controls the number to be hypothesized. This clear separation of policy from mechanism has facilitated experimentation with various control schemes. A trivial change to WORD-CTL such that goal hypotheses are generated only at the start of the utterance (left-hand end) results in MOW creating word hypotheses only at the start, thus forcing all top-end processing to be left-to-right (see Section 3.4.2).

In this example four words (ARE, BY, AND and FELDMAN) of the six in the utterance were correctly hypothesized; 86 incorrect hypotheses were generated (see Figure 3.4(e)). The 90 words that were hypothesized represent approximately 1.5% of the 1011-word vocabulary for each one of the six words in the utterance.

In addition, two unique word-level hypotheses are generated before the first and after the last segment of the utterance to denote the start and end of utterance, respectively. They are denoted by [and].

Step 6   KS: WORD-SEQ
    Stimulus: New words created bottom-up.
    Action: Create four word-sequence hypotheses:

       [–ARE*(97, 0:28),
       AND–FELDMAN–]*(90, 145:225),
       EIGHT(85, 48:57).
       SHAW–AND–MARVIN(75, 72:157),

The WORD-SEQ knowledge source (Lesser *et al.*, 1977) has the task of generating, from the bottom-up word hypotheses, a small set (about three to ten) of word-sequence hypotheses. Each of these sequences, or *islands*, can be used as the basis for expansion into larger islands, which it is hoped will culminate in a hypothesis spanning the entire utterance. Multiword islands are used rather than single-word islands because of the relatively poor reliability of ratings of single words. With multiword islands, syntactic and coarticulation constraints can be used to increase the reliability of the ratings.

WORD-SEQ uses three kinds of knowledge to generate multiword islands efficiently:

(1) A table derived from the grammar indicates for every ordered pair of words in the vocabulary (1011 × 1011) whether that pair can occur in sequence within some sentence of the defined language. This binary table, whose density of ones for the X05 grammar is 1.7%, defines a *language-adjacent* relation.

(2) Acoustic-phonetic knowledge, embodied in the JUNCT (juncture) procedure (Cronk, 1977) is applied to pairs of word hypotheses and is used to decide if that pair might be considered to be *time-adjacent* in the utterance JUNCT uses the dictionary pronunciations, and examines the segments at their juncture (gap or overlap) in making its decision.

(3) Statistical knowledge is used to assess the credibility of generated alternative word sequences and to terminate the search for additional candidates when the chance of finding improved hypotheses drops. The statistics are generated from previously observed behavior of WORD-SEQ and are based on the number of hypotheses able to be generated from the given bottom-up word hypotheses and their ratings.

WORD-SEQ takes the highest rated single words and generates multiword sequences by expanding them with other hypothesized words that are both time- and language-adjacent. This expansion is guided by credibility ratings generated by using the statistical knowledge. The best of these word sequences (which occasionally includes single words) are hypothesized.

The WORD-SEQ-CTL (Word-Sequence-Control) KS controls the amount of hypothesization that WORD-SEQ does by creating 'goal' hypotheses that WORD-SEQ interprets as indicating how many hypotheses to create. This provides the same kind of separation of policy and mechanism achieved in the MOW/WORD-CTL pair of KSs. WORD-SEQ-CTL fired at the start of processing, at step 3, in order to create the goal hypotheses. Subsequently, WORD-SEQ-CTL may trigger if stagnation is recognized; it then modifies the word-sequence goal hypotheses, thus stimulating WORD-SEQ to generate new islands from which the search may prove more fruitful. WORD-SEQ may generate the additional hypotheses by decomposing word sequences already on the blackboard or by generating islands previously discarded because their ratings seemed too low.

Step 6 results in the generation of four multiword sequences (see Figure 3.4(g)). These are used as initial, alternative anchor points for additional searching. Note that two of these islands are correct, each representing an alternative search path that potentially can lead to a correct interpretation of the utterance. This ability to derive the correct interpretation in multiple ways makes the system more robust. For example, there have been cases in which a complete interpretation could not be constructed from one correct island because of KS errors but was derived from another island.

High-level processing on the multiword sequences is accomplished by the following KSs: PARSE, PREDICT, VERIFY, CONCAT, STOP and WORD-SEQ-CTL. Since an execution of the VERIFY KS will often immediately follow the execution of the PREDICT KS (each on the same hypothesis), we have combined the descriptions of the two KS executions into one step for ease of understanding.

Because the syntactic constraint used in the generation of the word sequences is only pairwise, a sequence longer than two words might not be syntactically acceptable. The PARSE knowledge source (Hayes-Roth *et al.*, 1977a) can parse a word sequence of arbitrary length, using the full grammatical constraints. This parsing does not require that the word sequence form a complete nonterminal in the grammar or that the sequence be sentence-initial or sentence-final; the words need only occur contiguously in some sentence of the language. If a sequence hypothesis does not parse, it is marked as 'rejected'. Otherwise a phrase hypothesis is created. Associated with the phrase hypothesis is the word sequence that supports it, as well as information about the parse(s).

Steps 7 through 10 show the PARSE KS processing each of the multiword sequences. In this example all four multiword sequences were verified as valid language fragments. However, if a multiword sequence had been rejected, the WORD-SEQ KS might have been reinvoked to generate additional multiword sequences in the time area of the rejected one. WORD-SEQ would generate the additional hypotheses by decomposing (shortening) word-sequence islands already on the blackboard or by regenerating islands which may not have been hypothesized initially owing to low ratings. Additional word-sequence hypotheses might also be generated in response to the modification of 'goal' hypotheses at the word-sequence level by the WORD-SEQ-CTL. Such a structuring of a KS as a *generator* is a primary mechanism in Hearsay-II for limiting the number of hypotheses created on the blackboard and thereby reducing the danger of a combinatorial explosion of KS activity in reaction to those hypotheses.

The scheduling strategy is parameterized to delay phrase-level processing until an adequate number of highly rated phrase hypothesis islands is generated. This strategy is not built directly into the scheduler, but rather is accomplished by:

(1)   appropriately setting external scheduling parameters (i.e. the high setting of the priorities of WORD-SEQ and PARSE KS actions in contrast to those of PREDICT, VERIFY and CONCAT) – these settings are determined empirically by observing a number of training runs. They are not adjusted during test runs of the system.

(2)   taking into account the current state of hypotheses on the phrase level of the blackboard in evaluating the usefulness of potential KS actions as described by their response frames.

Step 7   KS: PARSE*
            Stimulus: [–ARE* (word sequence).
            Action: Create phrase: [+ARE* (97, 0:28).

Step 8   KS: PARSE*
            Stimulus: AND–FELDMAN–]* (word sequence).
            Action: Create phrase: AND+FELDMAN+]* (90, 145:225).

Step 9   KS: PARSE
            Stimulus: EIGHT (word sequence).
            Action: Create phrase: EIGHT (85, 48:57).

Step 10   KS: PARSE
            Stimulus: SHAW–AND–MARVIN (word sequence).
            Action: Create phrase: SHAW+AND+MARVIN (75, 72:157).

Each of the four executions of the PARSE KS (steps 7–10) results in the creation of a phrase hypothesis; these are shown in Figure 3.4(h). Each of these hypotheses causes an invocation of the PREDICT KS.

The PREDICT knowledge source (Hayes-Roth *et al.*, 1977a) can, for any phrase hypothesis, generate predictions of all words that can immediately precede and all that can immediately follow that phrase in the language. In generating these predictions this KS uses the parsing information attached to the phrase hypothesis by the parsing component. The action of PREDICT is to attach a 'word-predictor' attribute to the hypothesis that specifies the predicted words. Not all of these PREDICT KS instantiations are necessarily executed (and thus indicated as a step in the execution history). For instance, further processing on the phrases [+ARE and AND+FELDMAN+] is sufficiently positive that the scheduler never executes the instantiation of PREDICT for the phrase SHAW+AND+MARVIN (created in step 10).

The VERIFY KS can attempt to verify the existence of or reject each such predicted word in the context of its predicting phrase. If verified, a confidence rating for the word is also generated. The verification proceeds as follows. First, if the word has been hypothesized previously and passes the test for time-adjacency (by the JUNCT procedure), it is marked as verified and the word hypothesis is associated with the prediction. (Note that some word hypotheses may thus become associated with several different phrases.) Second, a search is made of the internal store created by MOW to see if the prediction can be matched by a previously generated word candidate which had not yet been hypothesized. Again, JUNCT makes a judgment about the plausibility of the time-adjacency relationship between the predicting phrase and the predicted word. Finally, WIZARD compares its word-pronunciation network with the segments in an attempt to verify the prediction.

For each of these different kinds of verification, the approximate begin-time (end-time if verifying an antecedent prediction) of the word being predicted following (preceding) the phrase is taken to be the end-time (begin-time) of the phrase. The end-time (begin-time) of the predicted word is not known, and in fact one function of the verification step is to generate an approximate end-time (begin-time) for the verified word. In general, it is possible to generate several different 'versions' of the word which differ primarily in their end-times (begin-times); since no context following (preceding) the predicted word is given, several different estimates of the end (beginning) of the word may be plausible solely on the basis of the segmental information. These alternatives give rise to the creation of competing hypotheses.

VERIFY is invoked when a KS (PREDICT) places a 'word-predictor' attribute on a phrase hypothesis. For each word on the attribute list that it verifies, it creates a word hypothesis (if one does not already exist), and the word is placed on a 'word-verification' attribute of the phrase hypothesis. Word hypotheses created by VERIFY are shown in Figure 3.4(f).

The CONCAT KS (Hayes-Roth et al., 1977a) is invoked on phrase hypotheses which have word-verification attributes attached. For each verified word, the phrase and new word are parsed together and a new, extended phrase hypothesis is created (as shown in Figure 3.4(h)). The new hypothesis receives a rating based on the ratings of its component words. If all word predictions preceding or following the phrase had been rejected, the phrase hypothesis itself would be marked as 'rejected'.

Similarly, the underlying word-sequence hypothesis is rejected if all the phrase hypotheses it supports are rejected. (This action would retrigger WORD-SEQ to generate more word sequences.)

Step 11   KS: PREDICT & VERIFY*
   Stimulus: [+ARE* (phrase).
   Action: Predict (from the grammar) 292 words following. Reject (using the acoustic information) 277 of them. The four highest rated of the 15 verified words are
   REDDY(85, 26:52),
   ANY*(65, 24:49),
   HUGH(55, 30:39), and
   YOU(55, 28:39).

Step 12   KS: CONCAT
   Stimulus: [+ARE* (phrase), REDDY (word).
   Action: Create phrase: [+ARE+REDDY (91, 0:52).

Step 13   KS: CONCAT*
   Stimulus: [+ARE* (phrase), ANY* (word).
   Action: Create phrase: [+ARE+ANY* (86, 0:49).

In steps 11 through 13 the highly rated phrase [+ARE is extended and results in the generation of the additional phrases [+ARE+REDDY and [+ARE+ANY. These phrases, however, are not immediately extended because the predicted words REDDY and ANY are not rated sufficiently high. Instead, the scheduler, pursuing a strategy more conservative than strict best-first, investigates phrases that look almost as good as the best one. This scheduling strategy results in the execution of the PREDICT and VERIFY KSs on two of the other initial phrase islands: AND+FELDMAN+] and EIGHT.

Step 14   KS: PREDICT & VERIFY*
   Stimulus: AND+FELDMAN+]* (phrase).
   Action: Predict 100 words preceding. Reject 76 of them. The best of the verified 24 (in descending rating order) are

   FEIGENBAUM*(80, 72:150),
   WEIZENBAUM(70, 72:150),
   ULLMAN(70, 116:150),
   NORMAN(70, 108:150), and
   NEWBORN(70, 108:150).

Step 15   KS: PREDICT & VERIFY
   Stimulus: EIGHT (phrase).
   Action: Predict the word NINE following and verify it (80, 52:82). Predict SEVEN preceding, but reject this because of mismatch with the acoustic segments.

The attempt to extend the phrase EIGHT at step 15 is not successful; none of the grammatically predicted words is acoustically verified, even using a lenient threshold. Thus this phrase is marked rejected and is dropped from further consideration.

Step 16 KS: CONCAT*
Stimulus: FEIGENBAUM* (word), AND+FELDMAN+]* (phrase).
Action: Create phrase: FEIGENBAUM+AND+FELDMAN+]* (85, 72:225).

Beginning with step 16, extending the phrase AND+FELDMAN+] with the highly rated word FEIGENBAUM looks sufficiently promising for processing to continue now in a more depth-first manner along the path FEIGENBAUM+AND+FELDMAN+] through step 25. The rating on a hypothesis is only one parameter used by the scheduler to assign priorities to waiting KS instantiations. In particular, the length of a hypothesis is also important. Thus, FEIGENBAUM with a rating of 80 looks better than REDDY with a rating of 85 because it is much longer. Processing on the path [+ARE+REDDY does not resume until step 26.

Step 17 KS: PREDICT & VERIFY*
Stimulus: FEIGENBAUM+AND+FELDMAN+]* (phrase).
Action: Predict eight preceding words. Reject one (DISCUSS). Find two already on the blackboard:

BY*(80, 52:72) and
ABOUT(75, 48:72).

Verify five others:

NOT(75, 49:82),
ED(75, 67:72),
CITE(70, 49:82),
QUOTE(70, 49:82),
CITES(65, 49:82).

In steps 18 through 24, alternative word extensions of FEIGENBAUM+AND+FELDMAN+] are explored. As a result of this exploration the phrase BY+FEIGENBAUM+AND+FELDMAN+] is considered the most credible.

Step 18 KS CONCAT*
Stimulus: BY* (word), FEIGENBAUM+AND+FELDMAN+]* (phrase).
Action: Create phrase: BY+FEIGENBAUM+AND+FELDMAN+]* (84, 52:225).

Step 19 KS: CONCAT
Stimulus: ABOUT (word), FEIGENBAUM+AND+FELDMAN+]* (phrase).
Action: Create phrase: ABOUT+FEIGENBAUM+AND+FELDMAN+] (83, 48:225).

Step 20   KS: PREDICT & VERIFY
Stimulus: ABOUT+FEIGENBAUM+AND+FELDMAN+] (phrase).
Action: Predict one preceding word: WHAT. Verify it (10, 20:49).

Step 21   KS: CONCAT
Stimulus: CITE (word), FEIGENBAUM+AND+FELDMAN+] (phrase).
Action: Create phrase: CITE+FEIGENBAUM+AND+FELDMAN+] (83, 49:225).

Step 22   KS: PREDICT & VERIFY
Stimulus: CITE+FEIGENBAUM+AND+FELDMAN+] (phrase).
Action: Predict four preceding words. Reject two of them: BOOKS, PAPERS. Verify
THESE (25, 28:49),
YEAR (20, 30:49).

Step 23   KS: PREDICT & VERIFY*
Stimulus: BY+FEIGENBAUM+AND+FELDMAN+]* (phrase).
Action: Predict ten preceding words. Reject five: ABSTRACTS, ARE, BOOKS, PAPERS, REFERENCED. Find two already on the blackboard:
ANY* (65, 24:49),
THESE (25, 28:49).

Verify three more:
ARTICLE (25, 9:52),
WRITTEN (25, 24:52),
ARTICLES (10, 9:52).

Step 24   KS: CONCAT
Stimulus: NOT (word), FEIGENBAUM+AND+FELDMAN+]*.
Action: Create phrase: NOT+FEIGENBAUM+AND+FELDMAN+] (83, 49:225).

Step 25   KS: CONCAT*
Stimulus: ANY*   (word),   BY+FEIGENBAUM+AND+FELDMAN+]*
(phrase).
Action: Create phrase: ANY+BY+FEIGENBAUM+AND+FELDMAN+]*
(82, 24:225). [+ARE+ANY+BY+FEIGENBAUM+AND+FELDMAN+]*
(85, 0:225) is also created, from [+ARE+ANY and BY+
FEIGENBAUM+AND+FELDMAN+].

In step 25 the word ANY is concatenated onto the phrase BY+FEIGENBAUM+AND+FELDMAN+]. However, instead of only creating this new combined phrase, the CONCAT KS also notices that the word ANY is the last word of the phrase [+ARE+ANY; this leads the CONCAT KS to merge the two adjacent phrases [+ARE+ANY and BY+ FEIGENBAUM+AND+FELDMAN+] into a single phrase, after first ascertaining that the resulting phrase is grammatical. This merging bypasses the several single-word PREDICT, VERIFY and CONCAT actions needed to generate the enlarged hypothesis from either of the two original hypotheses in an incremental fashion. Thus the recognition process is sped up in two ways:

(1)   several single-word actions are eliminated, and

(2)   the scheduler postpones KS actions on competing (incorrect) hypotheses since these potential actions seem less attractive than actions on the new, enlarged hypothesis.

Such mergings occur in approximately half of the runs on the 1011-word grammar with the small branching factor (X05); in grammars with higher branching factors, the merging of phrase hypotheses occurs with even higher frequency.

It has been our experience that just as a multiword island is more credible than the individual words that compose it, so a merged phrase hypothesis is more credible than its two constituent phrases. For example, about 80% of the mergings in X05 runs produce correct hypotheses. In more complex grammars this statistic drops to about 35%, but correspondingly more phrase mergings occur.

The newly created merged phrase also happens to be a complete sentence; i.e. it has begin- and end-of-utterance markers as its extreme constituents. Thus it is a candidate for the interpretation of the utterance.

Step 26   KS: STOP
   Stimulus: [+ARE+ANY+BY+FEIGENBAUM+AND+FELDMAN+]* (complete sentence).
   Action: Deactivation of several dozen competing hypotheses.

These start- and end-of-utterance 'words' (denoted by [and]) appear in the syntactic specification of the language as the first and last terminals of every complete sentence. Thus any verified phrase that includes these as its extreme constituents is a complete sentence and spans the entire utterance. Such a sentence becomes a candidate for selection as the system's recognition result.

In general, the control and rating strategies do not guarantee that the first such complete spanning hypothesis found will have the highest rating of all possible spanning sentence hypotheses that might be found if the search were allowed to continue, so the system does not just stop with the first one generated. (An alternative control strategy based on the shortfall density scoring function and assumptions of the completeness of processing at the word level can guarantee that the first complete interpretation generated is the best possible (see Section 3.3.1). This results in a more conservative, breadth-first search, in which more alternatives are explored.) However, the characteristics of such a hypothesis are used by the STOP knowledge source to prune from further consideration other partial hypotheses which, because of their low ratings, are unlikely to be extendible into spanning hypotheses with ratings higher than the best already-discovered spanning sentence. This heuristic pruning procedure is based on the form of the ratings function (i.e. how the rating of the phrase is derived from its constituent words). The pruning procedure considers each partial phrase and uses the ratings of other word hypotheses in the time areas not covered by the phrase to determine if the phrase might be extendible to a phrase rated higher than the spanning hypothesis; if not, the partial phrase is pruned. This pruning process and the rating and halting policies are discussed in Mostow (1977).

Of the hypotheses not discarded, extensions to the phrase [+ARE now appear as the most likely candidates to produce new and better complete phrases. This search for better complete phrases results, in steps 27 through 36, in the examination of numerous alternative extensions, each of which is promising.

Step 27   KS: PREDICT & VERIFY
  Stimulus: [+ARE+REDDY.
  Action: Predict three following words. Verify CITED (60, 52:86), OR (30, 52:67), AND (25, 52:82).

Step 28   KS: CONCAT
  Stimulus: [+ARE* (phrase), HUGH (word).
  Action: Create phrase: [+ARE+HUGH (83, 0:39).

Step 29   KS: CONCAT
  Stimulus: [+ARE (phrase), YOU (word).
  Action: Create phrase: [+ARE+YOU (83, 0:39).

Step 30   KS: CONCAT
  Stimulus: [ARE+REDDY (phrase), CITED (word).
  Action: Create phrase: [+ARE+REDDY+CITED (80, 0:86).

Step 31   KS: PREDICT & VERIFY
  Stimulus: [+ARE+REDDY+CITED (phrase).
  Action: Predict two following words. Verify BY (75, 83:98), IN (20, 86:114).

Step 32   KS: CONCAT
  Stimulus: [+ARE+REDDY+CITED (phrase), BY (word).
  Action: Create phrase: [ARE+REDDY+CITED+BY (80, 0:98).

Step 33   KS: PREDICT & VERIFY
  Stimulus: [+ARE+REDDY+CITED+BY (phrase).
  Action: Predict one following word. Verify ANY (30, 105:126).

Step 34   KS: PREDICT & VERIFY
  Stimulus: [+ARE+HUGH (phrase).
  Action: Predict one following word. Verify NAGEL (40, 42:63).

Step 35   KS: PREDICT & VERIFY
  Stimulus: [+ARE+YOU (phrase).
  Action: Predict three following words. Reject USUALLY. Verify
    REGULARLY (25, 39:116),
    ALWAYS (15, 39:72).

Step 36   KS: CONCAT
    Stimulus: [+ARE+REDDY (phrase), OR (word).
    Action: Create phrase: [+ARE+REDDY+OR (79, 0:67).

Step 37   KS: CONCAT
    Stimulus: [+ARE+REDDY (phrase), AND (word).
    Action: Create phrase [+ARE+REDDY+AND (78, 0:82).

Step 38   KS: STOP
    Stimulus: Stagnation
    Action: Stop search and accept [+ARE+ANY+BY+FEIGENBAUM+
    AND+FELDMAN+]*.

The recognition processing finally halts in one of two ways: First, there may be no more partial hypotheses left to consider for prediction and extension. Because of the combinatorics of the grammar and the likelihood of finding some prediction rated at least above the absolute rejection threshold, this termination happens when the heuristic pruning procedure used by STOP and RPOL has eliminated all competitors. Such a halt occurs here as STOP decides to terminate the search process and accept the phrase [+ARE+ANY+BY+FEIGENBAUM+AND+FELDMAN+] as the correct interpretation. In general there might be more than one complete sentence hypothesis at this point; STOP would select the one with the highest rating.

A second kind of halt occurs if the system expends its total allowed computing resources (time or space). (The actual thresholds used are set according to the past performance of the system on similar sentences, i.e. of the given length and over the same vocabulary and grammar.) In that case a selection of several of the highest rated phrase hypotheses is the result of the recognition process, with the selection biased toward the longest phrases which overlap (in time) the least.

Step 39   KS: SEMANT*.
    Stimulus: Recognized utterance: [+ARE+ANY+BY+FEIGENBAUM+
    AND+FELDMAN+]*.
    Action: Generate an interpretation for the database retrieval system.

The SEMANT knowledge source (Fox and Mostow, 1977) takes the word sequence(s) result of the recognition process and constructs an interpretation in an unambiguous format for interaction with the database that the speaker is querying. The interpretation is constructed by actions associated with 'semantically interesting' nonterminals (which have been prespecified for the grammar) in the parse tree(s) of the recognized sequence(s). In our example the following structure is produced:

```
F:[U:([ARE ANY BY FEIGENBAUM AND FELDMAN])
  N:($PRUNE!LIST
    S:($PRUNE!LIST!AUTHOR  K:(A:((FEIGENBAUM * FELDMAN)))))]
```

F denotes the total message. U contains the utterance itself. N indicates the main type of the utterance (e.g. PRUNE a previously specified list of citations, REQUEST, HELP), S the subtype (e.g. PRUNE a list according to its author). K denotes the different attributes associated with the utterance (e.g. A is the author, T is the topic).

If recognition produces more than one partial sequence, SEMANT constructs a maximally consistent interpretation based on all of the partial sentences, taking into account the rating, temporal position and semantic consistency of the partial sentences.

The DISCO (discourse) knowledge source (Hayes-Roth *et al.*, 1977b) accepts the formatted interpretation of SEMANT and produces a response to the speaker. This response is often the display of a selected portion of the queried database. In order to retain a coherent interpretation across sentences, DISCO maintains a finite-state model of the ongoing discourse.

3.3 Comparison with other speech-understanding systems

In addition to Hearsay-II, several other speech-understanding systems were also developed as part of the Defense Advanced Research Projects Agency (DARPA) research program in speech understanding from 1971 to 1976 (Medress *et al.*, 1978). As a way of concretely orienting the research, a common set of system performance goals, shown in Table 3.3, was established by the study committee that launched the project (Newell *et al.*, 1973). All of the systems are based on the idea of diverse, cooperating KSs to handle the uncertainty in the signal and processing. They differ in the types of knowledge, interactions of knowledge, representation of search space, and control of the search. (They also differ in the tasks and languages handled, but we do not address those here.) In this section we describe three of these systems: Bolt, Beranek and Newman's (BBN's) HWIM, Stanford Research Institute's (SRI's) system, and Carnegie-Mellon University's (CMU's) HARPY, and compare them with Hearsay-II along those dimensions. (IBM has been funding work with a somewhat different objective (Bahl *et al.*, 1976). Its stated goals mandate little reliance on the strong syntactic/semantic/task constraints exploited by the DARPA projects. This orientation is usually dubbed *speech recognition* as distinguished from *speech understanding*.) For consistency we will use the terminology developed in this paper in so far as possible, even though it is often not identical to that used by the designers of each of the other systems.

Although the performance specifications had the strong effect of pointing the various efforts in the same directions, the backgrounds and motivations of each group led to different emphases. For example, BBN's

Table 3.3 DARPA speech-understanding system performance goals set in 1971. (After Newell *et al.*, 1973 and Medress *et al.*, 1978)

The system should:
- accept connected speech
- from many
- cooperative speakers of the General American Dialect
- in a quiet room
- using a good-quality microphone
- with slight tuning per speaker
- requiring only natural adaptation by the user
- permitting a slightly selected vocabulary of 1000 words
- with a highly artificial syntax and highly constrained task
- providing graceful interaction
- tolerating less than 10% semantic error
- in a few times real time on a 100-million-instructions-per-second machine
- and be demonstrable in 1976 with a moderate chance of success.

---

expertise in natural-language processing and acoustic-phonetics led to an emphasis on those KSs; SRI's interest in semantics and discourse strongly influenced its system design; and CMU's predilection for system organization placed that in the central position (and led to the Hearsay-II and HARPY structures).

3.3.1 BBN's HWIM system

Figure 3.5 shows the structure of BBN's HWIM (Hear What I Mean) system (Woods *et al.*, 1976; Wolf and Woods, 1980). In overall form, HWIM's general processing structure is strikingly similar to that of Hearsay-II. Processing of a sentence is bottom-up through audio signal digitization, parameter extraction, segmentation and labeling, and a scan for word hypotheses; this phase is roughly similar to Hearsay-II's initial bottom-up processing up through the MOW KS.

Following this initial phase, the Control Strategy module takes charge, calling the Syntax and Lexical Retrieval KSs as subroutines:

- The grammar is represented as an augmented transition network (Woods, 1970) and, as in Hearsay-II, includes semantic and pragmatic knowledge of the domain (in this case, 'travel planning'). The Syntax KS combines the functions of Hearsay-II's PREDICT and CONCAT KSs. Like them, it handles contiguous sequences of words

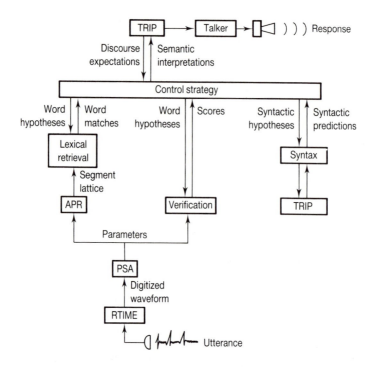

Figure 3.5   Structure of HWIM. (From Wolf and Woods, 1980)

in the language, independently of the phrase structure nonterminal boundaries, as well as the merging of phrase hypotheses (i.e. island collision).

- The Lexical Retriever functions in this phase much like Hearsay-II's VERIFY KS, rating the acoustic match of a predicted word at one end of a phrase. Some configurations of HWIM also have a KS which does an independent, highly reliable, and very expensive word verification; that KS is also called directly by the Control Strategy.

- The Control Strategy module schedules the Syntax and Lexical Retrieval KSs opportunistically. To this end it keeps a task agenda that prioritizes the actions on the most promising phrase hypotheses. The task agenda is initialized with single-word phrase hypotheses constructed from the best word hypotheses generated in the bottom-up phase.

Given these similarities between HWIM and Hearsay-II, what besides the content of the KSs (which we do not address) are the differences? The most significant differences involve the mechanisms for instantiating KSs, scheduling KSs (i.e. selective attention for controlling the search), and representing, accessing and combining KS results. These differences stem primarily from differing design philosophies:

- The Hearsay-II design was based on the assumption that a very general and flexible model for KS interaction patterns was required because the type, number and interaction patterns of KSs would change substantially over the lifetime of the system (Lesser *et al.*, 1975; Lesser and Erman, 1977). Thus we rejected an explicit subroutine-like architecture for KS interaction because it reduces modularity. Rather, the implicit data-directed approach was taken, in which KSs interact uniformly and anonymously via the blackboard.

- The HWIM design evolved out of an *incremental simulation* methodology (Woods and Makhoul, 1973). In this methodology the overall system is implemented initially with some combination of computer programs and human simulators, with the latter filling the role of components (i.e. KSs and scheduling) not fully conceptualized. As experience is gained, the human simulators are replaced by computer programs. Thus by the time the system has evolved into a fully operational computer program, the type of KSs and their interaction patterns are expected to be stable. Modifications after this point aim to improve the performance of individual KSs and their scheduling, with only minor changes expected in KS interaction patterns. From this perspective, developing specific explicit structures for explicit KS interactions is reasonable.

Thus HWIM has an explicit control strategy, in which KSs directly call each other, and in which the scheduler has built-in knowledge about the specific KSs in the system. The Hearsay-II scheduler has no such built-in knowledge but rather is given an abstract description of each KS instantiation by its creator condition program.

Similarly, one KS communicates with another in HWIM via *ad hoc* KS-specific data structures. The introduction of a new KS is expected to occur very rarely and requires either that it adopt some other KS's existing data representation or that its new formats be integrated into those KSs that will interact with it. Hearsay-II's blackboard, on the other hand, provides a uniform representation which facilitates experimentation with new or highly modified KSs.

When one KS in a hierarchical structure like that in HWIM calls another, it provides the called KS with those data it deems relevant. The called KS also uses whatever data it has retained internally plus what it might acquire by calling other KSs. Hearsay-II's blackboard, on the other hand, provides a place for all data known to all the KSs; one KS can use data created by a previous KS execution without the creator of the data having to know which KS will use the data and without the user KS having to know which KS might be able to create the data.

The ability to embed into the HWIM system a detailed model of the KSs and their interaction patterns has had its most profound effect on the techniques developed for scheduling. Several alternative scheduling policies were implemented in the Control Strategy module. The most interesting of these, the 'shortfall density scoring strategy' (Woods, 1977) can be shown formally to guarantee that the first complete sentence hypothesis constructed by the system is the best possible (i.e. highest rated) such hypothesis that it will ever be able to construct. Heuristic search strategies with this property are called *admissible* (Nilsson, 1971). This contrasts with the *approximate* Hearsay-II scheduling strategy, in which there is no guarantee at any point that a better interpretation cannot be found by continued search. Thus Hearsay-II requires a heuristic stopping decision, as described in Section 3.2.2. In HWIM an admissible strategy is possible because the scheduler can make some strong assumptions about the nature of KS processing: in particular, the algorithms used by the Lexical Retriever KS are such that it does not subsequently generate a higher rating for a predicted word than that of the highest rated word predicted in that utterance location by the initial, bottom-up processing.

An admissible strategy eliminates errors which an approximate strategy may make by stopping too soon. However, even when an admissible strategy can be constructed, it may not be preferable if it generates excessive additional search in order to guarantee its admissibility. More discussion of this issue in speech understanding can be found in Wolf and Woods (1980), Woods (1977), Mostow (1977) and Hayes-Roth (1980). Discussions of it in more general cases can be found in Pohl (1970, 1977) and Harris (1974).

Given that hypotheses are rated by KSs, combining on a single hypothesis several ratings generated by different KSs is a problem. A similar problem also occurs within a KS when constructing a hypothesis from several lower-level hypotheses; the rating of the new one should reflect the combination of ratings of its components. Hearsay-II uses *ad hoc* schemes for such rating combinations (Hayes-Roth *et al.*, 1977). HWIM takes a formal approach, using an application of Bayes' theorem. To implement this, each KS's ratings are calibrated by using performance statistics gathered on test data. This uniform scheme for calibration and combination of ratings facilitates adding and modifying KSs. The issue of evaluating the combination of evidence from multiple sources is a recurrent problem in knowledge-based systems (Shortliffe and Buchanan, 1975; Duda *et al.*, 1978).

3.3.2 SRI's system

The SRI system (Walker, 1978, 1980), though never fully operational on a large vocabulary task, presents another interesting variant on structuring a speech-understanding system. Like the HWIM system, it uses an explicit control strategy with, however, much more control being centralized in the Control Strategy module. The designers of the system felt there was 'a large potential for mutual guidance that would not be realized if all knowledge source communication was indirect' (Walker, 1978, p. 84). Part of this explicit control is embedded within the rules that define the phrases of the task grammar, each rule, in addition to defining the possible constituent structure for phrases in an extended form of BNF, contains procedures for calculating attributes of phrases and factors used in rating phrases. These procedures may, in turn, call as subroutines any of the knowledge sources in the system. The attributes include acoustic attributes related to the input signal, syntactic attributes (e.g. mood and number), semantic attributes such as the representation of the meaning of the phrase, and discourse attributes for anaphora and ellipsis. Thus the phrase itself is the basic unit for integrating and controlling knowledge-source execution.

The interpreter of these rules (i.e. the Syntax module) is integrated with the scheduling components to define a high-level Control Strategy module. Like Hearsay-II and HWIM, this control module opportunistically executes the syntax rules to predict new phrases and words from a given phrase hypothesis and executes the word verifier to verify predicted words. This module maintains a data structure, the 'parse-net', containing all the word and phrase hypotheses constructed, and the attributes and factors associated with each hypothesis. This data structure is similar to a Hearsay-II blackboard restricted to the word and phrase levels. Like the blackboard, it serves to avoid redundant computation and facilitates the detection of possible island collisions.

As with Hearsay-II and HWIM, the SRI Control Strategy module is parameterized to permit a number of different strategies, such as top-down, bottom-up, island-driving and left-to-right. Using a simulated word recognizer, SRI ran a series of experiments with several different strategies. One of the results, also substantiated by BBN experiments with HWIM, is that island-driving is inferior to some forms of left-to-right search. This appears to be in conflict with the Hearsay-II experimental results, which show island-driving to be clearly superior (Lesser et al., 1977). We believe the difference to be caused by the reliability of ratings of the initial islands: both the HWIM and SRI experiments used single-word islands, but Hearsay-II uses multiword islands, which produce much higher reliability. (See the discussion at step 6 in Section 3.2.2 and in Hayes-Roth (1978).) Single-word island-driving proved inferior in Hearsay-II as well.

3.3.3 CMU's HARPY system

In the systems described so far, knowledge sources are discernible as active components during the understanding process. However, if one looks at Hearsay-II, HWIM and the SRI system in that order, there is clearly a progression of increasing integration of the KSs with the control structure. The HARPY system (Lowerre, 1976; Lowerre and Reddy, 1980) developed at Carnegie-Mellon University is located at the far extreme of that dimension: most of the knowledge is precompiled into a unified structure representing all possible utterances; a relatively simple interpreter then compares the spoken utterance against this structure to find the utterance that matches best. The motivation for this approach is to speed up the search so that a larger portion of the space may be examined explicitly. In particular, the hope is to avoid errors made when portions of the search space are eliminated on the basis of characteristics of small partial solutions; to this end, pruning decisions are delayed until larger partial solutions are constructed.

To describe HARPY, we describe the knowledge sources, their compilation, and the match (search) process. The *parameterization* and *segmentation* KSs are identical to those of Hearsay-II (Goldberg *et al.*, 1977; Gill *et al.*, 1978); these are not compiled into the network but, as in the other systems, applied to each utterance as it is spoken. As in Hearsay-II, the *syntax* is specified as a set of context-free production rules; HARPY uses the same task and grammar definitions. *Lexical* knowledge is specified as a directed pronunciation graph for each word; for example, Figure 3.6 shows the graph for the word 'please'. The nodes in the graph are names of the phonelike labels also generated by the labeler KS. A graph is intended to represent all possible pronunciations of the word. Knowledge about phonetic phenomena at *word junctures* is contained in a set of rewriting rules for the pronunciation graphs.

For a given task language, syntax and lexical and juncture knowledge are combined by a *knowledge compiler* program to form a single large network. First, the grammar is converted into a directed

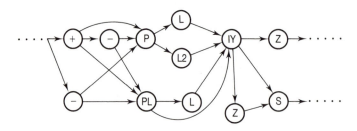

Figure 3.6   HARPY pronunciation network for the word 'Please'. (After Lowerre and Reddy, 1980)

Table 3.4   A tiny example grammar. (After Lowerre and Reddy, 1980)

⟨SENT⟩	::==	[⟨SS⟩]
⟨SS⟩	::==	please help ⟨M⟩ | please show ⟨M⟩ ⟨Q⟩
⟨Q⟩	::==	everything | something
⟨M⟩	::==	me | us

graph, the 'word network', containing only terminal symbols (i.e. words); because of heuristics used to compact this network, some of the constraint of the original grammar may be lost. Table 3.4 shows a toy grammar, and Figure 3.7 the resulting word network. Next, the compiler replaces each word by a copy of its pronunciation graph, applying the word-juncture rules at all the word boundaries. Figure 3.8 shows part of the network for the toy example. The resulting network has the name of a segment label at each node. For the same 1011-word X05 language used by Hearsay-II, the network has 15 000 nodes and took 13 h of DEC PDP-10 (KL-10) processing time to compile.

In the network each distinct path from the distinguished start node to the distinguished end node represents a sequence of segments making up a 'legal' utterance. The purpose of the search is to find the sequence which most closely matches the segment sequence of the input spoken utterance. For any given labeled segment and any given node in the network, a primitive match algorithm can calculate a score for matching the node to the segment. The score for matching a sequence of nodes with a sequence of segments is just the sum of the corresponding primitive matches.

The search technique used, called *beam search*, is a heuristic form of dynamic programming, with the input segments processed one at a time from left to right and matched against the network. At the beginning of the ith step, the first $i - 1$ segments have been processed. Some number of nodes in the network are *active*; associated with each active node is a path to it from the start node and the total score of the match between

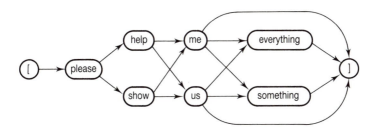

Figure 3.7   Word network for example language. (After Lowerre and Reddy, 1980)

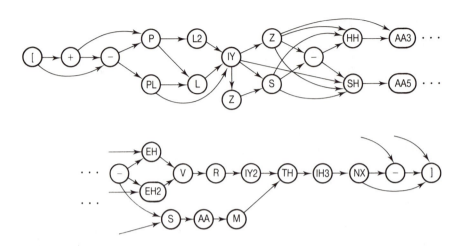

Figure 3.8 Partial final network for example language. (After Lowerre and Reddy, 1980)

that path and the first $i - 1$ segments of the utterance. All nodes in the network that are successors of the active nodes are matched against the ith segment and become the new active nodes. The score for a new active node is the best path score that reaches the node at the ith segment, i.e. the sum of the primitive match at the segment plus the best path score to any of its predecessor nodes.

The best path score among all the new active nodes is taken as the target, and any new active nodes with path scores more than some threshold amount from the target are pruned away. This pruning rule is the heuristic heart of the search algorithm. It reduces the number of active nodes at each step and thus reduces the amount of processing time (and storage) needed in the search; typically only about 3% of the nodes in the net need to be matched. Note that the heuristic does not fix the number of active nodes retained at each step but allows it to vary with the density of competitors with scores near the best path. Thus in highly uncertain regions, many nodes are retained and the search slows down; in places where one path is significantly better than most others, few competitors are kept, and the processing is rapid. The search strategy is, therefore, automatically cautious or decisive in response to the partial results. The threshold, i.e. the 'beam width', is tuned *ad hoc* from test runs.

There are two major concerns about the extensibility of HARPY. First, the compilation process requires all knowledge to be represented in a highly stylized form; adding new kinds of knowledge strains the developer's ingenuity. So far, however, several kinds of knowledge have been added within the basic framework of expanding a node by replacing it with a graph. For example, as mentioned previously, phonetic phenomena at word junctures are handled. Also, the expected length of each segment is stored at each node and influences the match score. The second concern is with the size and compilation cost of the compiled network; both grow very large as the task language becomes more complex. There have been proposals that the word network not be expanded explicitly, but rather that the word pronunciation graphs be interpreted dynamically, as needed. An alternative response to this concern is that computer memory and processing costs continue to decline, so that using larger networks becomes increasingly feasible.

HARPY's novel structure is also interesting in its own right and is beginning to have effects beyond speech-understanding systems. Newell has done a speculative but thorough analysis of HARPY as a model for human speech and understanding, using the production system formalism (Newell, 1980); Rubin (1978) has successfully applied the HARPY structure to an image-understanding task.

3.4 System performance and analysis

3.4.1 Overall performance of Hearsay-II

Overall performance of the Hearsay-II speech-understanding system at the end of 1976 is summarized in Table 3.5 in a form paralleling the goals given in Table 3.3.

Active development of the Hearsay-II speech system ceased at the end of 1976 with the conclusion of the speech-understanding program sponsored by DARPA (Medress *et al.*, 1978; Klatt, 1977). Even though the configuration of KSs at that point was young, having been assembled in August 1976, the performance described in Table 3.5 comes close to meeting the ambitious goals, shown in Table 3.3, established for the DARPA program in 1971 (Newell *et al.*, 1973). This overall performance supports our assertion that the Hearsay-II architecture can be used to integrate knowledge for resolving uncertainty. In the following sections we relate some detailed analyses of the Hearsay-II performance to the resolution of uncertainty. We finish with some comparison with the performances of the other systems described in Section 3.3.

3.4.2 Opportunistic scheduling

In earlier KS configurations of the system, low-level processing (i.e. at the segment, syllable and word levels) was not done in the serial, lock-step manner of steps 1, 4 and 5 of the example, that is, level-to-level, where each level is completely processed before work on the next higher

Table 3.5   Hearsay-II performance.

Number of speakers	One
Environment	Computer terminal room (>65 dB)
Microphone	Medium-quality, close-talking
System speaker-tuning	20–30 training utterances
Speaker adaptation	None required
Task	Document retrieval
Vocabulary	1011 words, with no selection for phonetic discriminability
Language constraints	Context-free semantic grammar, based on protocol analysis, with static branching factor of 10
Test data	23 utterances, brand-new to the system and run 'blind'. 7 words/utterance average, 2.6 seconds/utterance average, average fanout[†] of 40 (maximum 292)
Accuracy	9% sentence semantic error,[‡] 19% sentence error (i.e. not word-for-word correct)
Computing resources	60 MIPSS (million instructions per second of speech) on 36-bit PDP-10

[†] The *static branching factor* is the average number of words that can follow any initial sequence as defined by the grammar. The *fanout* is the number of words that can follow any initial sequence in the test sentences.

[‡] An interpretation is *semantically correct* if the query generated for it by the SEMANT KS is identical to that generated for a sentence which is *word-for-word* correct.

level is begun. Rather, processing was opportunistic and data-directed as in the higher levels; as interesting hypotheses were generated at one level, they were immediately propagated to and processed by KSs operating at higher and lower levels. We found, however, that opportunistic processing at the lower levels was ineffective and harmful because the credibility ratings of hypotheses were insufficiently accurate to form hypothesis islands capable of focusing the search effectively. For example, even at the relatively high word level, the bottom-up hypotheses created by MOW include only about 75% of the words actually spoken; and the KS-assigned ratings rank each correct hypothesis on the average about 4.5 as compared with the 20 or so incorrect hypotheses that compete with it (i.e. which overlap it in time significantly). It is only with the word-sequence hypotheses that the reliability of the ratings is high enough to allow selective search.

Several experiments have shown the effectiveness of the opportunistic search. In one (Hayes-Roth and Lesser, 1977) the opportunistic scheduling was contrasted with a strategy using no ordering of KS activations. Here, all KS precondition procedures were executed, followed by all KS activations they created; this cycle was repeated. For the utterances tested, the opportunistic strategy had a 29% error rate (word for word), compared with a 48% rate for the nonopportunistic. Also, the opportunistic strategy took less than half as much processing time.

The performance results given here and in the following sections reflect various configurations of vocabularies, grammars, test data, halting criteria and states of development of the KSs and underlying system. Thus the absolute performance results of each experiment are not directly comparable to the performance reported in Section 3.4.1 or to the results of the other experiments.

In another experiment (Lesser *et al.*, 1977) the island-driving strategy, which is opportunistic across the whole utterance, was compared with a left-to-right strategy, in which the high-level search was initiated from single-word islands in utterance-initial position. For the utterances tested, the opportunistic strategy had a 33% error rate as compared with 53% for the left-to-right; for those utterances correctly recognized by both strategies, the opportunistic one used only 70% as much processing time.

3.4.3 Use of approximate knowledge

In several places the Hearsay-II system uses approximate knowledge, as opposed to its more complete form also included in the system. The central notion is that even though the approximation increases the likelihood of particular decisions being incorrect, other knowledge can correct those errors, and the amount of computational resources saved by first using the approximation exceeds that required for subsequent corrections.

The organization of the POM and MOW KSs is an example. The bottom-up syllable and word-candidate generation scheme approximates WIZARD matching all words in the vocabulary at all places in the utterance, but in a fraction of the time. The errors show up as poor ratings of the candidate words and as missing correct words among the candidates. The POM–MOW errors are corrected by applying WIZARD to the candidates to create good ratings and by having the PREDICT KS generate additional candidates.

Another example is the WORD-SEQ KS. Recall that it applies syntactic and acoustic-phonetic knowledge to locate sequences of words within the lattice of bottom-up words and statistical knowledge to select a few most credible sequences. The syntactic knowledge only approximates the full grammar, but takes less than 1% as much processing time to apply. The errors WORD-SEQ makes because of the approximation (i.e. generating some nongrammatical sequences) are corrected by applying the full grammatical knowledge of the PARSE KS, but only on the few, highly credible sequences WORD-SEQ identifies.

Table 3.6   Hearsay-II performance under varying vocabularies and grammars.

Vocabulary	Grammar		
	05	*15*	*F*
S 250 words	err = 5.9% comp = 1.0 fanout = 10	err = 20.6% comp = 2.7 fanout = 17	err = 20.6% comp = 3.4 fanout = 27
M 500 words	err = 5.9% comp = 1.1 fanout = 18		
X 1011 words	err = 11.8% comp = 2.0 fanout = 36		

err = semantic error rate.
comp = average ratio of execution time to that of S05 case, for correct utterances.
fanout = fanout of the test sentences (see notes to Table 3.5, Section 3.4.2).
N = 34 utterances.

3.4.4 Adaptability of the opportunistic strategy

The opportunistic search strategy adapts automatically to changing
conditions of uncertainty in the problem-solving process by changing the
breadth of search. The basic mechanism for this is the interaction
between the KS-assigned credibility ratings on hypotheses and scheduler-
assigned priorities of pending KS activations. When hypotheses have
been rated approximately equal, KS activations for their extension are
usually scheduled together. Thus, where there is ambiguity among
competing hypotheses, the scheduler automatically searches with more
breadth. This delays the choice among competing hypotheses until further
information is brought to bear.

   This adaptiveness works for changing conditions of uncertainty,
whether it arises from the data or from the knowledge. The data-caused
changes are evidenced by large variations in the numbers of competing
hypotheses considered at various locations in an utterance, and by the
large variance in the processing time needed for recognizing utterances.
The results of changing conditions of knowledge constraint can be seen in
Table 3.6, which shows the results of one experiment varying vocabulary
sizes and grammatical constraints. Note that Table 3.6 shows imperfect
correlation between fanout and performance; compare, for example, X05
and SF. Fanout is an approximate measure of language complexity that
reflects the average uncertainty between adjacent words. While X05 has a
large fanout, it may be a simpler language to interpret than SF because
most of the fanout is restricted to a few loci in the language, as opposed
to the lower but more uniform uncertainty of SF.

Table 3.7 Goals and performance for final (1976) DARPA systems. (After Lea and Shoup, 1979)

GOAL: Accept continuous speech from many cooperative speakers

HARPY:		184		3 male, 2 female	
Hearsay-II:	tested	22	sentences	1 male	speakers
HWIM:	with	124	from	3 male	
SDC:		54		1 male	

GOAL: In a quiet room, with a good mic, and slight tuning/speaker

HARPY:			20	
Hearsay-II:	in a computer terminal room, with a close-talking mic,	and	20	training sentences per speaker,
HWIM:			no	
SDC:	in a quiet room, with a good mic,	and	no	

GOAL: Accepting 1000 words, using an artificial syntax and constraining task

HARPY:	1011 words, context-free	BF = 33	for document
Hearsay-II:	grammar,	BF = 33, 46	retrieval,
HWIM:	1097 words, restricted ATN grammar,	BF = 196,	for travel planning,
SDC:	1000 words, context-free grammar,	BF = 105,	for data retrieval,

GOAL: Yielding <10% semantic error, in a few times real-time (=300 MIPSS)

HARPY:		5%		28	million
Hearsay-II:	yielding	9%, 26%	semantic error, using	85	instructions per second of speech (MIPSS)
HWIM:		56%		500	
SDC:		76%		92	

3.4.5 Performance comparisons

It is extremely difficult to compare the reported performances of existing speech-understanding systems. Most have operated in different task environments and hence can apply different amounts of constraint from the task language to help the problem solving. Although some progress has been made (Goodman, 1976; Sondhi and Levinson, 1978; Bahl *et al.*, 1978) there is no agreed-upon method for calibrating these differences. Also, the various systems use different speakers and recording conditions. And finally, none of the systems has reached full maturity; the amount that might be gained by further debugging and tuning is unknown, but often clearly substantial.

Lea and Shoup (1979) contains an extensive description of the systems developed in the DARPA speech-understanding project and includes the best existing performance comparisons and evaluations. Table 3.7 and Figure 3.9 reproduced here from that report show some comparison of the performances of Hearsay-II, HARPY, HWIM and the SDC system (Bernstein, 1976).

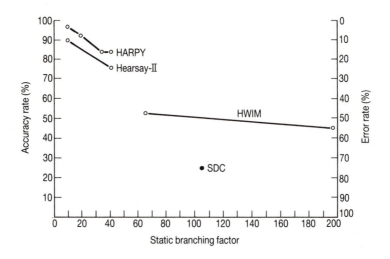

Figure 3.9   Effects of static branching factor on recognition error rate. (After Lea and Shoup, 1979)

Performance of the SRI system is not included because that system was run only with a simulated bottom-end. Also, there are slight differences between the Hearsay-II performance shown in Table 3.7 and that of Section 3.4.1; the former shows results from the official end of the DARPA project in September 1976, while the latter reflects some slight improvements made in the subsequent three months.

The Hearsay-II and HARPY results are directly comparable, the two systems having been tested on the same tasks using the same test data. HARPY's performance here dominates Hearsay-II's in both accuracy and computation speed. And, in fact, HARPY was the only system clearly to meet and exceed the DARPA specifications (see Table 3.3). It is difficult to determine the exact reasons for HARPY's higher accuracy, but we feel it is caused primarily by a combination of three factors:

(1)   Because of its highly compiled efficiency, HARPY can afford to search a relatively large part of the search space. In particular, it can continue pursuing partial solutions even if they contain several low-rated segments (and its pruning threshold is explicitly set to ensure this). Thus HARPY is less prone to catastrophic errors, that is, pruning away the correct path. Hearsay-II, on the other hand, cannot afford to delay pruning decisions as long and thus is more likely to make such errors.

(2)   Some knowledge sources are weaker in Hearsay-II than in HARPY. In particular, Hearsay-II's JUNCT KS has only a weak model of word juncture phenomena as compared with the more comprehen-

sive and sophisticated juncture rules in HARPY. This disparity is an accident of the system's development histories; there is no major conceptual reason why HARPY's juncture rules could not be employed by Hearsay-II.

(3) HARPY was debugged and tuned much more extensively than Hearsay-II (or any of the other DARPA speech understanding systems, for that matter). This was facilitated by the lower processing costs for running tests. It was also helped by fixing the HARPY structure at an earlier point; Hearsay-II's KS configuration underwent a massive modification very late in the DARPA effort, as did HWIM's.

It seems clear that for a performance system in a task with a highly constrained and simply structured language, the HARPY structure is an excellent one. However, as we move to tasks that require more complex kinds of knowledge to constrain the search, we expect conceptual difficulties incorporating those kinds of knowledge into HARPY's simple integrated network representation.

3.5 Conclusions

Hearsay-II represents a new approach to problem solving that will prove useful in many domains other than speech. Thus far, however, we have focused on the virtues, and limitations, of Hearsay-II as a solution to the speech-understanding problem *per se*. In this section we consider what Hearsay-II suggests about problem-solving systems in general. To do so, we identify aspects of the Hearsay-II organization that facilitate development of 'expert systems'. Before concluding, we point out some apparent deficiencies of the current system that suggest avenues of further research. A more detailed discussion of these issues can be found in Lesser and Erman (1977).

3.5.1 Problem-solving systems

The designer of a knowledge-based problem-solving system faces several typical questions, many of which motivate the design principles evolved by Hearsay-II. The designer must first represent and structure the problem in a way that permits decomposition. A general heuristic for solving complex problems is to 'divide and conquer' them. This requires methods to factor subproblems and to combine their eventual solutions. Hearsay-II, for example, divides the understanding problem in two ways: it breaks the total interpretation into separable hypotheses, and it modularizes different types of knowledge that can operate independently and cooperatively. This latter attribute helps the designer address the second basic question: How can I acquire and implement relevant knowledge? Because knowledge sources operate solely by detecting and modifying hypotheses on the blackboard, we can develop and implement each independently. This allows us to divide and conquer the knowledge acquisition problem.

Two other design questions concern the *description* and *use* of knowledge. First, we must decide how to break knowledge into executable units. Second, we must develop strategies for applying knowledge selectively and efficiently. Choices for these design issues should attempt to exploit sources of structure and constraint intrinsic to the problem domain and knowledge available about it. In the current context this means that a speech-understanding system should exploit many alternative types of speech knowledge to reduce uncertainty inherent in the signal. Moreover, the different types of knowledge should apply, ideally, in a best-first manner. That is, the most credible hypotheses should stimulate searches for the most likely adjoining hypotheses first. To this end, the Hearsay-II focusing scheduler considers the quality of hypotheses and potential predictions in each temporal interval and then selectively executes only the most marginally productive KS actions. Accomplishing this type of control required several new sorts of mechanisms. These included explicit interlinked hypothesis representations, declarative descriptions of KS stimulus and response frames, a dynamic problem state description, and a prioritized schedule of pending KS instantiations.

3.5.2 Specific advantages of Hearsay-II as a problem-solving system

This paper has covered an extensive set of issues and details. From these we believe the reader should have gained an appreciation of Hearsay-II's principal benefits, summarized briefly as follows.

Multiple sources of knowledge

Hearsay-II provides a framework for diverse types of knowledge to cooperate in solving a problem. This capability especially helps in situations characterized by incomplete or uncertain information. Uncertainty can arise from any of a number of causes, including noisy data, apparent ambiguities, and imperfect or incomplete knowledge. Each of these departures from the certainty of perfect information leads to uncertainty about both what the problem solver should believe and what it should do next. In such situations finding a solution typically requires simultaneously combining multiple kinds of knowledge.

Although each type of knowledge may rule out only a few alternative (competing) hypotheses, the combined effect of several sources can often identify the single most credible conclusion.

Multiple levels of abstraction

Solving problems in an intelligent manner often requires using descriptions at different levels of abstraction. After first finding an approximate or gross solution, a problem solver may work quickly toward a refined, detailed solution consistent with the rough solution. In its use of multiple levels of abstraction, Hearsay-II provides rudimentary facilities for such variable-granularity reasoning. In the speech task particularly, the different levels correspond to separable domains of reasoning. Hypotheses about word sequences must satisfy the constraints of higher-level syntactic phrase-structure rules. Once these are satisfied, testing more detailed or finely tuned word juncture relations would be justified. Of course the multiple levels of abstraction also support staged decision making that proceeds from lower-level hypotheses up to higher levels. Levels in such bottom-up processing support a different type of function, namely, the sharing of intermediate results, discussed separately in the following paragraph.

Shared partial solutions

The blackboard and hypothesis structures allow the knowledge sources to represent and share partial results. This proves especially desirable for complex problems where no *a priori* knowledge can reliably foretell the best sequence of necessary decisions. Different attempts to solve the same problem may require solving identical subproblems. In the speech domain these problems correspond to comparable hypotheses (same level, type, time). Hearsay-II provides capabilities for the KSs to recognize a hypothesis of interest and to incorporate it into alternative competing hypotheses at higher levels. Subsequent changes to the partial result then propagate to all of the higher level constructs that contain it.

Independent knowledge sources limited to data-directed interactions

Separating the diverse sources of knowledge into independent program modules provides several benefits. Different people can create, test and modify KSs independently. In addition to the ordinary benefits of modularity in programming, this independence allows human specialists (e.g. phoneticians, linguists) to operationalize their diverse types of knowledge without concern for the conceptual framework and detailed behavior of other possible modules. Although the programming style and epistemological nature of several KSs may vary widely, Hearsay-II provides for all of them a single uniform programming environment. This environment constrains the KSs to operate in a data-directed manner – reading hypotheses from the blackboard when situations of interest occur, processing them to draw inferences, and recording new or modified hypotheses on the blackboard for others to process further. This paradigm facilitates problem-oriented interactions while minimizing complicated and costly design interactions.

Incremental formation of solutions

Problem solving in Hearsay-II proceeds incrementally through the accretion and integration of partial solutions. KSs generate hypotheses based on current data and knowledge. By integrating adjacent and consistent hypotheses into larger composites, the system develops increasingly credible and comprehensive partial solutions. These in turn stimulate focused efforts that drive the overall system toward the final goal, one most credible interpretation spanning the entire interval of speech. By allowing information to accumulate in this piecemeal fashion, Hearsay-II provides a convenient framework for heuristic problem solving. Diverse heuristic methods can contribute various types of assistance in the effort to eliminate uncertainty, to recognize portions of the sequence, and to model the speaker's intentions. Because these diverse methods exist in the form of independent, cooperating KSs, each addition to the current problem solution consists simply of an update to the blackboard.

Opportunistic problem-solving behavior

Whenever good algorithms do not exist for solving a problem, we must apply heuristic methods or 'rules-of-thumb' to search for a solution. In problems where a large number of data exist to which a large number of alternative heuristics potentially apply, we need to choose each successive action carefully. We refer to a system's ability to exploit selectively its best data and most promising methods as 'opportunistic' problem solving (Nii and Feigenbaum, 1978; Hayes-Roth and Hayes-Roth, 1979b). Hearsay-II developed several mechanisms to support such opportunistic behavior. In particular, its focus policies and prioritized scheduling allocate computation resources first to those KSs that exploit the most credible hypotheses, promise the most significant increments to the solution, and use the most reliable and inexpensive methods. Similar needs to focus intelligently will arise in many comparably rich and complex problem domains.

Experimentation in system development

Whenever we attempt to solve a previously unsolved problem, the need for experimentation arises. In the speech-understanding task, for example, we generated several different types of KSs and experimentally tested a variety of alternative system configurations (specific sets of KSs) (Lesser and Erman, 1977). A solution to the overall problem depended on both developing powerful individual KSs and organizing multiple KSs to cooperate effectively to reduce uncertainty. These requirements necessitated a trial-and-error evaluation of alternative system designs. Throughout these explorations, the basic Hearsay-II structure proved robust and sufficient. Alternative configurations were constructed with relative ease by inserting or removing specific KSs. Moreover, we could test radically different high-level control concepts (e.g. depth-first versus breadth-first versus left-to-right searches) simply by changing the focus policy KS. The need for this kind of flexibility will probably arise in many future state-of-the-art problem-solving tasks. To support this flexibility, systems must be able to apply the same KSs in different orders and to schedule them according to varying selection criteria. These requirements directly motivate KS data-directed independence, as well as autonomous scheduling KSs that can evaluate the probable effects of potential KS actions. Because it supports these needs, Hearsay-II provides an excellent environment for experimental research and development in speech and other complex tasks.

3.5.3 Disadvantages of the Hearsay-II approach

We can identify two different but related weaknesses of the Hearsay-II approach to problem solving. One weakness derives from the system's generality, and the other concerns its computational efficiency. Each of these is considered briefly in turn.

Generality impedes specialization and limits power

The Hearsay-II approach suggests a very general problem-solving paradigm. Every inference process reads data from the blackboard and places a new hypothesis also on the blackboard. Thus blackboard accesses mediate each decision step. While this proved desirable for structuring communications between different KSs, it proved undesirable for most intermediate decision tasks arising within a single KS. Most KSs employed private, stylized internal data structures different from the single uniform blackboard links and hypotheses. For example, the word recognizer used specialized sequential networks, whereas the word sequence recognizer exploited a large bit matrix of word adjacencies.

Each KS also stored intermediate results, useful for its own internal searches, in appropriately distinctive data structures. Attempts to coerce these specialized activities into the general blackboard-mediated style of Hearsay-II either failed completely or caused intolerable performance degradation (Lesser and Erman, 1977).

Interpretative versus compiled knowledge

Hearsay-II uses knowledge interpretively. That is, it actively evaluates alternative actions, chooses the best for the current situation, and then applies the procedure associated with the most promising KS instantiation. Such deliberation takes time and requires many fairly sophisticated mechanisms; its expense can be justified whenever an adequate, explicit algorithm does not exist for the same task. Whenever such an algorithm emerges, equal or greater performance and efficiency may be obtained by compiling the algorithm and executing it directly. For example, recognizing restricted vocabulary and grammatical spoken sentences from limited syntax can now be accomplished faster by techniques other than those in Hearsay-II. As described in Section 3.3.3, by compiling all possible inter-level substitutions (sentence to phrase to word to phone to segment) into one enormous finite-state Markov network, the HARPY system uses a modified dynamic programming search to find the one network path that most closely approximates the segmented speech signal. This type of systematic, compiled and broad search becomes increasingly desirable as problem-solving knowledge improves. Put another way, once a satisfactory specific method for solving any problem is found, the related procedure can be 'algorithmetized', compiled and applied repetitively. In such a case the flexibility of a system like Hearsay-II may no longer be needed.

3.5.4 Other applications of the Hearsay-II framework

Both the advantages and disadvantages of Hearsay-II have stimulated additional research. Several researchers have applied the general framework to problems outside the speech domain, and others have begun to develop successors to the Hearsay-II system. We will briefly discuss one of these new applications and then mention the other types of activities underway.

Although the Hearsay-II framework developed around an understanding task, B. and F. Hayes-Roth et al. have extended many of its principal features to develop a model of planning (Hayes-Roth and Hayes-Roth, 1979b; Hayes-Roth et al., 1979). While understanding tasks require 'interpretive' or 'analytic' processes, planning belongs to a complementary set of 'generative' or 'synthetic' activities. The principal

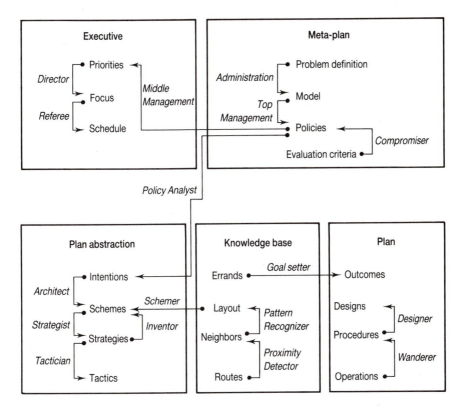

Figure 3.10   The planning blackboard and the actions of illustrative knowledge sources. (From Hayes-Roth and Hayes-Roth, 1979b)

features of the Hearsay-II system which make it attractive as a problem-solving model for speech understanding also suggest it as a model of planning.

The planning application shares all the principal features of the Hearsay-II system summarized in Section 3.5.2 but, as Figue 3.10 suggests, the planning model differs from the Hearsay-II framework in several ways. In particular, the designers found it convenient to distinguish five separate blackboard 'planes', reflecting five qualitatively different sorts of decisions. The Plan plane corresponds most closely to Hearsay-II's single blackboard, holding the decisions that combine to form a solution to the planning problem, i.e. what low-level operations can be aggregated to achieve the high-level outcomes of the plan. These kinds of decisions in generative tasks can be thought of as the dual of the successively higher level, more aggregated hypotheses constituting the blackboard for interpretation tasks. In the speech task, corresponding hypotheses express how low-level segments and phones can be aggregated to form the high-level phrases and sentences intended by the speaker. The other four planes of the planning blackboard hold intermediate decisions that enter into the planning process in various ways. For example, based on the Hearsay-II experience with selective attention strategies, resource allocation strategies were formalized and associated explicitly with an Executive plane.

Although the planning model is the only current application of the Hearsay-II framework to generative tasks, several interesting applications that transfer the approach to other interpretation problems have been made. Rumelhart (1976) has proposed to apply the Hearsay-II framework to model human reading behavior. In this application only one blackboard plane is used, the levels closely approximate those used in the speech-understanding task, and many additional KSs are introduced to represent how varying amounts of linguistic and semantic knowledge affect reading skills. Engelmore, Nii and Feigenbaum (Engelmore and Nii, 1977; Nii and Feigenbaum, 1978) describe other signal-processing applications, namely, protein crystallography and acoustic signal under-standing. These applications employ multiple levels and planes appro-priate to their specific domains. Soloway and Riseman (1977a) used the framework in a learning system that develops multilevel models of observed game behaviors. Hanson and Riseman (1978b) and Levine (1978) have developed systems that mirror the Hearsay-II speech-understanding components in the image-understanding task. Arbib and Caplan (1979) propose Hearsay-II-based multilevel, incremental problem-solving structures as a basis for neuroscience models, and Norman (1980, p. 383) states that Hearsay-II has been a source of ideas for theoretical psychology and that it 'fulfills [his] . . . intuitions about the form of a general cognitive processing structure'. Finally, Mann (1979) has adapted the Hearsay-II structure to the task of interpreting human–machine communication dialogues.

Several researchers have focused efforts on generalizing, refining or systematizing aspects of the Hearsay-II architecture for wider application. As previously mentioned, B. and F. Hayes-Roth have formalized some aspects of meta-planning and executive control and have treated this type of problem solving within one uniform framework. Nii and Aiello (1979) have developed a system that assists a programmer in developing a new special-purpose variant of a Hearsay-II system suitable for some particular new task. Balzer *et al.* (1980) have implemented a more formalized, domain-independent version of Hearsay-II and are applying it to an automatic-programming-like task. This system uses one blackboard for interpretation and another for scheduling decisions, in a manner akin to that proposed for the Executive decisions in the Hayes-Roth planning system. In a similar way, Stefik (1980) uses three distinct planes to record the plan, meta-plan and executive decisions arising in a system that incrementally plans genetic experiments.

Lesser and Erman (1979) have used Hearsay-II as a central component in a model for interpretation tasks in which the problem solving is accomplished cooperatively by distributed processors, each with only a limited view of the problem and with narrow-bandwidth intercommunication, and describe the model and some validating experiments using the Hearsay-II speech-understanding system. Hearsay-II has also influenced some attempts at developing general techniques for formal descriptions of complex systems (Fox, 1979a,b; Lesser *et al.*, 1980).

We predict that in the future the Hearsay-II paradigm will be chosen increasingly as a model of heuristic, knowledge-based reasoning. Improved compilation techniques, and increased computing power will further enhance its performance. In the final analysis, however, Hearsay-II will be remembered as the first general framework for combining multiple sources of knowledge, at different levels of abstraction, into a coordinated and opportunistic problem-solving system. Such systems seem certain to play a significant role in the development of artificial intelligence.

Appendix: System development

On the basis of our experience with the Hearsay-I system (Reddy *et al.*, 1973a,b), at the beginning of the Hearsay-II effort in 1973 we expected to require and evolve types of knowledge and interaction patterns whose details could not be anticipated. Because of this, the development of the system was marked by much experimentation and redesign. This uncertainty characterizes the development of knowledge-based systems. Instead of designing a specific speech-understanding system, we considered Hearsay-II as a model for a class of systems and a framework within which specific configurations of that general model could be constructed and studied (Lesser *et al.*, 1975; Erman and Lesser, 1975).

On the basis of this approach a high-level programming system was designed to provide an environment for programming knowledge sources, configuring groups of them into systems, and executing them. Because KSs interact via the blackboard (triggering on patterns, accessing hypotheses and making modifications) and the blackboard is uniformly structured, KS interactions are also uniform. Thus one set of facilities can serve all KSs. Facilities are provided for:

- defining levels on the blackboard,
- configuring groups of KSs into executable systems,
- accessing and modifying hypotheses on the blackboard,
- activating and scheduling KSs,
- debugging and analyzing the performance of KSs.

These facilities collectively form the Hearsay-II 'kernel'. One can think of the Hearsay-II kernel as a high-level system for programming speech-understanding systems of a type conforming to the underlying Hearsay-II model.

Hearsay-II is implemented in the SAIL programming system (Reiser, 1976), an ALGOL-60 dialect with a sophisticated compile-time macro facility as well as a large number of data structures (including lists and sets) and control modes which are implemented fairly efficiently. The Hearsay-II kernel provides a high-level environment for KSs at compile-time by extending SAIL's data types and syntax through declarations of procedure calls, global variables and macros. This extended SAIL provides an explicit structure for specifying a KS and its interaction with other KSs (through the blackboard). The high-level environment also provides mechanisms for KSs to specify (usually in nonprocedural ways) information used by the kernel when configuring a system, scheduling KS activity and controlling researcher interaction with the system.

The knowledge in a KS is represented using SAIL data structures and code, in whatever sylized form the KS developer chooses. The kernel environment provides the facilities for structuring the interface between this knowledge and other KSs, via the blackboard. For example, the syntax KS contains a grammar for the specialized task language to be recognized; this grammar is coded in a compact network form. The KS also contains procedures for searching this network, for example, to parse a sequence of words. The kernel provides facilities:

(1)   for triggering this KS when new word hypotheses appear on the blackboard,

(2)   for the KS to read those word hypotheses (in order to find the sequence of words to parse), and

(3)   for the KS to create new hypotheses on the blackboard, indicating the structure of the parse.

Active development of Hearsay-II extended for three years. About 40 KSs were developed, each a one- or two-person effort lasting from two months to three years. The KSs range from about 5 to 100 pages of source code (with 30 pages typical), and each KS has up to about 50 Kbytes of information in its local database.

The kernel is about 300 pages of code, roughly one-third of which is the declarations and macros that create the extended environment for KSs. The remainder of the code implements the architecture: primarily activation and scheduling of KSs, maintenance of the blackboard, and a variety of other standard utilities. During the three years of active development, an average of about two full-time-equivalent research programmers were responsible for the implementation, modification and maintenance of the kernel. Included during this period were a half-dozen major reimplementations and scores of minor ones; these changes were usually specializations or selective optimizations, designed as experience with the system led to a better understanding of the usage of the various constructs. During this same period about eight full-time-equivalent researchers were using the system to develop KSs.

Implementation of the first version of the kernel began in the autumn of 1973, and was completed by two people in four months. The first major KS configuration, though incomplete, was running in early 1975. The first complete configuration, C1, ran in January 1976. This configuration had very poor performance, with more than 90% sentence errors over a 250-word vocabulary. Experience with this configuration led to a substantially different KS configuration, C2, completed in September 1976. C2 is the configuration described in this paper.

Implementing a general framework has a potential disadvantage: the start-up cost is relatively high. However, if the framework is suitable, it can be used to explore different configurations within the model more easily than if each configuration were built in an *ad hoc* manner. Additionally, a natural result of the continued use of any high-level system is its improvement in terms of enhanced facilities, increased stability, reliability and efficiency, and greater familiarity on the part of the researchers using it.

Hearsay-II has been successful in this respect; we believe that the total cost of creating the high-level system and using it to develop KS configurations C1 and C2 (and intermediate configurations) was less than it would have been to generate them in an *ad hoc* manner. It should be stressed that the construction of even one configuration is itself an experimental and evolving process. The high-level programming system provides a framework, both conceptual and physical, for developing a configuration in an incremental fashion. The speed with which C2 was developed is some indication of the advantage of this system-design approach. A more detailed description of the development philosophy and tools can be found in Erman and Lesser (1978b) and a discussion of the relationships between the C1 and C2 configurations can be found in Lesser and Erman (1977) and in Chapter 4 of this book.

Acknowledgments

This research was supported chiefly by Defense Advanced Research Projects Agency contract F44620-73-C-0074 to Carnegie-Mellon University. In addition, support for the preparation of this paper was provided by USC-ISI, Rand, and the University of Massachusetts. We gratefully acknowledge their support. Views and conclusions contained in this document are those of the authors and should not be interpreted as representing the official opinion or policy of DARPA, the US government, or any other person or agency connected with them.

The success of the Hearsay-II project depended on many persons, especially the following members of the Carnegie-Mellon University Computer Science Department 'Speech Group': Christina Adam, Mark Birnbaum, Robert Cronk, Richard Fennell, Mark Fox, Gregory Gill, Henry Goldberg, Gary Goodman, Bruce Lowerre, Paul Masulis, David McKeown, Jack Mostow, Linda Shockey, Richard Smith, and Richard Suslick. Daniel Corkill, David Taylor and the reviewers made helpful comments on early drafts of this paper.

Figure 3.1 is adapted from A. Newell, A tutorial on speech understanding systems, in *Speech Recognition: Invited Papers of the IEEE Symposium*, D.R. Reddy (Ed.), Academic Press, New York, 1975. Table 3.3 is adapted from M.F. Medresse *et al.*, Speech understanding systems, Report of a steering committee, *Artificial Intelligence*, **9** (1978). Figure 3.5 is taken from J.J. Wolf and W.A. Woods, The HWIM speech understanding system, in *Trends in Speech Recognition*, W.A. Lea (Ed.) © 1980, by permission of Prentice-Hall, Inc., Englewood Cliffs, NJ. Figures 3.6–3.8 and Table 3.4 are taken from B.T. Lowerre and R. Reddy, The HARPY speech understanding system, in *Trends in Speech Recognition*, W.A. Lea (Ed.) © 1980, by permission of Prentice-Hall, Inc., Englewood Cliffs, NJ. Figure 3.10 originally appeared in B. Hayes-Roth and F. Hayes-Roth, A cognitive model of planning, *Cognitive Science*, **3** (1979) 275–310, Ablex Publishing Corporation, Norwood, NJ.

4

A Retrospective View of the Hearsay-II Architecture

Victor R. Lesser and Lee D. Erman

4.1 Introduction

The Hearsay model (Reddy *et al.*, 1973) has been developed for problem solving in domains that must use large amounts of diverse, errorful and incomplete knowledge in order to search in a large space. Other approaches for solving this class of problem include production systems, frames (Minsky, 1975), heterarchical structures (Walker *et al.*, 1977; Woods *et al.*, 1976), relaxation techniques (Barrow and Tenenbaum, 1976; Rosenfeld *et al.*, 1976), Planner (Hewitt, 1972), QA4 (Rulifson *et al.*, 1972) and the Locus model (Lowerre, 1976; Rubin and Reddy, 1977). The Hearsay-I architecture and system (Reddy *et al.*, 1973b; Erman, 1974) represented a first (and successful) attempt to apply that model to the problem of understanding connected speech in specialized task domains. In this first application, the size of the vocabulary (less than 100 words) and complexity of the grammar were very limited.

Experiences with Hearsay-I led to the more generalized Hearsay-II architecture (Lesser *et al.*, 1975; Erman and Lesser, 1975) in order to handle more difficult problems (e.g. larger vocabularies and less constrained grammars). The first configuration of knowledge sources (KSs) for Hearsay-II – configuration C1 – was complete in January 1976 (CMU, 1976). This implementation had poor performance (e.g. 10% sentences correct in 85 MIPSS (million instructions per second of speech) on a 250-word vocabulary). Experience with this configuration has led to a substantially different set of KSs – configuration C2 (CMU, 1977). This configuration performs substantially better (e.g. 85% correct in 60 MIPSS on a 1000-word vocabulary).

The Hearsay-II system, with the second configuration, has been successful: it comes close to the original performance goals set out in 1971 to be met by the end of 1976 for the ARPA speech understanding effort

(Newell *et al.*, 1973) and does so with a system organization that is of interest because of the potential for its application to other problem areas. Several other problems have been attacked with organizations strongly influenced by the Hearsay-II structure: image understanding (Prager *et al.*, 1977), reading comprehension (Rumelhart, 1976), protein-crystallographic analysis (Engelmore and Nii, 1977), signal understanding (Nii and Feigenbaum, 1978) and complex learning (Soloway and Riseman, 1977b).

This chapter is divided into two major parts. The first part presents an overview of the Hearsay model, the Hearsay-II architecture, which is a further specification of this model, and the two KS configurations. (More detailed descriptions of these configurations are contained in the appendix to the chapter.) The second part of the chapter discusses the implication of these experiences for the Hearsay model and the Hearsay-II architecture. In particular, those aspects of the architecture are identified that have contributed most strongly to the success of the system, as well as those parts that need the most future work. (The fact that certain parts of the implementation need further work does not necessarily indicate deficiencies with the basic Hearsay model, but rather points out inadequacies in the Hearsay-II implementation of the model. It is to the model's credit that even though some of its more sophisticated capabilities are not implemented effectively it still provides an appropriate framework for the successful solution of a complex task. Thus, one of the intents of this paper is to define some of the major design goals for the next iteration in the implementation of the Hearsay model.) This discussion is structured around two themes – the multilevel global database (blackboard) for KS cooperation, and the asynchronous, data-directed control structure for KS activation. Note that while this chapter discusses the means of organizing the knowledge and applying it to the problem, it does not describe in detail nor quantify the knowledge in the system. At least as much work has been expended on specifying and debugging the knowledge in the system as on building and refining the structure to hold and apply that knowledge.

4.2 Overview of the Hearsay model

A number of characteristics of the problem drive the Hearsay model:

(1) large search space;

(2) diverse sources of knowledge – many of the KSs are large, some have large internal search problems of their own;

(3) error and variability – these are characteristics of both the input data (the acoustic signal) and the processing of knowledge sources;

(4)   experimental approach needed for system development – this implies the need for iterating the system and running over large amounts of data;

(5)   performance requirement (accuracy and speed) – this is true of any practical solution to the problem as well as during development (because of the experimental nature).

The basic notions of the Hearsay model (Reddy *et al.*, 1973a) were developed in response to the requirements just stated:

(1)   The KSs are kept separate, independent and anonymous. This separation is felt to be a decomposition that is natural and can also help make the combinatoric problems more tractable. For development purposes, the separation should help with system modifications (especially adding and modifying KSs) and evaluation.

(2)   A global data structure – the blackboard – is the means of communication and interaction of KSs. This provides a hypothesize-and-test means of interaction. Each KS accesses and modifies the blackboard in a uniform way.

(3)   A KS responds to changes to the blackboard it is concerned with; it applies its knowledge within the context of such a change. This implies data-directed activation of KSs.

4.3 Overview of the Hearsay-II architecture

The Hearsay-II architecture is one framework for implementing the Hearsay model. In this section, a very brief overview of that architecture is given. More details are described in Lesser *et al.* (1975) and Erman and Lesser (1975).

4.3.1 The blackboard

The blackboard is partitioned into distinct information **levels**; each level is used to hold a different representation of the problem space. (Examples of levels are 'phrase', 'word', 'syllable' and 'segment'.) The decomposition of the problem space into levels is a natural parallel to the decomposition of the knowledge into separate KSs. For most KSs, the KS needs to deal with only a few (usually two) levels to apply its knowledge. Its interface to the rest of the system is in units and concepts that are natural to it.

The sequence of levels forms a loose hierarchical structure in which the elements at each level can be described approximately as abstractions of elements at the next lower level. The possible hypotheses at a level form a problem space for KSs operating at that level. A partial solution (i.e. a group of hypotheses) at one level can be used to constrain the search at an adjacent level. For example, consider a KS that can predict and rate words based on acoustic information and another KS that knows about the grammar of the language. The first KS can generate a set of candidate word hypotheses. The second KS can use these hypotheses to generate phrase hypotheses which can be used, in turn, to predict words likely to precede or follow. These predictions can now constrain the search for the first KS.

Associated with each level is a set of primitive elements appropriate for representing the problem at that level, e.g. the elements at the word level are the words of the vocabulary to be recognized. The major units on the blackboard are **hypotheses**. A hypothesis is an interpretation of a portion of the spoken utterance at a particular level. For example, a hypothesis might represent the assertion that the word GIVE was spoken at the beginning of the utterance. Each hypothesis at a given level is labeled as being a particular element of the set of primitive elements at that level.

Each hypothesis, no matter what its level, has a uniform attribute–value structure. Some attributes (and values) are required of all hypotheses and others are optional, as needed. Included among the required attributes of a hypothesis are its level (e.g. word), its element name (e.g. GIVE) and an estimate of its time coordinates within the spoken utterance (which can include notions of 'fuzziness' of estimate). The level and time attributes place a two-dimensional structure on hypotheses which partitions the blackboard and can be used for addressing hypotheses. Note that two or more hypotheses at the same level with significantly overlapping times are *competitors*, i.e. they represent competing interpretations of a portion of the utterance.

Other attributes of a hypothesis include information about its *structural relationships* with other hypotheses (forming an AND/OR graph), *validity ratings* (i.e. estimates by KSs of the 'truth' of the hypothesis) and *processing state*. The processing state attributes are summaries and classifications of the other attributes. For example, values of the rating attributes are summarized by the 'rating state' attribute that takes a value from the set Unrated, Neutral, Verified, Guaranteed, or Rejected. New attributes can be created by any KS and may be used for passing arbitrary information about a hypothesis between instantiations of the same or different KSs.

A KS can create new hypotheses, specifying values for attributes of the new hypothesis. Given the 'name' of a hypothesis, a KS can examine or modify attributes of that hypothesis. In addition, sets of hypotheses may be retrieved associatively, based on the values of their attributes (e.g. all hypotheses at the syllable level whose durations are greater than

250 ms). The hypothesis structure is uniform across all levels in the blackboard. Thus, the form of access and modification to hypotheses by KSs can also be uniform and is accomplished by calling kernel procedures; the set of these procedures comprises the **blackboard handler**.

In addition to the information in each hypothesis which can be accessed by KSs, *auxiliary state information* is maintained by the blackboard handler in specialized data structures. Examples of this information are:

(1)   a representation of hypotheses at each level arranged for efficient associative retrieval by time, and

(2)   the name of the highest-rated hypothesis in each time area.

These auxiliary structures are updated by the blackboard handler automatically as KSs make changes to the blackboard.

4.3.2 Structure of knowledge sources

Each KS has two major components: a **precondition** and an **action**. The purpose of the precondition is to find a subset of hypotheses that are appropriate for action by the KS and to invoke the KS on that subset; the subset is called the *stimulus frame* of the KS instantiation. For example, the precondition of the KS that generates word hypotheses based on syllables looks for new syllable hypotheses. When invoking the KS, the precondition provides the system scheduler with, in addition to the stimulus frame, a stylized description of the likely action that the KS instantiation will perform (if and when it is allowed to execute); this estimate of action is called the *response frame*. For example, a response frame for the syllable-based word hypothesizer (MOW) indicates that the action will be to generate hypotheses at the word level and in a time area that includes at least that of the stimulus frame. The action part of a KS is a program (written in SAIL (Reiser, 1976)) for applying the knowledge to the stimulus frame and making appropriate changes to the blackboard. In general, the changes made will serve to trigger more KS activations.

To keep from having to fire the precondition continuously to search the blackboard, each precondition declares to the blackboard handler in a nonprocedural way the primitive kinds of blackboard changes in which it is interested. Each precondition is triggered only when such primitive changes occur (and is then given pointers to all of them). This changes a polling action into an interrupt-driven one and is more efficient, especially as the number of preconditions gets large. After being triggered (and when scheduled for execution), the precondition (also a

SAIL procedure) can do arbitrary searching of the blackboard for hypothesis configurations of interest to its KS.

Several KSs may be grouped together into **modules**. The KSs within a module may share code and long-term built-in data. A discussion of the module construct, including its implications for KS independence, is given below in the section on KS independence.

4.3.3 Scheduling

Whenever a precondition is executed, it checks all blackboard events in which it is interested that have occurred since the last time it executed. For example, a 'new hypothesis' to a precondition is any hypothesis that was created between the last time the precondition executed and its current execution. Thus, a precondition may be thought of as executing, then 'sleeping' for a time while retaining state, then waking (executing again) and being able to find all new events of interest to it.

However, whenever a KS executes, it uses the stimulus frame specific to that invocation. Each KS execution goes to completion; that is, the KS cannot put itself to sleep, waiting for some other event (on the blackboard) to occur.

At any point, there are, in general, a number of pending tasks to execute – both invoked KSs and triggered preconditions. (In practice, the number of pending tasks often exceeds 200.) A **scheduler** in the kernel (Hayes-Roth and Lesser, 1977) calculates a priority for each waiting task and selects for execution the task with the highest priority. The priority calculation attempts to estimate the usefulness of the action in fulfilling the overall system goal of recognizing the utterance. This estimation is based on the specific stimulus and response frames of the actions and on overall blackboard state information, which includes such notions as the best hypotheses in each time area in the utterance, and how much time has elapsed since the current best hypothesis was generated. The priority of a KS is recalculated if the validity of its stimulus frame is changed or the auxiliary state pertinent to evaluating the significance of the response frame is modified.

Some KSs are not directly involved in hypothesizing and testing partial solutions; instead, these control the search by influencing the activation of other KSs. These *policy* KSs can be used to impose global search strategies on the basic priority scheduling mechanism.

4.4 The configurations

Following are brief overviews of configurations C1 and C2, to provide a basis for subsequent discussion. The appendix contains more detailed descriptions of the KSs, as well as pointers to published papers.

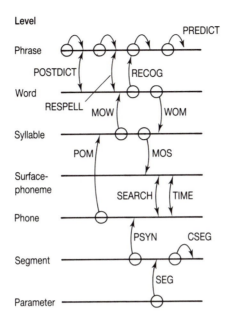

Figure 4.1 The levels and knowledge sources of configuration C1 (as operational in January, 1976).

Figure 4.1 gives a schematic of configuration C1 as it was operational in January 1976. The levels are indicated by solid horizontal lines and are labeled at the left. KSs are indicated by vertical arcs with the circled end indicating the level where its stimulus frame is and the pointed end indicating the level of its response frame. As segment hypotheses were generated from the acoustic data (SEG), they might be combined to form larger segment hypotheses (CSEG). Phone hypotheses were created, based on one or more contiguous segments (PSYN). Syllables were predicted from the phones (POM) and words from the syllables (MOW). Phrase hypotheses were constructed from contiguous word or phrase hypotheses which were syntactically consistent (RECOG). Other KSs (PREDICT, RESPELL and POSTDICT) accomplished various syntactic extension and prediction functions at the phrase and word levels. Verification of predicted words was carried out by expanding the words into their expected syllables (WOM), expanding the syllables into expected phonemes (MOS), and matching the sequences of expected phonemes with the recognized phones (TIME and SEARCH). Changes of ratings of hypotheses were propagated to structurally connected hypotheses (RPOL). The FOCUS policy KS controlled the search by setting priorities for various kinds of KS actions.

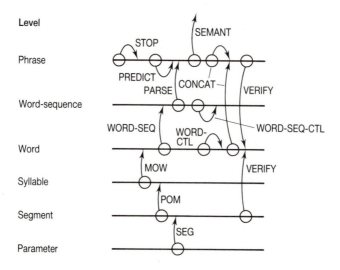

Figure 4.2   The levels and knowledge sources of configuration C2 (as operational in September, 1976).

Figure 4.2 gives a schematic of configuration C2 as it was operational in September 1976. First, all segment hypotheses are generated from the parametric representation of the acoustic signal (SEG). Next, syllables are predicted from the segments (POM). Then, words are predicted from the syllables (MOW); the most likely words in each time interval placed on the blackboard (WORD-CTL). Next, a heuristic word-sequence hypothesizer (WORD-SEQ) attempts to identify the most probable sequences of word hypotheses (consisting of successive language-adjacent word pairs). Because this KS exploits statistical methods to improve credibility, the initial word sequence hypotheses are much more accurate than are hypotheses based on single words. Subsequently, KSs are invoked to attempt to parse the hypothesized word sequences to determine if they are grammatical (PARSE), to predict possible time-adjacent grammatical word extensions (PREDICT), to hypothesize and verify new words satisfying these predictions (VERIFY), to concatenate grammatical and time-adjacent word sequences (CONCAT), to propagate ratings (RPOL), to reject phrases and to determine when the search should be terminated (STOP), and to generate new word sequence hypotheses (WORD-SEQ-CTL).

The major system-related differences between these configurations are listed here; they will be discussed individually throughout the paper.

(1)   C1 has asynchronous processing throughout. C2 has an initial pass of sequential, bottom-up processing at the word level; i.e. all segments are created, then all syllables, then a selection of words.

(2) C1 used the blackboard extensively for intra-KS state-saving between instantiations of a KS (e.g. SEARCH and RECOG-PREDICT-RESPELL-POSTDICT). In C2, this was greatly reduced, with KSs doing more computation internally and in larger units (e.g. VERIFY and PARSE-PREDICT-CONCAT).

(3) C2 generated simpler hypothesis networks than those in C1. For example, SEARCH and TIME built complex structures to represent verifications of words; VERIFY builds very simple ones for the same purpose.

Though we are here concerned with systems issues, it is worth pointing out that WORD-SEQ is a novel KS which significantly contributes to the success of C2. It limits the search space by providing large hypotheses which act as islands of reliability and bases for further search. This KS uses *approximate* syntactic knowledge to examine efficiently many alternative sequences of low-reliability word hypotheses and generate a small number of more reliable phrase hypotheses.

4.5 Experiences with Hearsay-II

This section addresses the following questions: How well did the Hearsay-II system meet its original design goals and were these goals appropriate for problem solving in the speech understanding domain (and more generally in errorful domains which require extensive search)? This discussion is based on approximately three years of experience with the Hearsay-II architecture, including numerous iterations of both the system architecture and KS configurations. These questions will be discussed in the context of two major aspects of the Hearsay-II architecture: the blackboard global database, and KS interaction and control. The emphasis on the two configurations as fixed points can be misleading; rather than appearing full-grown, the configurations evolved over time, with numerous iterations required first to develop C1 and then C2 from C1.

4.5.1 Blackboard database

There are two major design themes reflected in the structure of the blackboard. The first theme is the avoidance of expensive and complicated backtracking control structures by the representation of alternative, distributed hypotheses in an integrated multilevel manner. The second design theme is the representation of all information levels with a high-level, uniform structure, in order to allow all KSs to contribute their information to the blackboard in an identical and anonymous manner.

Distributed representation

It was hoped that the first design theme would avoid the redundant calculation of previously-generated results and allow KSs to apply their knowledge selectively to places in the blackboard where further processing would resolve contradictory evidence supporting likely, alternative hypotheses. Hayes-Roth (1978), in discussing how to evaluate the potential usefulness of a KS action, introduces the concept of *diagnosticity* as an important component in a KS priority function. Diagnosticity is a measure of how much contradictory evidence could potentially be resolved by a particular KS action.

The ability to save partial results on the blackboard in an integrated manner, in terms of hypothesis subnetworks, has been a very positive characteristic of the architecture; it avoids a significant amount of unnecessary recalculation of results previously generated. (The usual manner of accomplishing this is having each KS, as it is about to create a new hypothesis, first check that a hypothesis does not already exist which is sufficiently similar to the one it is about to create.) This was especially true for KSs operating at the word and phrase levels. This was also true for KSs in the C1 configuration operating at lower information levels, for example the TIME and SEARCH KSs. However, later versions of these KSs (e.g. VERIFY in C2), for reasons of efficiency (to be discussed later), do not save partial results on the blackboard.

The use of an integrated representation as a way of efficiently resolvng competition among KSs wanting to work on the same hypotheses has not been exploited, nor has the ability to bring to bear specialized knowledge dynamically to resolve the conflict among competing, alternative hypotheses (for example, a specialized KS to resolve ambiguity between two word hypotheses that are very close acoustically, e.g. 'sit' and 'split'). In addition, the ability given by the integrated representation to re-evaluate automatically (i.e. without KS intervention) the credibility of a hypothesis when its supporting environment is modified is not exploited in the C2 configuration (although it was in C1). In the C2 configuration, hypothesis credibility is never modified in an explicit sense; rather, new and different hypotheses are created. A side-effect of this approach is that hypotheses are never deleted from the blackboard.

One explanation for the lack of full use of the integrated, multilevel representation of hypotheses could be just that the particular task domain of speech understanding does not need these capabilities. However, it is our feeling that there are fundamental weaknesses in the Hearsay-II representation of an integrated, multilevel hypothesis; these weaknesses (to be discussed below) make it difficult, both in terms of execution time and programming complexity, to perform the desired analyses of the hypothesis structure and its surrounding environment. This type of analysis is the key to the effective use of the sophisticated processing capabilities that are possible within the framework of the Hearsay model.

Hypothesis network structure

A major problem in using the blackboard is that one cannot operate on a network (in its simplest form, a tree) of interconnected hypotheses as a composite unit. There is a basic confusion in Hearsay-II's implementation of hypothesis networks between the hypothesis at the top of the tree (the highest level of interpretation) and the whole tree; the state information associated with a hypothesis is very local and does not adequately characterize the state(s) of the hypothesis network(s) connected to it. In order to operate effectively in a distributed manner on interconnected multilevel hypothesis networks, the state information associated with an individual hypothesis must allow a KS to analyze quickly the local environment of a hypothesis and, more importantly, the role that the hypothesis plays in the larger context of the hypothesis networks it is part of. One of the consequences of this deficiency is the difficulty encountered in making appropriate scheduling decisions because the more global import of a potential KS action cannot be determined easily. (It is expensive to trace through a hypothesis network to determine the global import of a potential KS action, but this cost is not unreasonable relative to the total system execution time for a configuration that contains KSs that perform moderately large amounts of internal computation. However, the major computational expense comes in dynamically updating the global import of a pending KS action as modifications are made to the blackboard, since there are a large number of these modifications. It is necessary both to find which waiting KS instantiations have priorities that are affected by the modification and then to recalculate the priorities for those affected.)

For example, in configuration C1, a hypothesis at the phrase level was constructed out of hypotheses at the phrase, word, syllable, surface-phoneme, phone and segment levels. Because of the asynchronous nature of processing, a phrase hypothesis could be supported by word hypotheses in different stages of verification – some might be fully verified, others only partially verified, or some totally unverified. Possible KS actions waiting to work on this hypothesis network could be a separate verification of each unverified word, an attempt to extend the phrase in either the right or left direction, a search for co-articulation effects among different word pairs, or a full verification of a partially verified word. These actions represent processing at different information levels. Given the existing hypothesis interconnection primitives, there is no way to determine easily that all these actions relate to the same hypothesis network, nor what import each action could potentially have in judging the credibility of the entire network.

Another symptom of this problem is the inability to express, except in a very limited way, what type of processing has already been applied to a hypothesis network and what further processing could possibly be applied. This inability again impacts the scheduler because it makes it difficult to schedule 'competing' KSs (i.e. KSs that could work on the same or different parts of a specific hypothesis network) appropriately. Because of these difficulties there has been, in later KS configurations, only a very limited (and simply represented and analyzable) form of KS competition.

Another aspect of the inadequate network structure is that the primitives for specifying structural relationships between hypotheses require many intermediate levels to represent certain types of connectivity patterns. This need for many intermediate levels is expensive in storage space and, more importantly, time; it requires a great deal of network searching through the connection structure to analyze the relationship of a hypothesis to its immediate surrounding environment. These intermediate levels represent a level of detail which is unnecessary for some types of KS analysis and which interfere with these analyses by making then unwarrantedly complex. Once it has been constructed, it is impossible to bypass this level of detail in situations in which it is not pertinent. For example, an information level may contain many intermediate sublevels built out of the connection primitives; a KS using information at this level may want to examine only those hypotheses that are the highest sublevel in each time area. This type of operation, given the current blackboard retrieval primitives, requires the examination of all hypotheses in a specified time area. Another complication of not being able to hide these intermediate levels is that a KS in some cases has to know the exact structure of the intermediate levels used by another KS in order to be able to skip over them, thus making the KSs less independent.

In summary, the experience to date on the distributed representation approach indicates that the implementations of this concept explored so far are neither general nor efficient enough in two major interrelated aspects – how hypotheses can be combined into a network and how the state information associated with an individual hypothesis reflects the hypothesis networks connected to it. To elaborate further, what is missing from the blackboard structure is a way of viewing the shared network structure from a different perspective. This perspective should permit the particular path through the network that defines a specific composite hypothesis to be both viewed in isolation from other paths that are intertwined with it, and also in a way that eliminates superfluous substructure. From this type of perspective, the importance of potential KS actions could be judged efficiently and related to the history of previous processing. A possible approach for implementing this different type of perspective is discussed in work by Hendrix (1975) on partitioned semantic networks.

Uniform blackboard structure

Let us now examine the second major design theme used to structure the blackboard: a uniform structure at all information levels. From a programming point of view, in terms of both KS writers and system implementers, the uniform structure of the blackboard has been a good design choice. By having a uniform structure, a variety of standard blackboard creation, accessing, display, analysis and debugging functions could be developed that are usable by all KSs. These standard functions, some of which are quite complex, make it convenient for a KS writer to interface a knowledge source with the system. The ease with which this interfacing could be accomplished is exemplified by the fact that, in a period of six months, configuration C2, which is almost entirely new relative to C1, was developed and debugged. Because of this uniform structure of hypotheses and their connections, it is often possible for a KS to be recoded so that it generates a different local hypothesis structure without requiring the recoding of other KSs in the system; this is true because a KS can probe the blackboard with sophisticated built-in retrieval operations which, in many cases, shield the KS from changes made by other KSs. For example, there is the *structural-adjacency* blackboard primitive which, given a hypothesis, finds all hypotheses at a particular information level that are immediately adjacent to the given hypothesis based on the AND/OR connection structure among hypotheses.

The uniformity of the attribute structure of hypotheses also makes it possible to monitor efficiently for blackboard changes that are to trigger preconditions. Each precondition needs only to declare to the blackboard handler the names of the attributes at each level in which it is interested. When an attribute is changed, the blackboard handler then triggers all preconditions interested in it.

The uniform blackboard structure, though efficiently implemented, is not appropriate as a scratchpad for the internal computations of a KS. This type of use of the blackboard is often inappropriate because its uniform, general structure does not come completely free in the storage requirements for a hypothesis and the cost of creation and access; most internal computations of a KS do not need this generality. An example of a misuse of the blackboard was the case of the syntax analyzer knowledge source, SASS. In early versions of this KS, the blackboard was used to hold the partial parse trees developed in attempting to parse a language fragment; current versions of this KS, which use a tailored, internal data structure for parsing, are two orders of magnitude faster than the original blackboard-based version of this KS. This case history seems to confirm the notion that there are advantages to specialization of structures: one for KS interaction (i.e. the blackboard), and separate ones for each KS.

The blackboard has also proven to be useful as a database for the scheduler (Hayes-Roth and Lesser, 1977). Because of the uniform hypothesis structure, instantiations of KSs can specify scheduling information in a uniform way (as stimulus and response frames), allowing new KSs to be introduced without having to modify the scheduler. The representation of alternative hypotheses in an integrated, uniform fashion also makes it possible to compare directly the pending KS instantiations to determine which will likely contribute most to further progress; the scheduler can determine those areas on the blackboard that most need further work and locate the pending KS instantiations that are relevant to those areas, and estimate the amount that a KS instantiation will improve the quality of hypotheses in the area of its action.

Long-term information structures

Associated with each information level of the blackboard, there is, as previously discussed, a set of primitive elements which are used to label hypotheses at that level. The kernel interface provides facilities for creating, accessing and displaying these labels. In addition, arbitrary data structures can be associated with each label. These structures, for example at the word information level, can be simple, such as the average expected duration of each word, or complex, such as a network which specifies alternative syllabic spellings for each word. In the complex case, this structure is often used to relate labels at one information level with labels at another; this relationship is used by a KS which operates between different levels (e.g. in the example given here, WOM in configuration C1). These data structures related to labels constitute much of the long-term (built-in) KS-defined information structures of the system and often represent most of the problem-specific knowledge in a KS.

Each KS (or group of KSs) defines whatever *ad hoc* structure seems appropriate for the particular kind of information to be represented. There has been no attempt to define a uniform set of kernel interfaces for creating and accessing these long-term data structures, nor a set of relationships (connection primitives) for relating labels at different levels. However, it seems possible to attempt to define a small number of representations within the kernel; these structures would mimic the hierarchical structure of the blackboard. (Hanson and Riseman in their work on image understanding have a system architecture (Prager *et al.*,

1977) very similar to the blackboard and have included a complementary long-term memory structure.)

The major drawback of not having a predefined long-term memory is that if KSs want to share this information they have to agree among themselves upon a specific structure, thus violating independence considerations. In addition, uniform structures could makes KSs easier to understand, develop and analyze.

On the other hand, these long-term structures must be highly optimized because of their large size and the high frequency with which they are accessed. For example, the description of the grammar used by the KSs within the SASS module in configuration C2 is a network of 3100 nodes. Each node has about seven pointers to other nodes, plus several pieces of auxiliary information. A typical KS action, e.g. parsing a four-word phrase, might make 100 to 5000 node accesses. The approach taken of tailoring these structures to the particular KS(s) using them allowed for efficient implementations in terms of both time and space. It is also possible that explicit tailoring has led to KSs that are easier to understand than if they were forced to fit their requirements into a uniform structure.

Thus, there are still open questions about the desirability of providing uniform structures for representing the knowledge in KSs; hopefully, future implementations will explore these possibilities.

Conclusions about blackboard usage

In trying to draw some conclusions about our experiences with the use of the blackboard, the main issue that constantly comes up is time and space efficiency. In errorful task domains, such as speech understanding, a large number of alternative interpretations of the data must be examined and analyzed. The blackboard concept is effective in the Hearsay-II implementation to the degree that it allows this search to be efficient. Analysis of the C1 configuration indicated that certain types of KS processing on the blackboard were not efficient. Reimplementation of the KSs in order to eliminate those types of processing resulted in the C2 configuration. The major uses of the blackboard in the C2 configuration are:

(1)   a storage area for high-level intermediate results generated by the search – this storage area avoids the unnecessary recalculation of these results if they are encountered on future search paths;

(2)   a communication area for KSs, with strong and simplified assumptions by a KS of what structures can be generated by other KSs;

(3)   a database for the scheduler;

(4)   a common display, debugging and performance evaluation area.

4.5.2 Knowledge source interaction and control

The asynchronous, data-directed control structure used in Hearsay-II was designed to permit:

(1)   the quick refocusing of attention to appropriate hypotheses in the blackboard;

(2)   the flexible reconfiguration of the system with different sets of independent (and possibly competing) KSs, and different global control strategies;

(3)   the exploration of parallel processing.

This section will examine each of these requirements along two dimensions: Were the capabilities embodied in the requirement important to the project, and how well did the control structure (in terms of time, space and ease of representation) implement these capabilities?

Appropriateness of a data-directed control structure

The first requirement, quick refocussing, was based on the following model for processing in the speech domain. Processing can be organized in terms of the incremental additions of small units of information to a limited number of alternative hypotheses. The limited number of alternatives derives from the view that there are islands of reliability in the acoustic data that can be used to anchor the search. Each small increment of information should help to verify, refute or augment (expand) a hypothesis. A KS action, though performed in a local context, could also have the side-effect of contributing information useful in the evaluation of alternative hypotheses (i.e. in other contexts). Thus, after each incremental addition of information (through the execution of a KS), it is necessary to re-examine the set of potential actions that now can be activated and determine which of these will most likely resolve ambiguity. An asynchronous, data-directed architecture makes it convenient to implement such a processing strategy by permitting KS action to be directed by the data: it delays the application of knowledge until there is enough information for a meaningful result (decision), and it re-applies the knowledge when, at a later time, additional information is generated that bears on the original decision.

In those parts of the blackboard where processing followed this model, the data-directed control structure was very effective. However, at lower levels of speech processing (i.e. segmentation and labeling, syllable hypothesis generation based on segments, and word spotting based on syllables), this model was found to be inappropriate because there is not enough reliability in credibility scores of hypotheses to form hypothesis islands that can reliably anchor the search. Thus, processing at these levels cannot be selective (depth-first), and instead requires a complete scan (breadth-first), for which asynchronous control has no advantages (and considerable costs).

A major change in going from configuration C1 to C2 was making the lower levels of processing more sequential and bottom-up. Not until the word level is reached do hypothesis credibility scores have enough reliability to justify the more complex processing required of an asynchronous, data-directed control structure. The presence of these islands of reliability is in itself not a sufficient condition for the use of this sophisticated control structure. What is additionally required is that there is either a significant cost to evaluate each alternative or a large number of alternatives (combinatoric explosion in the search space); only then is the overhead involved in implementing a data-directed control structure worthwhile.

In addition to the control overhead, an asynchronous control structure requires a more complex internal structure for a KS. This complexity arises because, as new information is asynchronously generated, a KS must have the additional logic to determine whether this new information allows it to make a decision it could not previously make or whether this information contradicts a previous decision. In the latter case, it must modify the previous decision, which may involve modifying decisions made as a consequence of the original one. Where processing involves a complex hypothesis network structure with much detailed structure, the nature of asynchronous processing in response to a change at the detailed level is costly, in terms of both processing time and complexity of the KS, and should be avoided unless the compensatory benefits are large. As previously mentioned, the inadequacies in the blackboard structure which make it difficult to skip over detailed structure exacerbate these problems. (The SEARCH KS in configuration C1 is an example of a KS working asynchronously at a detailed level. Although the acoustic-phonetic knowledge applied by SEARCH was represented by a relatively simple data structure within the KS, the code necessary for examining and incrementally building large, integrated and competing AND/OR structures on the blackboard was very complex and the number of KS executions needed to verify a word was large – of the order of 10 to 100. In C2, the function of word verification was replaced by the VERIFY KS. Here, verifying a word is an atomic act (as far as other KS actions are concerned) and is carried out using tailored structures internal to the KS. Each execution of VERIFY forced a recalculation of the detailed structure, rather than sharing such structures across executions.)

Overhead costs of data-directed control

The overhead cost of implementing an asynchronous data-directed control structure for computation of medium level granularity (i.e. a KS action which involves greater than 0.1 s of internal computation) is not significant. The major cost involves monitoring each modify operation to the blackboard to determine whether any preconditions are interested in being notified of this specific change. This cost of monitoring and notification makes a modify operation 12 times as expensive as a read operation. However, in the C2 configuration there are 29 times as many reads as modify operations, thus making this aspect of implementing a data-directed control only 4% of the total cost of a run.

Another cost associated with implementing this type of control structure involves maintaining a scheduler queue of waiting KS instantiations and performing priority calculations to decide which instantiation to run next. However, these focus of control calculations, possibly expressed in a different way, are necessary in any problem-solving system that involves a dynamic search. The more general implementation of these calculations in the context of an asynchronous control structure does not appear to generate significantly more system overhead than a specialized implementation of them in a system with more explicit control structure. The cost of maintaining and updating the scheduler queues and calculating the priorities was about 5–7% of a total run.

Further costs involved in implementing this type of asynchronous control structure arise because of the delay between the invocation of a KS and its execution. The KS must, in general, contain code that revalidates its invocation context before beginning execution. However, by making some assumptions about the type of processing other KSs could effect at particular information levels, there was in practice very little need for context revalidation. KSs did not in general interact by modifying previously made assumptions and detailed structures constructed by other KSs, but rather through the incremental addition of new hypotheses to existing structures or the verification of previously unverified hypotheses.

KS independence

As indicated above, complete independence among KSs was not accomplished. However, information about the processing characteristics of other KSs is generally very restricted, and relates only to KSs that share either dynamic information on the blackboard or long-term static information. To facilitate such data sharing, the concept of a *module* was introduced into the architecture. A module contains a set of preconditions and KSs which share common structures and related accessing procedures. The KSs contained in a module generally operate at the same or adjacent information levels and thus also share specialized accessing and display routines for these information levels of the blackboard. A module usually represents the code of one KS programmer and typically contains one to four KSs and one to four preconditions. Each module is implemented as a separately compiled body of code. A configuration is specified at load time by selecting the desired modules. Additionally, any KS or precondition can be *inhibited* at run-time, effectively excising it from the system. The clustering of KSs by their long-term information structures turned out to be a convenient decomposition for separably instantiable but related activity. The KS module is the atomic unit which is the basic building block for different KS configurations.

How important is the property of independence of KSs? For the two configurations discussed here, the KS modules are not completely independent. However, during the lifetime of the project, which involved numerous iterations of KSs, there has been very little difficulty encountered by this lack of complete independence (i.e. the 'subroutine interaction problem' did not haunt us). It has been possible to configure systems with subsets of KS modules (e.g. a top-end system that deals only with word and phrase hypotheses or a bottom-end system that deals only at and below the word level) without modifications to the modules involved.

The reason for having little difficulty with the subroutine interaction problem can be traced to the data-directed activation of KSs. In general, interaction among KSs is accomplished by having a KS modify the attribute structure of a hypothesis in a way which causes some other KS(s) to be activated and attend to that hypothesis. In order for KSs to communicate information which is not representable using the standard, kernel-supplied attributes, the communicating KSs need only agree on the name of a new attribute and the form of its value; this new attribute can then be used to pass the information. Thus, it is not necessary for a KS to know the names of the other KSs involved. Individual KSs which create, are activated by, or use this information may be added to or deleted from the system without requiring modifications to the other KSs.

A KS as a hypothesis generator

There are two major reasons, in addition to the one already discussed about context validation, why total independence was not achieved; both of these relate to a KS as a generator of hypotheses. The first reason concerns the control of the number of hypotheses a KS should initially generate and the reinvocation of it to generate additional, alternative hypotheses. The parameters associated with hypothesis generation should be set by a policy KS which has a more global view of the current state of the recognition process. The need then arises for a mechanism by which a policy KS can transmit its desires, in an anonymous and independent manner, to the appropriate KS.

It was hoped initially that these 'processing goals' could be specified in terms of the basic hypothesize-and-test paradigm (i.e. by having the policy KS create the appropriate type of hypotheses which would in turn trigger the desired activity). However, 'asking for something to be done' cannot always be specified conveniently in this way nor in an anonymous manner. For example, if there is a need for more word hypotheses to be generated in a particular time area, the action of creating a new hypothesis at the phrase level which will then be expanded at the word level does not precisely capture the desired activity, nor does the somewhat clumsy approach of modifying some attribute of the lower level data (e.g. the syllable level) to force a KS to reprocess this data so as to accomplish the desired activity. Note, in this example, that by trying to force the concept of processing goals into the hypothesize-and-test paradigm the policy KS must know the type of input stimulus that will trigger a KS to produce the desired results, thus violating the independence among modules. In addition, a KS which is designed to do hypothesizing-and-testing does not necessarily produce a response that will precisely match the desired processing goal. Due to these difficulties of directly embedding goal processing control in the hypothesize-and-test paradigm, an alternative approach was developed (but not implemented) which integrates smoothly with the data-directed control flow of Hearsay-II.

This alternative approach is based on introducing the concept of a *goal node* into the blackboard, with types of attributes distinct from those of a hypothesis, and a means of relating goals at different levels. The action of creating a goal at a particular level is a monitorable event that triggers a KS that can do processing at that level. By making a goal node distinct from a hypothesis, a policy KS can generate goals without interfering with KSs that operate at that information level but that cannot respond to the goal. If the triggered KS cannot directly satisfy the goal, it can generate a subgoal, linked to the original goal, to generate data at another level which could be used by the KS to satisfy the original goal. In this way, a policy KS can interact with KSs in an anonymous and independent way. For example, if there is no KS to react to the goal, processing can still continue. In the same manner, if there is more than one KS that can respond to the goal (i.e. competing KSs), the scheduler can resolve this conflict without the need for any action by the KS that generated the goal. A goal node can also be used as a convenient place for a generator type of KS action to leave internal state information about how much and what type of further processing it can do in this area.

The other major reason for violating the independence criterion was based on an efficiency consideration. As previously mentioned, it is comparatively expensive to create a hypothesis on the blackboard. The cost of hypothesis creation is especially critical with a KS that can potentially generate a large number of hypotheses. For example, the syntax prediction KS (EXTEND, in C2) can create, based on a prediction from a single-phrase hypothesis, several hundred word hypotheses. Each of these must then be processed by the word verifier KS (VERIFY) and verified or rejected. Before these hypotheses are verified they share almost identical structures. All but 20, perhaps, will be rejected by VERIFY. To avoid the expense of expanding these as distinct blackboard word hypotheses, special data structures have been constructed to store the predicted words compactly; these data structures are then attached as an attribute of the phrase hypothesis. This example further illustrates the weakness in the current Hearsay-II implementation of efficiently representing and processing groups of hypotheses.

Uniformity of control

Another issue associated with the data-directed control structure is the ease with which different global control strategies can be explored. The uniform interface conventions used for specifying and activating KSs and preconditions, together with treating policy (strategy) KSs in the same way as other KSs makes the total system easy to modify and understand.

As part of the uniform convention for specifying each KS, nonprocedural declarations are required which tell the system the type of pattern that triggers the KS and the type of action that can result from the activation of the KS. By separating the activation of a KS from its scheduling, it has been easy to introduce new global strategies by applying a new priority evaluation function to the information supplied by each KS. In addition, by allowing a policy KS to be able to trigger upon certain conditions that occur in the scheduling 'database' (such as the absence of any invoked KSs, or the lack of any invoked KSs above a certain priority level), it is possible to add different types of policy KSs into the system in a modular manner (e.g. WOSCTL in configuration C2).

In the initial specification of the Hearsay-II architecture, the approach required for focus of control was not well developed and represented one of the major conceptual problems that would determine the success of the design. As a result of work on this problem over the last three years, it is felt that the problem, though not completely solved, is now understood well enough that it no longer represents a major obstacle to the effective use of the architecture. It is interesting to note that much of the discussion in preceding sections is based on a better understanding of what features need to be present in the architecture in order to efficiently support complex focus of control strategies.

Parallel processing

One of the initial design goals of the Hearsay-II architecture was that it should be efficiently (and correctly) executable on a multiprocessor (Lesser, 1975; Fennel, 1975). In order to test the parallel processing capabilities of this architecture on an actual KS configuration, a multiprocessor simulation system was embedded in the multiprocess implementation of Hearsay-II. Each KS in this configuration was modified with the appropriate synchronization primitives.

The result of this simulation, which used an early version of the C1 configuration that was strictly bottom-up in its processing (because it did not include the SASS module), showed that effective parallelism factors of four to six could be achieved (Fennel and Lesser, 1977). Unfortunately, there does not exist similar simulation data for a fully configured C1 or C2 configuration, both of which include top-down processing. However, it is expected that the C2 configuration would exhibit a much higher degree of parallelism, because KS interaction is more loosely coupled and the system does a large amount of breadth-first type of search.

The parallelism factors of four to six that were achieved were less than expected. Further experiments were performed to determine the reason for these low factors. One of these experiments was to run the system with all uses of the synchronization primitives turned off. In this mode, the parallelism factors increased to 14. This dramatic increase is due to the fact that much superfluous synchronization was performed in each KS to maintain data consistency because no assumptions were made about how the blackboard was modified by other KSs. This superfluous synchronization, combined with synchronization primitives whose granularity of locking was too coarse, led to unnecessarily large areas of the blackboard being locked in order to maintain data consistency; this resulted both in significant interference among concurrently executing KS processes and a high system overhead (between 50 and 100%) in order to support parallel processing. As with context validation (discussed above), this was a price paid for complete independence among KSs.

A surprising result was that system performance, in terms of accuracy, was as good with the synchronization disabled as its performance with the full synchronization. The explanation for this phenomenon is that the asynchronous, data-directed control of Hearsay-II is robust in the face of certain types of synchronization errors. For example, consider the normal activity sequence of a KS which involves first examining the blackboard, and then, based on the values read, modifying the blackboard. Suppose that between the time when the KS read the value of an attribute on the blackboard and when it modified the blackboard, the value of the attribute was changed; therefore, the modification was inconsistent with the current state of the blackboard data. However, because of the data-directed nature of KS activation, the changing of the attribute will probably trigger the same KS to be reinvoked to recalculate its original modification. Thus, the need is obviated for a KS, while executing, to lockout the areas of the blackboard it has read, in order to maintain the consistency of its modifications. In addition, other types of inconsistency can often be resolved because another KS with a different view of the problem will correct an incorrect hypothesis whether it resulted from a synchronization error, a mistake in the theory used by the KS, or errorful data. Thus, this self-correcting nature of information flow among KSs, created through the use of a data-directed form of the hypothesize-and-test paradigm, in many cases obviates the need for explicit use of synchronization.

Another example of this self-correcting type of computational structure is a class of iterative refinement methods used to solve partial differential equations. This type of computational structure can be decomposed for multiprocessor implementation so as to avoid most explicit synchronization at the expense of more cycles to reach convergence (Baudet, 1976). This decomposition is accomplished by not requiring each point in the differential grid to be calculated based on the most up-to-date value of its neighboring points.

4.6 Conclusions

The major conclusions on the use of the multilevel blackboard structure are the following:

(1) The paradigm of viewing problem solving in terms of hypothesize-and-test actions distributed among distinct representations of the problem (where these representations form a hierarchy of abstractions) has been shown to be a computationally feasible approach to solving knowledge-intensive tasks. This paradigm also provides a convenient framework for structuring and applying knowledge. This has been demonstrated both by the successful application of the Hearsay-II architecture to the speech-understanding task and also its adoption as an approach to problem solving in a diverse set of other domains such as image understanding (Prager *et al.*, 1977), reading comprehension (Rumelhart, 1976), protein-crystallographic analysis (Engelmore and Nii, 1977), signal understanding (Nii and Feigenbaum, 1978) and complex learning (Soloway and Riseman, 1977b).

(2) The representation of alternative hypotheses in an integrated manner on the blackboard has been shown to have positive aspects. In particular, the integrated representation avoids unnecessary

recalculation and makes it easy to compute a global view of the current state of the problem solution, for the purpose of focussing. The problems still to be resolved arise because the integrated representation permits hypotheses to be used simultaneously in (shared by) multiple contexts (hypothesis networks). Existing primitives for grouping alternative hypotheses are inefficient in space, and, more importantly, make it difficult to determine easily the different contexts that use a hypothesis; these primitives also do not provide a convenient framework for representing and determining the fact that two contexts have very similar hypothesis structures.

(3) There are problems with the current formulation of a partial solution as a distributed network of hypotheses at different information levels. There is a basic confusion in the Hearsay-II implementation between the hypothesis in the network which is at the highest level of abstraction (interpretation) and the entire network. This confusion, combined with the problem of handling of multiple uses of a hypothesis, makes it difficult to perform some of the complex focus-of-attention strategies possible in the architecture.

(4) The uniform structure of the blackboard at all information levels has turned out to be a very positive feature of the architecture. It has made it possible to integrate new KSs into the system easily and to develop a large set of utilities applicable to all KSs. It has also permitted numerous reimplementations of the internal structure of the blackboard without requiring KS modification.

The major conclusions on the uniform, asynchronous, data-directed control are the following:

(5) The use of an implicit and uniform control structure for KS cooperation makes the system easy to modify and understand. The separation permitted between the invocation of a KS and its scheduling makes it convenient to implement a variety of scheduling policies without KS modification.

(6) The overhead costs involved in implemeneting this type of control structure are acceptable for KSs which do moderate amounts of internal computation at each invocation (e.g. more than 0.1 s in the current implementation).

(7) This control structure is not appropriate for domains in which the hypothesis credibility ratings are not selective enough to suggest strongly good paths to search.

(8) The problem of focus of attention in this type of control environment, though not completely solved, is now understood well enough that it no longer represents a major obstacle to the effective use of the architecture. The integrated representation of alternatives on the blackboard, which permits a global view of the current state of problem solution, and the data-directed control structure make it possible to quickly refocus attention to the appropriate places on the blackboard.

(9) The initial attempt to have complete KS independence (in both a sequential and parallel processing environment) resulted in a significant amount of overhead, and thus seems not to be worth the cost. A more balanced approach, based on some knowledge about the type of processing done by other KSs in the configuration, has been more effective. This knowledge does not violate anonymity of KSs because it is based on a functional characterization of their activity and not on their 'names'. Using this approach, KS configurations are still highly modular (i.e. there has been no serious subroutine interaction problem) without paying the severe costs (in complexity of KS programming and execution time) of complete independence.

(10) Parallel processing can be exploited effectively in this architecture. The techniques which are needed because of the errorful nature of the processing in this problem domain provide a form of processing which is also robust in the face of data inconsistency caused by not imposing complete synchronization among parallel processes. Thus, the overhead costs of the synchronization are reduced substantially, allowing effective use of parallelism.

Acknowledgments

Raj Reddy has provided much of the vision and energy for this work, most of the central ideas in the Hearsay model, and much technical expertise in many of the knowledge sources in the Hearsay-II system. Richard Fennell and Rick Hayes-Roth have been particularly instrumental in formulating and testing the Hearsay-II architecture. All members of the CMU Speech Group have contributed to this work; their substantial efforts are gratefully acknowledged. Dan Corkill, Mark Fox, Doug Lenat, Jack Mostow, Don McCracken, John McDermott, Allen Newell, Ed Riseman and Elliot Soloway have made helpful suggestions for this chapter.

Appendix: Configurations of knowledge sources

Configuration C1

The KSs of C1 (see Figure 4.1) are functionally described here briefly. The name given in parentheses following the name of the KS is the module in which it was embedded.

SEG (SEG)   The SEG KS (Goldberg, 1976) generated, from the digitized acoustic signal, a sequence of contiguous, variable-length segment hypotheses.

CSEG (PSYN)   This KS (Shockey and Adam, 1976) combined segment hypotheses into larger segment hypotheses. The stimulus frame was a sequence of three contiguous segment hypotheses; the action was to generate one or more new segment hypotheses, each of whose times lay within the time span of the three hypotheses in the stimulus frame. The precondition for this KS was triggered highly asynchronously – whenever a new segment hypothesis was created. The KS was then invoked once for every pair of segment hypotheses immediately preceding and following the new one.

PSYN (PSYN)   This KS (Shockey and Adam, 1976) created phone hypotheses, based on segment hypotheses. The stimulus frame was also a sequence of three contiguous segment hypotheses; the action was to generate one or more phonetic hypotheses, again with times within the boundaries of the stimulus hypotheses. The comment above about asynchrony of execution of CSEG also holds for PSYN.

POM (POMOW)   The POM KS (Smith, 1976) generated syllable hypotheses from phone hypotheses. The stimulus frame contained phone hypotheses that were classified as syllable nuclei; the action of the KS was to create syllable hypotheses based on the stimulus frame and adjacent segment hypotheses. The precondition for this KS was very complex because it made no assumptions about the order in which phone hypotheses would be created. Thus, the creation of a new phone hypothesis of any kind (syllable nucleus or other) triggered the precondition and caused an invocation of the KS for each nucleus hypothesis with which the new phone hypothesis might possibly interact.

MOW (POMOW)   The MOW KS (Smith, 1976) generated word hypotheses from contiguous syllable hypotheses. The stimulus frame consisted of a newly created syllable hypothesis; the output word hypotheses covered the same time as the stimulus hypothesis, but could also encompass syllable hypotheses on either side of the stimulus hypothesis (i.e. for multisyllabic words). If the stimulus hypothesis suggested a multisyllabic word but the hypothesis for the other syllables did not exist, the word would not be hypothesized; however, if at some later time the required syllable hypothesis did appear, the KS would be triggered (by the new syllable) and the word hypothesized.

RECOG (SASS)   This recognition KS (Hayes-Roth and Mostow, 1976) used syntactic knowledge to generate phrase hypotheses from contiguous word or phrase hypotheses. The precondition triggered on a new phrase or word hypothesis (or one with a changed rating). If the triggering hypothesis completed, with existing hypotheses, a phrase and the constituents were rated sufficiently high, the KS was invoked. This was a bottom-up parsing action.

PREDICT (SASS)   The prediction KS (Hayes-Roth and Mostow, 1976) used syntactic knowledge to generate a new phrase hypothesis, given another phrase hypothesis that was highly rated. This was essentially a 'sideways' or 'outward' action.

RESPELL (SASS)   This KS (Hayes-Roth and Mostow, 1976), given a predicted phrase hypothesis (i.e. one with no links to lower level hypotheses, either phrase or word) with a sufficiently high prediction rating, generated hypotheses of the constituents (words and/or phrases) of the predicted hypothesis. Thus, respelling drove processing downward, from predicted hypotheses towards the word level, so that predictions could ultimately be matched to acoustic data and verified or rejected.

POSTDICT (SASS)   Given a weakly recognized or predicted phrase or word hypothesis, this KS (Hayes-Roth and Mostow, 1976) looked for other hypotheses that tended to confirm it. Such hypotheses were linked to the 'postdicted' hypothesis, increasing its rating.

WOM (WOMOS)   This KS (Cronk and Erman, 1976) was triggered on new word hypotheses that were not linked to syllable hypotheses (i.e. ones that were generated 'from above', by RESPELL or PREDICT). For each such hypothesis, it generated (via a dictionary lookup) expected syllable hypotheses which were likely to describe it.

MOS (WOMOS)   The MOS KS (Cronk and Erman, 1976), given a new syllable hypothesis, generated (via a dictionary lookup) a set of surface-phonemic hypotheses that described the syllable.

TIME (POSSE)   This KS (Cronk and Erman, 1976) responded to the creation of a new phone or surface-phonemic hypothesis and attempted to create a link between the new hypothesis and an existing hypothesis at the other level.

SEARCH (POSSE)   This KS (Cronk and Erman, 1976) responded to the creation of a new link between a phone hypothesis and a surface-phoneme hypothesis and attempted to create new links adjacent to the triggering one. Thus, TIME and SEARCH together incrementally built, through structural connections on the blackboard, a synchronization of a sequence of surface phonemes representing a syllable with a sequence of lower-level, acoustically based phones. The SEARCH KS was very complex in that it built up competing synchronizations (multiple interpretations); this was done with localized, incremental actions and while attempting to have the competing interpretations share maximal consistent substructures.

RPOL (RPOL)   This policy KS (Hayes-Roth *et al.*, 1976) was responsible for propagating validity ratings. It triggered on the creation of a hypothesis, the establishment of a structural connection between two hypotheses, or the change of rating of a hypothesis. It calculated ratings for a hypothesis based on the values of KS-assigned attributes and the ratings of its structurally connected neighboring hypotheses.

FOCUS (FOCUS)   This policy KS imposed a global control strategy on the function of all other KSs in the system. It imposed this control through the setting of goal hypotheses which indicated to a KS both that it should attempt to generate particular types of hypotheses and also what internal criteria (thresholds) it should apply in order to generate such hypotheses.

The strategy implemented by this KS was based on a progressive enlarging of the search space of hypotheses as existing hypotheses prove fruitless; the idea behind this strategy is that one should open up the combinatorics in the search space only when absolutely necessary. The strategy was implemented by setting up initial goal hypotheses with very high criteria for hypothesis generation and then successively lowering these thresholds when the search stagnated.

Configuration C2

This section gives a description of the knowledge sources of configuration C2 from September 1976. See Figure 4.2 for a summary of knowledge sources and levels of C2.

Signal acquisition, parameter extraction, segmentation, labeling (SEG)

An input utterance is spoken into a medium-quality Electro-Voice RE-51 close-speaking headset microphone in a fairly noisy environment (>65 dB). The audio signal is low-passed filtered and 9-bit sampled at 10 kHz. All subsequent processing, as well as controlling the A/D converter, is digital and is done on a time-shared PDP-10 computer. Four parameters (called ZAPDASH) are derived by simple algorithms operating directly on the sampled signal (Goldberg *et al.*, 1977). These parameters are extracted in real time and are used initially to detect the beginning and end of the utterance.

The ZAPDASH parameters are next used by the SEG knowledge source as the basis for an acoustic segmentation and classification of the utterance. This segmentation is accomplished by an iterative refinement technique. First, silence is separated from nonsilence; then the nonsilence is broken down into the sonorant and nonsonorant regions, etc. Eventually, five classes of segments are produced: silence, sonorant peak, sonorant non-peak, fricative and flap. Associated with each classified segment is its duration, absolute amplitude, and amplitude relative to its neighboring segments (i.e. local peak, local value or plateau). The segments are contiguous and nonoverlapping, with one class designation for each.

Finally, the SEG KS does a finer labeling of each segment. The labels are allophonic-like; there are currently 98 of them. Each of the 98 labels is defined by a vector of autocorrelation coefficients (Itakura, 1975). These templates are generated from speaker-dependent training data that have been hand labeled. The result of the labeling process, which matches the central portion of each segment against each of the templates using the Itakura metric, is a vector of 98 numbers; the ith number is an estimate of the (negative log) probability that the segment represents an occurrence of the ith allophone in the label set.

Word spotting (POM, MOW, WORD-CTL)

The initial generation of words, bottom-up, is accomplished by a three-step process.

First, using the labeled segments as input, the POM knowledge source (Smith, 1976) generates hypotheses for likely syllable classes. This is done by first identifying syllable nuclei and then parsing outward from each nucleus. The syllable-class parsing is driven by a probabilistic 'grammar' of 'syllable-class → segment' productions; the rules and their probabilities are learned by an off-line program which is trained on hand-labeled utterances. (The current training, which is speaker dependent, uses 60 utterances containing about 360 word tokens.) For each nucleus position, several competing syllable-class hypotheses are generated – typically three to eight.

The syllable classes are used to hypothesize words. Each of the 1011 words in the vocabulary is specified by a pronunciation description. For word hypothesization purposes, an inverted form of the dictionary is kept, in which there is associated with each syllable-class all the words which have some pronunciation containing that syllable-class. The MOW KS (Smith, 1976) looks up each hypothesized syllable class and generates word candidates from among those words containing that syllable-class. For each word that is multisyllabic, all of the syllables in one of the pronunciations must match above a threshold. Typically, about 50 words of the 1011-word vocabulary are generated at each syllable nucleus position.

Since the September 1976 version, the POM and MOW KSs have been replaced by Noah (Smith, 1977). This KS outperforms POM-MOW on the 1011-word vocabulary (in both speed and accuracy) and is able to handle much larger vocabularies. It has a performance degradation which is only logarithmic in vocabulary size in the range of 500 to 19 000 words.

Finally, the generated word candidates are rated and their begin- and end-times adjusted by the WIZARD procedure (McKeown, 1977). For each word in the vocabulary, WIZARD has a network which decribes the possible pronunciations. This rating is calculated by finding the path through the network which best matches the labeled segments, using the distances associated with each label for each segment; the rating is then based on the difference between this best path and the segment labels. WIZARD is, in effect, a miniature version of the HARPY speech recognition system (Lowerre, 1976; Lowerre and Reddy, 1980), except that it has one network for each word, rather than one network with all words and all sentences.

The result of the processing to this point is a set of words. Each word includes a begin-time, an end-time and a confidence rating. MOW selects a subset of these words, based on their times and ratings, to be hypothesized; it is these selected word hypotheses that form the base for the 'top-end' processing. Typically, these hypotheses include about 75% of the words actually spoken (i.e. 'correct' word hypotheses). Each correct hypothesis has a rating which ranks it on the average about three, as compared to the five to 25 or so incorrect hypotheses that compete with it (i.e. which significantly overlap it in time). The nonselected words are retained internally by MOW for possible later hypothesization.

The amount of hypothesization that MOW does is controlled by the WORD-CTL (Word Control) KS. WORD-CTL creates 'goal' hypotheses at the word level; these are interpreted by MOW as indicating how many word hypotheses to attempt to create in each time area. One can think of MOW as a generator of word hypotheses (from the candidates it creates internally) and WORD-CTL as embodying the policy of how many to hypothesize. This clear separation of policy from mechanism has facilitated experimentation with various control schemes. For example, a trivial change to WORD-CTL, such that goal hypotheses are generated only at the start of the utterance ('left-hand end'), results in MOW creating word hypotheses only at the start, thus forcing all top-end processing to be left-to-right.

WORD-CTL fires at the start of processing of an utterance in order to create goal hypotheses. Subsequently, it may re-trigger if the overall search process stagnates; this condition is recognized as there being no waiting KS instantiations above a certain priority (as described in the section below on attention focusing) or as the global measures of current state of the problem solution not having increased in the last several KS executions.

Top-end processing

Word-island generation (WORD-SEQ, WORD-SEQ-CTL)

The WORD-SEQ knowledge source (Lesser *et al.*, 1977) has the job of generating, from the word hypotheses generated bottom-up, a small set (about three to ten) of word sequence hypotheses. Each of these sequences, or *islands*, can be used as the basis for expansion into larger islands, hopefully culminating in a hypothesis that spans the entire utterance. Multi-word islands are used rather than single-word islands because of the relatively poor reliability of ratings of single words as well as the limited syntactic constraint supplied by single words.

WORD-SEQ uses two kinds of knowledge to generate multi-word islands:

- A table derived from the grammar indicates for every ordered pair of words in the vocabulary (1011 × 1011) whether that pair can occur in that order in some sentence of the defined language. This binary table (which contains about 1.7% 1s) thus defines language-adjacency.

- Acoustic-phonetic knowledge, embodied in the JUNCT (juncture) procedure, is applied to pairs of word hypotheses and is used to decide if that pair might be considered to be time-adjacent in the utterance. JUNCT uses the dictionary pronunciations and examines the segments at their juncture (gap or overlap) in making its decision.

WORD-SEQ takes the highest-rated single words and generates multi-word sequences by expanding them with other hypothesized words that are both time- and language-adjacent. This expansion is controlled by heuristics based on the number and ratings of competing word hypotheses. The best of these words sequences (which occasionally includes single words) are hypothesized.

The WORD-SEQ-CTL (Word-Sequence-Control) KS controls the amount of hypothesization that WORD-SEQ does by creating 'goal' hypotheses which are interpreted by WORD-SEQ as indicating how many hypotheses to create. This provides the same kind of separation of policy and mechanism achieved in the MOW/WORD-CTL pair of KSs. WORD-SEQ-CTL fires at the start of processing of an utterance in order to create the goal hypotheses. Subsequently, WORD-SEQ-CTL triggers if stagnation is recognized; it then modifies the word-sequence goal hypotheses, thus stimulating WORD-SEQ to generate new word-sequence islands from which the search may be more fruitful. WORD-SEQ will generate the additional hypotheses by decomposing word-sequence islands already on the blackboard or by re-generating islands which were initially discarded because their ratings were too low.

Word-sequence parsing (PARSE)

Because the syntactic constraint used in the generation of the word sequences is only pairwise, a sequence longer than two words might not be syntactically acceptable. The PARSE knowledge source of the SASS module (Hayes-Roth et al., 1977a, 1978a) can parse a word sequence of arbitrary length, using the full constraints given by the language. This parsing does not require that the word sequence form a complete nonterminal in the grammar or that the sequence be sentence-initial or sentence-final – the words need only occur contiguously somewhere in some sentence of the language. If a sequence hypothesis does not parse, the hypothesis is marked as 'rejected'. Otherwise, a *phrase hypothesis* is created. Associated with the phrase hypothesis is the word sequence of which it is composed, as well as information about the way (or ways) the words parsed.

Word predictions from phrases (PREDICT)

The PREDICT knowledge source of the SASS module can, for any phrase hyothesis, generate predictions of all words which can immediately precede and all which can immediately follow that phrase in the language. In doing the computation to generate these predictions, this KS uses the parsing information attached to the phrase hypothesis by the parsing component.

Word verification (VERIFY)

An attempt is made to verify the existence of or reject each such predicted word, in the context of its predicting phrase. This verification is handled by the VERIFY knowledge source. If verified, a confidence rating for the word must also be generated. First, if the word has been hypothesized previously and passes the test for time-adjacency (by the JUNCT procedure), it is marked as verified and the word hypothesis is associated with the prediction. (Note that a single word hypothesis may thus become associated with several different phrases.) Second, a search is made of the internal store created by MOW to see if the candidate can be matched by a previously generated candidate which had not been hypothesized. Again, JUNCT makes a judgment about time-adjacency. Finally, WIZARD compares its word-pronunciation network to the segments in an attempt to verify the prediction.

For each of these different kinds of verification, the approximate begin-time (end-time) of the word being predicted to the right (left) of the phrase is taken to be the end-time (begin-time) of the phrase. The end-time (begin-time) of the predicted word is not known and, in fact, one requirement of the verification step is to generate an approximate end-time (begin-time) for the verified word. In general, several different 'versions' of the word may be generated which differ primarily in their end-times; since no context to the right (left) of the predicted word is given, several different estimates of the end (beginning) of the word may be plausible based solely on the segmental information.

Word-phrase concatenation (CONCAT)

For each verified word and its predicting phrase, a new and longer phrase may be generated. This process, accomplished by the CONCAT knowledge source of SASS, which is similar to the PARSE knowledge source, involves parsing the words of the original phrase augmented by the newly verified word. The extended phrase is then hypothesized and includes a rating based on the ratings of the words that compose it.

If a verified word is already associated with some other phrase hypothesis, CONCAT tries to parse that phrase with the predicting phrase. If successful, a new, larger phrase hypothesis is created which represents the merging of the two phrases.

Complete sentences and halting criteria (STOP)

Two unique 'word' hypotheses are generated before the first and after the last segment of the utterance to denote begin and end of utterance, respectively. These same 'words' are included in the syntactic specification of the language and appear as the last terminals of every complete sentence. Thus, any verified phrase that includes these as its extreme constituents is a complete sentence and spans the entire utterance. Such a sentence becomes a candidate for selection as the system's recognition result.

In general, the control and rating strategies do not guarantee that the first such complete spanning hypothesis found will have the highest rating of all possible spanning sentence hypotheses that might be found if the search were allowed to continue, so the system does not just stop with the first one generated. However, the characteristics of such a hypothesis are used by the STOP knowledge source to prune from further consideration other partial hypotheses which, because of their low ratings, are unlikely to be extendible into spanning hypotheses with ratings higher than the best already-discovered spanning sentence. This heuristic pruning procedure is based on the form of the ratings function (i.e. how the rating of the phrase is derived from its constituent words). The pruning procedure considers each partial phrase and uses the ratings of other word hypotheses in the time areas not covered by the phrase to determine if the phrase might be extendible to a phrase rated higher than the spanning hypothesis; if not, the partial phrase is pruned. This pruning process and the rating and halting policies are discussed in Mostow (1977).

The recognition processing finally halts in one of two ways. First, there may be no more partial hypotheses left to consider for predicting and extending. Because of the combinatorics of the grammar and the likelihood of finding some prediction that is rated at least above the absolute rejection threshold, this form of termination happens when the pruning procedure has been effective and has eliminated all competitors. Second, the expenditure of a predefined amount of computing resources (time or space) also halts the recognition process; the actual thresholds used are set according to the past performance of the system on similar sentences (i.e. of the given length and over the same vocabulary and grammar).

Once the recognition process is halted, a selection of one or more phrase hypotheses is made to represent the result. If at least one spanning sentence hypothesis was found, the highest-rated such hypothesis is chosen; otherwise, a selection of several of the highest-rated of the partial phrase hypotheses is made, biasing the selection to the longest ones which tend to overlap (in time) the least.

Hypothesis ratings (RPOL)

The RPOL KS runs in high priority immediately after any KS action that creates a new hypothesis or that modifies an existing hypothesis. RPOL uses rating information on the hypothesis, as well as rating information on hypotheses to which the stimulus hypothesis is connected, to calculate the overall rating of the stimulus hypothesis.

Attention focusing

The top-end processing operations include: (1) word-island generation, (2) word sequence parsing, (3) word prediction from phrases, (4) word verification, and (5) word–phrase concatenation. Of these, (3), (4) and (5) are the most frequently performed. Typically, there are a number of these actions waiting to be performed at various places in the utterance. The selection at each point in the processing of which of these actions to perform is a problem of combinatoric control, since the execution of each action usually generates other actions to be done.

To handle this problem, the Hearsay-II system has a statistically based scheduler (Hayes-Roth and Lesser, 1977) which calculates a priority for each action and selects, at each time, the waiting action with the highest priority. The priority calculation attempts to estimate the usefulness of the action in fulfilling the overall system goal of recognizing the utterance. The calculation is based on the stimulus and response frames specified when the action is triggered. For example, the word verifier is triggered whenever words are predicted from a phrase hypothesis; the information passed to the scheduler in order to help calculate the priority of this instantiation of the verifier includes such things as the time and rating of the predicting phrase (in the stimulus frame) and the number of words predicted (as given in the response frame). In addition to the action-specific information, the scheduler keeps track of the overall state of the system in terms of the kinds and quality of hypotheses in each time area.

Interpretation and response (SEMANT, DISCO)

The SEMANT knowledge source (Fox and Mostow, 1977) accepts the word sequence(s) result of the recognition process and generates an interpretation in an unambiguous format for interaction with the database that the speaker is querying. The interpretation is constructed by actions associated with 'semantically interesting' nonterminals (which have been pre-specified for the grammar) in the parse tree(s) of the recognized sequence(s). If recognition results in two or more partial sequences, SEMANT constructs a consistent interpretation based on all of the partial sentences, taking into account for each partial sentence its rating, temporal position and semantic consistency, as compared to the other partial sentences.

The DISCO (discourse) knowledge source (Hayes-Roth *et al.*, 1977b) accepts the formatted interpretation of SEMANT and produces a response to the speaker. This response is often the display of a selected portion of the queried database. In order to retain a coherent interpretation across sentences, DISCO has a finite-state model of the discourse which is updated with each interaction.

Part II

5

Early Applications (1975–1980)

R.S. Engelmore, A.J. Morgan and H.P. Nii

Part II contains five chapters that capture the spirit of the earliest Hearsay-II-inspired applications. In each case, the types of problems being considered did not admit a 'conventional' solution, in the sense that there appeared to be a consistent algorithm that could produce reliable solutions. For these problems, the single most important feature of the blackboard model was the capability for opportunistic problem solving. Put simply, the direction taken by the system is determined by the current state of progress toward the solution, and not by some predetermined plan. Of course, the actions the system can take are determined by pre-specified code. However, a number of individual actions can be combined in many different ways to give a wide range of system behaviors.

The most important of the early applications was HASP, developed at Systems Control by Nii and co-workers (Feigenbaum was a consultant to the project). Originally this project could not use the name HASP, for security reasons, and the system was referred to as SU/X in early papers (e.g. Nii and Feigenbaum, 1978). Chronologically, HASP was overlapped by the Hearsay-II project. During the time that Hearsay-II was being developed, the staff of the HASP project was looking for an approach to solve its application problem. The search for a new methodology came about because the plan-generate-and-test problem-solving method that was successful for interpreting mass spectrometry data in the DENDRAL program (Lindsay et al., 1980) was found to be inappropriate for the problem of interpreting passive sonar signals. In the history of blackboard systems, HASP represents a branching point in the philosophy underlying the design of blackboard systems. Generally, later systems can be thought of as modifications of or extensions to either the Hearsay-like or HASP-like designs.

By way of introduction, it is interesting to trace the early development of HASP and see how its designers came to adopt the blackboard model over one with which they were more familiar. The following discussion is taken from Nii (1986b). The task of HASP was to interpret continuous sonar signals passively collected by hydrophone arrays monitoring an area of the ocean. Signals are received from multiple arrays, with each array consisting of multiple hydrophones. Each array has some directional resolution. One can get a pretty good understanding of the situation by visualizing a large room full of plotters, each recording digitized signals from the hydrophones. Imagine an analyst going from one plotter to the next trying to discern what each one is hearing, and then integrating the information from all the plots in order to discern the current activity in the region under surveillance. This interpretation and analysis activity goes on continuously day in and day out, for the purpose of detecting enemy submarines. The objective of the HASP project was to write a program that 'emulated' the human analysts, that is, to incorporate, in a computer program, the expertise of the analysts, especially their ability to detect submarines. (This was in 1973, before the term 'expert system' was coined. The only expert system in existence at the time was DENDRAL, and MYCIN was on its way.) The HASP problem was chosen to work on because it appeared to be similar to the DENDRAL problem, a signal interpretation problem for which there were experts who could do the job. The system designers were confident that the problem-solving approach taken in DENDRAL would work for HASP. What was DENDRAL's task, and what was its approach? To quote from Feigenbaum (1977), the task was:

> to enumerate plausible structures (atom-bond graphs) for organic molecules, given two kinds of information: analytic instrument data from a mass spectrometer and a nuclear magnetic resonance spectrometer; and user-supplied constraints on the answers, derived from any other source of knowledge (instrumental or contextual) available to the user.
>
> DENDRAL's inference procedure is a heuristic search that takes place in three stages, without feedback: plan-generate-and-test.
>
> Generate is a generation process for plausible structures. Its foundation is a combinatorial algorithm that can produce all the topologically legal candidate structures. Constraints supplied by the user or by the Plan process prune and steer the generation to produce the plausible set and not the enormous legal set.
>
> Test refines the evaluation of plausibility, discarding less worthy candidates and rank-ordering the remainder for examination by the user. . . . It evaluates the worth of each candidate by comparing its predicted data with the actual input data. . . . Thus, Test selects the best explanation of the data.

Plan produces direct (i.e. not chained) inference about likely substructures in the molecule from patterns in the data that are indicative of the presence of the substructure. In other words, Plan worked with combinatorially reduced abstracted sets to guide the search in a generally fruitful direction.

If some of the words in this description were replaced, the plan-generate-and-test approach seemed appropriate for the HASP tasks:

Generate plausible ship candidates and their signal characteristics. Test by comparing the predicted signals with the real signals. Plan by selecting types of ships that could be in the region of interest. The Plan phase would use intelligence reports, shipping logs, and so on.

The system designers had already talked with the analysts and had read their training manuals. They knew that the necessary knowledge could be represented as rules, a form of domain knowledge representation that had proven its utility and power in DENDRAL. Difficulties were encountered immediately; some of these were:

(1) The input data arrived in a continuous stream, as opposed to being batched as in DENDRAL. The problem of a continuous data stream was solved by processing data in time-framed batches.

(2) The analysis of the activities in the ocean had to be tracked and updated over time. Most importantly, past activities played an important role in the analysis of current activities.

(3) There were numerous types of information that seemed relevant but remote from the interpretation process; for example, the average speeds of ships.

To address the second problem, it was immediately clear that a data structure was needed that was equivalent to a 'situation board' used by the analysts; the data structure was called the Current Best Hypothesis (CBH). The CBH reflected the most recent hypothesis about the situation at any given point in time. This could serve as the basis for generating a 'plan'; that is, the CBH could be used as a basis for predicting the situation to be encountered in the next time frame. The prediction process could also utilize and integrate the variety of information mentioned in item 3 above. The predicted CBH would then be used:

(1) to verify that the interpretation from the previous time frame was correct;

(2)   to reduce the number of alternatives generated during past time-frames – there was only one solution hypothesis, but some attributes, for example platform type, could have alternative values; and

(3)   to reduce the number of new signals not accounted for in the predicted CBH that needed to be analyzed in full.

The CBH was thought of as a cognitive 'flywheel' that maintained the continuous activities in a region of ocean between time frames. The initial design, a modified version of DENDRAL, was sketched out in December of 1973 (Figure 5.1).

Then there came the bad news: there was no plausible generator of the solution space, and there was no simulator to generate the signals of hypothesized platforms. The bad news had a common root: given a platform, there was a continuum of possible headings, speeds and aspects relative to a hydrophone array. Each parameter, in addition to variations in the water temperature, depth, and so on, uniquely affected the signals 'heard' at an array. Consequently, there was a continuum of possibilities in the solution space as well as for the simulator to simulate. The designers tried to limit the number of possibilities, for example, by measuring the headings by unit degrees, but this left an enormous search space. Moreover, there was not enough knowledge to prune the space to make the generate-and-test method practical. The DENDRAL approach was abandoned. The HASP developers then learned of the Hearsay-II

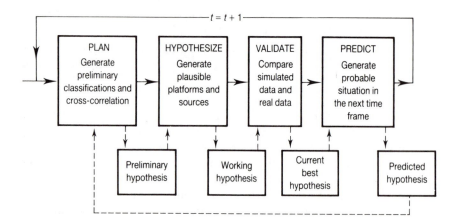

Figure 5.1   HASP design based on DENDRAL. There was one global data structure that contained a hypothesis about the situation. After each of the plan, hypothesize, validate and predict phases the hypothesis changed states. These states were called the preliminary hypothesis, the working hypothesis, the current best hypothesis, and the predicted hypothesis. (—, control flow; ---, data flow.)

approach. The description of the approach produced enough of a mental shift in the way the HASP problem was viewed that a new solution could be designed. It should be noted in passing that Hearsay-II in fact had generators and used them. It was the idea of fusing uncertain and partial solutions to construct solutions, combined with 'island driving', that intrigued the designers. Island driving is a problem-solving strategy. A relatively reliable partial hypothesis is designated as an 'island of certainty', and the hypothesis building pushes out from this solution island in many directions. This is sometimes called a 'middle-out' strategy. There can be many islands of certainty driving the problem-solving process.

The sonar analysts solved the problem piecemeal. They first identified a harmonic set in the signals. The 'accounted-for' signals were then 'subtracted' from the data set. Then another harmonic set would be formed with the remaining data and so on until all the signals were accounted for. As easy as it sounds, the task of harmonic set formation was a very difficult one, given noisy and missing data, and could produce large combinatorial possibilities. Addressing this problem became one of the major concerns in HASP. Each harmonic set implied a set of possible sources of sound (for example, a propeller shaft), which in turn implied a set of possible ship types from which the sounds could be emanating. Certain signal characteristics directly implied platform types, but this type of diversion from the incremental analysis was very rare. What the human analysts were doing was what might be called logical induction and synthesis. This point is discussed in Pentland and Fischler (1983). Hypotheses were synthesized from pieces of data using a large amount of domain-specific knowledge that translated information in one form to information in another form; that is, transformed a description in one vocabulary to one in another vocabulary. For example, a set of frequencies was transformed into a set of possible ship parts (for example, a shaft or a propeller) by using knowledge of the form: If the harmonic set consists of . . . , then it is most likely to be due to . . . . The partial solutions thus formed were then combined using other knowledge to construct acceptable solutions.

The analysts were also strongly model driven. There were common shipping lanes used by merchant ships traveling from one port to another. These platforms usually maintained a steady speed and heading. This and similar knowledge served to constrain the number of possible partial solutions. For example, if a hypothetical surface platform traveled across a shipping lane, the possibility that it might be a merchant ship could be eliminated. In this example, a model of ship movements was able to aid in the platform classification process. Moreover, knowledge about the characteristics of platforms was used to combine lower-level, partial solutions. Suppose a platform type was hypothesized from an acoustic source, for example a propeller shaft. Knowledge about the platform type (a model) was then used to look for other acoustic sources (for example, an engine) belonging to that platform. This type of top-down, model-driven analysis was used as often as the bottom-up signal analysis.

Once it was clear that interpretation in HASP, as in Hearsay, was a process of piecemeal generation of partial solutions that were combined to form complete solutions, the Hearsay-II system organization could be exploited. The CBH was partitioned into levels of analysis corresponding to the way analysts were used to thinking (that is, harmonic sets, sources and ship types). The rule-based knowledge gathered for the purposes of pruning and guiding the search process was organized into sets of rules (knowledge sources) that transformed information on one level to information on another level. It is interesting to note that many of the pieces of knowledge intended for pruning purposes could be converted into inductive knowledge. For example, a pruning rule that read, 'If a signal is coming from outside the normal traffic lane, then its source could not be cargo or cruise ships', could be used directly for reducing alternatives or could be converted to read '. . . , then its source is either military ships or fishing boats'. One can hold the view that this is not surprising, because knowledge is knowledge and what counts is how and when it is used.

Nothing is as easy as it appears. There were many differences between the speech and the sonar signal understanding tasks that drove the HASP system architecture in a different direction from Hearsay-II. The use of the blackboard as a situation board that evolves over time has already been mentioned. This is somewhat equivalent to asking a speaker to repeat his utterance over and over again while moving around, and having the interpretation improve with each repeated utterance as well as being able to locate the speaker after each utterance. After each utterance, the CBH would reflect the best that the system could do up to that point. It was also mentioned that sets of rules were used as opposed to procedures in Hearsay-II to represent knowledge sources. Rules were chosen because they were used in DENDRAL and in MYCIN. This is one example of the cultural influence. No other representation was even considered. This choice of knowledge representation had a great influence in simplifying the HASP scheduler.

Another example is in the choice of problem-solving method. HASP was built in a culture that had a tradition of using problem-solving approaches that focused on applying large amounts of situation-specific knowledge rather than applying a weak method – search – using general knowledge about the task. The methodology used to select and apply knowledge in HASP is, therefore, quite different philosophically from the one reflected in the Hearsay-II scheduler.

The following characteristics influenced the final design of HASP.

(1) *Events* The concept of events is inherent in the HASP problem. For

example, a certain type of frequency shift in the signal would be an event that implied the ship was changing its speed. An appearance or disappearance of a signal would be an event that implied a new ship was on the scene or a known ship was getting out of the range of the sensors, or it implied an expected behavior of certain types of ships. This inherent task characteristic made it natural for the HASP system to be an event-based system; that is, an occurrence of a particular event implied that new information was available for some *a priori* determined knowledge source to pursue. The goals of the task dictated which events were significant and which were not. This, in turn, meant that the programmer (the knowledge engineer of today) could, *a priori*, decide what changes in the blackboard, that is, events, were significant for solving the problem (as opposed to the system noticing every change). Furthermore, the only time a knowledge source needed to be activated was when some events occurred that it knew about. These task characteristics, together with the use of a rule-based knowledge representation, helped redefine and simplify the task of the scheduler in the sense that each piece of knowledge was more or less self-selecting for any given event.

(2) *Temporal events*   In Hearsay-II 'time' meant the sequence in which the words appeared in a spoken sentence. Based on the sequence of words, one could predict or verify the appearance of another set of words later or earlier in the sequence. In HASP time had different connotations. In one sense, time was similar to the separate utterance in the hypothetical repetitive utterances problem mentioned earlier. There was information redundancy, as well as new and different information (no two utterances sound exactly the same), as time went on. Redundancy meant that the system was not pressed to account for every piece of data at each time frame. It could wait to see if a clearer signal appeared later, for example. Also, time meant that the situation at any time frame was a 'natural' consequence of earlier situations, and such information as trends and temporal patterns (both signal and symbolic) that occur over time could be used. One of the most powerful uses of time in this sense was the generation and use of expectations of future events.

(3) *Multiple input streams*   Aside from the digitized data from many hydrophones, HASP had another kind of input – reports. Reports contained information gathered from intelligence or normal shipping sources. These reports tended to use descriptions similar to those used on the ship level on the blackboard (CBH). Whereas the ordinary data came in at the bottom level for both Hearsay and HASP, HASP had another input 'port' at the highest level. Given the input at this level, the system generated the kinds of acoustic sources and acoustic signatures it expected in the future based on

information in its taxonomic knowledge base. This type of model-based expectation was one of the methods used to 'fuse' report data with signal data.

(4)   *Explanation*   The purpose of explanation is to understand what is going on in the system from the perspective of the user and the programmer. Because the needs of the users are different from those of the programmers, explanation can take on many forms. Explanation for the user was especially important in HASP, because there was no way to test the correctness of the answer. The only way to test the performance of the system was to get human analysts to agree that the system's situation hypotheses and reasoning were plausible. CBH, with its network of evidential support, served to justify the hypothesis elements and their hypothetical properties. It served to 'explain' the relationships between the signal data and its various levels of interpretation. The explanation of the reasoning, that is, 'explaining' which pieces of knowledge had been applied under what circumstances, was made possible by 'playing back' the executed rules. In MYCIN and other similar rule-based programs, explanation consists of a playback of rule firings. In HASP the ordinary method of playback turned out to be useful only to programmers for debugging purposes. For the user, the rules were either too detailed or were applied in a sequence (breadth first) that was hard for the user to understand. In HASP the explanation of the line of reasoning was generated from an execution history with the help of 'explanation templates' that selected the appropriate rule activities in some easy-to-understand order.

There were many other differences, but these characteristics had the most impact on the design of the eventual system. The list serves to illustrate how strongly the task characteristics influence blackboard architectures.

Overlapping the HASP project, but slightly later, was a second Stanford application; the analysis of the structure of proteins. The project originally called SU/P (Waterman and Hayes-Roth, 1978) later came to be known as CRYSALIS. The main goal of the CRYSALIS system, from an AI perspective, was to investigate the use of strategic knowledge in problem solving. The blackboard model was chosen because it appeared to offer a way of partitioning both the solution space and the knowledge into manageable units. Some considerable time was spent in the design of the blackboard structure for CRYSALIS. The final design included two blackboard panels, rather than the single panel of Hearsay-II and HASP. The use of multiple panels later became an important feature of other systems. The control mechanism of CRYSALIS was developed from HASP, by removing the real-time aspects of HASP and adding a hierarchical structure. On each problem-solving cycle, CRYSALIS transferred control to a strategy-level knowlege source, which evaluated the current state of the problem-solving process and selected a task to pursue. The execution of the task was determined by a task-level knowledge source, which in turn called upon an appropriate domain-level knowledge source. As we will see in Part III, the idea of knowledge sources for control was extended in a natural way to include a control blackboard in the Hearsay-III and BB1 frameworks.

Two of the applications in this part are vision systems. As with HASP and CRYSALIS, the objective is to impose structure upon complex input data. The design of the VISIONS system, developed at the University of Massachusetts, shows clearly the influence of the Hearsay-II architecture as well as the influence (also from CMU) of production systems in its use of terms like long-term and short-term memory. The task domain is the interpretation of static color images of natural scenes. Hypotheses are proposed in the STM, which is actually a seven-level blackboard, representing an abstraction hierarchy, on which are stored instances of classes of objects. The object classes are stored in the LTM, which is another seven-level blackboard structure with levels corresponding to the STM. Partial hypotheses can be formulated in either a bottom-up or a top-down manner. The knowledge sources use both declarative and procedural forms and are used to generate and verify hypotheses at the different levels of abstraction. VISIONS went well beyond Hearsay-II in the richness of representations used for expressing the system's knowledge, including the use of a directed graph implemented in a graph processing language. The problem solving approach is more like Hearsay-II than HASP in its reliance on search, but differs from Hearsay-II in its representation of alternative hypotheses. VISIONS keeps a history of the sequence of hypothesis generation, whereas Hearsay-II maintains a network of alternatives directly on the blackboard without a record of their order of creation. The control strategy employs a fixed sequence of activities, organized hierarchically much like the method employed in CRYSALIS, but using a more elaborate hierarchy of control modules.

A description of the original VISIONS system can be found in the book *Computer Vision Systems* (Hanson and Riseman, 1978a). Further developments were reported in an article entitled 'The VISIONS image understanding system – 1986', by A. Hanson and E. Riseman, which appears in the book *Advances in Computer Vision*, Edited by Chris Brown and published in 1987 by L. Erlbaum. More recently, the VISIONS system has evolved into the UMass Schema System, and that is the system described in Chapter 8. The Schema System advances the earlier work by providing 'a framework for building a general interpretation system by combining many special-purpose ones', and permitting schema instances to run concurrently. Chapter 8 is a condensed and slightly revised version of an article that appeared in the *International Journal of Computer Vision* (Vol. 2, 1988). Although this chapter was written much later than other chapters in this section, its focus is on a blackboard system whose origins belong in the era of early applications. We are grateful to the authors and to Professors Takeo Kanade, editor of the *IJCV*, for permission to use the material in this chapter, which we believe gives a clearer description of the system than the earlier papers.

In the system developed at Kyoto University (which for brevity we refer to as SACAP, for Structural Analysis of Complex Aerial Photographs), the input to the system is an aerial photograph. The use of a blackboard framework was motivated by the availability of different kinds of specialized knowledge that can be applied to the problem, by the possibility of describing the problem in a structured way, and by the need to focus on a particular part of the problem using specific problem-solving procedures.

SACAP's input is a processed image consisting of a large number of regions characterized by properties such as homogeneity and shape. Its task is to identify various object types (road, roof, car, grassland, etc.) in those regions. Associated with each object are knowledge sources for detecting it. The knowledge sources are individual production systems that share the common data on the blackboard. Conflicts can arise when more than one object is hypothesized in a region, or if an object identification is incompatible with identifications made in neighboring regions. Such conflicts are resolved by associating a reliability factor with each identification. Only the highest ranking hypothesis is maintained on the blackboard at any one time.

Scheduling is straightforward: the knowledge sources are applied to each region for which they are appropriate.

A further refinement of the concepts in Hearsay-II and HASP was carried out at the Rand Corporation in the late 1970s. The application was centered on planning, rather than the analytic tasks performed by Hearsay-II, HASP and CRYSALIS. The objective of the Rand project was to simulate human problem solving in the context of planning, and to explore the capabilities of the blackboard model as a model of human planning behavior. The simulation system was called OPM. The underlying concepts are described in two papers, (Hayes-Roth *et al.*, 1979; Hayes-Roth and Hayes-Roth, 1979b), the former of which is reproduced in Chapter 10. Like CRYSALIS, OPM used multiple blackboard panels to structure the problem and to record the output from individual knowledge sources.

The particular problem addressed by OPM was generating a sensible plan for carrying out errands, e.g. picking up a repaired watch, ordering a book or meeting a friend for lunch, around a small town. Plan generation required a knowledge of the spatial and temporal constraints that could be applied. Control of the application of these constraints was of central importance here, and this concern was influential in the design of BB1, which is presented in Part III.

6

Signal-to-Symbol Transformation: HASP/SIAP Case Study

H. Penny Nii, Edward A. Feigenbaum, John J. Anton and A.J. Rockmore

Artificial Intelligence is that part of Computer Science that concerns itself with the concepts and methods of symbolic inference and symbolic representation of knowledge. Its point of departure – its most fundamental concept – is what Newell and Simon called (in their Turing Award Lecture) 'the physical symbol system' (Newell and Simon, 1976).

But, within the last 15 years, it has concerned itself also with signals – with the interpretation or understanding of signal data. AI researchers have discussed 'signal-to-symbol transformations', and their programs have shown how appropriate use of symbolic manipulations can be of great use in making signal processing more effective and efficient. Indeed, the programs for signal understanding have been fruitful, powerful and among the most widely recognized of AI's achievements.

HASP, and its follow-on, SIAP, are among these programs. HASP arose from an important national defense need. It appeared to be impossible to satisfy the computational requirements of a major ocean surveillance system of sensors (at least within the bounds of economic feasibility) with conventional methods of statistical signal processing. AI's signal understanding methods were maturing in the early 1970s. Vision research had been underway for several years. The ARPA Speech Understanding Project was well into its first phase (Newell *et al.*, 1973). And the DENDRAL project for the interpretation of mass spectral data in terms of organic molecular structures had achieved significant success in certain narrow areas of chemical analysis (Lindsay *et al.*, 1980). The time was ripe to attempt the application of the emerging techniques to ocean surveillance signal understanding problem. This insight was made by Dr Lawrence Roberts, then Director of Information Processing Technology for ARPA.

135

At his request, and with ARPA support, scientists at the Stanford Heuristic Programming Project, with the help of scientists at Systems Control Technology, Inc. (SCI), began in 1972 to study the feasibility of the project. System design and programming began in 1973. The project was located at SCI because of the company's expertise in the military problem and because of the classified nature of the work. Feigenbaum was the principal investigator, and Nii was responsible for the detailed design and much of the programming. Scottie Brooks also contributed significant programming. The primary expert in this Expert System project was John Miller, a recently retired officer from the military. Scottie Brooks acquired expertise about acoustic and other data characteristics and took over some of the expert's role during SIAP development. Many others contributed (see Acknowledgments).

The first year was spent in understanding the nature of the signals, the signal-generating objects, the symbolic context in which the signal analysis was taking place, and in demonstrating that one could not 'DENDRALize' this problem. Systematic generation and pruning of the hypothesis space was not the appropriate model. But we learned a great deal, and were able by the end of the year to recognize the appropriate framework when it presented itself. That framework was the blackboard model of the Hearsay-II effort in speech understanding being done at Carnegie-Mellon University (CMU) (Lesser and Erman, 1977; Erman *et al.*, 1980).

The second year and beyond consisted of a rush of activity to program, adapt and alter the CMU model to fit the problem at hand, to finish the acquisition and encoding of the knowledge, and to perform a series of tests to demonstrate and validate the work. The HASP phase ended in the fall of 1975.

SCI scientists continued the work in SIAP, which began in 1976. The HASP project had intentionally evaded one difficult part of the overall signal-to-symbol transformation problem, the part that is sometimes called 'low-level' processing, the processing activity closest to the signal data. HASP never saw real signals. It saw descriptions of signals, albeit low-level descriptions. The identification of line segments and their characterization were done by people. SIAP was an attempt to automate this phase, and involved as well some necessary modifications to HASP to allow it to cope with this additional confrontation with reality. The SIAP work was complicated by the fact that the SCI scientists were constrained by their sponsor to use signal processing programs that had been developed in another context by another ARPA contractor. The SIAP effort ended early in 1980 after showing significant demonstration on real ocean data in real time.

(Some purists insist that the only valid use of the term 'signal' is the set of digitized voltages that arise from the normal functioning of the sensor. But we are not that rigid in our view. We are willing to consider as signal those low-level algorithmic transformations of the raw data that are in the standard toolkit of the signal processing community (such as the Fast Fourier Transform). Indeed, the humans who do the HASP/SIAP task manually never see the numbers either. Their job begins after some elementary transforms have been computed. This is not to imply that there isn't additional leverage in pushing AI methods one last level closer to the numbers, but to assert that HASP/SIAP is not really looking at the signal is to be splitting hairs.)

6.1 System operation – what it does

6.1.1 The problem

The embassy cocktail party problem captures important features of the ocean surveillance mission. Suppose microphones are concealed for intercepting important conversations of foreign dignitaries at a party. Because bug emplacements are near the heavily trafficked bar and buffet tables, the basement sleuth who monitors the phones must contend with the babble of simultaneous speakers. The party-goers move into and out of range of the microphones in imperfectly predictable patterns. Their speaking patterns also change, as does the background clatter of plates, glasses, orchestra, and so on. Room echoes confound otherwise discernible conversations. Worst of all, the guests of greatest concern to the basement sleuth are prone themselves to covertness, using low voices and furtive movements in pursuit of their business.

HASP/SIAP sleuths in the deep ocean. Using data from concealed hydrophone arrays, it must detect, localize and ascertain the type of each ocean vessel within range. The presence and movements of submarines are most important. Nevertheless, there are strategic and tactical motives for monitoring all vessel types.

Just as for the embassy sleuth, the program has to overcome the problems of noncooperative subjects in a noisy, complex medium. Ocean-going vessels typically move within fixed sea lanes, but storms and currents cause shifts in routes and operations. The background noise from distant ships is mixed with storm-induced and biological noises. Sound paths to the arrays vary with diurnal and seasonal cycles. Arrival of sound energy over several paths may suddenly shift to no arrivals at all, or arrivals only of portions of vessel radiation. Sound from one source can appear to arrive from many directions at once. Characteristics of the receivers can also cause sound from different bearings to mix, appearing to come from a single location. Finally, the submarine targets of most interest are very quiet and secretive.

6.1.2 What HASP/SIAP does to solve the problem

The program starts with digitized data from hydrophone arrays that monitor an ocean region from its periphery. The arrays have some directional resolution. Ideally each look direction produces a data channel with sound energy only from vessels near its axis, a spatial partition resembling spoke gaps on a bicycle wheel. In practice, radiation from a single vessel may spread across several gaps, and many vessels may be located in any one gap, or in adjacent gaps; a situation that can produce a kaleidoscope of sound.

Rotating shafts and propellers, and reciprocating machinery on board a ship are major sources of the intercepted radiation. The **signature**, or sound spectrum, of a ship under steady operation contains persistent fundamental narrow-band frequencies and certain of their harmonics. Imagine the ship's propeller saying 'ahhhhh' on its way across the ocean. On a speech analyst's sonogram, this sound would appear as a collection of dark vertical stripes against a fuzzy gray background.

Sonar analysts have been trained to recognize the sound signature traits of ships on their sonogram displays, and to classify a signature into one of several important classes. If only one ship is present on a channel, the problem is essentially to match the measured signature (it may be imperfectly measured or partially present) to a collection of stored references for the best fit. Most computer-aided ship classification schemes have achieved some measure of success at this level.

When several ships radiate into the same array channels, the problem becomes more demanding. Highly skilled analysts use a collection of tricks in sonogram interpretation to disentangle the signatures for classification. Their procedures are not strictly separable for these tasks. That is, they do not disentangle signatures first without regard to classification information. ('Disentangle' means to separate correctly signature components of different vessels. This process is aided by contextual information about the plausible behavior of the sources on ships.) HASP/SIAP is unique among current machine-aided classifiers in imitating this nonseparable approach.

Sonogram displays used by a sonar analyst are analog histories of the spectrum of received sound energy. New data on a channel are portrayed by varying the intensity of pixels on the display. Greater concentrations of energy at a given frequency are translated into higher intensities at corresponding horizontal positions. Synchronous horizontal sweeps, therefore, leave vertical lines on a display where persistent frequencies are present. (See Figure 6.1 for a simulated sonogram.) Starting, stopping, frequency shifting, and even subtle traces, are discernible to a trained eye. Recognition of these analysis elements must also be carried out automatically if the program is to emulate human analysts' procedures in subsequent processing. The data streams from

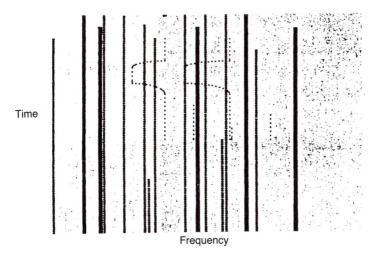

Figure 6.1   A simulated sonogram (with noise suppressed).

each hydrophone array channel are then converted into hypotheses on the class type of each detected vessel. The data, rules and procedures associated with a particular hypothesis can be recalled, so supporting evidence for the program's conclusions are also available for operator scrutiny.

6.2 System organization – how it does it

6.2.1 Major terms and concepts

The *understanding* of sonograms often requires using information not present in the signals themselves. Major sources of information are reports from other arrays and intelligence reports. More general knowledge, like the characteristics of ships and common sea-lanes, also contributes significantly. Each such source of knowledge may at any time provide an inference which serves as a basis for another knowledge source to make yet another inference, and so on, until all relevant information has been used and appropriate inferences have been drawn.

Essential to the operation of the program is its *model* of the ocean scene. The model is a symbol-structure that is built and maintained by the program and contains what is known about the unfolding situation. The model thus provides a context for the ongoing analysis. More commonly known as the *situation board* to the analysts, the model is used as a reference for the interpretation of new information, assimilation of new events, and generation of expectations concerning future events. It is the program's *cognitive flywheel*.

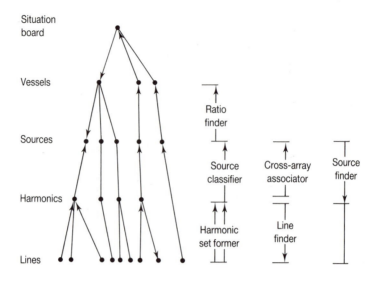

Figure 6.2   Levels of analysis and some of the knowledge sources.

The task of understanding the situation from the sonogram and other data is accomplished at various *levels of analysis*. These levels are exhibited in Figure 6.2. The most integrated, or the highest, level represents the situation board describing all the ships hypothesized with some confidence. The lowest level, that is, the level closest to the data, consists of connected line segments containing features derived from the signal data. During the HASP design an assumption was made that a front-end program could be written to extract major signal features – intensity, stability, bandwidth, duration, etc. SIAP, in fact, integrates such a front-end signal processor into the system.

At each level, the *units of analysis* are the *hypothesis elements*. These are symbol-structures that describe what the available evidence indicates in terms that are meaningful at that particular level. Thus, on the Vessel level, in Figure 6.2, the descriptive properties that each Vessel element can have are Vessel class, Location, Current speed, Course and Destination. Each of the values of the properties has associated with it *weights*, an informal measure of confidence in the hypothesis. The example below shows a part of a hypothesis element on the Source level with different expressions of confidence.

```
SOURCE-1
    TYPE        (Engine .5) (Shaft .3) (Propeller −.3)
    LOCATION    ((Lat 34.2) (Long 126.5) (Error 9))
```

Links between the levels of analysis are built from *sources of knowledge*. A knowledge source (KS) is capable of putting forth the *inference* that some hypothesis elements present at its 'input' level imply some particular hypothesis element(s) at its 'output' level. A source of knowledge contains not only the knowledge necessary for making its own specialized inferences, but also the knowledge necessary for checking the inferences made by other sources of knowledge. The inferences which draw together hypothesis elements at one level into a hypothesis element at a higher level (or which operate in the other direction) are represented symbolically as links between levels as shown in Figure 6.2. The resulting network, rooted in the input data and integrated at the highest level into a descriptive model of the situation, is called the *current best hypothesis* (CBH), or the *hypothesis* for short.

Each source of knowledge holds a considerable body of specialized information that an analyst would generally consider 'ordinary.' Sometimes this is relatively 'hard' knowledge, or 'textbook' knowledge. Also represented are the *heuristics*, that is, 'rules of good guessing' an analyst develops through long experience. These judgmental rules are generally accompanied by estimates from human experts concerning the *weight* that each rule should carry in the analysis.

Each KS is composed of 'pieces' of knowledge. By a piece of knowledge we mean a *production rule*, that is, an IF–THEN type of implication formula. The IF side, also called the *situation* side, specifies a set of conditions or patterns for the rule's applicability. The THEN side, also called the *action* side, symbolizes the implications to be drawn (or various processing events to be caused) if the IF conditions are met. Following is a heuristic represented as a production rule:

IF   Source was lost due to fade-out in the near-past, and
        Similar source started up in another frequency, and
        Locations of the two sources are relatively close,

THEN   They are the same Source with confidence of .3.

Source refers to some noise-producing objects, such as propellers and shafts on ships.

Hypothesis formation is an 'opportunistic' process. Both **data-driven** and **model-driven** hypothesis-formation techniques are used within the general hypothesize-and-test paradigm. The *knowledge of how to perform*, that is, how to use the available knowledge, is another kind of knowledge that the analysts possess. This type of knowledge is represented in the form of *control rules* to promote flexibility in specifying and modifying analysis strategies. One of the tasks of the control knowledge source is to determine the appropriate techniques to use for different situations.

The unit of processing activity is the **event**. Events symbolize such things as 'what inference was made', 'what symbol-structure was modified', 'what event is expected in the future', and so on. The basic control loop for these **event-driven** programs is one in which lists of events and a set of control rules are periodically scanned to determine the next thing to do.

6.2.2 HASP/SIAP organization

Most signal processing programs are organized in a pipeline fashion starting with signal data, segmenting the signals, identifying the segments, and so on. One way to view HASP/SIAP is as a signal-processing paradigm with multiple feedbacks and many data input points. The primary input data is a sequence of *described line segments* (from each channel, for each array) present in the frequency *vs* time data. The secondary inputs are information available from other arrays and a variety of reports routinely available to the analysts. The output of the program is a data structure containing the program's best explanation of the current input data considered in conjunction with previous analyses of earlier-received data. This data structure is the machine equivalent of the analyst's situation board, except that it contains more information. In particular, it contains the basis for the explanation as recorded by the program during its analysis process. Figure 6.3 shows the general program structure of HASP/SIAP, and Figures 6.4 and 6.7 show some of the output.

Integration of many diverse data and knowledge sources is accomplished through a hierarchic data structure, as shown in Figure 6.2. The interpretation process is viewed as a problem of bidirectional,

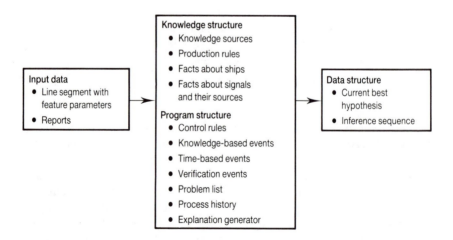

Figure 6.3   General program structure.

The Current Best Hypothesis at time 20455

Vessel-1

Class	(OR (Cherry 8.4) (Iris 6.9) (Tulip 6.2) (Poppy 4.8) 20455 ...)
Location	((Lat 37.3) (Long 123.1) (Error 37))
Speed	15.7
Course	135.9
Sources	(AND Source-1 Source-5)

Source-1

Type	(OR (Cherry Propeller 5.5) (Poppy Shaft 2.5)
	(Poppy Propeller 2.0) (Cherry Shaft 2.5) 20455 ...)
Dependency	Unknown
Regain	(20230)
Harmonics	(Harmonic-1)

Harmonic-1

Fundamental	(224.5 20520)
Evolution	(fade-in 20230 fade-out 20210 ...)
Lines	(AND Line-1 Line-2 Line-6 Line-12)

Source-5

Type	(OR (Cherry Shaft 6.0) (Poppy Shaft 4.0)
	(Iris Propeller 5.0) (Tulip Propeller 2.0) 20455)
Dependency	6
Harmonics	(Harmonic-5)

Harmonic-5

Fundamental	(162.4 20455)
Evolution	(fade-in 20455)
Lines	(AND Line-25)

ASSIMILATION (RATIO Source-1 Source-5 .5) 20455)

Problem-list
(EXPECT Vessel-1 (SUPPORT Cherry) (Dependency Propeller 5))
(EXPECT Vessel-1 (PRED.LOC (Lat 37.2) (Long 123.) (Error 41.3))
(REPORT REPORT-GEN Rose (Signature (Engine 30 166.7) ....))

Figure 6.4 A part of a current best hypothesis. The class of Vessel-1, located in the vicinity of Latitude 36.3 and Longitude 123.1 at time day 2, 4 hours, 55 minutes, can be either Cherry, Iris, Tulip or Poppy class. Two distinct acoustic sources, supported by respective harmonic sets, have been identified for Vessel-1. Source-1 could be due to a shaft or propeller of vessel class Cherry or Poppy. Similar source possibilities exist for Source-5. These two sources were assimilated into Vessel-1 because of the possibility of a known mechanical ratio that exists between the two sources. If a dependency of the Cherry propeller for Source-1 can be determined to be 5, then the supporting evidence that Vessel-1 is a Cherry class can be increased. Additional information on the Problem-list suggests the expected position of Vessel-1 computed at the next time interval on the basis of its currently hypothesized location, course, and speed. In addition, there is a report that a Rose class vessel is expected in the area. (Also see Figure 6.7 for a program-generated summary explanation.)

stepwise transformations between signals and the symbolic description of objects at various levels of abstraction, using as many intermediate steps as needed. Thus, for each level in the hierarchy, there must be at least one KS that can transform information on one level into information that is meaningful on some other level. For example, the following rule transforms a line segment into a line by attaching it to a previously identified line:

IF   Characteristics of a new segment "match" an earlier line, and
        Source associated with the line is not currently heard, and
        Source had disappeared less than 30 minutes ago,

THEN   Source is being picked up again with confidence 0.5, and
        Segment is assigned to the old line.

The word 'transformation' is used loosely to mean a shift from one representation of an object (e.g. signal segment) to another (e.g. propeller) using any formal or informal rules.

6.2.3 The current best hypothesis

As KSs are applied to a stream of input data, a solution hypothesis emerges. The hypothesis structure represents the 'best hypothesis' at any given time for the data available up to that time. It is the most up-to-date situation board and contains all supporting evidence. The structure of the CBH is a linked network of nodes, where each node (hypothesis element) represents a meaningful aggregation of lower-level hypothesis elements. A link between any two hypothesis elements represents a result of some action by a KS and indirectly points to the KS itself. A link has associated with it directional properties. A direction indicates one of the following:

(1)   A link that goes from a more abstract to a less abstract level of the hypothesis is referred to as an *expectation-link*. The node at the end of an expectation-link is a model-based hypothesis element, and the link represents *support from above* (i.e. the reason for proposing the hypothesis element is to be found at the higher level).

(2)   A link that goes in the opposite direction, from lower levels of abstraction to higher, is referred to as a *reduction-link*. The node at the end of a reduction-link is a data-based hypothesis element, and the link represents *support from below* (i.e. the reason for proposing the hypothesis element is to be found at a lower level). An example of hypothesis elements generated by the KSs is shown in Figure 6.4.

6.2.4   Kinds of knowledge represented

There are several kinds of knowledge used in HASP/SIAP, each represented in a form that seems the most appropriate.

(1)   *Knowledge about the environment*   The program must know about common shipping lanes, location of arrays and their relation to map coordinates, and known maneuver areas. This knowledge is represented in procedures that compute the necessary information.

(2)   *Knowledge about vessels*   All the known characteristics about vessel types, component parts and their acoustic signatures, range of speed, home base, etc., are represented in frame-like structures. These constitute the static knowledge used by rules whenever a specific class of vessels is being analyzed. In addition, when some vessel class is inferred from a piece of data, detailed information is available to help make that hypothesis more credible. The use of this information by model-driven KSs reduces the amount of computation by directing other KSs to look for specific data.

(3)   *Interpretation knowledge*   All heuristic knowledge about trans-forming information on one level of the CBH to another level is represented as sets of production rules. The rules in a KS usually generate inferences between adjacent levels. However, some of the most powerful KSs generate inferences spanning several levels. For example, a line with particular characteristics may immediately suggest a vessel class. This type of knowledge is very situation-specific. It was elicited from human experts who know and use much of the specialized, detailed knowledge now in the program. (It is said that chess masters can immediately recognize approximately 50,000 board patterns.) There are more examples of rules in the next section.

(4)   *Knowledge about how to use other knowledge*   Since the strategy is opportunistic, the program must know when an opportunity for further interpretation has arisen and how best to capitalize on the situation. In HASP/SIAP this type of knowledge is made explicit as will be explained in the following section.

6.2.5 How the knowledge is organized and used

How well an expert system performs depends both on the competence of the KSs and on the appropriate use of these KSs. Thus, the primary considerations in the design of expert systems revolve around the availability and the quality of the KSs, and the optimal utilization of these KSs. When and how a KS is used depends on its quality and its relevancy at any given time. The relevance of a KS depends on the state of the CBH. The control mechanism for KS selection needs to be sensitive to, and be able to adjust to, the numerous possible solution states which arise during interpretation. Given this viewpoint, what is commonly called a *control strategy* can be viewed as another type of domain-dependent knowledge, albeit a high-level one. Organizing the knowledge sources in a hierarchy is an attempt to unify the representation of diverse knowledge needed for the interpretation task.

In a *hierarchically organized control structure*, problem-solving activities decompose into a hierarchy of knowledge needed to solve problems. On the lowest level is a set of knowledge sources whose charter is to put inferences on the CBH. We refer to KSs on this level as *Specialists*. At the next level there are *KS-activators* that know when to use the various Specialists. On the highest level a *Strategy-KS* analyzes the current solution state to determine what information to analyze next. The last activity is also known as *focusing-of-attention*.

The execution cycle consists of:

(1)   focusing attention on pending time-dependent activities, on verification of a hypothesis, or on one of the hypothesized elements;
(2)   selecting the appropriate KSs for the attended event; and
(3)   executing the selected KSs.

The KSs will generate a new CBH or expectations for some future events. The cycle is then repeated. Figure 6.5 shows the major flow of information and control. Since the program is event-driven, it is impossible to show the detailed flow of control in this type of a diagram.

The KS hierarchy should be clearly distinguished from the hierarchy of analysis levels. The hypothesis hierarchy represents an *a priori* plan for the solution determined by a *natural* decomposition of the analysis problem. The KS hierarchy, on the other hand, represents a plan for organizing the problem-solving activities, or control, needed to form hypotheses. Figure 6.6 shows a general relationship between the organization of the hypothesis hierarchy and the KS hierarchy.

6.2.6 KSs on the Specialist level

Each Specialist has the task of creating or modifying hypothesis elements, evaluating inferences generated by other Specialists, and cataloging missing evidences that are essential for further analysis. Its focus of attention is generally a hypothesis element containing the latest changes. Although a KS has access to the entire hypothesis, it normally

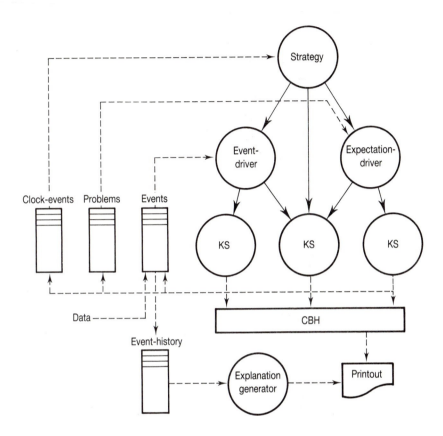

Figure 6.5   Information and control flow. Incoming data are treated as events and are put on the Event-list. At the beginning of the processing cycle at time t, the items on the Clock-event list are scanned to see if it's time for any particular item to be processed. If so, the appropriate KS is called. Next, the Expectation-driver is called to see if any pending problems can be resolved with the events on the Event-list. All resolvable problems are taken care of at this point. Next, the Event-driver is called to process the events. It first determines what changes of the CBH to focus on. (Note that each event represents either a new piece of data or a change made to the CBH during the last process cycle.) The Event-driver then calls the appropriate KSs to make further inferences on the basis of the focused event. The invoked KSs make changes to the CBH and add new events to the Event-list. A processing cycle terminates when the Event-list becomes empty.

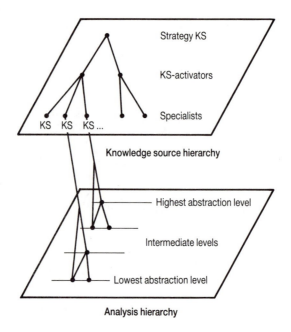

Figure 6.6   Relationship between the analysis levels and the KS levels.

'understands' only the descriptions contained in two levels, its input level and its output level. Some examples of different types of Specialists are listed below.

Inference-Generation:
IF   Characteristics of a Harmonic set match another set on another channel,
THEN   Both sets are coming from the same source with confidence of .6.

Inference-Evaluation:
IF   Source belongs to Vessels of class Cherry or Iris, and
        Harmonics associated with Source have been stable for a while,
THEN   Increase the confidence of Cherry and Iris by .3.

Problem-Cataloging:
IF   Report exists for a vessel class Rose to be in the vicinity, and
        Source likely to be associated with Rose has been detected,
THEN   Expect to find other Source types associated with Rose class.

6.2.7 KSs at the KS-activation level

A KS on this level has the task of invoking the appropriate Specialists given the kind of strategy being employed. For example, a KS charged with calling the appropriate KSs within a model-driven strategy has a different goal than one charged with a data-driven strategy. Different KS-activators can be made to reflect different policies, ranging from using the fastest-first to the most-accurate-first. HASP/SIAP has two KS-activators, the Event-driver and the Expectation-driver. If there is more than one Specialist available to process an event, some policy is needed to guide the order in which these KSs are to be used. The Event-driver chooses items on the Event-list and activates Specialist-KSs based on the degree of specialization (and assumed accuracy) of the KSs. The Expectation-driver processes items on the Problem-list on the basis of how critical the needed evidence is to the emerging hypothesis.

Event-driver

An event type represents an *a priori* grouping of similar changes to the hypothesis (i.e. it represents the abstractions of possible changes to the hypothesis). An example event is 'source-type-identified'. The changes, together with the identity of the rules that produced the changes, are put on a globally accessible list called the *Event-list*. The Event-driver invokes the appropriate Specialist-KSs based on the focused event or group of events.

Expectation-driver

The Expectation-driver monitors the items on the Problem-list to see if any event that might satisfy an expectation on the Problem-list has occurred. If an expected event does occur, the Expectation-driver will call the Specialist-KS which put the expectation on the Problem-list. For example, in Figure 6.4, if a source belonging to a reported Rose class is detected, the REPORT-GEN (the KS that put the item on the Problem-list) will be called.

6.2.8 KS on the strategy level

The Strategy-KS reflects a human analyst's problem-solving strategy. Its expertise consists of determining how accurate the current hypothesis is and in deciding what task will have the highest impact on the CBH. It has a variety of possible activities to choose from:

'Is it time to check for specific data?'

'Has anything happened since the last processing cycle that might invalidate the hypothesis?'

'Has an expected event occurred?'

'What is the best region in the CBH to work on next (i.e. what is the region of minimal ambiguity)?'

In HASP/SIAP there are no formal mechanisms to measure the differences between the current best hypothesis and the 'right answer'. The program detects when the solution hypothesis is 'on the right track' by a periodic use of heuristic criteria. A consistent inability to verify expectation-based hypothesis elements may signal an error in the hypothesis. A more general indication of ineffective hypothesis formation appears as a consistent generation of conjectures whose confidence values are below a threshold value; and which therefore indicates that the analysis is 'bogged down'.

6.2.9 Dealing with time-dependent analysis

The task of HASP/SIAP is to interpret continuous streams of data and to maintain a current situation model. The primary input data currently consists of 5 minute segments describing, in effect, a summary of observed signals at various frequencies. These segments must be integrated into the existing Line-level elements. In addition, lines must be integrated into harmonic sets; sources must be attributed to vessels. The CBH serves as the historical context by which the integration can occur. Through the CBH one can incorporate appearances and disappearances of signals over time, using only common-sense reasoning, such as, 'ships can't just disappear, or appear, from nowhere'. The CBH must keep track of the times when specific events occurred, as well as maintain a network of relationships between Lines, Sources and Vessels. Time markers are placed with hypothesized values; new time markers are added only when the values change. In the example below, there were no changes to the source type for two hours even though weights may have been changed during that time. (See also Figure 6.4.)

```
SOURCE-1
    TYPE [(OR (Cherry Propeller 7.5)) 10650
         (OR (Cherry Propeller 6.0)
         (Poppy Propeller 2.5)) 10450]
```

HASP/SIAP must also analyze time-oriented signatures and move-ments of vessels over time. The signature analysis is similar to trend analysis. The signature analysis depends on the type of vessel – some vessel signatures may last 15 min, others may last for hours or days. This type of time-dependent analysis is accomplished through the use of a mechanism called *Clock events*. When a Specialist-KS needs to look at or verify signatures, it puts on the Clock-event list a request to be recalled at a specific time. The request contains information that needs to be reviewed at that time. The Strategy-KS also generates Clock events in order to review certain hypothesis elements periodically at specified time intervals. In the example below a Specialist-KS called **RATIO-FINDER** will be called at time 22055 to check for a ratio between the Shaft and the Propeller for the Cherry class hypothesis.

> **Clock Event**
> (22055 RATIO-FINDER Source-1 Source-5
> (Cherry Shaft Propeller))

6.2.10 Explanation and summary of the CBH

Every so often an explanation of the current best hypothesis is printed, together with unresolved issues. There were difficulties in generating an explanation that the analysts could understand. Although the basic processing strategy of the program had to be breadth-first, the analysts wanted to know all the supporting rationale for the situation one vessel at a time, that is, depth-first. Furthermore, analysts were not interested in every inference step, only the 'important' ones. These requirements eliminated the use of a straightforward back-trace explanation currently in use in most expert systems. Another knowledge source had to be brought to bear on the History-list to identify 'important' events and to present these events in a sequence acceptable to the analysts. Figure 6.7 contains a small sample of a HASP/SIAP summary explanation. The first statement requires a search through the History-list to collect several events that support the Vessel-1 hypothesis. These are widely separated events in the processing cycle.

6.3 AI and signal processing

Decomposition of the HASP/SIAP program offers an interesting avenue for highlighting the value of combining AI with signal processing. The two segments of importance are the following:

(1)   translation of the data into sonogram lines and measurement of line parameters; and

(2)   the disentanglement of intermingled target signatures and their classification.

The HASP system used skilled human perception to perform the first step in the signal-to-symbol transformation – the encoding of the signal data into segments and features. For a largely automated classification program this is a task that requires substantial signal processing. Complex algorithms have now been developed for this front-end application, incorporating many of the skills of the analyst.

Summary of Events at this Time Slot

- Newly reported line segment which does not seem to be a part of any previously observed lines is assigned to a new line: Line-25. This line is assigned to a new lineset Harmonic-5, from which in turn a new source Source-5 is created.

- Sources Source-1 and Source-5 of vessel Vessel-1 have a known ratio; this provides further evidence for the association of these two sources with this vessel.

- Source type of Source-5 is updated due to an observed ratio: (Cherry Shaft 6.0) (Poppy Shaft 4.0) (Iris Propeller 5.0) (Tulip Propeller 2.0).

- Source type of Source-1 is updated due to an observed ratio: (Cherry Propeller 4.0).

- Based on modified Source types (Source-1), the class types of Vessel-1 are weighted as follows: (Cherry 7.2).

- Based on modified Source types (Source-5), the class types of Vessel-1 are weighted as follows: (Cherry 8.4) (Iris 6.9) (Tulip 6.2) (Poppy 4.8).

Pending Problem

There is evidence that Vessel-1 is a Cherry class, because there is a relation between Shaft and Propeller.

If it is a Cherry class, there should be a dependency of 5 in the propeller and dependency of 6 in the shaft. We have not yet observed the dependency 5.

Problem list = (EXPECT Vessel-1 (SUPPORT Cherry) (Dependency Propeller 5))

Figure 6.7 Example of a summary explanation. A summary explanation is printed with the current best hypothesis, shown in Figure 6.4. The CBH describes the current situation; the summary explanation provides the rationale for the changes in the situation since the last processing cycle.

However, in the SIAP project the sponsor required that a particular front-end be used. This program unfortunately smoothed over many of the key clues that permitted the HASP program to perform so well. To compensate for this setback, some AI had to be moved into the signal-processing front-end and the processing adjusted in the second segment. For example, the automated front-end had a tendency to break certain wideband lines into several adjacent narrow-band lines. An uninformed grouping of these lines can be incorrect, since in some cases they could be neighboring narrow-band lines. The grouping needs to be accomplished within the context of what is already known about the relationship among the lines, and between the lines, the sources, and the vessel classes. A new knowledge source was added that used the context to process the algorithmic outputs.

Two other major issues involving AI and signal processing surfaced in the course of building HASP/SIAP. They are:

(1)   the feedback to the signal processing front-end; and

(2)   the allocation of signal processing resources.

There are two kinds of feedback that the situation model can provide to signal processors. First, special-purpose detection and parameter measurement algorithms depend on higher level information – the CBH has the necessary information. Second, threshold values for the front-end need to be adjusted according to the current need and expectations. In both cases, the processing of information over a period of time leads to modifications of parameters in the front-end for more accurate subsequent processing.

In the undersea surveillance problem, a variety of signal processing techniques can be brought to bear in the front-end. Some of these fall in the category of standard algorithms that are more or less always used, but others are specialized algorithms that cannot be used for all channels at all times because of their cost. Because these algorithms can provide important processing clues when used, the allocation of these scarce resources is an important issue. The appropriate use of the resource is especially important because the use of these special algorithms can significantly reduce the time required to produce an accurate situation model.

The resource allocation problem is knowing *when* to invoke the special signal processors. The approach to its solution lies in rules that can recognize when the context will permit the special processor to resolve important ambiguities. In HASP/SIAP only a rudimentary capability for this process was used, but its value was conclusively demonstrated.

The resource allocation problem pointed out another 'signal-processing' capability that can be utilized on a demand basis to resolve ambiguities. This resource is the human operator, who generally has great expertise in the entire process, including the processing of the sonogram information. This interaction was performed off-line in HASP/SIAP, but on-line capabilities are being incorporated in the HASP/SIAP derivatives. This approach is more in line with using the expert system as an analyst aid, rather than a stand-alone system, but the combination of man and machine will be far more powerful than either alone.

The HASP/SIAP experience indicates that some good AI can cover a multitude of signal processing inadequacies and can direct the employment of signal processing algorithms. The intelligent combination of AI and signal processing views the signal processing component as another knowledge source, with rules on how best to employ algorithms and how to interpret their output.

6.4 Evaluation

MITRE Corporation undertook a detailed analysis of the performance of SIAP in a series of experiments conducted between December 1976 and March 1978 at DARPA's Acoustic Research Center. The experiments compared HASP/SIAP performance with those of two expert sonar analysts in three task categories.

The first experiment, designed to test the performance in detection and classification of vessels using data derived from actual ocean events, led to the general conclusion that 'HASP/SIAP has been shown to perform well on ocean derived data. . . . For this restricted ocean scene, the program is not confused by extraneous data and gives results comparable to an expert analyst.'

The second experiment, designed to test the information integration capability, using derived data for multi-arrays, led to the conclusion that 'HASP/SIAP understood the ocean scene more thoroughly than the second analyst and as well as the first analyst. . . . The program can work effectively with more than one acoustic array. SIAP classified an ocean scene over a 3 h time period indicating the plausibility of SIAP efficacy in an evolving ocean situation.'

The third and final experiment, documented by MITRE, was designed to test the automatic parameter extraction capability added during the SIAP phase of HASP/SIAP development. It led to the conclusion that 'with the exception that the SIAP program obtained significantly more contacts than the human analysts, the descriptions of the ocean scene are very similar.' Moreover, 'SIAP can perform vessel classification in increasingly difficult ocean scenes without large increases in the use of computer resources.' Hence, continued better-than-real-time performance could be expected if the system were deployed.

In a later experiment, it was shown that the additional contacts seen by SIAP in the third experiment were due to the front-end processor provided by the sponsor – namely, taking relatively wideband lines and decomposing them into erratic collections of narrow-band lines. These problems were essentially eliminated by additional heuristics in the line-formation knowledge source.

6.5 Conclusions

In signal-processing applications, involving large amounts of data with poor signal-to-noise ratio, it is possible to reduce computation costs by several orders of magnitude by the use of knowledge-based reasoning rather than brute-force statistical methods. We estimate that HASP/SIAP can reduce computation costs by two to three orders of magnitude over conventional methods. *It makes little sense to use enormous amounts of expensive computation to tease a little signal out of much noise, when most of the understanding can be readily inferred from the symbolic knowledge surrounding the situation.*

There is an additional cost saving possible. Sensor bandwidth and sensitivity is expensive. From a symbolic model it is possible to generate a set of signal expectations whose emergence in the data would make a difference to the verification of the ongoing model. Sensor parameters can then be 'tuned' to the expected signals and signal directions; not every signal in every direction needs to be searched for.

6.5.1 Suitable application areas

Building a signal interpretation system within the program organization described above can best be described as *opportunistic* analysis. Bits and pieces of information must be used as opportunity arises to build slowly a coherent picture of the world – much like putting a jigsaw puzzle together. Some thoughts on the characteristics of problems suited to this approach are listed below.

(1) *Large amounts of signal data need to be analyzed* Examples include the interpretation of speech and other acoustic signals, X-ray and other spectral data, radar signals, photographic data, etc. A variation involves understanding a large volume of symbolic data; for example, the maintenance of a global plotboard of air traffic based on messages from various air traffic control centers.

(2) *Formal or informal interpretive theories exist* By informal interpretive theory we mean *lore* or heuristics which human experts bring to bear in order to *understand* the data. These inexact and informal rules are incorporated as KSs in conjunction with more formal knowledge about the domain.

(3) *Task domain can be decomposed hierarchically in a natural way* In many cases the domain can be decomposed into a series of data reduction levels, where various interpretive theories (in the sense described above) exist for transforming data from one level to another.

(4) *Opportunistic strategies must be used* That is, there is no computationally feasible *legal move generator* that defines the space of solutions in which pruning and steering take place. Rather, by reasoning about bits and pieces of available evidence, one can incrementally generate partial hypotheses that will eventually lead to a more global solution hypothesis.

6.5.2 Data-driven *vs* model-driven hypothesis-formation methods

Data- and model-driven methods of hypothesis formation were combined in the design of HASP/SIAP. By *data-driven* we mean 'inferred from the input data'. By *model-driven* we mean 'based on expectation', where the expectation is inferred from knowledge about the domain. For example, a hypothesis generated by a KS which infers a source type from a harmonic set is a data-driven hypothesis. On the other hand, a hypothesis about the possible existence of a harmonic set based on the knowledge about a ship is a model-based hypothesis. In the former case, the data are used as the basis for signal analysis; in the latter case, the primary data are used solely to verify expectations.

There are no hard-and-fast criteria for determining which of the two hypothesis formation methods is more appropriate for a particular signal-processing task. The choice depends, to a large extent, on the nature of the KSs that are available and on the power of the analysis model available. Our experience points strongly toward the use of a combination of these techniques; some KSs are strongly data dependent, while others are strongly model dependent. In HASP/SIAP the majority of the inferences are data-driven, with occasional model-driven inferences. The following are guidelines we have used in the past to determine which of the two methods is more appropriate:

(1) *Signal-to-noise ratio* Problems which have inherently low *S/N* ratios are better suited to solutions by model-driven programs; the converse is true for problems with high *S/N* ratios. However, designers should beware that the model-driven approach is prone to 'finding what is being looked for'. Model-driven approaches should be supplemented with strong verification heuristics.

(2) *Availability of a model* A model, sometimes referred to as the *semantics of the task domain*, can be used in various ways: (i) as input at some level of the hypothesis structure, (ii) to make inferences based on general knowledge about the task domain, or (iii) to make inferences based on specific knowledge about the particular task. In HASP/SIAP, the model is drawn from general knowledge about the signal sources and from external reports that serve to define the context. If a reliable model is available, the data-interpretation KSs can be used as *verifiers* rather than *generators* of inferences; this reduces the computational burden on the signal-processing programs at the front-end.

The general methodology used in HASP/SIAP has been applied in many other problem areas. A small sampling includes the Hearsay-II speech understanding program, the original blackboard program (Erman *et al.*, 1980; Lesser and Erman, 1977); CRYSALIS, a program that interprets protein X-ray crystallographic data (Engelmore and Terry, 1979); a program that generates plans (Hayes-Roth *et al.*, 1979); and a program that interprets aerial photographs (Nagao *et al.*, 1979). In addition, program packages that help users implement a variety of blackboard programs have been under development for the past few years (Erman *et al.*, 1981; Nii and Aiello, 1979).

Acknowledgments

Many different people helped in building HASP/SIAP in many different capacities. The people acknowledged below are project leaders (*), consultants and programmers who waded through the myriad of technical problems and codes. We are also indebted to John Miller, Jay Seward, Dan Sestak and Ken McCoy – our experts. They cheerfully took on the frustrating and time-consuming jobs of having their brains picked by knowledge engineers, and their own performance then outstripped by the program. Those who helped with HASP include John Anton, Scottie Brooks, Edward Feigenbaum, Gregory Gibbons, Marsha Jo Hanna, Neil Miller, Mitchell Model, Penny Nii* and Joe Rockmore. Those who helped with SIAP include John Anton,* Al Bien, Scottie Brooks, Robert Drazovich,* Scott Foster, Cordell Green, Bruce Lowerre, Neil Miller,* Mitchell Model, Roland Payne, Joe Rockmore and Reid Smith.

7

Using Explicit Strategic Knowledge to Control Expert Systems

Allan Terry

7.1 Introduction

As artificial intelligence research matures, the programs that are produced use increasingly large amounts of knowledge in increasingly complex ways. This is particularly true of expert systems research, where programs are often viewed as having exactly two elements: the knowledge base and the inference engine. This arrangement works well as long as the power of the inference engine matches the size of the knowledge base. As the amount of knowledge increases, the inference engine must cope with what is often referred to as the *focus-of-attention problem*: how should limited resources be allocated at any given time when many plausible ways of making progress exist? The focus-of-attention problem appears in many guises, but essentially the inference engine must select relevant pieces, or 'chunks', of knowledge from a large knowledge base.

The point of this chapter is that the focus-of-attention problem in expert systems can be solved, or at least reduced, by the use of domain-specific control knowledge, which will be called *strategic knowledge* or *strategies*. This chapter presents a program architecture that permits explicit use of expert strategies.

More specifically, this chapter demonstrates one method for incorporating explicit strategies into a production system formalism. Any problem can be viewed at many levels of abstraction; different heuristics and strategies may be appropriate at different levels. In view of this, we define a *hierarchical production system* in which control proceeds through many levels of strategy heuristics until one specific action at the problem-solving, bottom-most, level is selected. This control structure has been implemented using a blackboard architecture and tested in an expert system that solves a problem from the field of X-ray protein crystallography. The goal of this system, called CRYSALIS, is to infer the atomic structure of a protein of known composition but unknown conformation from X-ray diffraction data. The knowledge in this domain cannot be successfully cast into a traditional, single-level production system because there are so many places the model-building rules seem to apply that the system would thrash in the absence of some higher control. A description of this domain follows in the next section.

The CRYSALIS project, originally called SU/P, was initiated in 1976 by R. Engelmore, E. Feigenbaum, C.K. Johnson and H.P. Nii (Engelmore and Nii, 1977). Work was substantially completed by 1983.

7.2 The task domain of protein crystallography

7.2.1 Steps in determining protein structure

There are many steps in understanding the structure and function of a protein (see Figure 7.1). The first is to chemically isolate one protein for study and then to grow a crystal of it (a process that can take years). Next, the crystallized protein is studied by X-ray diffraction. The crystal is placed in a beam of X-rays of 1.0–2.0 Å wavelength, and the position and intensity of diffracted waves are recorded. Each atom in the protein contributes to the total, unique diffraction pattern, which is sampled at points on a three-dimensional lattice. If the intensity and phase of the diffracted wave could be measured accurately at enough points, the problem would be solved. The diffraction pattern is a Fourier transformation of the original molecule, so an inverse Fourier transform would in principle yield an atomic model (a list of atoms and their coordinates). As it is, the intensities cannot be measured with perfect accuracy and the phases cannot be measured at all, Moreover, the number of lattice points on which intensity data are collected is limited by experimental parameters, effectively limiting the resolution, i.e. the degree to which individual atoms can be resolved.

A cycle of approximation and refinement now begins that often lasts months or years. The crystallographer uses one of many mathematical and chemical methods to estimate the phases. A Fourier transform then recreates an image of the molecule based on the observed intensities and the approximated phases. This image is an **electron density map** (EDM), a function $\rho(x, y, z)$ that gives the density of the protein's electron cloud (which is all the X-rays interact with). The crystallographer can now derive a model of the protein's structure and can use this model to improve the phases for the next cycle. The EDM is often represented as a three-dimensional contour map presented as sections drawn on large plates of clear plastic. Crystallographers view these plates through a half-silvered mirror or use computer graphics so that they can build a brass ball-and-stick model 'into' the density.

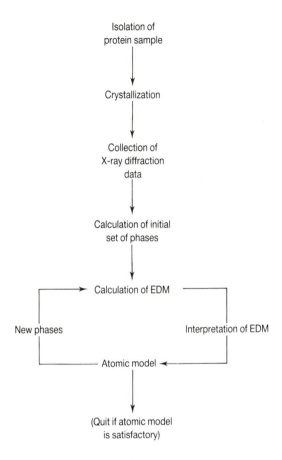

Figure 7.1   The cycle of interpretation and refinement.

The EDM is noisy and unclear to the degree to which the phases are in error, or equivalently, to the degree to which the atoms in the model used to generate the EDM are incorrectly placed. The process of refinement continues with a map improved by a better estimate of the phases or by the addition of higher resolution data. When the refinement is nearly complete, most of the protein's structure has been found and need not be solved again. However, because little of the structure is known the first few times through the cycle, the interpretation can take weeks or months.

Crystallographers who solve and partially refine a new protein usually do so early in their careers and rarely carry out the entire process a second time. If map interpretation could be partially or completely automated, especially for the initial cycle, much time and effort could be saved.

7.2.2 Protein structure

A protein is a polypeptide: a single strand of units variously called *amino acids*, *residues* or *peptides*. Each amino acid consists of two parts: a peptide bond which is the same for all amino acids and a sidechain which distinguishes one kind of amino acid from another. Twenty kinds of amino acids are found in proteins. Each peptide links to the next, forming a continuous, nonbranching backbone.

While the amino acid sequence of the protein forms a linear sequence, the actual backbone of the protein forms a complex three-dimensional configuration in space. This structure is central to the biological activity of the molecule. The protein's configuration is often stiffened by hydrogen bonds between parts of the molecule, bonds between the sulfurs in pairs of sulfur-bearing cystine residues, and sometimes by large atomic groups called *cofactors*, such as the heme group found in hemoglobin and the cytochrome family of proteins.

Although the most detailed and accurate description of the protein is a list of its atoms and their locations in 3-space, it is often useful to describe the structure in more abstract terms. This description is called the *secondary structure*. Pieces of the protein's backbone frequently assume stereotyped configurations for structural reasons; these configurations form the vocabulary of secondary structure. Of the three major categories, the simplest is strands of backbone that have no overall structure, called random coils. The second category is the *helices*, of which the α-helix is the most familiar member. The final category consists of the structures based on the β-*sheet*, which occurs when two or more strands lie parallel to each other and are extensively cross-linked with hydrogen bonds. The description of secondary structure is then a list of the helices, β-sheets and random coils of the protein, and their associated sequences of amino acids.

A few comments on scale should put proteins in better perspective. A small protein (such as rubredoxin) has around 50 peptide units or about 500 nonhydrogen atoms. Many proteins being studied today have 200–400 peptides, sometimes even more. Interatomic distances are of the order of the carbon–carbon bond, which is about 1.5 Å. This should be compared to the resolution of a high-quality EDM, which is 2.0–2.5 Å.

7.3 The CRYSALIS program

7.3.1 Statement of the task

CRYSALIS is designed to do the initial interpretation of protein electron density maps. The program is given an EDM of 2.0–2.5 Å resolution and an amino acid sequence. It is also told what cofactors the protein has and accepts whatever information the crystallographer has discovered by chemical means (usually the location of metal ions in the cofactor, if any). CRYSALIS's job is to infer an atomic model that is as complete as possible. It is not expected that all atoms will be located, but it is expected that enough will be found, to sufficient accuracy, that standard refinement procedures can begin. The system is also able to summarize the secondary structure, if a complete atomic model cannot be found. (The description of secondary structure can locate the backbone even if the program cannot place individual atoms.)

7.3.2 Constraints imposed on CRYSALIS

CRYSALIS was built in its present form because of five major constraints on its design:

(1)   Uncertainty in the data is a fundamental constraint on the program. The EDM is a noisy, blurred image of an object that has no hard surfaces, seen at a resolution insufficient to resolve individual atoms. The complementary data, the amino acid sequence, is more accurate but may also contain errors. The sequence might not be complete and it may contain mistakes where two similar amino acids are confused. Domain knowledge allows us to filter out some of the errors in these data but not all.

(2)   The knowledge for interpreting maps is also uncertain. People interpret EDMs mostly by visual pattern recognition guided by their interpretations of what is reasonable. They, like the program, have a few basic physical and chemical facts available for guidance, but these are usually only general principles that must be interpreted for the specific situation. Protein crystallography lacks any formal theory to guide map interpretation. (There is, however, a strong theory for predicting the observed data from the hypothesis.) The knowledge is relatively weak, confirmatory in nature rather than predictive, and requires a consensus of heuristics before making a positive identification.

(3)   Knowledge about model building is largely judgmental. There is no written body of expertise and few experts to consult. EDM interpretation seems to be an art handed down from student to student within each laboratory; it is rarely taught explicitly since it is based on individual interpretations of general principles.

(4)   The size of the search space prohibits brute-force search. A small protein contains up to a thousand atoms that must be located within an EDM of up to half a million data points. The system has hundreds of heuristics to try, most of which are applicable somewhere in this large data set at any given moment.

(5)   The data provides little guidance to reduce the search. The EDM is a very indistinct, unresolved image of the protein, while the amino acid sequence constrains the search only within an atom or two of any given location. These two facts mean that it is easy for a problem solver in this domain to be misled. There is little *a priori* guidance as to what to do next and often no way to tell when a misinterpretation has been made until considerable effort has been wasted.

Despite these difficulties, humans solve this task by using many heuristics of how to interpret EDMs. Crystallographers work opportun- istically; they jump from place to place in the search space and from task to task. They also make many shallow hypotheses but rarely expend much effort on them until some group of these local interpretations begins to form a mutually supportive whole. This method capitalizes on 'islands of certainty' (or 'toeholds') as they appear by using the one solid identification to anchor many tentative hypotheses in the same region.

Our response to these constraints and to human methods was to adopt a variant of the Hearsay-II blackboard architecture, since CRYSALIS faces many of the same problems. In their retrospective examination of Hearsay-II, Lesser and Erman (1977) (see Chapter 4) note a large search space, error and variability in both knowledge and data, and existence of diverse sources of knowledge as characteristics of their domain. They also cite a need for modularity in structure so that the system can be reconfigured easily to permit experimentation with individual parts of the knowledge base. Knowledge in CRYSALIS is partitioned into independent, anonymous knowledge sources (KSs). These KSs communicate by means of a global 'blackboard' containing a multilevel hypothesis structure (which is the common KS language) and the data. Finally, the system is event driven in that KSs react to changes in the blackboard. The only characteristic CRYSALIS does not share with Hearsay-II is the requirement for speed.

7.3.3 The data

CRYSALIS requires two kinds of data: the amino acid sequence and the EDM. The amino acid sequence is a linear approximation to the three- dimensional solution. It specifies exactly what atoms there are and most of their connections (hydrogen bonding must be discovered), but says nothing about three-dimensional structure.

The electron density map provides information on the three- dimensional location of atoms. The EDM itself is usually represented as density values on a three-dimensional grid. There can be 60 000 to 500 000 of these points, only 1–6% of them representing the actual protein. In the EDM, the signal-to-noise ratio is low, very few points are significant, and the resolution is less than that required to see individual atoms. Thus, single points in the EDM convey little information. Features are visible only as patterns of density values. For this reason, we have developed several abstractions of the EDM:

(1) *The EDM viewed as a function* When the EDM is viewed as a function $\rho(x, y, z)$ of electron density, its maxima (peaks) usually represent one atom or several atoms that form a compact group. The height of a peak is an approximate function of the atomic number of the atom or atoms producing the peak. For the data used by CRYSALIS, peak height is a linear function of atomic number with an error of about 15%. The presence of a peak can then indicate that a region in the EDM is interesting, and the peak's height is a clue to what atoms might be in that region. Unlike the EDM, which is on a grid of about 1.0 Å spacing, peaks are interpolated so that their locations are accurate to better than 0.1 Å. Peaks provide the most positionally exact information available.

(2) *The EDM viewed as a graph* One aspect of the EDM not preserved by abstraction into peaks is connectivity. The notion of connected regions within the map is essential because the association of regions defined by the sequence with regions of the EDM is the core of map interpretation. A data abstraction that preserves this information is the skeleton, a representation first proposed by Greer (1974). Skeletonization can be visualized as a process of stripping away insignificant points of the EDM until only a graph structure is left. The object is to build a skeleton of the protein that preserves as many high-density EDM points as possible linked in such a way that a smoothly connected set is obtained. The result is a graph-structure representation of the high-density parts of the EDM: nodes whose properties are a position and a list of neighboring nodes. Skeletonization is a purely numerical process that does not constrain the result to look like a protein. The skeleton often has gaps and regions of overconnectivity (regions so interconnected that any structure due to the protein is totally lost).

(3) *The EDM viewed as connected regions* A skeletal description of the EDM is too low level for some purposes, so we also partition the skeleton into significant groups of nodes called segments. Each node in the skeleton can have zero or more neighboring nodes, but most have exactly two neighbors. Tip nodes (nodes with only one neighbor) occur where the electron density drops below threshold while junction nodes (nodes with more than two neighbors) occur where the density is particularly high and the skeleton branches. So, to capture the notion of significant regions, segments are defined as

starting at a tip or junction node, proceeding through an unbroken string of connected bivalent nodes, and terminating at another tip or junction node.

7.3.4 The hypothesis structure

The hypothesis acts as a central repository for all tentative and partial solutions and also forms the common language for inter-KS communication. In this section we describe CRYSALIS's hypothesis structure and examine how it fulfills both roles.

The three levels of abstraction for the EDM are also used for the hypothesis structure and are called the atomic, superatomic and stereotypic levels of abstraction. With a few exceptions, these levels form a loose hierarchy based on the PART-OF relation – atoms are parts of superatoms which are themselves parts of stereotypes. The most fundamental description of a protein is a list of the protein's atoms and their locations. This atomic model is 'the answer' because it is required for evaluating the quality of the interpretation, for display of results, and as input to any of the standard crystallographic refinement algorithms.

Atoms, superatoms and stereotypes

As shown in Figure 7.2, atoms, superatoms and stereotypes are represented as LISP atoms A*n*, SA*n* and ST*n* respectively, and their properties. The properties of atoms record location within the amino acid sequence and note position within the hypothesis hierarchy. Lists of peaks, skeletal nodes or EDM coordinates record hypothesized location within the data.

Whereas atoms describe point-like entities, superatoms are small, coherent groups of atoms, primarily PEPTIDE, SIDECHAIN, CHAINEND and COFACTOR. We have split a single amino acid into two superatoms; this allows us to discuss the protein's backbone as a series of PEPTIDEs before knowing what the sidechains are. Superatoms are not indended to cover objects larger than a residue or a cofactor. Anything more extensive should be a stereotype.

The highest level of the hypothesis has a slightly different interpretation than groupings of superatoms. Stereotypes are intended to capture what the crystallographer calls secondary structure, a description of the protein in terms of common configurations assumed by parts of its backbone. Some of the objects at this level are β-sheets of two or more strands, β-barrels, several varieties of helix, hydrogen-bonded atoms, and random coils.

```
A62    TYPE          C
       NAME          C-ALPHA
       BELONGSTO     (PROLINE . 20)
       SKELNODES     ((SK245 . 40))
       EDM.PEAKS     ((PK098 . 355) (PK104 . 109))
       EDM.COORD     (((89 -132 43) . 560))
       MEMBEROF      (SA90 SA85)


SA85   TYPE          PEPTIDE
       BELONGSTO     (PROLINE . 20)
       SEGMENTS      (((SEG168 SEG114 SEG106 SEG105 SEG98) . 714)
                      ((SEG168) . 10))
       NEARBY.PEAKS  (PK020)
       MEMBEROF      (ST9)
       MEMBERS       (A62 A65)


ST9    TYPE          BACKBONE
       MEMBERS       (SA93 SA95 SA94 SA91 SA92 SA90 SA85 SA84)
       RANGE         (17 . 21)
       BLOCKED.ENDS  BOTH
       WT            627
```

Figure 7.2 Sample hypothesis elements at the atomic (**A**), superatomic (**SA**), and stereotypic (**ST**) levels of abstraction.

Weights

CRYSALIS measures the 'goodness' of a hypothesized location by a value called the weight. Weights are numbers that range from −1000 to 1000. Positive values indicate belief that the identification is correct, negative values indicate disbelief, and values near zero indicate the highest uncertainty. Weights are combined by simple addition within the interval −1000 to 1000. The weight of a hypothesis element is then an *ad hoc* measure of the system's belief that the given location is the best location. Our use of weights was inspired by MYCIN's certainty factors (Shortliffe and Buchanan, 1975) but weights are not certainty factors. Our domain is much less tractable than MYCIN's; we could not derive a consistent set of certainties or probabilities from knowledge that is essentially a personal interpretation of first principles.

Weights are used in several ways. One is to capture some of the judgmental knowledge of model building in these numbers by attaching them to rules and knowledge sources (see Section 7.3.6). Another use is to indicate how much effort has been expended on verifying a given data identification. Most importantly, weights are used to compare hypothesis elements. Every link into the data carries a weight and each data property (e.g. PEAKS) is sorted by these weights. (In Figure 7.2, the weight of each location appears immediately after the link to the data panel; e.g. (SK245 . 40) in A62.) Weights are placed on data links because the location, not the existence, of the object is in question. The current location of any hypothesis element (and its weight) is taken from its highest-weighted location. The current best hypothesis, the most accurate answer available so far, consists of the best locations of all hypothesis elements.

7.3.5 The division of the blackboard into panels

The data and the hypothesis in CRYSALIS form two distinct panels on the system's blackboard as shown in Figure 7.3. This division was made for clarity and because the two panels are treated differently. The lowest level on the data panel contains the observable data – the EDM. Other levels correspond to the different views of the EDM given by the data

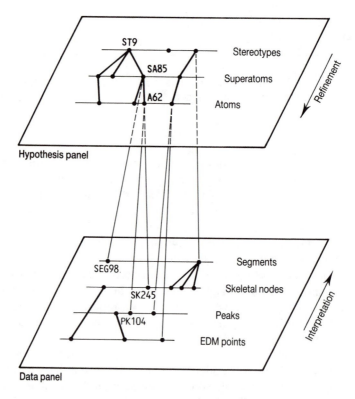

Figure 7.3 Blackboard hypothesis and data panels. Inferences may be made from any level to any other, but the two major directions of inference are shown as interpretation in the data panel and refinement in the hypothesis panel.

abstractions discussed above. The levels of the hypothesis panel are dictated by the kind of heuristics we collected. Crystallographers find it useful to view proteins at three charcteristic scales – individual atoms, peptide-sized groups of atoms (superatoms, e.g. lysine) and groups of peptides (stereotypes, e.g. an α-helix) – and express their knowledge in these terms.

Elements on the data panel are created by a set of heuristic preprocessing programs and are rarely changed during the execution of CRYSALIS itself. The panel is interpreted bottom-up; from the given EDM is derived a skeleton and a set of segments, and, independently, a set of peaks. In contrast, all elements on the hypothesis panel are created by CRYSALIS. This panel is processed in an opportunistic manner with elements at any level supporting elements at any other hypothesis level. Over the course of a protein interpretation, however, the hypothesis processing can be considered as a process of refinement. The goal of an interpretation is a description at the atomic level; superatomic and stereotypic hypothesis elements are ultimately refined ino sets of atoms.

During interpretation, inferences may be made from any level to any other level, and from either panel. Elements on the hypothesis panel can be inferred from other hypothesis elements or have independent support from the data panel. CRYSALIS makes heavy use of this independence in the way it looks for toeholds in the data. We find that the ability to create solutions incrementally and to work in either direction – general to specific or vice versa – is essential to the success of the system.

The use of multiple blackboard panels is a new extension to the blackboard architecture that permits additional modularity in the hypothesis elements, the associated knowledge sources and the control. Problem solving within each panel can involve different types of data, different knowledge sources and different control schemes. In some applications, where the requirement for synchronization between the activities on the two panels is weak, one could use this architecture as a basis for concurrent processing.

7.3.6 The knowledge base

Both factual and heuristic knowledge are required to interpret an electron density map. These are discussed below.

Factual knowledge and access functions

Most of the facts and 'handbook knowledge' that might be represented declaratively are implicit in the set of access functions. There was little need for a general declarative representation that was reusable for other purposes (e.g. explanation), so access functions were chosen for their ease of implementation. The only explicitly stored facts are the properties of the 20 amino acids, the peptide bond, the amino and carboxy ends of the protein's backbone, and the cofactors. Of these items, only the set of cofactors known to the system is likely to change, and then usually by addition of new members.

CRYSALIS has about 250 functions that manipulate the hypotheses and the data. These functions are meant to hide implementation detail from the user, who can treat them as a crystallographic language when writing knowledge sources. All but a few of these functions are written in LISP; the exceptions are the heavily numeric template matchers, which are written in FORTRAN.

Knowledge for EDM interpretation

The heuristics for map interpretation form the largest part of the knowledge base. We selected a production rule formalism for representing this knowledge because it is easy to read and modify, and because it matches the natural grain size of the available knowledge. Our rules are partitioned into sets based on function and topic. For example, one rule set contains all the rules about verifying hydrogen bonds, and another contains all the rules about locating heme cofactors.

```
KS-variables:
      (MAXWT  if MAP.QUALITY is GOOD then 400 else 300)
      (SC     the best segment-level data identification of the current
                 hypothesis element in focus)
      (SCROOT the skeletal node closest to the base of the sidechain SC)
      (PEAKS  a list of all peaks within 1.2 Ang. of SCROOT)
      (DIST   the distance from the highest of PEAKS to SCROOT)
Comment: Given a sidechain, try to find an atomic hypothesis for the
         alpha-carbon at its base
Rules:
      1) if an alpha-C atomic hypothesis already exists for this residue
            then (KSQUIT)
      2) if SCROOT exists then create a new atomic hypothesis called ALPHA-C
                  with residue = CURRENT.RESIDUE and
                  SKELNODES = SCROOT with WT of 50
      3) if no PEAKS found then (KSQUIT)
      4) if DIST < 0.5 Ang. then add highest of PEAKS to atomic hypothesis with
            a WT of 600
      5) if DIST is between 0.5 and 0.9 Ang. then add highest peak with WT of 500
```

Figure 7.4   A portion of the `Possible.alpha-C` KS.

Each rule set forms a knowledge source with two parts: KS-variables and rules. KS-variables create local variables for the KS, remove redundant computations from the rules, and encourage the user to create a clearer, more meaningful vocabulary in which to express the KS's expertise. Some of the KS-variables have meaning to the interpreter, the most important of which states how the KS is to be interpreted. The user can specify that only the first rule that matches is to be fired (Single-hit), all rules that match on a top-to-bottom sweep are to be fired (Multiple-hit), or rules are to be fired in successive sweeps until none match (Cyclic).

The heuristic knowledge of the system also includes the weights that appear in rules and KSs. Rules that modify the hypothesis contain weights that are added to the existing weight. In this way the user's judgment on the importance of each rule can be expressed. In addition, the KS-variable MAXWT expresses the user's judgment about the power of the KS as a whole. The weights in the KS's rules are all written in terms of -1000 to 1000 and are then modified by the MAXWT, which ranges from 1 to 1000. The weight of a hypothesis element is computed as the minimum of 1000 and (Old Wt + 0.001 * MAXWT * Rule Wt). Thus a rule with a weight of 250 is assumed to contain roughly one-fourth of that KS's information. Figure 7.4 shows a portion of a CRYSALIS KS.

7.3.7 Current status of the system

CRYSALIS is a successful demonstration system, although not developed enough to be useable by the general crystallographic community. For perspective, we give a few statistics on the speed and size of the system. The system interprets an EDM at the rate of about six residues per CPU hour (using compiled LISP code) on the SUMEX dual PDP KI-10. Even though the system is not coded for speed, CRYSALIS can solve a medium sized protein in about a day. The contents of the knowledge base are categorized in Table 7.1.

Table 7.1   Distribution of knowledge in CRYSALIS.

Level	Number of KSs	Number of rules
Strategy	0	29
Task	9	112
Model building	56	461
	66	602

7.4 Hierarchical control

7.4.1 The problem of focus

The focus-of-attention problem in CRYSALIS is that there is a large number of heuristics to choose among and that their ordering is often important. There are also many data points and hypothesis elements to focus on. Finally, the system's resources are far too limited and the knowledge is far too weak to permit either exhaustive invocation of rules or much undirected exploration and backtracking. If the system is to find the correct answer it must pick an efficient sequence of rules to apply in response to the specific problem. This is especially true for a production system that does not exhaustively apply the rules in the conflict set. If some rules are not fired when they match, some solutions may be lost. Proper focus is then critical.

Fortunately, crystallographers have expert knowledge about using their knowledge – strategies on how to interpret the data. This is a collection of hints suggesting what course of action is likely to be useful in certain situations. Typical examples are: 'Look for cofactors first since they are highly visible' and 'If two well interpreted regions are close together in the amino acid sequence, try to find the protein backbone connecting them.' Control knowledge (strategies) is knowledge about how to choose among plausible courses of action.

7.4.2 Using strategic knowledge

Strategies choose among object-level actions, so control rules must execute before object-level rules. We accomplish this with a hierarchical production system (HPS) consisting of many levels. Each level is a complete production system containing rules that examine the current situation and choose actions at the next lower level. The bottom-most, and largest, of these levels consists of the object-level rules that actually construct the solution. All higher levels are composed of control rules that invoke other KSs instead of performing object-level actions.

Control within a hierarchical production system proceeds from the top down. The highest level consists of a single control KS (the basic conceptual unit of execution being the KS rather than a single rule) that examines the knowledge base and the current state of the hypothesis and data panels in order to select a KS or sequence of KSs to invoke at the next level. This process then repeats, the execution of rules in a KS at one level causing KSs at the next level to be invoked, until the bottom level is encountered. When a KS is invoked, control passes to it *from* the

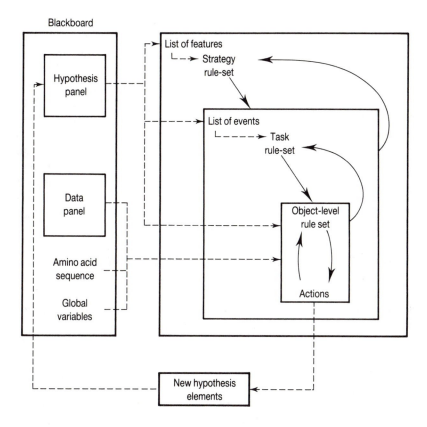

Figure 7.5 Control flow in CRYSALIS. Each of the nested boxes on the right is a production system composed of a loop of rule selection and rule execution. In the lowest-level production system, rule executions change the blackboard by creating hypotheses. In all higher levels, rule actions invoke rule sets of the next level production system. (—, control flow; ---, data flow.)

KS that invoked it, i.e. the higher-level KS is suspended until the KS it has invoked either runs out of rules that match or terminates itself. When this lower-level KS is done, control returns *to* the KS that invoked it. The flow of control in CRYSALIS is summarized in Figure 7.5.

Focus-of-attention is achieved in two ways. First, instead of picking a set of KSs as possibly useful and then ruling most of them out during conflict resolution, the control rules directly state which KSs to run next. A secondary mechanism of focus is to pass the data matched by a control rule to the KS it invokes. The control rule states what to do by the KSs it selects and where to do it by the focus it passes.

7.4.3 CRYSALIS as a hierarchical production system

The highest level of rules is called the *strategy level* because these rules are closest to what crystallographers recognize as strategy. This is a single rule set (KS) responsible for monitoring the overall progress of the solution and for directing the largest movements in the interpretation process. Strategy rules do not examine the hypothesis directly, but use a summary of the blackboard computed each time control returns to the strategy level. This summary, the FEATURESLIST, is a partition of the amino acid sequence into backbones, toeholds and unsolved regions, computed by examining the current best hypothesis. The conditions of strategy rules then consist of patterns using these features and their attributes. The action of a strategy rule is to invoke one or more task KSs in response to some meaningful pattern it sees in the developing hypothesis.

The middle level of control is called the *task level*. There appear to be only a few standard tasks (subproblems) involved in solving a protein, e.g. looking for the backbone that connects two located peptides. A task KS is a rule set that guides the application of object-level KSs to solve one of these subproblems. Each task KS is focused on its own particular domain of expertise and on the region of the data/hypothesis space defined by the pattern of features matched in that space by the strategy rule that invoked it.

Task KSs examine the blackboard but react only to changes. For efficiency, each change is packaged into an event as it is created and put onto an EVENTLIST. Task KSs can then scan the EVENTLIST rather than the entire blackboard. This event-driven control for tasks also allows each task to specify its own mode of processing. Task rule matching always starts at the front of this list, so the task can work depth-first, breadth-first or best-first depending on whether new events are placed on the front, back or some functionally mediated best place within the EVENTLIST. A further dimension of control is gained by specifying the task rule set's method of interpretation. Like any other KS in the system, this can be cyclic (the default for all control KSs), single hit or multiple hit. Both of these execution modes (i.e. event scheduling and rule processing modes) are specified by the values of KS-variables in the task rule set.

The conditions of task rules are predicates whose arguments are descriptions of events and values of KS-variables and global variables. At least one event expression must appear so that a focus can be passed to the next level. The primary action of a task rule is to specify a sequence of object-level KSs to execute, passing the event or events matched to each in turn as a focus. Tasks operate until no rules match or until a rule explicitly calls for termination.

The final level is the *model-building level*. This level is not composed of control KSs but of KSs that actually create and modify hypotheses. KSs at this object level are not restricted, but examine the entire blackboard: data, hypothesis, amino acid sequence and global variables. These KSs are also the only ones allowed to change the data or the hypothesis.

The language used to specify KS rules is much more complex than that used in the control levels because the world of crystallography is much richer than the world of KS control. The conditions of KSs are usually simple predicates on the values of KS-variables. This simplicity is achieved by pushing complex expressions involving many access functions out of rules and into the KS-variables section. The actions of a KS are much more varied than the actions of control rule sets. These actions consist mostly of calls to the system's blackboard manipulation functions and to LISP functions that manipulate descriptions of protein structures.

An example of the execution of an HPS can be found in Appendix A. This brief example shows one cycle of CRYSALIS's execution, starting with the strategy rules, descending through task and object-level KSs, and ending back at the strategy level.

7.4.4 Additions to the basic HPS architecture

CRYSALIS requires one addition to the general structure discussed above. A task KS may be unable to change the hypothesis in any way. If this happens, the present strategy interpreter could go into an infinite loop because the condition that originally invoked the task is unaltered. To help the system detect this problem (and to record data for a future explanation system) we record each event and each strategy rule that fires on a 'history list'. Avoiding endless loops becomes a matter of preventing a strategy rule from firing more than once on the same focus. We note that a similar problem might be found at the task level if a KS does not change the hypothesis. The problem does not occur because events that are not matched as they reach the front of the EVENTLIST are removed under the assumption that they do not have meaning in the current task. If any other task has need of them, a function is provided that can search the history list for them.

A second observation is that in the beginning of this section we did not intend to imply that hierarchical production systems and backtracking are incompatible. A common form of heuristic search is to pick one of many actions, try it, and backtrack if it fails so that another alternative may be tried. The frequency of backtracking is directly related to how intelligent the original choice of action was. If strategies exist for selecting the correct action in the first place, an HPS allows the programmer to use them. If a backtrack facility is required, all that is needed are KSs to do the bookkeeping and control rules to specify when to use them.

Since the data are so uncertain, CRYSALIS uses backtracking as conservatively as possible. Our strategy for interpretation is to avoid backtracking by seeking as much context as possible to constrain the chances for error. The data may clearly support the hypothesis that the current subgraph of the skeleton is a valine sidechain; it probably will also support the assumption that it is one of several other very similar sidechains, or that the subgraph represents VALINE-34 instead of VALINE-57 or VALINE-109. Rather than proposing a shaky hypothesis element, the strategy directs the system's focus to more promising areas. Often by working on surrounding areas that are more certain, the abandoned area becomes sufficiently constrained to permit work to resume. The HPS is ideal for this kind of opportunistic problem solving.

Our final observation is that an HPS can be goal directed as well as event directed. Perhaps the easiest and most general method for accomplishing this fusion is to allow it on a KS-by-KS basis. CRYSALIS currently allows each KS to specify how it is to be interpreted and what the conflict resolution criterion will be. This is accomplished by building the simplest possible interpreter and then adding the desired set of options in a user-accessible way. It would be possible in CRYSALIS (or any HPS) to extend this idea by providing two basic interpreters so that each KS could choose to be either goal directed or event directed.

7.5 Related work on control

The ideas behind the hierarchical production system architecture were inspired by Hearsay-II and by some of the work in the MYCIN project. The HPS structure was first implemented early in 1979 after an evaluation of our initial program architecture. The work since that time has mainly been focused on building up the knowledge base in order to test our ideas and to attain an adequate level of performance. We have surveyed other relevant work in Terry (1983).

7.6 Conclusions

7.6.1 Results

Rules were derived from the examination of data from rubredoxin and five other proteins. Our demonstration of the system has two parts. We ran CRYSALIS on rubredoxin to show that the system can solve a small protein to an acceptable level of accuracy and completeness. We also ran the program on a different protein, cytochrome *c2*, to demonstrate the generality of the system.

The protein rubredoxin, from the bacteria *Clostridium pasteur-*

ianum, is a small, relatively simple protein containing 54 amino acids, with no α-helix or β-sheet, but with a cofactor consisting of a single iron atom tetrahedrally coordinated by the sulfurs of four cystine sidechains. Our data is an EDM calculated to 2.0 Å resolution from a model provided by Dr Keith Watenpaugh of the University of Washington. (Note that the EDM is calculated, not derived from X-ray crystallographic data.) Although we were able to obtain a very sharp EDM characterized by a relatively high S/N ratio, this apparent quality is deceptive. We have since discovered that the model has not been checked for stereochemical accuracy as many bond lengths and angles are very nonstandard. This is typical of the early stages in the model-building cycle: the crystallographer must find atoms before worrying about refining their positions.

CRYSALIS solves the map in terms of superatoms, finding PEPTIDEs and SIDECHAINs for as many residues as possible. At this level, the program found at least one superatom of acceptable weight for 45 of the 54 residues in the protein, or 83% (see Terry (1983) for details of this solution). Before the solution can be used and evaluated by crystallographers, these superatoms must be refined into sets of component atoms. The system currently accomplishes this with FORTRAN routines based on fitting standard templates into the EDM, directed by the location of the superatom. The atomic model CRYSALIS produces for rubredoxin contains 206 atoms. When compared with the original model, the average error is 0.57 Å with a standard deviation of 0.28 Å.

Our other data set is from the protein cytochrome *c2* from *Rhodospirillum rubrum*: a refinement of the original solution made by our collaborators at UCSD. This protein is a much tougher challenge for CRYSALIS as it is bigger (112 amino acids), has a poorer-quality EDM, and has more features. Cytochrome *c2* is a globular protein with a heme cofactor. The shape of the protein is maintained by several α-helices, hydrogen bonding between different residues, and the bonds that fix the heme to the protein's backbone. Since this is a larger protein with features the program has little knowledge about (the helices), and since the overall quality of the data is poorer, we do not expect CRYSALIS to find as complete a solution as it found for rubredoxin.

CRYSALIS found superatoms for 25 out of the 112 residues in this protein before we stopped the program. Our objective was to show that the knowledge is valid for problems other than rubredoxin. The atomic model contains 119 atoms, and has an error of 0.45 Å with a standard deviation of 0.14 Å. Since the map is at 2.3 Å resolution and has a much lower S/N ratio, these results are better than we expected. We stopped at 25 residues because we ran out of address space. Given more time and address space, there are several places in which the program could continue working.

7.6.2 Evaluation as an expert system

Given these results, we need a method for evaluating their quality. Fortunately, there are standard crystallographic methods for evaluating a solution independently of the way it was obtained. Before discussing our results, we need to digress a little to provide background.

One of the most important measures of the quality of an EDM is its resolution. Obviously, finer resolution means that more detail can be seen. The crystallographer frequently begins work on a new protein by examining an EDM of about 3.0 or 3.5 Å resolution to get his or her bearings. The first real attempt at an atomic model is usually at 2.5 Å as that is as much resolution as the data will bear without further work. The crystallographer can iteratively increase the resolution of the EDM, each time using more of the collected data. With each iteration he or she adds knowledge by locating more atoms. Through successive Fourier transforms, atoms that are correctly located have the effect of making the rest of the map more clear. In this way the crystallographer can bootstrap from using a small, poor resolution set of data, to using all the collected data. Our choice of resolution range, 2.0–2.5 Å, and our choice of Fc maps (see Electron density map in the Glossary in Appendix B) means that CRYSALIS has been tested only on high-quality maps which are at or just beyond the resolution limit for generating first solutions.

There are two aspects to evaluating CRYSALIS's performance. We can see how many atoms in the amino acid sequence it finds and then apply standard tests to measure how well the predicted positions fit the data. This kind of test, however, is unfair to the program without considering how well humans perform at the same task. A more useful performance standard is: can the program find enough atoms with sufficient accuracy that standard crystallographic refinement procedures can begin? This is roughly the same level of performance required of humans. Our expert collaborators refined this criterion to 'can the program find 75% of the nonhydrogen atoms given in the amino acid sequence with an accuracy of 0.8 Å (about half a bond length) or better?' This accuracy is to be measured on the average as not every atom is equally localizable. Atoms that are very constrained by their neighbors, such as the atoms in peptide bonds, have little freedom to move. Other atoms that are not so constrained, such as atoms at the tips of sidechains or near the molecular surface, have so much freedom of movement that they frequently fail to appear even in high-quality data.

CRYSALIS passes this test, which is especially encouraging considering the primitive nature of the template matchers. As these programs are more in the domain of numerical analysis than AI, we built only simplistic versions. We have every reason to believe a complete and more intelligent set of template matchers will yield a more accurate final model.

However, we can regard the program's success only as the successful demonstration of a prototype. Before the system can perform at a professional level, it must incorporate a much wider set of crystallographic concepts. Our goal in this research is not to build a completely functional, polished product, but to test and demonstrate some ideas about control in expert systems by using them to solve a difficult problem.

7.6.3 Observations on strengths and weaknesses of the HPS architecture

We view the separation of control heuristics from object-level heuristics and their use as a hierarchical production system to be our main contribution to AI. We discuss here the strengths and weaknesses of hierarchical production systems we discovered while building one.

We have found the HPS structure very easy and natural to work with because the knowledge is localized and clearly expressed. We found that the KSs within the HPS are very modular and independent. The effects of modifying a KS rule are almost always limited to the KS it appears in, and never extend beyond the task that calls the KS. This is partly due to the use of a blackboard as a communication and coordination device, but is also due to the separation of control knowledge and inference rules into different levels. We have found that the HPS structure allows us to express expertise more cleanly than the 'standard' production system for two reasons. First, each rule performs either control or inference. A further simplification occurs in that most screening clauses are removed from individual rules by the use of rule sets. This leads into the second reason: division of the knowledge into explicit sets of rules highlights the expertise encoded in these rules. Each set of rules can be understood as a single action within a broader conceptual view of the knowledge base. Finally, an HPS can augment the standard production system's match-and-execute cycle with other control constructs without cluttering up the basic inference rules. Counting down lists, watching for stopping conditions, and complex passing of control is done with rules separate from inference rules, making the system easier to understand.

A more specific estimation of the HPS's strengths can be derived from examination of the distribution of rules given at the beginning of Section 7.3.7. Almost a quarter of the rules are control rules. We could have built CRYSALIS as a traditional production system but it would have taken much longer and would be much more difficult to maintain. The HPS structure allowed us to create a pool of single-purpose KSs that are shared among many tasks. For example, nearly half of the inference KSs deal with tracing the protein backbone (matching sidechains and peptides, making backbone stereotypes, etc.). Since control is separate, these KSs can be shared between several tracing tasks with changes only in the task KSs, not in the inference KSs.

We found two major problems with using an HPS to structure CRYSALIS. The first is that control strategies are expressed with too much domain detail. The other is the system's current inability to invoke KSs other than by name. Neither problem is fatal, but solutions to these research questions are needed before hierarchical production systems can be as elegant and easy to use as we envision them to be.

We find it interesting that while other researchers have postulated hierarchies of control strategies, CYRSALIS is one of the first systems actually to implement and use the idea. Davis conjectured (in a private communication) that meta-rules are not used because no system is big enough yet to need them. CRYSALIS is slightly larger than MYCIN, at least by rule count, yet CRYSALIS has two levels of control now and could easily have four. The two new levels would go on either end of the current hierarchy. When there is enough knowledge, we contemplate adding a new top level that would choose between strategy KSs for 'opening, middle and endgames' during interpretation. These rules could also choose between strategy KSs for first solutions of a protein, and reinterpretations during refinement. Since the line between the lowest rules and the access functions they call is arbitrary, we could also add a level to the bottom. We draw the line at the level we want knowledge to be visible: rules can be explained, functions are to be invisible. Still, the access functions themselves are not all at the same level. Many of the functions called from KS rules involve thresholds, have built-in knowledge about proteins, and are the result of design decisions some other expert might want to change. If a user thought visibility at this level was important, we could turn the higher access functions into rule sets and the current KS level into a control level for invoking the new rule sets.

Why does CRYSALIS need all these control levels when other systems like MYCIN do not? The first reason is that CRYSALIS's possible hypotheses are much less constrained by the data. The quantity of the data and the need for considering data points only in context of other points means that the control component must guide the interpretation rather than just follow the data. Another reason is that each hypothesis level can almost be derived from a subset of the data levels. For example, the atomic level can be derived from the EDM and skeletal points, the superatomic level from segments. In theory, a complete solution should be derivable independently at each hypothesis level. In practice, interaction between levels is needed because extensions at any one level drop below any reasonable certainty. Control knowledge at one level is needed to guide the different individual and quasi-independent lines of reasoning while another is needed to coordinate them all. Finally, relatively more control is needed in CRYSALIS because the consequences of making mistakes are greater. The knowledge is such that it is easy to make an incorrect identification, create many other hypotheses from that point, and then not be able to decide what hypothesis elements should be retracted. In summary, CRYSALIS faces an acute focus-of-attention problem: at each step there are many plausible, but ultimately bad, choices of what to do. Our solution is a strong control based on expert strategies at many levels of detail.

This work touches on four themes in current expert systems research. These are:

(1) *Separate representation and use of different kinds of expert knowledge* A knowledge base that represents everything in a single, uniform set of rules can be very difficult to understand. Each clause in a rule can have a different function, but none of these functions is explicit. When all these functions are separately represented, the system can optimize how they are used, and the user can understand what is going on without voluminous documentation of how each rule was written. The three kinds of knowledge most commonly used in rules are control, context and inference knowledge. Control knowledge defines when to use the basic inference knowledge. Context can be as simple as a set of clauses common to a group of rules, or it can augment the rules by information not otherwise represented (e.g. a representation of what is currently 'normal' so that rules can be written in terms of normal and abnormal values of parameters).

(2) *Multiple uses of the rule set* While the rule set is initially built for the performance task of the domain, other uses emerge as the system matures. Examples of other uses of the same rule set include explanation of the system's reasoning, teaching the expertise contained in the rules, acquisition of new knowledge, and maintenance of the rule base. Needless to say, the task of these new system modules is simplified if each kind of knowledge is clearly delineated.

(3) *More complex control* Simplicity is elegant but, as in knowledge representation, the available control mechanisms must be sufficiently expressive. Expert systems research is starting to explore domains that require more than one method of processing information, or that need strong guidance from expert strategy. This is where hierarchical production systems make their main contribution. The HPS allows the knowledge engineer to capture and use expert strategies in a natural way. The HPS also provides a framework for the use of many kinds of problem solving within the same system by allowing each KS (at whatever level) to specify how it is to be interpreted.

(4) *Increased concern for the size of knowledge bases* As expert systems

grow in size and complexity, efficiency becomes an important issue. While there are many aspects to this problem, the HPS can help cut the interpreter overhead. When sets of relevant rules cannot be precompiled, the focus provided by the HPS can greatly reduce the number of rules examined in each cycle.

An important trend discernible in these four themes is the increasing size and importance of the control component. In particular, other researchers have advocated control components that are capable of extensive reasoning. (See, for example, Corkill and Lesser, 1981; Hayes-Roth, 1985.) The control of large expert systems is being accepted as a task worthy of an expert system solution. While we fully agree with this philosophy, most of this work has been done using descendants of the Hearsay-II variant of the blackboard paradigm. Our variant is not oriented towards such general planning and reasoning, but the representation and use of different types of control knowledge is well worth exploring. Some of these types of control knowledge are:

(1)   *Domain-specific control knowldge*   This is what CRYSALIS currently uses. This knowledge specifies what tasks the system should be pursuing, and in what order. An example is:

> IF   The protein has any cofactors that contain metal ions
> THEN   Search for these cofactors before doing anything else.

(2)   *Variant strategies for the same task*   While the overall task is the same, the first solution of a protein proceeds somewhat differently than subsequent solutions. One might also imagine a 'quick and dirty' strategy for obtaining rough answers, a cautious strategy, and other strategy variants for solving the same basic problem. At the top level of CRYSALIS, for example:

> IF   This protein is one of the cytochromes, and
>   Atomic models of the same cytochrome from other species are available
> THEN   Use the Cytochrome-family-strategy KS instead of the standard strategy KS.

(3)   *Control knowledge based on problem-solving context*   Each specific problem has unique characteristics. If the control mechanism can recognize these characteristics as the solution proceeds, it may be able to optimize subsequent problem solving. In CRYSALIS's domain, parts of the protein's backbone in any given EDM might be invisible because of high thermal disorder. A rule to prevent the system from wasting its time on such regions might be:

> IF   X is a blank region longer than 8 residues, and
> Some tracing task has failed to find any hypothesis elements inside X, and
> Some secondary toehold task has failed to find any hypothesis elements inside X
> THEN Don't bother to try any other tasks on region X.

However, this kind of control knowledge can easily extend into more general heuristics about loop avoidance, efficiency, and other execution-dependent problems. For example:

> IF   Task X has been applied to region Y, and
> Task X did not create any hypothesis elements
> THEN Do not apply task X to region Y again, or to any subregion of Y.

(4) *Control knowledge for dealing with resource limitations* If the system is aware of its resource usage and of the resources available to it, the control component can try to provide the best possible answer within these constraints. This is very important for forward-chained interpretation systems like CRYSALIS that do not have clearly-defined stopping criteria. A sample rule is:

> IF   Have used 75% of the available resources, and
> Have completed 50% or less of the solution
> THEN Switch to a 'quick and dirty' strategy.

A proposal for how CRYSALIS might be augmented by different sources of control knowledge at different levels can be found in Terry (1983).

7.6.4 Summary

A hierarchical production system architecture offers several benefits not offered by traditional production systems. The first is clarity. By expressing strategies in control rules, the program makes this form of knowledge explicit and highly visible. Object-level rules do not need extra conditions sensitive to control goals because control is stated outside them. Since they are collected into KSs, the rules can also do without clauses whose intent is to state implicit context. Rules can be briefly stated because each serves only one function. If multiple levels of strategy are available, the structure of the system captures and highlights that aspect of the domain. The second benefit is the directness of control. If the expert's strategies are specific on what to do and when to do it, there should be no need to wait until the action comes to the top of some agenda, or for the right goal to appear. Allowing a control rule to invoke a knowledge source gives the directness of procedural languages without sacrificing the spirit of the production rule formalism. Finally, an HPS brings efficiency to the rule-based architecture. Our metaphor is a binary search. Control proceeds down one path in the tree of possible paths through the control hierarchy in much the same way a binary search zeroes in on the desired element. Instead of matching through a very large set of productions, most of which have nothing to do with the situation in question, an HPS focuses on the best rule quickly and with few tests along the way.

Appendix A Example of CRYSALIS's execution

We are now in a position to follow an HPS in action. Execution in CRYSALIS starts and ends with the strategy rules. In each cycle, these rules examine the FEATURESLIST, looking for meaningful patterns. Assume this summary contains:

```
( ... (BACKBONE 10 13 ST4) (BLANK 14 22) (TOEHOLD 23 A9) (BLANK 24 27)
      (BACKBONE 28 33 ST2) (BLANK 34 37) (TOEHOLD 38 A2) (BLANK 39 56) ...)
```

where (BACKBONE 10 13 ST4) means 'a backbone covering residues 10 to 13, further details can be found in stereotype ST4'. Also assume the strategy rule being examined is:

```
((AND (BACKBONE WITH WT > 600 THAT IS UNBLOCKED)
      (BLANKAREA WITH SIZE < 7)
      (TOEHOLD WITH WT > 450))
 (POINT.TO.POINT.TRACE) SIZE-THEN-WT T)
```

The interpreter finds two places in the FEATURESLIST for the rule to fire: the region specified by hypothesis elements A9 and ST2 (residues 23 through 28) and that specified by ST2 and A2 (residues 33 to 38). Each strategy rule specifies a tie-breaking criterion chosen from a set provided by the system. In this case it is SIZE-THEN-WT which directs the interpreter first to look for the candidate with the smallest blank space (assuming a pattern of A − BLANK − B) and then the largest of WT(A) + WT(B). Both choices have BLANKAREAs with SIZE of 4, but the second one wins out because A2 has a WT of 720. The WT of A9 is only 355 (these weights are found on the blackboard associated with hypothesis elements A2, A9 and ST2).

Control now passes to each task KS named in the strategy rule's right-hand side in turn (only POINT.TO.POINT.TRACE in this case). Each task is focused on the region of the data/hypothesis space specified by the features that were matched: ((BACKBONE 28 33 ST2) (BLANK 34 36) (TOEHOLD 37

A2)). When invoked, each task runs (with no interference from the strategy rules) by matching events on the EVENTLIST and calling object-level KSs in response. At some point during the trace, the EVENTLIST might be:

```
(EVENT-294 EVENT-293 EVENT-292 EVENT-288 EVENT-251 ...)

Where EVENT-294 has properties:
        Name = SIDECHAIN
        Hypo = SA46
        New properties = ((SEGMENTS ((1 SEG78) . -300))
                          (NEARBY.PEAKS (PK3 PK108)))
```

The task rule that will fire on this data is:

```
( (AND (SIDECHAIN WITH WT < $SIDECHAIN.MATCH.THRESHOLD)
       (MEMBER START STEREOTYPES))
    BACKUP.RESIDUE EXTEND.BACKBONE PTOP.REVERSE)
```

A translation of this rule is, 'If the SIDECHAIN fails to match and we are tracing from a backbone, back the trace up to the previous matched SIDECHAIN hypothesis element, extend the backbone with whatever residues have been found so far, and decide if the trace should restart at the other toehold or quit.' START is a KS-variable of the task that is set to the hypothesis element the task is tracing from. In this case it would be bound to either ST2 or A2, depending on which end of the blank area the task decides to examine first.

Each time an object-level KS is invoked, the event or events matched by the task rule are passed as arguments, and then it runs until completion. Continuing our example, each of the three KSs above would be passed the superatom SA46 as an argument. The SEGMENTS and NEARBY.PEAKS properties of this superatom fix the focus within the data panel of the blackboard, and the other properties fix the focus within the hypothesis panel. During the course of its execution, each KS will probably create or modify hypothesis elements, thereby creating new events. When all the object-level KSs in the task rule are done, control returns to the task level where the new events may mean new task rule firings. If not, control returns a further level up to the strategy rules, where the hypothesis is resummarized and the cycle continues. Execution ends when no strategy rule matches.

The EXTEND.BACKBONE KS examines the hypothesis between the current residue in the trace (specified by the KS focus SA46) and the start of this trace (specified by the value of START). All new PEPTIDE and SIDECHAIN superatoms are sorted by position in the amino acid sequence and are stored on the KS-variable NEWMEMBERS. The last rule in this KS is:

```
(NEWMEMBERS (MAKE.EVENT 'BACKBONE START
                       ((MEMBERS NEWMEMBERS T)
                        (RANGE NEWRANGE)
                        (BLOCKED 'LOW.END)
                        (WT (COMPUTE.BBWT NEWMEMBERS))))))
```

This rule says, 'If the trace has found more pieces of the backbone, create a new event called BACKBONE using the old stereotype hypothesis element given in START, plus the following new properties.' The backbone is extended by adding the new members to its list of member superatoms, updating the range of residues it covers and its total WT. Finally, it is marked as blocked, meaning that an attempt to trace has failed at this end. This new event will go on the EVENTLIST, possibly to stimulate another task rule to fire. When the task is done the FEATURESLIST is updated. If the task traces two residues from the end of the backbone ST2 toward A2, but cannot trace back from A2, the FEATURESLIST will be:

```
( ... (BACKBONE 10 13 ST4) (BLANK 14 22) (TOEHOLD 23 A9)
      (BLANK 24 27) (BACKBONE 28 35 ST2) (BLANK 36 37)
      (TOEHOLD 38 A2) (BLANK 39 56) ...)
```

Appendix B Glossary

Amino acid (also called peptide or residue)   An amino acid has the following topological structure:

$$
\begin{array}{ccc}
R & & O \\
| & & \| \\
NH_2 - C\alpha H - & C & - OH
\end{array}
$$

The central α-carbon is surrounded by an amino group, a carboxylic acid group, a hydrogen and a sidechain (R). There are 20 amino acids found in proteins, each distinguished by a unique sidechain which varies from a single hydrogen atom to a double ring structure. By removal of a water molecule (the hydroxyl on one and a hydrogen from the amino group of another), two amino acids can be linked together. In this way a polypeptide can be formed.

Amino acid sequence (also called the primary structure)   A description of the protein in terms of the amino acids of which it is composed. This sequential listing specifies all atoms in the polypeptide chain but gives no locations.

Angstrom unit   1 angstrom unit ($\text{Å} = 10^{-10}$ m).

Backbone   *see* polypeptide.

Beta sheet   Two strands of the polypeptide chain can run in parallel, locked together by extensive hydrogen bonding. Beta sheets are composed of two or more such parallel strands and can form a very important part in the protein's structure.

Cofactor A small group of atoms bound to the protein. Cofactors are integral parts of the protein, often essential to the biological function, but are not part of the amino acid sequence. Some proteins have no cofactors, others have many.

Electron density map (EDM) The electron density function for a protein crystal sampled on a set of three-dimensional grid points. This map is calculated from a set of intensity measurements and a set of phases (which are always estimated). Two kinds of EDM are commonly used: Fo and Fc maps. In an Fo map, the experimentally observed intensities are used in the calculation. An Fc map is one derived from calculated intensities rather than observed ones.

Helix Under some conditions, sections of a polypeptide chain can assume a helical form in space. The backbone lies along the helix, held in place by hydrogen bonding, while the sidechains protrude out into space. In a common form (the α-helix) there are approximately 3.5 α-carbons per turn of helix.

Hydrogen bond A hydrogen bond is a link between two atoms in the form of $X - H \cdots Y$, where X and Y are usually oxygen or nitrogen. This bond is much longer and weaker than the usual covalent bonds found in proteins. Hydrogen bonds often play an important role in stabilizing the structure of a protein.

Polypeptide A repeating sequence of atoms which forms the backbone of proteins:

$$- C\alpha - (C = O) - NH - C\alpha - (C = O) - NH - C\alpha \ldots$$

where $C\alpha$ is the α-carbon to which the amino acid sidechain is attached.

Protein A nonbranching chain of amino acids, folded in space, and possibly containing one or more cofactors.

Secondary structure A description of the protein in terms of common substructures such as α-helices and β-sheets.

Tertiary structure A complete specification of the positions of all atoms in the molecule.

Acknowledgments

Many friends and colleagues contributed time and suggestions to this work. Of these, I particularly wish to thank Robert Engelmore. Carroll Johnson and Stephan Freer. I would also like to thank Bruce Buchanan whose interest and valuable editorial suggestions made this paper possible. Dr Keith Watenpaugh provided the rubredoxin data set. This research was funded in part by grant MCS-7923666 from the National Science Foundation and contract DAHC 15-73-C-0435 from DARPA. Computer facilities were provided by the SUMEX-AIM facility at Stanford University, funded by the NIH under grant RR-00785-07.

8

Issues in the Development of a Blackboard-Based Schema System for Image Understanding

Bruce A. Draper, Robert T. Collins, John Brolio, Allen R. Hanson and Edward M. Riseman

8.1 Vision and knowledge engineering

8.1.1 Introduction

Special-purpose vision systems have shown considerable success within their limited task domains (e.g. Ikeuchi, 1987; Tsotsos, 1985; Tucker, 1984; Nagao and Matsuyama, 1980; Ballard, 1978). To date, however, there have been no general-purpose systems that work effectively across a variety of task domains. Why do special-purpose systems succeed where general systems fail? We believe that special-purpose systems have succeeded because they are better able to define, structure and apply knowledge relevant to their task domain. Knowledge in vision includes domain-independent knowledge about occlusion, perspective, physical support, etc., as well as domain-dependent knowledge about domain objects and ways of recognizing these objects (i.e. control knowledge). Domain-dependent knowledge includes information about objects the system is expected to encounter, their three-dimensional structure and appearance, their expected appearance in a two-dimensional image, and their relationships with other objects. Control knowledge addresses how the information stored in an image can be efficiently extracted, organized and matched against stored models, and when object knowledge can be used to support or refute portions of the evolving interpretation.

Systems working in restricted domains can bring very specific recognition and control knowledge to bear on their task. This allows them to perform sophisticated inferencing with relatively little computational effort. General-purpose systems, on the other hand, require generalized knowledge and inference machinery that may not be applicable to a specific task with the same efficiency and reliability. The situation is analogous to finding the greatest common denominator of two numbers by using Euclid's algorithm versus finding it through deduction from Peano's axioms. The axiomatic approach is perhaps more mathematically appealing, but performing complex tasks in a reasonable amount of time demands efficiency.

In the field of AI, researchers have tended to move from the development of general problem solvers (e.g. Newell and Simon, 1972; Ernst and Newell, 1969) towards systems that apply more specialized expertise (e.g. Lindsay *et al.*, 1980; Shortliffe, 1976). Experience has shown that many real-world problems are not amenable to simple, universally applicable methods that must reason from first principles. Instead, task-specific information is needed, in the form of empirical associations or of particular chains of inference through a large body of general knowledge. The high level of sophistication required has led to the notion of *expert* or *knowledge-based* systems. The process of building the knowledge base is called *knowledge engineering*.

The computational issues associated with the large search space of possible interpretations is particularly onerous for image understanding. The usual problems are intensified by the large volume of data and the uncertainty that almost always accompanies inferences associated with local subsets of data. Much of the process of scene understanding involves extracting descriptions, at varying levels of abstraction, from arrays of sensory data and relating these descriptions to *a priori* expectations in the knowledge base. Systems designed for small domains can be tailored to generate the minimal space of descriptions needed to recognize their restricted set of objects. Thus, control knowledge is implicitly hardwired within them. A multi-domain/viewpoint system can make fewer assumptions about what types of image descriptions may be necessary for later object verification. The tendency therefore is to generate as many different types of description as possible in order to avoid excluding the necessary ones. This leads to serious consequences in terms of storage space and processing time, particularly given the computational demands of vision.

The subject of this paper, the UMass Schema System, is a knowledge-based system for interpreting static color images. Our goal is to identify and locate the significant objects present in the scene and to identify their relationships. In a sense, the Schema System represents an attempt to build a general-purpose vision system out of many special-purpose ones. Each special-purpose system, or *schema*, is an expert at identifying one particular type of object, combining object-specific interpretation and control knowledge to provide an efficient means of object recognition. This information is supplied by 'knowledge engineers' who design a knowledge base of schemas for each application. The UMass Schema System provides an environment in which to build and extend schema knowledge bases.

A primary characteristic of our design philosophy is that coarse-grained parallelism should be exploited at the semantic level. A schema instance is invoked for each object instance hypothesized to be in the scene. These schema instances run concurrently, communicating asynchronously through a global blackboard when necessary. This leads to cooperation and competition among the schema instances. Collectively, the schemas produce a set of semantically and geometrically consistent (2D) object hypotheses.

Other researchers have addressed the problems of knowledge-directed vision. Nagao and Matsuyama (1980) used a variant of a production system in which the rules were actually complex visual subsystems. He was arguably the first to achieve a significant measure of success in a fairly complex natural scene domain. Ohta (1980) used a more traditional production system, supplemented with certain non-modular mechanisms for control knowledge. SPAM (McKeown *et al.*, 1985) has a production system knowledge base of over 500 rules, organized into five processing phases, for interpreting aerial images of airports. Glicksman (1982) used a frame-based knowledge representation in his human-aided interpretation system, and Hwang (1984) controlled a frame system by means of a blackboard-based scheduler. Shafer *et al.* (1986) have developed a system for real-time navigation whose global organization is similar to the one described here in that they use a set of visual knowledge sources, each running continuously on its own processor.

Research into knowledge-based vision at UMass has been underway for a number of years. Hanson and Riseman (1978b) first described a frame-like 'schema system' for computer vision. Their ideas were influenced in part by the earlier work of Arbib (1978) (on which our interpretation of the word *schema* is primarily based) and Minsky (1975, 1979). In the VISIONS environment (Hanson and Riseman, 1987), Terry Weymouth (1986) first demonstrated success at interpreting natural images with schemas running in a simulated distributed environment. The current UMass Schema System represents the continuing evolution of these ideas. Concerns about development time have led to increased standardization of schemas and the adoption of the blackboard as the only communication mechanism. At the same time, issues in distributed systems have led to splitting the blackboard into one global and many local blackboards. Another development has been to explore the use of symbolic endorsements (Cohen, 1985) in an effort to deal with the old and difficult problems of uncertainty and evidence combination.

8.1.2 Issues

A knowledge-engineering approach to image interpretation encounters many hard problems familiar to computer vision researchers (see also Rosenfeld *et al.*, 1986):

- the absence of experts able to introspect about their vision expertise,
- the problem of indexing into a potentially vast knowledge base of objects,
- the degree of uncertainty inherent in the data, and
- the sheer quantity of low-level data involved.

In addition to the difficulties associated with visual processing, a number of AI issues must be considered when designing a knowledge-based system, two of which are of particular concern to us:

- the power-generality tradeoff, and
- choosing a knowledge representation.

Knowledge engineering in the field of expert systems begins with interviewing recognized experts in the domain. Unfortunately, we lack experts in vision who can introspectively explain the processes they use. Cognitive science and the neurosciences are providing some insight, particularly in the early stages of processing (Arbib and Hanson, 1987), but to a great extent machine vision practitioners are left with only their intuition and the results of experimental investigations. Consequently, a new, experimentally oriented set of knowledge engineering support tools needs to be developed. We have made it a requirement of the Schema System that it support a knowledge engineering environment which is comfortable for the vision system designer.

The *object-indexing problem* involves the access of particular object knowledge or models on the basis of extracted image events. Systems working in constrained domains can afford to consider all possible objects known to the system, since these are usually relatively few in number. Such exhaustive search, however, is impractical in the unconstrained natural world. The 'real world' requires a framework for storing object information in a way that it may be efficiently and reliably retrieved using *a priori* knowledge cues extracted from the two-dimensional image.

Uncertainty is present in every stage of visual processing. Fundamentally, visual data is locally ambiguous, as can be demonstrated by the difficulty human beings have in interpreting small areas of an image when the surrounding context is unavailable (Riseman and Hanson, 1984; Hanson and Riseman, 1987). Noise is introduced by the limitations of sensor and transmission hardware and through the aliasing involved in discrete digitization. Ambiguity also results from collapsing the three-dimensional world into a two-dimensional image, and then occlusion, variations in lighting, perspective distortion, varying points of view, highlights and shadows all play havoc with the two-dimensional appearance of objects and their parts.

The *volume of data* input to an image understanding system is tremendous. Processing typical color images (RGB) in real time at a reasonable resolution (512 × 512) and frame rate (30 frames per second) would involve processing over 20 million bytes of data per second. A single *image operator* such as a 3 × 3 convolution would require almost half a billion arithmetic instructions per second, and many researchers believe that vision requires 2 to 4 orders of magnitude more computation than this (Hanson and Riseman, 1987). Even on a massively parallel architecture a vision system will need to be very selective in its choice of processing strategies.

The *power-generality tradeoff* (Feigenbaum, 1977) concerns the types of knowledge in the system and how that knowledge is applied. There is a distinction made in the AI literature between *strong* and *weak* methods (Laird and Newell, 1983). Strong methods apply task-specific inference mechanisms to domain-specific knowledge. Such methods are powerful, in that they can solve problems that are too difficult to be feasibly solved through less specific approaches. At the same time, they lack generality, and are of use only in their limited domain. The WORD-SEQ KS in Hearsay-II (Erman *et al.*, 1980), which used a formal grammar to propose word sequence extensions, is a good example of a strong method. In contrast, weak methods, such as *means–ends analysis* (Newell and Simon, 1972), are general in nature. They can solve problems from many different domains through the use of universal problem-solving techniques. The price paid for this generality, however, is that problems that can be efficiently solved using strong techniques are often too costly when solved using weak methods.

The choice of a *knowledge representation* can greatly affect the ease with which a system is built, and its efficiency when running. Most knowledge-based systems encode information in the form of rules, frames, blackboard knowledge sources or logic-based approaches. These representations are epistemologically equivalent; any system implemented in one could be rewritten using another. The differences are in efficiency, documentability and ease of implementation/extension.

In the next section we describe the UMass Schema System. In Section 8.3 we will return to the issues raised above and show how the Schema System addresses them.

8.2 The Schema System design

It has been our goal to build a system that could overcome the difficulties mentioned earlier. The idea behind the Schema System is to build a general-purpose vision system by building many special-purpose ones. Our system contains many single-object vision systems called *schemas*. When analyzing an image, the active schemas cooperate and compete with each other to arrive at a consistent interpretation of the image. Each schema is an expert at recognizing one object; together they recognize the scene.

For every class of objects to be recognized there is a schema. A sample part–subpart graph of the types of objects in our house-scene schema databases is shown in Section 8.4, Figure 8.10. To identify an instance of an object class, a *schema instance* is created. (We sometimes refer to schema *instances* simply as *schemas* when the context makes the reference clear.) A schema instance is a fully instantiated copy of the schema, and each schema instance is a separate process which maintains its own local state. Schema instances can be invoked by the user (for debugging purposes), but are usually invoked by other schema instances. One schema instance may invoke another for a variety of reasons, including, but not limited to: (1) gaining support for a hypothesis by finding a subpart, (2) accounting for inexplicable or contradictory data, or (3) predicting the existence of objects that often co-occur with a currently believed object hypothesis. The system's initial expectations about the world are represented by one or more schema instances which must be active to begin an interpretation (e.g. ROAD-SCENE, HOUSE-SCENE or the more general OUTDOOR-SCENE). These instances predict the existence of other objects, and invoke the appropriate schemas. The new schemas in turn invoke still more schemas until a large set of instances is created. The set of object hypotheses posted by successful schema instances form the interpretation of the image.

As in the case of OUTDOOR-SCENE, object classes are not necessarily restricted to tangible objects; contextual or *scene* configurations also have schemas. A scene bears a relation to its objects similar to that between an object and its parts; both scenes and objects have parts that are related in predictable ways. Thus, the distinction between a scene and an object is largely a function of point of view. Seen from a sufficient distance, a house is an object that must be recognized as a whole. Closer, the same house becomes a context for recognizing its subparts (roof, wall, etc.). Instead of separating the notions of object and context, contextual abstractions such as HOUSE-SCENE and OUTDOOR-SCENE are given their own schemas.

8.2.1 The Schema System

The Schema System can be described from two perspectives. The first considers what object-specific schemas are and what types of knowledge they contain; the second is the system level, which describes how schema instances interact. We will adopt the system viewpoint in this section, and describe individual schemas in Section 8.2.2.

Communication needs

Schema instances must be able to communicate with each other to arrive at a consistent interpretation of the image. While each schema can be viewed as an expert subsystem for recognizing its designated object, achieving this capability often requires awareness of other objects in the image. A schema must process information about the presence or absence of subparts or contextually associated objects, and the possibility of occluding or shadowing objects, as a necessary part of its own recognition process. Conflicting hypotheses, which offer alternative explanations of image events, are another important source of information.

Any two schema instances should be able to exchange information at any stage through global communication about the partial interpretation. This is necessary in the long run to allow the system to include new objects without a great deal of schema rewriting. It is also necessary in the short run since it is impossible to completely predict how objects will interrelate in the two-dimensional image space. Necessary physical relations between objects can be predicted, but data-dependent relations (such as conflicts over object labels) will vary from one image to the next, and can occur between any two object types. An efficient method of conflict recognition requires that the schema instance generating the conflict notify the instance which had originally claimed the disputed area. This requirement makes it impossible to predict *a priori* which schema instances will need to communicate with each other. At the same time, system modularity must be preserved in order to limit the difficulty of building and maintaining a large complex software system. Since knowledge engineering is an incremental process in which new schemas are continually added and old ones updated, it is very difficult effectively to build a knowledge base if changing one schema requires altering other schemas that depend on it. We have therefore adopted, in addition to the principle that any two schemas should be permitted to communicate, a principle of modularity that no schema should depend on the internal details of any other schema. This suggests the need for a uniform method of publicizing partial interpretations and the associated conflicts and corroborations.

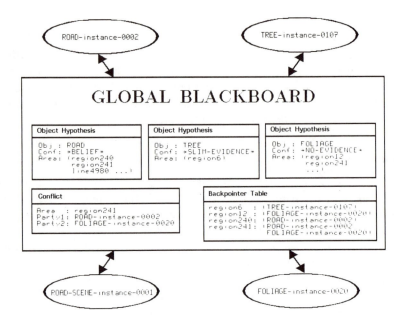

Figure 8.1   The global system blackboard.

The global blackboard

In the Schema System, schema instances communicate through a global blackboard (see Figure 8.1). The blackboard allows any schema to make public its own contribution to the partial interpretation, and to access public information about the contributions of other schemas. Each schema instance posts information to the blackboard about possible members of its object class in the form of an *object hypothesis*. Other schema instances can read this global hypothesis, enabling schemas to compute relations between objects. At the same time, the blackboard's decoupled communication preserves modularity. The posting schema does not need to know which (if any) schemas will look at its hypothesis, nor do the posting and reading schemas have to be simultaneously active. For example, in the road scene domain, this means that the stop-sign schema can utilize the road schema's hypothesis, even though the road schema may already have finished its processing. In fact, the stop-sign schema can be added to the knowledge base without modifying the road schema, even though road hypotheses will be used to suggest possible stop sign locations.

In the current Schema System implementation, the global blackboard is divided into sections. A separate blackboard section exists, for example, for the hypotheses of each object type. Any schema can read or write to any section of the blackboard; the partitioning is done to gain greater efficiency in retrieval. All messages written to the global blackboard are in one of a few, fixed formats, the semantics of which are the same throughout the system. The most common message type is the object hypothesis, which includes the object class, the portions of the image explained by the proposed object, and a confidence value (more about this in Section 8.2.2.). Each schema may acquire information about its hypotheses in an idiosyncratic, object-dependent manner; gathering support for a sky hypothesis may be completely different from verifying the presence of a proposed telephone pole. To 'publish' these results on the global blackboard, however, requires that the schema first translate its internal memos into the globally understood object hypothesis format. This allows information about objects to be passed without violating modularity. A stop sign instance may access the highest confidence road hypothesis, for example, without knowing how it was produced or what knowledge sources were invoked to support it. Other message formats currently in use are a table of spatial backpointers from image area to object hypothesis, and a potential conflict message that is posted whenever two hypotheses (from any objects) overlap spatially.

8.2.2 Schemas

Each schema is supposed to be its own special-purpose vision system. However, if each schema were uniquely constructed the knowledge engineering task would be unmanageable. Instead, the Schema System provides a set of building blocks – knowledge sources and representations – which are useful in object recognition. A schema is then assembled using object-specific knowledge about what knowledge sources and representations might be appropriate, when they should be used, and how relevant the information they provide is to the object under consideration. More precisely, the schema designer (1) defines an object-specific *problem space*, that is, the possible sources of positive or negative support for the presence of the object, (2) provides control knowledge for traversing that space, and (3) supplies a function to translate the evidence from knowledge sources into a degree of confidence in the object's presence in the scene.

Internal hypotheses and endorsements

Each schema instance develops and maintains *internal hypotheses* about possible instances of its object class in the scene. Internal hypotheses consist of *tokens* which represent image events, and *endorsements*, which are a symbolic record of the object-specific evidence supporting or denying the presence of an object instance. Tokens are abstract image descriptions which can represent any type of image event in the schema's problem space. Low-level tokens are those extracted directly from the pixel data, such as region or straight-line segementations (Beveridge *et al.*, 1987; Burns *et al.*, 1986); more abstract tokens result from grouping lower-level tokens into more complex entities (Reynolds and Beveridge 1987; Weiss and Boldt, 1986), or from describing the relationship between tokens of different types (Belknap *et al.*, 1986). To take an example from our road scene domain, roadline hypotheses initially contain straight-line segments extracted from the image via a straight-line extraction algorithm. (Roadlines are the white or yellow painted lines that usually bound a road and mark the lane boundaries.) Later processing builds more abstract tokens representing parallel pairs of these line segments, and after that forms regions corresponding to the area between line pairs. Future development of the roadline schema might include the construction of three-dimensional surface tokens from monocular, motion, stero or active range data. An object hypothesis is strengthened whenever several tokens, having been extracted or abstracted in a variety of ways, substantiate the existence of that object in the image.

In addition to image event tokens, a set of symbolic endorsements providing measures of support are maintained with each internal hypothesis. These endorsements are what the schema 'reasons over' to determine what knowledge sources have been run, and how successful they have been. The road schema, for instance, recognizes ten endorsements: centerline-present, sideline-present and shoulder-present (all of which are variations on subpart support); adjacent-to-road; correct-color and correct-texture (as compared with *a priori* expectations stored in the knowledge base); wrong-color and wrong-texture (which discredit hypotheses whose color/texture is too far from the expected norm); and telephone-pole-present and road-sign-present (denoting co-occurrence support). The set of possible endorsements spans the schema's problem space.

Strategies

Strategies are simple control programs that run concurrently within each schema. They represent an encoding of control knowledge encompassing both the order of knowledge source invocation and the addition of endorsements based on the results. In principle, the scheduling of knowledge sources could become an arbitrarily complex task. In a parallel processing environment, however, some of this complexity can be dismissed. Instead of writing a single-scheduler which must integrate all possible methods of recognizing the object, a strategy is written for each method. The house schema, for instance, might have one strategy for finding houses at a distance and another for recognizing them when nearby, one strategy for a frequently seen viewpoint, and another, more computationally expensive strategy, for recognizing houses from any arbitrary position. Our assumption is that trying to determine the proper order of actions motivated by different approaches to recognizing an object is going to be a somewhat arbitrary process. Instead, each strategy has an ordering of the actions it might take, and only executes actions as they become warranted by the success or failure of some other operation.

Schemas may also have strategies for subtasks of the recognition task. The sky schema, for instance, has one strategy for generating internal hypotheses, and another for verifying them. Each individual strategy can therefore be quite simple. The goal is to constrain processing enough so that several strategies of a given schema, and several schemas associated with different objects, may be executed in parallel.

One special strategy, associated with every schema instance, is the Object Hypothesis Maintenance strategy, or OHM. This strategy monitors the activity of the other strategies of a schema instance, and updates the object hypothesis message on the global blackboard when necessary. The global object hypothesis thus reflects the most current information at all times.

Local blackboards

A schema instance may contain many internal hypotheses, each of which must be available to all of its currently active strategies. At the same time, these internal hypotheses should not be visible to other schema instances. Therefore, each schema instance contains its own *local* blackboard, depicted in Figure 8.2. Local blackboards are also partitioned into sections. Each section often corresponds to a different level of internal hypothesis abstraction (the level of abstraction of the hypothesis token determines the abstraction level of the hypothesis).

The local blackboard is accessible to all the strategies making up a schema instance, but only those strategies. As a result, while messages to the global blackboard need to conform to a strict protocol, local blackboard messages can be highly schema specific, since the privacy of the schema's internal state is assured.

Global hypotheses and confidences

A schema reasons in terms of object-specific endorsements within its own local environment. At some point, however, the schema will need to communicate with other schemas or with the user. As was mentioned earlier, this is done by posting object hypotheses to the global blackboard. Concerns of modularity dictate that a schema should avoid transmitting its own idiosyncratic endorsements to other schemas. If endorsements were transmitted from one schema to the next, each schema would potentially need to know about other classes of objects and

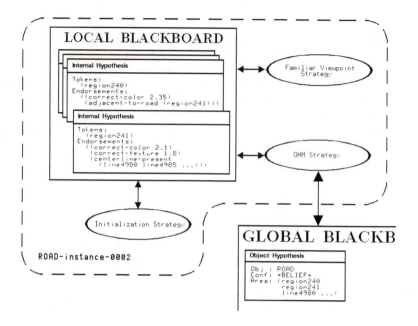

Figure 8.2   A schema instance's local blackboard.

their forms of evidence, making the resulting system very difficult to comprehend and extend. For this reason, schemas first translate their internal endorsements into a uniform object-hypothesis confidence scale.

The goal of translating endorsements into a universal confidence scale is to remove object-specific knowledge, and transmit just an object-*in*dependent knowledge of degree of belief in a hypothesis. While endorsements are symbolic representations of support, we have chosen a coarse, five-point ordinal scale for global confidence values. Values on this scale range from *no-evidence*, the lowest value, through *slim-evidence*, *partial-support*, *belief* and, finally, *strong-belief*. In this paper, an object hypothesis that has attained a confidence level of *belief* will sometimes be said to be *believed*; likewise, a hypothesis with a confidence level of *partial-support* will be described as *partially-supported*, and so on.

The task of translating endorsements into confidence values is performed within the OHM strategy (see Strategies, above) of the schema by an object-specific function that maps sets of endorsements into confidence values. Invariably this means losing information, since different sets of endorsements lead to the same confidence value. We have found, however, that collapsing information in this way represents an adequate compromise between posting all of a schema's internal information on the global blackboard and posting no intermediate results at all. The mapping function is provided at the time of schema definition by the schema designer. This forces the designer to explicitly consider the relationship between the degree of evidence provided by the knowledge sources, and the resulting strength of the object hypothesis. Of course, the combinatorics of dependencies between schema endorsements are similar to the combinatorics of joint probability distributions associated with a set of features. This is a difficult and open problem, which we do not fully address in this chapter.

8.2.3 Knowledge sources

Knowledge sources are general-purpose tools called by the schema strategies. While they may contain knowledge associated with their particular task, they do not contain object-specific knowledge, and thus are useful over a variety of objects and domains. Sometimes a knowledge source is a complex subsystem that is itself a topic of research, as in the case of the Graph-Based Matcher (GBM) or the Initial Hypothesis System (IHS). Besides the specific utility of a particular KS, it is important that the amount of computational work that takes place should be controlled by the calling strategy. For complex KSs this means that the major control factors must be parameterized, thereby allowing control decisions to be encoded in the schema strategy.

As part of an experimental methodology governing our research, knowledge sources have been developed on a needs-driven basis. This has slowed schema development, since writing a new schema often means coding a new KS and adding it to a library. As this KS library grows, however, the time required to write a schema should decrease, since most KSs will already exist. To some extent that has already happened, although it is premature to draw any conclusions with our still limited experience in two scene domains (house scenes and road scenes).

An interesting development has occurred with the KS library, however. From the original concept of many highly specific KSs there has been a trend towards a few large subsystems that are flexible enough to provide a wide range of services. As a result, there have been instances in which many small KSs have been subsumed by a single system. In anticipation that this trend will continue, we now group our KSs into five categories: (1) feature-based classification; (2) perceptual organization and grouping; (3) geometric model matching; (4) relations (spatial, geometric and hypothesis space); and (5) low-level processes (including bottom-up image segmentation and knowledge-directed resegmentation). Four of these five groups (all but the relations) are now being developed into large, controllable subsystems, not by *a priori* design, but rather by implied research interests in these areas by our colleagues at UMass. It is not yet the case that all of the knowledge sources in any one area have

Figure 8.3 256 × 256 intensity image of a
sample road scene.

Figure 8.4 Region segmentation of
the road scene in Figure 8.3.

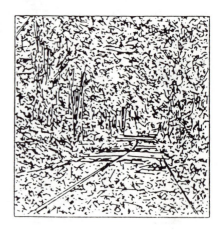

Figure 8.5 Straight-line
segmentation of the road scene in
Figure 8.3.

been replaced by the more general system. Nevertheless, the schema
designer is slowly being relieved of the task of hand-constructing
knowledge sources.

8.2.4 An example of schema processing

Let us illustrate the activity of the system by taking as an example the
recognition of the objects ROAD and ROADLINE in a sample road scene.

Figure 8.6   Regions returned by the IHS KS (in gray) as having the correct color and texture of ROAD. Used to form the initial road hypothesis.

Figure 8.7   Pairs of parallel lines touching the initial road hypothesis. These lines are the starting point for the roadline schema.

Figure 8.8   Final hypothesis region (in black) produced by the roadline schema instance.

Figure 8.9   Initial road hypothesis region (in black) with extensions (in gray) suggested by the final roadline hypothesis.

The image used for this example can be seen in Figure 8.3. This figure shows just the intensity image; the original data is a 256×256 color image, with 24 bits of data per pixel (8 bits in each color plane). Figure 8.4 shows a region segmentation of this image (Beveridge *et al.*, 1987), and Figure 8.5 a straight-line segmentation (Weiss and Boldt, 1986). Low-level image descriptors, or tokens, such as these are routinely extracted through bottom-up processing. Similar results should be obtainable selectively in a top-down manner under control of the schemas (see the Goal-Directed Intermediate-Level Executive (GOLDIE) KS

(Kohl, 1987; Kohl *et al.*, 1987)), but the present hardware configuration makes this infeasible. A machine currently under construction, the Image Understanding Architecture (Weems *et al.*, 1987), will permit this approach to be tested.

Quite often a system will have some *a priori* expectations or knowledge about where it is and what it can expect to see. Our example begins with an active road-scene schema instance, corresponding to an initial expectation that the scene will contain a road, seen from the viewpoint of a vehicle on the road. The following discussion begins at the point where the road-scene schema has invoked a road schema instance.

The default road schema strategy begins by generating a set of initial hypotheses using the IHS knowledge source to find regions with features matching the expected color and texture of previously seen roads, as defined through a set of prior training instances. The IHS KS returns the regions in Figure 8.6. Since these regions are contiguous, the road schema creates an initial hypothesis with a new token corresponding to their union, and with the endorsements correct-color and correct-texture. (The IHS is actually reinvoked on the new token, since it is possible (albeit pathological) for two tokens to have the color or texture of an object class, but for their union not to.) These two endorsements are enough to give a confidence of *partial-support* to the corresponding public object hypothesis posted on the global blackboard. From this point on, the road schema has two goals: to generate more support for this internal hypothesis, and to extend it to include corresponding region segments that the IHS might have missed.

One way an object schema can generate support is to verify the existence of subpart objects in the image. The most significant subparts of a road are roadlines: elongated regions with pairs of bounding parallel lines. Any strong linear structure within the area covered by the initial road hypothesis regions is a good initial candidate for a roadline. For each distinct linear structure found, a roadline schema instance is generated to either verify or refute that structure as a roadline. The road strategy which looks for subparts suspends processing, waiting for a suitable roadline hypothesis to be written to the blackboard. The specific logic and strategies used by the roadline schema are unknown to the road schema, but if the roadline schema *does* verify a proposed roadline then a roadline object hypothesis will be written to the global blackboard with a confidence value of at least *belief*. (*belief* is a system-wide threshold. Anything with that level confidence is considered recognized.) Although the subpart strategy of the road schema is suspended pending roadline recognition, other strategies of the road schema instance may still be actively verifying the internal road hypothesis.

In this example, one roadline schema is instantiated. Since the lines given to it by the road schema upon creation can be merged to form a parallel pair (see Figure 8.7), the roadline schema instance checks whether the pixels lying between the lines are the correct color for a roadline (yellow or white), as determined by the IHS. Since this is indeed the case, the roadline schema then applies a hypothesis extension strategy in an attempt to extend its hypothesis using other lines in the original line segmentation, until the color of the pixels between line pairs no longer matches the color of this roadline. Figure 8.8 is the resulting roadline. Its object hypothesis is posted on the global blackboard, and given a confidence of *belief*, since this is considered satisfactory evidence for roadline's existence.

Once this global roadline hypothesis is written, the road schema resumes processing (in a manner to be discussed shortly) and attempts to integrate it. The orientation of the roadline is checked for consistency against the road shoulder schema hypothesis (i.e. adjacent gravel or grassy strips) which is not described here. Also, by examining the spatial relationship of the roadline hypothesis to the road hypothesis, it is determined that this roadline is a centerline. The centerline-present endorsement is added to the road's internal hypothesis. The identification of an important road subpart is enough extra support to boost the confidence of the public road hypothesis to *belief*.

The road schema has not completed its processing, however. The roadline hypothesis extends to an area above the road hypothesis, suggesting that portions of the road may still be missing. A new internal hypothesis, corresponding to the additional regions adjacent to either side of the roadline, is created (Figure 8.9). When checked with the IHS, these regions are given support correct-color, but the texture data is indeterminate (which explains why the regions were not found by the IHS in the first place), hence neither correct-texture nor wrong-texture is given. The new road hypothesis gets two other endorsements, however: centerline-present and adjacent-to-road (for being contiguous with an already believed road hypothesis). These three endorsements, in the absence of wrong-texture, are enough support to post this hypothesis with a confidence level of *belief*. Since the original road hypothesis is also posted with *belief*, the two global object hypotheses are merged together into a single token. In contrast, the internal hypotheses are kept separate, since they originated in different ways and have been supported by different knowledge sources – as represented by their differing sets of endorsements. Further processing may affect the status of one or the other, or both.

Now that all of its internal hypotheses have reached the *belief* stage, and there are no more relevant knowledge sources to try, this road schema strategy suspends itself again. It suspends, rather than terminates, because its results are based partly on the roadline schema's hypothesis. If that hypothesis were to be altered or revoked, the road hypothesis might need to be changed as well. The road schema therefore 'goes to sleep', waiting for the roadline hypothesis to change. This is a procedural approach to the *truth maintenance* problem. Each object hypothesis has an associated process (the schema instance), which knows what other hypotheses it is based on. If one of those other hypotheses changes, the process awakens and performs whatever updates are necessary.

In general, a sleeping schema may wait for any number of potentially relevant events to happen. This is accomplished by writing predicates to the appropriate blackboard sections before suspension. A wakeup predicate should evaluate to true for any 'interesting' messages, those that the schema should be woken up for. Whenever a message is written to a blackboard section, each of the predicates stored there are applied, and those that evaluate to true have their appropriate schema instances awakened by the scheduler. This scheme avoids polling of the blackboard by sleeping schemas, at the cost of some slight overhead for message writing (the number of sleeping schema instances with predicates on any particular blackboard section is usually quite small).

8.3 System design review

In this section, we return to the issues discussed in Section 8.1. In particular, we consider how the Schema System's design addresses the issues of

- the power-generality trade off,
- knowledge engineering,
- knowledge representation,
- the treatment of uncertainty,
- coarse-grained parallelism as a solution to the expected volume of data,
- the object indexing problem.

8.3.1 Power-generality tradeoff

The Schema System embodies the assumption that, at this point in the development of the field, the vision problem is too difficult to be solved by weak methods alone and that object-specific recognition techniques will be a component of any successful general-purpose vision system. We do not reject generally applicable techniques; our KSs, for example, are general-purpose routines which can be run across several domains. The main point is that weak methods should not be applied blindly, but rather applied in just those situations for which they are well suited.

General-purpose recognition mechanisms can also be used to generate efficient, object-specific techniques automatically, as shown in the work of Ikeuchi (1987) and of Burns and Kitchen (1987) in pre-compiling two-dimensional viewpoints from three-dimensional object models. Techniques such as these, and others such as the generalized geometric representations of ACRONYM (Brooks, 1981), would fit naturally into our system. Unfortunately, many objects cannot be expressed in terms of simple geometric models and standard recognition strategies. The goal of the Schema System is to avoid incurring the cost of complete generality when object-based expectations can be used to constrain processing.

8.3.2 Knowledge engineering

The Schema System is only useful if the knowledge base for a new domain can be developed with a reasonable amount of speed. This requires tools for supporting the schema design process; in Draper *et al.* (1987) we present several such tools. The *Schema Shell* is a domain-independent research kernel which provides the distributed environment (currently simulated on a single processor, see Section 8.3.5), maintains the global and local blackboards, and provides facilities for creating, tracing and debugging schemas, as well as for saving and restoring partial or complete interpretations. The *Intermediate Symbolic Representation* (ISR) is a database for storing and retrieving tokens associated with extracted sensory events and their derived abstractions. In addition to data storage, it supplies routines for the associative and spatial retrieval of tokens required by many knowledge sources, and provides for selective 'on-demand' calculation of computationally expensive token attributes.

Our recent experiences in schema design have been encouraging. The original Weymouth (1986) Schema System, working in the house scene domain, took over 2 years to develop. The house scene knowledge base of the current Schema System took a little under a year to complete, including time for redesigning and reimplementing the basic system. In the most recent knowledge engineering experiment (Draper *et al.*, 1987), a reasonable road scene knowledge base was developed in 2½ man-months. The eventual aim is to be able to produce similar results in one man-week. Current work towards this goal involves expanding the knowledge source libraries, developing methods for specifying strategies and confidence-mapping functions, and building additional debugging tools.

8.3.3 Knowledge representation

Frames, rules and blackboard knowledge sources

Earlier we noted that knowledge has typically been represented in frames, rules, blackboard knowledge sources or logic-based approaches. (For the sake of the arguments in this chapter, logic-based approaches can be thought of as equivalent to backward-chaining rule systems.) In this section we compare and contrast the representation of knowledge in the Schema System with these better-known alternatives, and argue that the Schema System architecture can be viewed as the natural outgrowth of using a blackboard architecture in a distributed environment.

Frame systems have been popular in AI because they offer the advantages of inheritance and the 'active value' concept, as well as the benefits of a network database and of record structures. Inheritance saves time in constructing and documenting a system in a domain with a strong and meaningful taxonomy. Active values enable procedures to be called during access of individual frame slots, while network database capabilities enable a set of frames to operate as a semantic network. Some frame system capabilities are spread throughout the VISIONS+ Schema System. The ISR offers the *active-value* capability of a good frame system, whereby slots may have attached procedures. The *endorsement* representation of support for hypotheses generates a semantic network which is threaded through the blackboard. We have not yet encountered enough taxonomic structure in the scene domains we have been working in to lead us to expend effort on an inheritance network beyond what our implicit schema invocation network supplies; there is, however, nothing to prevent a schema designer from using frames in conjunction with the Schema System. Additionally, it is important to remember that a frame system by itself offers no special control or execution capabilities. These must be supplied by integrating a frame system with a rule-based system or other AI architecture.

It is an interesting observation that systems that make successful use of rich taxonomic structure operate in domains where the taxonomy has been discovered or imposed by human experts for the purposes of high-level reasoning (e.g. medicine, botany, geology). This suggests that the first generally useful taxonomy domain for vision would be in the area of interpretation tools and their usefulness for various domains and situations. This suggests that our first use for a full-frame system will be to enhance the organization of our knowledge source libraries.

Compared to other processing representations, *rule systems* are relatively easy to build. Knowledge is encapsulated in IF–THEN rules, or condition–action pairs, which in turn interact with the body of data in working memory. Working memory in our system would be equivalent to the ISR, the VISIONS image planes (Burrill, 1987), and the global system blackboard. Because of the large number of rules needed in a real-world task domain, the simple production system control paradigm is usually supplemented by structuring the rule-base into classes (Soloway *et al.*, 1987; Ohta, 1980) or phases (McKeown *et al.*, 1985), or by implementing additional rule sets which make control decisions. This last approach is clearly undesirable since it requires that knowledge about a domain rule reside in a control rule, which makes system modification difficult. Rule classes or phases alleviate this problem somewhat since the source of control is now explicitly represented in the domain rule, but the power to run a rule still resides in at least two separate locations (the rule's condition part and any rules that invoke the class) so that a change to either location may have unforeseen effects on the computation. In addition, there is a tradeoff between class size and the number of classes. At one extreme is a system with a few clearly marked classes or phases, each of which contains a large number of fine-grained rules; at the other extreme would be a large number of classes, each having a few complex, coarse-grained rules (e.g. Nagao and Matsuyama, 1980). This latter solution naturally leads to a blackboard style of control, where *events* on the blackboard signal when a rule's condition part should be matched against working memory.

A *blackboard knowledge source* (BBKS) is the equivalent of a rule. There is a *condition* and an *action* component to each BBKS. Additionally, each BBKS declares a set of events it is interested in. An event in a blackboard system may occur whenever a specified blackboard item is written, modified or deleted (or even when a slot value is modified, in some systems). When any event in a BBKS's triggering set occurs, the BBKS is put on a *triggered* queue. Once triggered a BBKS may have its preconditions (condition part) tested; if the test is successful, the BBKS body (action part) is then run. This declaration of triggering events gives the BBKS a measure of the state of the system which is more fine-grained than classes or phases, but more economical than just testing condition predicates to see if a rule (or BBKS) should be selected. The BBKSs fall somewhere between our schemas and our knowledge sources (KSs) in both power and grain size. The two types of knowledge source (KS and BBKS) should not be confused. Our knowledge source is a function or set of functions that do not conceptually interact with the blackboard at all in our system.

We have adapted much of the structure of the basic blackboard system, with a few significant adjustments. A great deal of work on control and scheduling in blackboard systems (Hayes-Roth, 1985; Johnson et al., 1987) uses centralized control, so that a BBKS must have some way of indicating to the central controller why it is running, what resources it will consume, and what it might produce in the way of output. There may be a large number of parameters that a BBKS must 'tweak' in an effort to influence the scheduler (Hayes-Roth, 1985). Where a group of BBKSs form a natural processing sequence or tree, it may thus become quite difficult for the system user to manipulate the scheduler in order to achieve the necessary effect. Furthermore, it is possible that a large investment in centralized control might prove fatal to what should be a distributed paradigm.

Schemas

The Schema System gives the schema instances more intelligence, more autonomy and more continuity than their BBKS counterparts, thereby reducing the centralized control duties of the blackboard and the scheduler. The state of the interpretation is already public on the blackboard; if the available processing resources can be published in a similar manner, there is no intrinsic reason why a schema cannot determine its own priority. The benefits we expect are greater efficiency in a distributed system, with reduction in control communication overhead, and reduced burden on the schema designer because there is no longer a need to manipulate global parameters in a monolithic external control module to achieve reasonable process goals, and a schema can be treated as a uniquely structured program which can read the blackboard as often as necessary and suspend processing for long or short periods with no difficulty. From the schema designer's point of view, a schema is simply a program that has a set of concurrent strategies, an internal measure of success and a means of translating its internal results into a uniform public hypothesis.

Schemas are continuous processes which can invoke other schemas directly and invoke subprocesses of their own (*strategies*) serially or in parallel as the interpretation may demand. A schema runs first when it is invoked. Subsequently, a schema may suspend itself while waiting for information to be written to the blackboard. A schema has internal criteria by which it can measure the quality of its current local interpretation, and it may suspend itself temporarily or permanently if current results and information do not justify further processing. To reduce the scheduling burden, we permit the sectioning of the blackboard to be arbitrarily fine-grained by supporting dynamic, as well as static, creation of blackboard sections.

8.3.4 The management of uncertainty

There is uncertainty at all stages of visual processing. Local errors are introduced by the imaging and digitization process, by imperfect knowledge sources (segmentation, line grouping, etc.), as the result of incorrect heuristics, or of inherent ambiguity in the scene itself. Computer vision systems must generate global interpretations in spite of such local uncertainty, so most systems represent and reason about it explicitly.

In AI, both *numeric* and *symbolic* methods (Cohen, 1985) have been used in reasoning about uncertainty. Bayesian probability theory (Hummel and Landy, 1985), fuzzy set theory (Zadeh, 1983) and the Shafer-Dempster theory of evidence (Wesley and Hanson, 1982; Wesley *et al.*, 1984) are all examples of the numeric approach, which has dominated work in computer vision and pattern recognition. Numerical approaches manipulate uncertainty arithmetically with some degree of mathematical justification, but in the typical AI domain they may suffer a serious loss of information when combining support from numerous, potentially nonindependent, sources. Symbolic approaches, on the other hand, explicitly record the sources of uncertainty in order to facilitate situation-specific combination methods and recovery from errors. Cohen's *endorsements* (Cohen, 1985) are an example of this approach. (It was Cohen's paper that led us to adopt the term 'endorsement'.) One of the possible difficulties with a symbolic method springs from its very flexibility: in order to take advantage of the added information about the interaction of supporting knowledge sources, it might be necessary to analyze many combinations of support (up to the power set of sources). In many cases, however, only a very few combinations will be significant, which suggests that if the grain size is appropriate the local combinatorics may not be a problem.

The Schema System uses a hybrid approach: for global communication it uses a simple five-point numeric scale, while locally (i.e. within a schema) uncertainty is treated symbolically. To our knowledge, this is the first vision system to handle uncertainty symbolically. For example, our model of sky regions excludes linear structure, so that the presence of high contrast lines inside a hypothesized sky region reduces the confidence rating of that hypothesis. Rather than just lower the numeric confidence value, the sky schema also records in its internal hypothesis the presence of unexplained lines. This is a source of negative support, weakening the confidence in that hypothesis. The schema instance can then take steps to remove this negative evidence, invoking another schema, for example, to account for the lines by recognizing an occluding object such as a telephone wire. If a hypothesis is subsequently posted for such an object, the previously unexplained item is accounted for, and the hypothesis regains its higher confidence rating. The Schema System thus arrives at more reliable conclusions by reasoning about the sources of uncertainty. The symbolic representation of uncertainty facilitates this.

8.3.5 A distributable system

The Schema System has been designed to run in a parallel environment. Schemas running concurrently allow many hypotheses to be pursued simultaneously as available processors permit. Explicit parallelism is further expressed by the strategy sets which may run concurrently within each schema. Since this system was conceived as a distributed system from the beginning, we have gone to some lengths to avoid certain bottlenecks that are peculiar to serial implementations of blackboard systems.

Distributed control

We have already discussed the potential control bottleneck embodied in the centralized blackboard agenda and scheduler. As we pointed out, we hope to reduce the control bottleneck by distributing scheduling decisions among the schemas themselves. The issue of when the cost of control processing outweighs the benefits is still an open research question. In general, that process should run which incurs the least computational cost while providing the greatest contribution. Although cost is not too difficult to calculate, a potential contribution can only be assessed in the light of the goals of the computation.

In current blackboard systems (Hayes-Roth, 1985), the solution is for the control knowledge sources to test at one time or another all of the other scheduled BBKSs in the system to determine which ones should be run and in which order. We feel it will prove more economical, more modular and more effective to publish the goal information that the control KSs in a blackboard would use, and let the schemas themselves decide whether or not to run. In the worst case, control in the Schema System should have a cost–benefit behavior identical to that of the traditional blackboard. Generally, the advantage should lie with the Schema System. Schemas suspend processing while waiting for *a particular piece* of control information, so that the processing queue (agenda) should be significantly smaller. Thus, control processing should benefit from the same modularity and opportunistic focus behavior as does the domain processing.

The Schema System is not yet large enough to begin testing our control assumptions. The current system goal is to continue the interpretation until all reasonable hypotheses have been examined. The system stops when it has interpreted everything it possibly can and has marked as unknown anything in the image it can't explain. Because of the localization of control, the system is able to use any generic process scheduling mechanism. The current implementation of the Schema System relies on the TI Explorer process scheduler.

Distributed communication

We have attempted to reduce the blackboard *information* bottleneck in two ways:

(1)   The small set of strategies within a given schema instance share a local blackboard.

(2)   The global blackboard is sectioned by object with efficient parallelism in mind.

A schema's local blackboard can be located at a node where the schema's strategies will generally run. Since there is limited parallelism within a schema, there will be a small amount of potential processor-to-processor communication (or memory contention in a shared memory system). Although in theory any schema can access any section of the global blackboard, in practice most schemas access only a very few sections. Since the set of sections most likely to be accessed is known before a schema is run, we should be able to determine a good distribution of the blackboard information and schemas across several processors.

About 75% of all blackboard messages written during interpretations were written to local blackboards rather than the gloal blackboard. This number is interesting, but preliminary; we have not yet begun to explore the space of factors that affect it. The local-to-global message ratio does seem to be influenced by the number of distinct objects present in the scene. This is to be expected, since fewer schemas mean less inter-schema communication. Other important factors include how much of the image was successfully interpreted, the complexity of the individual schemas in terms of knowledge sources, and the frequency with which a schema's global hypothesis is updated to reflect changes in the internal hypotheses. Regarding the latter, the current strategy is to update the external hypothesis whenever its confidence level or token field is affected by a change to an internal hypothesis. This results in a large number of global blackboard messages, since each update involves erasing the old hypothesis.

Distributed implementations

We currently simulate parallelism on a TI Explorer LISP machine. A forthcoming implementation of the Schema System will work on a Sequent Balance 21000 parallel processor. This 16-processor (expandable to 30) shared memory machine will run a local implementation of concurrent COMMON LISP. The target machine for our system is the proposed Image Understanding Architecture (IUA) (Weems *et al.*, 1987), which will provide 64 parallel symbolic processors with channels to more massively parallel environments for low and intermediate level vision algorithms. The IUA will offer an excellent environment for the Schema System since there will be enough processors to support a large number of schemas running concurrently. While there are many issues inherent in distributed processing, we expect that the system design will free us from some of the problems of adapting to a parallel environment. We expect the Schema System to port well to any set of distributed processors that have shared memory or reasonable communication capabilities.

8.3.6 The object indexing problem

A vision system may index its object types according to visual features such as color or geometry, or contextual relations such as co-occurrence, functional association and part–subpart relations. Although many vision systems index objects based on extracted visual features, the Schema System's design allows one schema to invoke another for any of the indexing methods mentioned. Subpart and co-occurrence associations can be expressed through schema invocations or through blackboard communication. Feature-based indexing is accomplished by calls to knowledge sources. The Initial Hypothesis System, for example, returned a set of rank-ordered object types whose appearance is consistent with the feature values of a given region.

Testing object indexing solutions requires a large knowledge base of objects in a working interpretation system. This may explain why so few knowledge-based vision systems address this problem. Although we believe the Schema System's design addresses several aspects of this problem with a variety of approaches, our two domains of natural scenes, involving approximately 15 objects each, are inadequate for a serious test of this belief. Our current work is aimed at speeding the process of schema development and expansion of the knowledge base. As our knowledge bases grow, we expect to experiment with solutions to this problem more thoroughly.

Often it is necessary not only to predict the presence of an object, but to provide spatial bounds on that prediction. For example, although telephone wire is a part of the house scene, it is invoked by the sky hypothesis. This is because the house-scene schema cannot provide constraints as to where to look for wire, while the sky schema can. We have therefore adopted the simplest solution, allowing the sky schema to

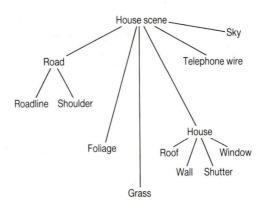

Figure 8.10   House scene subpart network.

call the telephone wire schema directly. While sufficient for a small knowledge base, this solution lacks modularity. Other solutions are being considered, such as having the house-scene schema activate a telephone wire *context* (similar to the notion of *class* in object-oriented programming) which would invoke wire schema *instances* as constraints become available from other sources. We are avoiding the adoption of additional mechanisms, however, until we can generalize from more examples.

8.4 House scene results

The results in this section were generated using the house scene knowledge base whose subpart hierarchy is shown in Figure 8.10. Interpretations are presented as images in which believed hypotheses (i.e. those with a confidence level of *belief* or *strong-belief*) are colored according to the object label; uninterpreted areas of the image are left black. A color code for the house scene interpretations, which appear in Plates 1–3, is shown in Table 8.1. The schema system from which these results were obtained was an old version. Significant improvements have been made in the system on the basis of those experiments, although no new house scene results have been obtained yet. For example, the knowledge sources available at the time the house scene results were obtained were primarily region based. As a result, the system had a hard time recovering from window and shutter mis-segmentations (as in Plate 3). In addition, the top-down creation of tokens was difficult in the software environment of the time. As a result it was only done for roofs and telephone wires.

Table 8.1   House scene interpretation color codes.

Color	Object type
Black	UNKNOWN
Brown	ROAD
Orange	CENTERLINE
White	HOUSE-WALL
Yellow	HOUSE-ROOF
Red	SHUTTER
Blue	SKY
Light blue	WIRE
Green	GRASS
Lime green	BUSH
Cyan	TREE
Magenta	SLIDE BORDER

8.5 Conclusion and future work

8.5.1 Summary

The UMass Schema System is an experiment in knowledge-directed vision. The goal is to provide the breadth of a general-purpose vision system while retaining the efficiency of a special-purpose one. The approach is to build generic mechanisms that avoid incurring the cost of complete generality when object-based expectations can be used to constrain visual processing. To this end, the system has been designed to provide a flexible environment for encoding both object and control knowledge. Assembled within an object-specific schema is knowledge about what knowledge sources and representations are appropriate, when they should be used, and how relevant each knowledge source is.

Each schema is an expert at recognizing one type of object. In an attempt to exploit coarse-grained parallelism, each instantiated schema runs in parallel with other schemas, and communicates with them asynchronously through a global blackboard. Together, the set of running object schemas cooperate to interpret the scene. Further parallelism is provided within each schema by the use of multiple *strategies*. Strategies are simple control programs which encode knowledge about what knowledge should be used and how to evaluate partial hypotheses. The Schema System architecture is an extension of the blackboard paradigm into a distributed environment that eschews centralized control mechanisms in favor of intelligent and autonomous schemas.

The Schema System approaches the management of uncertainty with a hybrid of numeric and symbolic techniques. For global communication, a simple five-point numeric confidence scale is used. Within each schema, uncertainty is managed through symbolic endorsements. The schema considers possible and existing endorsements when making its control decisions. Endorsements also record the *sources* of information, providing a backtrace of the reasons why an object hypothesis is being entertained, as well as how reliable it may be.

Knowledge sources are called by the schemas to perform low- and intermediate-level image processing. The KSs fall into five rough categories: feature-based classification, perceptual organization and grouping, geometric model matching, general relations, and low-level process control. Most knowledge sources can be used in either a data-driven or a model-driven fashion. All are required to be parameterized so that they can be invoked by the schemas to perform specific tasks within certain resource constraints.

8.5.2 Future research

The Schema System is one of only a handful of vision systems to rely on object-specific knowledge; it is unique with respect to its architecture and its approaches to control, uncertainty, parallelism and knowledge engineering. While all of these approaches need further study, the authors feel that two issues are paramount: system performance in an actual parallel environment, and the object indexing problem in a large knowledge base.

From its inception, the schema system has been designed to run on a parallel processor. Care has been taken to distribute the vision task while avoiding communication bottlenecks. However, without a specification of the parallel hardware, we have not been able to estimate system run times, only measure communication patterns. Without such measurements, the effectiveness (or ineffectiveness) of our control strategies cannot be measured. Will the cost of process creation overwhelm the benefits of coarse-grained parallelism? Can the allocation of a fixed number of processors be handled effectively without introducing a centralized mechanism? These are questions that cannot be answered until the Schema System runs on an actual parallel processor.

While it is imperative that the Schema System be exercised in a truly parallel environment, our target machine, the IUA (Weems *et al.*, 1987) is still a couple of years from completion. Therefore we have begun to port the system to a Sequent Balance 21000 multiprocessor. Although this machine is not adequate for real-time vision, it should allow us to test our schema control framework in a parallel, shared-memory environment.

Another major question for all knowledge-based vision systems is how well its knowledge base can expand to accommodate new objects and domains. This is no less true of the Schema System. The system must become sufficiently good at object indexing that only a few relevant schemas are ever invoked on any given image. In addition, the effects of knowledge base size on communication patterns, control, etc., must be determined. Unfortunately, our current knowledge bases of 15 objects each are inadequate for such an investigation. Serious research into the construction and maintenance of large knowledge bases can probably begin when a system is able to recognize 50–100 objects.

We also plan to integrate our house and road scene knowledge bases in the near future. While these domains have many objects in common, the resulting database should contain around 20 objects, and enable the system to recognize objects from a wider variety of images. Work on aerial images is also being considered.

Other aspects of the work are ongoing. We continue to expand the knowledge source library. The integration of a low-level monitor and a curve extractor is already in progress. The incorporation of motion data and better three-dimensional modeling techniques is planned. Work on simplifying the knowledge engineering task also continues. Recent changes have greatly improved the debugging facilities provided by the Schema Shell; future work is geared toward easing the burden of knowledge base construction.

Acknowledgments

This research was supported in part by DARPA and RADC under contract F30602-87-C-0140, by DARPA and Army ETL under contract DACA76-85-C-0008, by AFOSR under grant AFOSR-86-0021, and by NSF under grant DCR-8500332.

9
Structural Analysis of Complex Aerial Photographs

Makoto Nagao, Takashi Matsuyama and
Hisayuki Mori

9.1 Introduction

Recently several systems for the analysis of aerial photographs have been developed to locate objects on the ground surface (Barrow *et al.*, 1978; Quam, 1978; Nevatia and Price, 1978). When we are going to get a description of the structure on the ground surface by analyzing an aerial photograph, we find several difficulties which are not encountered in other image-analysis areas:

(1) The size of a picture is very large.

(2) As it is impossible to control photographing conditions, the quality of a picture is apt to change.

(3) The sizes and the textural properties of objects vary quite widely.

(4) Variation of objects in a scene entails calculation of many different features and the diverse knowledge of the world.

(5) There are too many situations on the ground surface to build a general model which can represent all possible spatial arrangements of objects.

In order to overcome these difficulties and to realize an efficient and reliable analysis, we have developed a new system based on the 'production system' (Davis and King, 1977). The system consists of a group of object-detection subsystems which individually search for specific objects by communicating with each other via a common blackboard (Erman and Lesser, 1975; Lesser and Erman, 1977).

The analysis process of this system is divided into the following steps:

(1)   *Segmentation*   After noise removal, an aerial photograph is segmented into elementary regions according to the multispectral property.

(2)   *Global survey of the whole scene*   Regions with characteristic properties are extracted. These are used to confine the spatial domains of objects where object-detection subsystems work.

(3)   *Detailed analysis of focused local areas*   Each object-detection subsystem focuses its attention on a specific local area and checks the existence of a specific object.

(4)   *Communication among object-detection subsystems*   All the information about the properties of regions and recognized objects is stored in the blackboard. Object-detection subsystems interface with it in a uniform way. The system controls the overall flow of the analysis by managing the information in the blackboard. It solves conflict among object-detection subsystems, and corrects errors by backtracking.

This chapter mainly describes the control structure of the system, and demonstrates its performance with experimental results. The detailed algorithms of picture processing routines are described in Nagao *et al.*, (1978).

9.2 Focus of attention in the analysis of aerial photographs

Aerial photographs we want to analyze are four-band multispectral images of complex suburban areas taken from a low altitude (Figure 9.1). (Figure 9.1).

As the size of a picture is very large, the analysis should be done as efficiently as possible. If each object-detection subsystem, which is very sophisticated and time consuming, were applied to the whole picture area, it would take a prohibitive time to complete the analysis. In order to solve this problem, we adopted the focusing mechanism which human beings seem to use when they interpret a complex scene. When they see a scene, at first they globally survey it to find the characteristic areas which attract their interest. Then they go into the detailed examination of some local area to find out objects using their knowledge of the world. The more intensively they focus, the more specialized knowledge they come to use.

In our system, several kinds of regions with prominent features (characteristic regions) are extracted by simple picture processing programs. Then object-detection subsystems apply sophisticated programs only in the local areas where specific objects are supposed to exist.

Figure 9.1   A picture of a complex suburban area.

As the time-consuming processing is applied only in small local areas, the total processing time can be reduced very much. Figure 9.2 shows the schematic drawing of this focusing process.

In order to specify the spatial domains of objects as correctly as possible, we utilize such features as size, shape, brightness, multispectral properties, texture and spatial relations among regions. We extract seven types of characteristic regions, i.e. large homogeneous regions, elongated regions, shadow regions, shadow-making regions, vegetation regions, water regions and high-contrast texture regions.

All the features used here are stable against change of photographing conditions, and all parameters are automatically and adaptively determined from the picture data under analysis. Therefore extracted characteristic regions can be the reliable basis for the subsequent detailed analysis.

Figure 9.3 shows the characteristic regions extracted from the picture in Figure 9.1.

9.3 Object-detection subsystem

An aerial photograph contains a variety of objects such as crop fields, forest areas, grasslands, roads, rivers, houses, and so on. The diverse knowledge should be incorporated to describe the structure on the ground surface. In addition, these objects, especially in a small country such as Japan, are intricately arranged without definite spatial relationships.

Taking these conditions into account, it seems to be natural to divide the system into a group of object-detection subsystems. Each of them is designed to find specific objects using the knowledge of their intrinsic properties and the environments in which they are embedded. The diverse knowledge of the world is distributed in object-detection

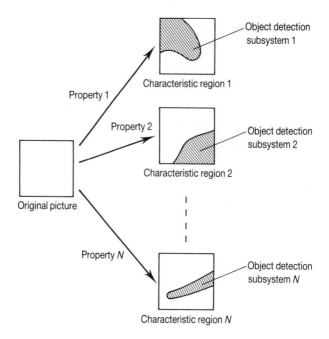

Figure 9.2   Focusing mechanism of the system.

subsystems. This facilitates the implementation of the system.

The types of object-detection subsystems can be classified into two categories according to the information they use in selecting the candidate regions of objects.

(1)   *Picture data-driven subsystem*   Subsystems of this type check the existence of the local areas with specified properties by combining characteristic regions. If there are such local areas, they examine them in detail by activating special-purpose feature-extraction programs.

(2)   *Model-driven subsystem*   Subsystems of this type pick up the candidate regions by using the spectral and spatial relationships with already recognized objects. For example, it is very difficult to detect cars by a simple knowledge that they are rectangular unless we impose the condition that they are on the roads or the parking lots. Therefore the subsystem for the detection of cars entails the recognition of roads or parking lots.

The present system has 13 object-detection subsystems for eight kinds of objects: crop field, bare soil (crop field without plantation), forest, grassland, road, river, car and house. Figure 9.4 shows the intermediate results of detection of these objects.

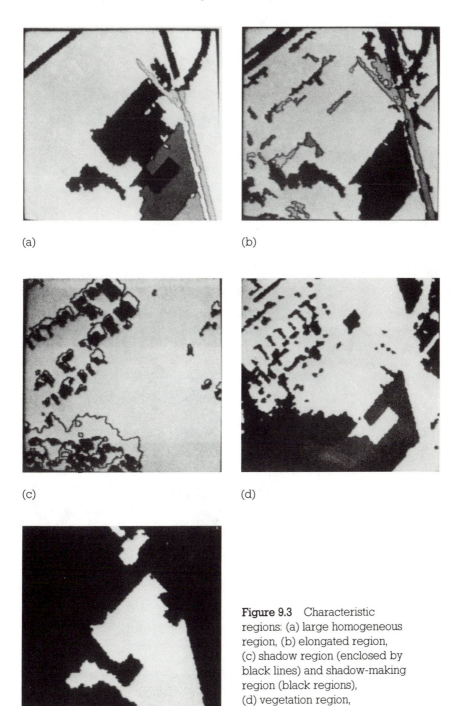

(a)

(b)

(c)

(d)

(e)

Figure 9.3 Characteristic regions: (a) large homogeneous region, (b) elongated region, (c) shadow region (enclosed by black lines) and shadow-making region (black regions), (d) vegetation region, (e) high-contrast texture region.

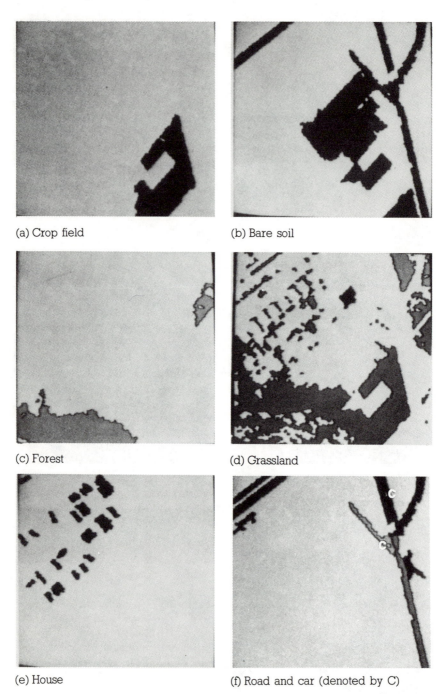

(a) Crop field

(b) Bare soil

(c) Forest

(d) Grassland

(e) House

(f) Road and car (denoted by C)

Figure 9.4 Intermediate results of object detection. Several regions are recognized as different objects. These conflicts are solved by the system (see Section 9.5).

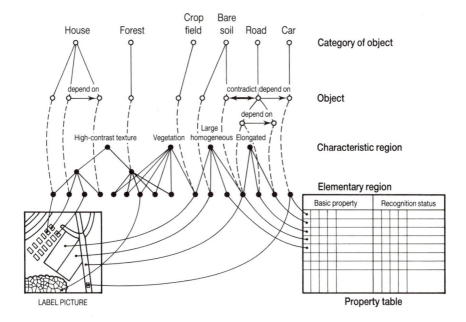

Figure 9.5   Structure of the blackboard.

9.4 The structure of the blackboard

Each object-detection subsystem interfaces with the common database, the blackboard, in order to test conditions for activation and to write in the result of the analysis. All the communications among object-detection subsystems are made via this blackboard. Figure 9.5 shows the schematic drawing of the structure of the blackboard.

The blackboard contains global parameters as well as the properties of regions and objects. They denote the global properties of the picture data, that is, photographing conditions of an aerial photograph such as the direction of the sun, threshold values for checking the similarity of multispectral properties, and so on. From these global parameters, each object-detection subsystem gets the information of the quality of the picture data under analysis. Therefore, it can successfully find out objects in spite of unstable photographing conditions of aerial photographs.

In this system, elementary regions, which are segmented according to the multispectral property in segmentation, are considered as the basic units for all higher level processing. Their fundamental properties (the average gray level in each spectral band, size, location and some basic shape features) are stored in the property table in the blackboard (Figure 9.5).

Figure 9.6   LABEL PICTURE: each pixel in an elementary region (enclosed by black lines) is labeled with a unique region number.

We store LABEL PICTURE in the blackboard in order to denote the spatial relationships among elementary regions. It is the symbolic picture where each pixel in an elementary region is labeled with the same unique region number (Figure 9.6). The reason for this is that the spatial relationships among regions used by object-detection subsystems are very different and depend on the properties of objects they want to find. Therefore it is not economical, and is even sometimes impossible to calculate all spatial relationships in advance. For example, when we want to estimate the location of a house by using the regularity of the spatial arrangement of already recognized ones, it will take a long time to find a candidate region of a house if we do not use the two-dimensional image.

As each pixel in LABEL PICTURE contains a unique region number, we can easily get the properties of the region to which it belongs. On the other hand, the location of a region in LABEL PICTURE is denoted by the two coordinate pairs, (BX, BY) and (EX, EY), in the property table (Figure 9.7). When one wants to calculate a new feature of a region, one only has to scan within the rectangle area specified by these coordinate pairs (Minimum Bounding Rectangle). This is very useful to save the processing time of picture processing programs.

Each characteristic region in the blackboard is represented by a characteristic region node which denotes a group of elementary regions. Two-dimensional images of characteristic regions can also be constructed from LABEL PICTURE. These are very useful in locating clusters of elementary regions such as forest and residential areas.

When each object-detection subsystem recognizes an object, it generates an object node in the blackboard, and the object node and its constituent elementary regions are connected by part/whole relations. If the recognition of an object depends on the properties of already recognized ones, the node of a new recognized object is linked with those

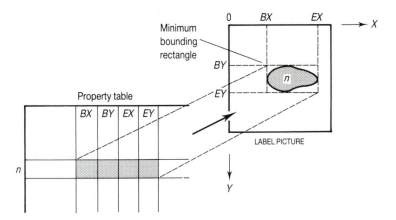

Figure 9.7 Specification of the location of an elementary region in **LABEL PICTURE**.

of old ones (Figure 9.5). By storing the history of the recognition process, the system can give back the state of the blackboard to the correct one when it finds an error in it.

9.5 Control mechanism of the system

As each object-detection subsystem recognizes objects independently of the others, the system incorporates the mechanism to solve conflicts between these subsystems.

The property table has the field where each object-detection subsystem returns one of the following recognition statuses: 'unanalyzed', 'recognized', 'irregular shaped' and 'rejected'. The system checks this field, and, if some elementary region is recognized as different objects by multiple subsystems, it evaluates the reliability value of each object to which that region belongs. Then the objects nodes except the most reliable one are deleted, and the corresponding recognition statuses of the region are changed from 'recognized' to 'rejected'.

If there are other objects that have been recognized in connection with rejected objects, the system also deletes those object nodes by traversing the dependency links from rejected objects. In this case, the recognition statuses of their constituent regions are given back to 'unanalyzed', as they might be recognized by using the properties of the other objects of the same kind.

Errors in segmentation are also repaired by the system. Object-detection subsystems check various properties of regions to recognize objects. They return the recognition status 'irregular shaped' if the shape

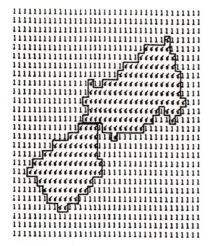

Figure 9.8   Splitting a region with a bottleneck.

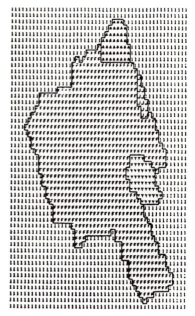

Figure 9.9   An irregular-shaped region: the central large region is merged with neighboring small regions.

of a region is not suitable for an object while all the other properties are satisfactory. Then, the system reanalyzes that region by applying the split/merge program. If the region has a bottleneck as shown in Figure 9.8, it is divided into small regions. If the boundary of the region is very rough and irregular (Figure 9.9), neighboring small regions with the similar color are merged with it. These newly generated regions are added to the blackboard as temporary regions and analyzed by object-detection subsystems. If a temporary region is successfully recognized, it is registered as a new elementary region in connection with its related object, and the original region is deleted from the blackboard. If the result of the recognition of the new region contradicts that of the original one, the system deletes one of them depending on reliability. When the temporary region is not recognized, it is removed from the blackboard, and the corresponding recognition status of the original region is changed to 'rejected'.

In the case of Figure 9.8, the bottleneck results from the error of mismerging two adjacent houses. When this region is split into two regions, the house detection subsystem recognizes them successfully. The region in Figure 9.9 corresponds to a crop field, but it is not recognized because of the irregularity of the boundary. After the merging process, it comes to take the smooth boundary, and is recognized as a crop field.

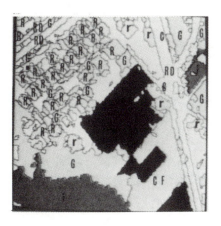

Figure 9.10   Final result of the analysis. White regions without mark are unrecognized (20% of the whole picture area). BS, bare soil (crop field without plantation); CF, crop field; G, grassland; F, forest; RD, road; R, roof of a house; C, car; r, misrecognized roof (these regions have similar multispectral properties to that of a true roof).

By the benefits of the above-mentioned control mechanisms of the system, each object-detection subsystem can use the properties of already-recognized objects without considering the results of recognition by the others. The system stops the analysis when no new objects are recognized.

Figure 9.10 shows the final result of the analysis. Although white regions with no marks are left unanalyzed, we can see that almost all objects which belong to clear semantic categories are successfully recognized. (As we do not have the ground truth data, the evaluation of the result is done by visual inspection.)

9.6 Conclusions

The system for the structural analysis of complex aerial photographs has been presented. The major conclusions on this system are the following:

(1)   The focusing mechanism realizes the efficient analysis and successfully isolates objects. Table 9.1 shows the efficiency of this focusing mechanism.

(2)   The production system architecture gives us the following benefits:

   (a)   *Modularity*   Diverse knowledge required to describe the structure of the ground surface can be individually implemented in object-detection subsystems.

   (b)   *Model-driven analysis*   We can use the properties of already-recognized objects in order to analyze unrecognized areas and to find context-dependent objects.

   (c)   *General control mechanism*   The system takes full responsibility for the maintenance of the blackboard. It solves the

Table 9.1   Efficiency of the focusing mechanism.

Scan area	Candidate region	Time (s)
in MBR*	large homogeneous regions	0.14
whole area	large homogeneous regions	0.39
in MBR*	all regions	0.84
whole area	all regions	28.95

Time denotes the processing time for the crop field detection subsystem to calculate straightness of region boundaries. As we focus only on large homogeneous regions, we can save considerable processing time.
* MBR denotes a minimum bounding rectangle (see Figure 9.7).

conflicts among object-detection subsystems and corrects the errors in segmentation. If necessary, it undoes the content of the blackboard to remove the effects of errors. These mechanisms of the system integrate mutually independent object-detection subsystems.

This system is implemented on a large computer (a FACOM M-190). The total CPU time was about 150 s in the picture of Figure 9.1. Experiments on several different aerial photographs have shown that this system works fairly well.

10

Modeling Planning as an Incremental, Opportunistic Process

Barbara Hayes-Roth, Frederick Hayes-Roth,
Stan Rosenschein and Stephanie Cammarata

We have been studying planning – the process by which a person or a computer program formulates an intended course of action. Our goal is to develop a model of the planning process that is both computationally feasible and psychologically reasonable. Toward this end, we have found it useful to adopt many of the basic features of the Hearsay-II system (CMU, 1977; Erman and Lesser, 1975; Hayes-Roth and Lesser, 1977; Lesser and Erman, 1977; Lesser *et al.*, 1975). In this chapter, we describe our model of the planning process, the current version of an INTERLISP implementation of the model, and some of the psychological research that supports it.

10.1 The errand-planning task

We have focused our initial efforts on an errand-planning task. The planner begins with a list of desired errands and a map of a town in which he or she must perform the errands. The errands differ implicitly in importance and the amount of time required to perform them. The planner also has prescribed starting and finishing times and locations. Ordinarily, the available time does not permit performance of all of the errands. Given these requirements, the planner decides which errands to perform, how much time to allocate for each errand, in what order to perform the errands, and by what routes to travel between successive errands.

In performing this task, the planner makes many decisions. These decisions exploit different kinds of knowledge and address different aspects of the planned activity. The following examples illustrate the variability in decisions a planner might make:

(1)   I'll go to the drug store after the bank.

(2)   I'm going to do all of the errands in the north-east corner of town and then the errands in the south-east corner.

(3)   The dentist is more important than the hardware store.

(4)   The drugstore, the dentist and the bank are all in the same general area.

(5)   I'm going to try to find an errand that is on my route to the north-east corner of town.

(6)   I'm going to see where the errands are on the map.

(7)   I'm going to avoid backtracking.

(8)   First I'd better decide which errands are the most important ones.

Planners can also vary considerably in the order in which they make these decisions. For example, a planner might begin by making very abstract decisions about the gross features of the plan (e.g. decision 2 above) and use these decisions to guide subsequent decisions about the details of the plan (e.g. decision 1 above). Alternatively, the planner might begin by making decisions about certain details of the plan before deciding on any particular gross organization for the plan. Similarly, the planner might decide upon intended actions in the order in which he or she plans to perform them. Alternatively, the planner might decide upon intended actions in some other order.

To accommodate the different kinds of decisions, the different kinds of knowledge they reflect, and differences in the order in which planners make them, we built our model around the following features of the Hearsay-II system: (1) multiple cooperating knowledge sources (referred to below as specialists); (2) incremental, opportunistic problem-solving behavior; (2) structured communication among knowledge sources via a blackboard; and (4) an intelligent scheduler to control knowledge source activity.

10.2   The planning model

In our model, the planning process comprises the independent and asynchronous operation of many distinct *specialists* (knowledge sources). Each specialist makes tentative *decisions* for incorporation into a tentative *plan*. All specialists record their decisions in a common data structure called the blackboard. They also establish *linkages* on the blackboard to reflect causal or logical relationships among various decisions. The blackboard enables the specialists to interact and communicate. Each specialist can retrieve decisions of interest from the blackboard regardless of which specialists recorded them. A specialist can

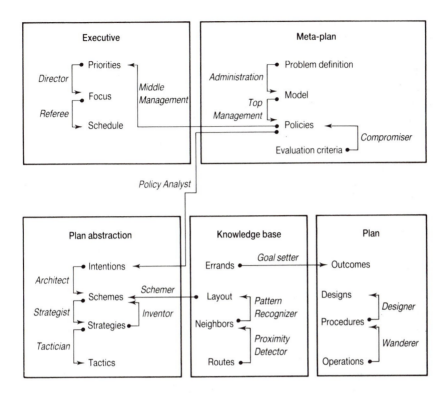

Figure 10.1   The planning blackboard and the actions of illustrative specialists.

combine earlier decisions with its own decision-making heuristics to generate new decisions.

We partition the blackboard into five *planes* containing conceptually different categories of decisions. Each plane contains several levels of abstraction of the planning space. Most specialists deal with information that occurs at only a few levels of particular planes. Figure 10.1 shows the five planes of the blackboard and their constituent levels of abstraction. It also shows the activities of several illustrative specialists. We discuss these below.

Meta-plan decisions indicate what the planner intends to do during the planning process. This plane has four levels. Beginning at the top, the *problem definition* describes the planner's conception of the task. It includes descriptions of the goal, available resources, possible actions and constraints. In the errand-planning task, for example, the problem definition would include the list of errands, contextual information and associated instructions. The problem-solving *model* indicates how the planner intends to represent the problem symbolically and generate potential solutions. For example, the planner might view the errand-planning task as an instance of the familiar traveling salesman problem

(Christophides, 1975), searching for the most efficient route among the errands. Alternatively, the planner might view the task as a scheduling problem, deciding which errands to perform before deciding when to perform them. *Policies* specify general criteria the planner wishes to impose on the problem solution. For example, the planner might decide that the plan must be efficient or that it should minimize certain risks. *Solution evaluation criteria* indicate how the planner intends to evaluate prospective plans. For example, the planner might decide to speculate on what could go wrong during execution and ensure that the plan is robust over those contingencies.

Plan decisions indicate actions the planner actually intends to take in the world. Decisions at the four levels form a potential hierarchy, with decisions at each level specifying a more refined plan than those at the next higher level. Beginning at the most abstract level, *outcomes* indicate what the planner intends to accomplish by executing the finished plan. In the errand-planning task, for example, outcomes indicate what errands the planner intends to accomplish by executing the plan. *Designs* characterize the general approach by which the planner intends to achieve the outcomes. For the errand-planning task, designs characterize the general route the planner intends to take to accomplish the intended errands. *Procedures* specify specific sequences of actions. For the errand-planning task, procedures specify sequences of errands. *Operations* specify sequences of more specific actions. In the errand-planning task, operations specify the route by which the planner will proceed from one errand to the next.

In addition to the levels of abstraction, the plan plane has a second dimension corresponding to the time period spanned by proposed decisions. It also permits representation of competing alternative decisions and simultaneous and event-contingent decisions.

Plan-abstraction decisions characterize desired attributes of potential plans. These abstract decisions serve as heuristic aids to the planning process suggesting potentially useful qualities of planned actions. Each level of the plan-abstraction plane characterizes types of decisions suggested for incorporation into the corresponding level of the plan plane. For example, the planner might indicate an *intention* to do all of the critical errands. This intention could stimulate efforts to partition the errands into critical and noncritical sets. At a lower level, the planner might generate a *scheme* to fabricate a design employing gross spatial clusters of errands. This scheme might motivate a search for coherent clusters. At the next level, the planner might develop a *strategy* suggesting that errands in the current cluster be completed before moving on to errands in another cluster. This strategy would presumably constrain procedural sequences eventually incorporated into the plan. Finally, the planner might adopt a *tactic* that suggested searching for a shortcut between one errand and the next. This tactic might lead to the discovery and use of one particular shortcut.

The **knowledge base** records observations and computations about relationships in the world which the planner generates while planning. This knowledge supports two types of planning functions: *situation assessment*, the analysis of the current state of affairs; and *plan evaluation*, the analysis of the likely consequences of hypothesized actions. Again, the levels of the knowledge base form a hierarchy and correspond to the levels of the plan and plan-abstraction planes. Each level of the knowledge base contains observations and computations useful in instantiating decisions at the corresponding level of the plan-abstraction plane or generating decisions at the corresponding level of the plan plane. Thus, the levels of the knowledge base are problem specific. At the *errand* level, for example, the planner might compute the time required to perform all of the currently intended errands to evaluate the plan's gross feasibility. At the *layout* level, the planner might observe that several errands form a convenient spatial cluster and, as a consequence formulate a design organized around clusters. At the *neighbor* level, the planner might observe that two planned errands are near one another and, as a consequence, adopt a procedural decision to sequence those two errands. At the *route* level, he or she might detect a previously unnoticed shortcut and then exploit it in an operation-level decision to establish a route between two planned errands.

Before describing the executive plane of the planning blackboard, we must discuss planning specialists. Specialists generate tentative decisions for incorporation into the plan in progress. Decisions become final only after the planner has accepted an overall plan. This ordinarily requires that he or she has formulated a complete plan and determined that it satisfies solution evaluation criteria recorded on the meta-plan plane.

Most specialists work with decisions at only two levels of the blackboard. One level contains decisions (previously generated by other specialists) that stimulate the specialist's behavior. The other is the level at which the specialist records its own modifications to the blackboard. The circle and arrow ends of the arc associated with each specialist in Figure 10.1 indicate these two levels, respectively. For example, the strategist (on the plan-abstraction plane) responds to prior scheme decisions by generating strategies useful in implementing those schemes. Suppose, for example, that one specialist had geneated a scheme to travel around among spatial clusters of errands, doing the errands in one cluster before moving on to the next. The strategist would generate a strategy for sequencing individual errands according to this scheme. One such strategy would be to perform all pending errands in the current cluster before performing errands in any other cluster.

Note that the arcs in Figure 10.1 indicate that both bottom-up and top-down processing occur and that the two levels indicated by an arc need not be adjacent or even on the same plane of the planning blackboard.

We operationalize specialists as pattern-directed condition-action modules (Waterman and Hayes-Roth, 1978). The condition component of a specialist characterizes decisions whose occurrences on the blackboard warrant a response by the specialist. The occurrence of any of these decisions invokes the specialist. For example, the occurrence of a new scheme on the plan-abstraction plane invokes the strategist. The action of a specialist module defines its behavior. For example, the strategist generates strategies for implementing schemes. In addition to recording new decisions, each specialist records relational linkages among the decisions with which it deals. For example, the strategist records support linkages connecting the scheme decision that invokes it to the strategies generated for implementing that scheme.

We have selected the specialists shown in Figure 10.1 for illustrative purposes. The mnemonic names of the specialists and the preceding discussion of levels make most of the specialists self-explanatory, so we will not discuss them in detail here (but see Hayes-Roth and Hayes-Roth (1979a) for elaboration).

During planning, each of the independent specialists monitors the blackboard for the occurrences of decisions specified in its condition. Invoked specialists queue up for execution, and an **executive** decides which will execute its actions.

We have formalized executive decisions as the fifth plane of the blackboard. Decisions made at the three levels on this plane form a hierarchy, with decisions at each level potentially refining ones at the level above. Starting at the top, *priority* decisions indicate preferences for allocating processing activity to certain areas of the planning blackboard before others. For example, given a traveling salesman model, the planner might decide to determine what errand sequences *could* be done conveniently, rather than deciding what errands *ought* to be done. *Focus* decisions indicate what kind of decision to make at a specific point in time, given the current priorities. For example, the planner might decide to focus attention on generating an operation-level refinement of a previously generated procedure. Finally, *schedule* decisions indicate which of the currently invoked specialists, satisfying most of the higher-level executive decisions, to execute. If, for example, given current priorities and focus decisions, both the architect and the pattern recognizer had been invoked, the planner might decide to execute the pattern recognizer first.

Like the other planes of the planning blackboard, the executive plane includes decisions motivated by prior decisions on the same or other blackboards. For example, middle management responds to policies on the meta-plan plane by generating appropriate priorities on the executive plane. The referee uses focus decisions in deciding which of the currently invoked specialists to schedule. The executive plane differs from the other four planes of the planning blackboard because decisions recorded there do not motivate decisions recorded on other blackboards. Instead, they determine which invoked specialists can execute their action on their designated planes of the blackboard.

Under the control of the executive, the planning process proceeds through successive invocation and execution of the various operational specialists. The process continues until the planner has decided that the existing plan satisfies the evaluation criteria recorded on the meta-plan plane of the blackboard.

10.3 Implementation of the planning model

We have implemented a simulation of the planning model in INTERLISP. We describe the data structures, specialists and control structure for the simulation below. We then note the main differences between the present implementation and Hearsay-II and assess the current performance of the simulation.

10.3.1 Data structures

The simulation has four global data structures: the map, the blackboard, the agenda and the event list.

The map is an internal representation of the map our human subjects use in performing the errand-planning task. It is a two-dimensional grid, with 38 cells and 30 cells on the east–west and north–south dimensions, respectively. Each cell contains a number indicating the object it represents. For example, all cells representing a particular street, store, park or intersection have the same number. Thus, the system refers to an object on the map as the area covered by the corresponding number.

The blackboard contains all decisions generated during the planning process. Each decision appears as a node, residing at a particular level of abstraction on a particular plane of the blackboard (see above discussion). In addition, each node holds an arbitrary number of attribute–value pairs. Different nodes may have different attributes. However, all nodes have the TAG attribute which serves as a type designation. Once a node appears on the blackboard, its attributes may change, but it never disappears.

The following node might appear at the procedure level of the plan plane:

```
NODE N17
    PLANE       plan
    LEVEL       procedure
    TAG         thread
    ELEMENTS    (errand (x) errand (y))
    POSITION    last
```

This node represents a decision to create a procedure thread (an ordered sequence of errands) in which errand y follows errand x. It further specifies that this errand sequence will occur last in the plan.

The agenda contains all currently invoked specialists and complete descriptions of the nodes that triggered them. This information is used in scheduling specialists, as discussed below.

The event list provides a history of all blackboard activities. It maintains a complete description of each node creation or modification, in the order in which these changes to the blackboard occurred. We currently use the event list for tracing and debugging.

10.3.2 Specialists

Specialists add new nodes to the blackboard or modify the attributes of existing nodes. Each specialist has a two-part condition component and an action component, as discussed below.

The condition component of a specialist determines whether it gets invoked. It has two parts, a trigger and a test. Both are predicates which get applied to various nodes on the blackboard. They differ in complexity and time of application. A specialist gets invoked only after both its trigger and test have been satisfied.

The trigger provides a preliminary test of the specialist's relevance. Ordinarily it requires only that the focus node (the most recently added or modified node on the blackboard) reside at a particular level of the blackboard and that it have a particular TAG. The system tests all specialists' triggers for each new focus node. It adds to the agenda each specialist whose trigger has been satisfied.

The test specifies all additional prerequisites for the applicability of the specialist. It may require that the focus node have particular attributes or particular values of attributes. It may require the existence of a specific configuration of decisions on the blackboard. The system performs tests only for specialists on the agenda.

The action component of a specialist defines the modification it makes to the blackboard when executed. The actions of most specialists produce new nodes with particular attributes at particular levels of the blackboard. A few simply modify attributes of existing nodes.

The cluster recognizer illustrates the specialists in our simulation. It notices clusters of errands in the same geographic neighborhood. The trigger for the cluster recognizer requires that a node whose TAG is 'location' should appear at the neighbors level of the knowledge base. Such a node indicates that the simulation has located a particular errand on the map. The cluster recognizer is relevant in this context. The test requires that two other nodes whose TAGs are 'location' should also appear at the neighbors level of the knowledge base. It also requires that all three nodes have a common value (NE, NW, SE or SW) of the attribute REGION. Satisfying both the trigger and the test of the cluster recognizer indicates that three errands are in the same neighborhood – i.e. a cluster exists. The cluster detector's action records a new node whose TAG is 'cluster' at the layout level of the knowledge base. It also records MEMBERS and REGION attributes whose values are the names of the errands in the cluster and the region of the cluster, respectively.

10.3.3 Control structure

Like Hearsay-II, our simulation is event-driven. On each cycle, the current focus node triggers some number of specialists, which the system adds to the agenda. At this point, the agenda contains relevant specialists whose actions the system might be able to execute. The system processes these pending specialists in three phases: invocation, scheduling and execution.

During the invocation phase, the system evaluates the test of all specialists on the agenda. Specialists whose tests have been satisfied are invoked. If there are no invoked specialists, the simulation terminates. If there is exactly one invoked specialist, the system executes that specialist's action. In general, however, there will be several invoked specialists and the system will have to schedule these specialists for execution.

During the scheduling phase, the system recommends one of the invoked specialists for immediate execution. It currently bases this recommendation on two considerations: recency of invocation and the current focus decision. Other things being equal, the system will recommend a recently invoked specialist in favor of one invoked earlier in the planning process. Similarly, the system will recommend a specialist whose action would occur in an area of the blackboard currently in focus, in favor of one whose action would occur elsewhere. (Recall that decisions at the focus level of the executive plane designate areas of the blackboard as in focus.) If more than one specialist satisfies either of these criteria, the system chooses one of them at random. (The other specialists remain on the agenda for possible scheduling and execution on subsequent cycles.)

During the execution phase, the system executes the action of the scheduled specialist, adding a new node or modifying an existing node on the blackboard. The system immediately evaluates the trigger of each specialist against the new focus node and adds those specialists whose triggers are satisfied to the agenda. At this point, the agenda contains all of the newly triggered specialists along with any previously triggered but unexecuted specialists. Then the next cycle begins with the invocation phase, and so forth.

10.3.4 Major departures from the Hearsay-II framework

Our simulation differs from Hearsay-II in several ways. Obviously, the planning model embodies different specialists (knowledge sources) and different blackboard partitions. Our specialists are much more molecular than the Hearsay-II knowledge sources. While Hearsay-II comprised about ten very powerful knowledge sources, our model will eventually comprise about 50 much simpler specialists. In addition, we have enumerated a much larger number of levels for the planning blackboard than Hearsay-II used for speech understanding, and we have found it useful to group these levels in conceptual planes (see also Engelmore and Nii, 1977). The proposed model's most important departure from the Hearsay-II framework lies in its elaboration of executive decision making. The model treats executive decision making as it treats other kinds of decision making within the planning process. Thus, it permits a potential hierarchy of executive decisions, each recorded by an independent specialist (see also Hayes-Roth and Hayes-Roth, 1979a; Nii and Feigenbaum, 1978).

10.3.5 Performance of the simulation

Our main purpose in creating this simulation is to test the sufficiency of the planning model as a psychological theory. Toward this end, we wish to use the simulation to replicate a thinking aloud protocol (Newell and Simon, 1972) produced by a typical subject while performing the errand-planning task. In its current form (with about 30 specialists), the simulation can produce the exact sequence of decisions in the first half of a 2000-word protocol. We expect to be able to replicate the complete protocol with the addition of about 20 more specialists to our operational set. We will then attempt to replicate other protocols produced by other subjects for other versions of the errand-planning task.

We also want an experimental environment for evaluating different planning strategies. Accordingly, the simulation permits the user to override the executive and directly control the scheduling of invoked knowledge sources for execution. Thus, while the simulation can reproduce the exact sequence of decisions in the protocol, it can also produce other sensible decision sequences. We intend to evaluate the differences in decision sequences and resulting plans under alternative executive decisions.

10.4 Psychological support for the planning model

We have collected a variety of data which suggests that the proposed model provides a reasonable description of human planning. We summarize these data below.

10.4.1 General features of planning behavior

We have collected 30 thinking-aloud protocols from subjects performing the errand-planning task. These protocols exhibit statements from each of the levels of abstraction of each of the five planes of the blackboard. In addition, these protocols exhibit decision sequences which do not conform to any obvious systematic pattern. Instead, the decision sequences appear fairly opportunistic – each decision is motivated by one or two immediately preceding decisions, rather than by some high-level executive program. Thus, the general features of these protocols confirm the basic assumptions of the model (see Feitelson and Stefik, 1977, for additional evidence).

10.4.2 Details of planning behavior

As discussed above, our simulation can replicate the thinking-aloud protocol of one of our subjects. The protocol we chose to replicate is one of the most complex of the 30 we collected. It includes decisions at each level of abstraction on each of the five planes of the blackboard. It includes instances of both top-down and bottom-up decision sequences. It includes a considerable amount of opportunism. The ability of the simulation to replicate this protocol demonstrates the sufficiency of the model to account for these features of planning behavior as well as for the other more general features.

10.4.3 Levels of abstraction

The model assumes that people make decisions at different levels of abstraction and that the levels of abstraction have functional significance in the planning process. This assumption implies that theoretically naive subjects should recognize that various decisions made during planning represent particular levels of abstraction. In order to test this hypothesis, we drew statements from the thinking-aloud protocols described above and presented them in a random order to a second group of subjects. We asked them to group statements that communicated similar kinds of information. These subjects reliably grouped the statements to correspond to the postulated levels of abstraction.

10.4.4 Multi-directional processing

The model assumes that decisions at a given level of abstraction can influence subsequent decisions at either higher or lower levels of abstraction. We tested this assumption by effectively placing subjects in the middle of the planning process and examining their choices of subsequent decisions. We gave subjects errand-planning problems, required them to make particular prior decisions and asked them to choose one of two alternative subsequent decisions. By carefully specifying required prior decisions, we could predict which subsequent decision a subject would choose. The manipulation had comparable effects on subjects' choices regardless of whether the subsequent decisions were at higher or lower levels of abstraction than the prior decisions.

10.4.5 Alternative executive decisions

The model assumes that subjects can make different executive decisions and that these decisions determine the order in which other kinds of decisions occur. For example, subjects can treat the errand-planning task as a scheduling problem or a traveling salesman problem. The former constitutes a roughly top-down approach to the task, while the latter constitutes a roughly bottom-up approach. In addition to the differences in decision order, these different approaches should introduce differences in the plans subjects form. The traveling salesman approach should produce plans for performing all of the desired errands. The scheduling approach should reduce the number of planned errands, preserving only the most important errands.

We have been able to induce subjects to take these alternative approaches to the errand-planning task with three different methods. In one experiment, we gave subjects explicit instructions to use one or the other approach. Most subjects followed the instructions successfully and produced plans with the expected characteristics. In another experiment we instructed subjects to adopt one or the other approach on several priming tasks and then gave them a transfer task with no instructions. In this situation, most subjects adopted the approach they used on the priming tasks. In a third experiment, we instructed subjects to use each approach on some of the priming tasks and then gave them various transfer tasks with no instructions. Most of these subjects adopted the traveling salesman approach on the transfer task. However, some subjects discriminated transfer tasks for which the scheduling approach was more appropriate (tasks with time limitations) and adopted it instead.

10.5 Conclusions

As discussed above, our primary goal is to develop a computationally feasible and psychologically reasonable model of planning. We believe that the current performance of our simulation and the empirical results reported above provide good support for the proposed model. Our future work will focus on experiments with the simulation to evaluate its generality over specific planning tasks and planning strategies. We will also conduct additional psychological experiments to evaluate predictions derived from the simulation.

Our success in modeling planning also attests to the utility of the Hearsay-II framework as a general model of cognition. Several researchers have adapted the Hearsay-II framework to a variety of tasks, including image understanding (Prager *et al.*, 1977), reading comprehension (Rumelhart, 1976), protein-crystallographic analysis (Nii and Feigenbaum, 1978) and inductive inference (Soloway and Riseman, 1977b). Note, however, that all of these tasks are interpretation problems: problems which present the individual (or computer system) with the lowest level representation of the problem content (e.g. the speech signal) and require interpretation of the highest level representation (e.g. the meaning). Our application of the Hearsay-II framework to planning takes it into a qualitatively different task domain – generation problems: problems which present the highest level presentation (e.g. the goal) and require generation of the lowest level representation (e.g. the sequence of intended actions).

Interpretation and generation problems differ in important ways. For example, interpretation problems lend themselves well to initial bottom-up strategies, while generation problems lend themselves well to initial top-down strategies. Interpretation problems generally permit only one (or a small number) of solutions, while generation problems permit an arbitrary number of different solutions. Further, interpretation problems typically have correct solutions, while the correctness of solutions to generation problems varies under different evaluation criteria. Despite these differences, the Hearsay-II framework appears robust enough to guide solution of both interpretation and generation problems.

Acknowledgments

The work reported here was supported by Contract No. N00014-78-C-0039 from the office of the Director of Personnel and Training Research Programs, Psychological Sciences Division, Office of Naval Research. Perry Thorndyke and Doris McClure made valuable contributions to the research reported.

Part III

11

Generalizations (1977–1984)

R.S. Engelmore and A.J. Morgan

11.1 Introduction

In Parts I and II we looked at systems developed for specific applications. These systems demonstrated that the blackboard model could be applied to complex problems with some success. A natural extension of this experience was a desire to produce frameworks that were more generalized than the preceding application-oriented systems. The end-product of such an exercise would be a set of tools to allow future applications to be engineered with greater ease and speed than the early 'custom-built' application systems. Although intended as generalizations, each system described here was driven by its developer's perception of the needs (immediate or anticipated) of certain classes of applications. In this sense, each of the generalizations emphasizes a different view of what really constitutes 'the problem'.

The first generalization was called AGE (Attempt to GEneralize). Developed at Stanford, AGE reflects the experience gained on the HASP and CRYSALIS projects. As a result, AGE permits the user to build a restricted class of blackboard systems, in which changes to the blackboard are posted on event lists, attention is focused on a particular node at any point in the problem solving (rather than on a particular KS), and scheduling is based on a set of priorities. The AGE developers perceived a real need for helping the user 'engineer' his or her knowledge, and gave considerable attention to providing on-line help to the user at development time as well as explanation facilities at run-time. More of the system (in terms of lines of code) was concerned with these aids than with the blackboard architecture itself. Interestingly, the on-line help system was eventually discarded because of its large space requirements and relatively little use (users preferred reading manuals to reading a terminal screen with a 300 baud refresh rate). Graphical approaches to providing on-line help were also tried, but with similar results. The AGE designers discovered that users really needed help in formulating and designing their application, and were much less concerned with getting help with the mechanics of the system. In retrospect, the main influence of AGE has been on the design of subsequent blackboard systems, rather than as a solution to the knowledge-engineering problem. At least a dozen applications were built with AGE. A commercial product of Fujitsu, called ESHELL, is basically a reimplementation of AGE. Several versions of the product (ESHELL/X, ESHELL/FM, ESHELL/SB) have been developed for different size applications and hardware. Over 200 copies of ESHELL have been distributed as of late 1987, making it the most popular domestically produced knowledge-engineering tool in Japan.

The next generalization was Hearsay-III, developed at USC Information Sciences Institute (ISI). Hearsay-III is a domain-independent framework for constructing knowledge systems. Although not specifically a speech-understanding system, Hearsay-III 'draws strongly on the architectures of the Hearsay-I and Hearsay-II speech-understanding systems'.

One of the experiences gained with the Hearsay-II project was the complexity of the scheduling of knowledge sources. As Hearsay-II evolved, the special-purpose scheduling mechanism had become progressively more complex. As a result, a major aim of Hearsay-III was to make control of the system a knowledge-based procedure in its own right, using a separate scheduling blackboard to make control information visible and accessible to schedule knowledge sources. Similar aims had also appeared in the OPM project, which was discussed in Chapter 10.

A number of other new features appeared in Hearsay-III. Nodes on the blackboard were generalized into more complex structured objects called 'units' (although the reader should not confuse these with units as defined by Stefik (1978) and used in AGE and, later, in KEE). Units facilitated, among other things, the maintenance of and reasoning about alternative hypotheses. A context mechanism was introduced as an integral part of the system to allow simultaneous, alternative interpretations. Much of the functionality of the system depended on an underlying relational database, which in turn was implemented on top of the host INTERLISP programming language.

Hearsay-III was intended as a vehicle to explore the principles of problem solving in chosen domains. The performance of the system (in terms of computational efficiency) appears to have been low, although performance was never a design aim in the project. The complexity of the system, coupled with its performance, limited its use to a small number of experimental applications. However, the concepts it introduced have since been carried over into other systems; for example, the context mechanism was incorporated in the commercial ART knowledge-engineering tool.

The third generalization was the BB1 system, developed at Stanford by Barbara Hayes-Roth and co-workers (Micheal Hewett was the primary implementor). BB1 goes beyond Hearsay-III in establishing control as a first-class knowledge-based activity in its own right, and uses a separate, full blackboard architecture for controlling the execution of the domain knowledge sources. BB1 is based strongly on the concepts underlying OPM (see Chapter 10), and also benefitted from experiences with AGE.

The core elements of BB1 conform closely to the blackboard control architecture discussed in Hayes-Roth (1985). BB1 provides separate domain and control blackboards on which user-specified knowledge sources reason about the problem at hand and about control of problem-solving actions. The framework has been developed extensively since 1983, and provides many user aids, including graphical editors for building knowledge bases, blackboards and knowledge sources; a graphical run-time user interface that displays the evolving solution and control plan and provides access to all other data structures in the application system; and a graphical explanation facility.

The BB1 system is implemented in both COMMON LISP and INTERLISP, and has been distributed to about 30 university and industrial research laboratories. The system strongly influenced the recent development of another blackboard framework at Boeing Computer Services, called ERASMUS (Jagannathan et al., 1987).

Chapter 14 was prepared especially for this book by Barbara Hayes-Roth. It consists of excerpts from Hayes-Roth (1985) and from Hewett and Hayes-Roth (1987), plus new material. Hayes-Roth presents her view of control within the blackboard architecture. The BB1 system is then described from both a user's and a software engineer's perspective.

MXA grew out of a British Admiralty Research Establishment requirement for a Signal Understanding System (originally called SUS). The problem faced by the developers was the need to produce a description of the air–sea environment around a naval task force in close to real-time. The sources of information were various sensors, of different types, which produced overlapping (and sometimes conflicting) information. MXA was originally inspired by HASP, which attacked a similar problem, but its design was influenced largely by Hearsay-II. The MXA designers set out to solve the signal-understanding application with a set of generalized facilities that would allow other applications to be built. Moreover, many architectural decisions were motivated by the possibility of parallel processing, in which MXA would run on a heterogeneous system of associative memories for fast pattern matching (J.P. Rice, private communication).

MXA provides a language for the system designer to describe the application. An unusual feature is that the MXA language compiles into Pascal, which is then itself compiled for the host machine. The compiler generates static structures which are linked to the dynamically changing hypotheses on the blackboard. Like Hearsay-III, the hypotheses are grouped by class, rather than level.

As discussed in Chapter 22, MXA was used extensively in its original signal-understanding application. However, the lack of an incremental compilation facility has limited its application in other areas to relatively small experimental systems.

One of the features normally associated with real-time expert systems is that they have to act continuously. This is in distinction to the more common 'session'-oriented expert systems, which move progressively towards providing the user with a solution during a consultative session. The BLOBS system (discussed in Chapter 16) evolved from two earlier systems that formed parts of a simulator for an air defense environment. BLOBS is an attempt to reason about time, including the ability to intelligently discard outdated information. One of the chief concerns of the designers of BLOBS was the need to modify the basic blackboard model, in restricting access to blackboard data in order to simplify its management over an extended period. The resulting system is a fusion of blackboard and object-oriented systems.

12

AGE (Attempt to GEneralize): A Knowledge-Based Program for Building Knowledge-Based Programs

H. Penny Nii and Nelleke Aiello

12.1 Introduction

This chapter reports the goals and the current status of the AGE project. Appendix A contains a protocol of a user solving a specific problem using AGE. The intent of the protocol is to show AGE from the user's point of view. The main body describes the motivations for and the description of the facilities in AGE.

12.1.1 Objectives

The general goal of the AGE project is to demystify and make explicit the art of knowledge engineering. It is an attempt to formulate the knowledge that we knowledge engineers use in constructing knowledge-based programs and put it at the disposal of others in the form of a software laboratory.

The design and implementation of the AGE program is based primarily on the experience gained in building knowledge-based programs at the Stanford Heuristic Programming Project in the last decade. The programs that have been, or are being, built are: DENDRAL, meta-DENDRAL, MYCIN, HASP, AM, MOLGEN, CRYSALIS (Feigenbaum, 1977) and SACON (Bennett *et al.*, 1978). Initially, the AGE program will embody artificial intelligence methods used in these programs. However, the long-range aspiration is to integrate methods and techniques developed at other AI laboratories. The final product is to be a *collection of building-block programs* combined with an *intelligent front-end* that will assist the user in constructing knowledge-based programs. It is hoped that AGE will speed up the process of building knowledge-based programs and facilitate the dissemination of AI techniques by: (1) packaging common AI software tools so that they need not be reprogrammed for every problem; and (2) helping people who are not knowledge-engineering specialists write knowledge-based programs.

The task of building such a software laboratory for knowledge engineers is divided into two main sub-tasks:

(1)   *The isolation of techniques used in knowledge-based systems*   It has always been difficult to determine if a particular problem-solving method used in a knowledge-based program is 'special' to a particular domain or whether it generalizes easily to other domains. In existing knowledge-based programs, the domain-specific knowledge and the manipulation of such knowledge using AI techniques are often so closely coupled that it is difficult to make use of the programs for other domains.

(2)   *Guiding the user in the initial application of these techniques*   Once the various techniques are isolated and programmed for use, an intelligent agent is needed to guide the user in the application of these techniques.

12.1.2 User profile

The design of the AGE system would depend, to a great extent, on the type of users we expect will benefit most from using AGE. Initially, AGE is designed for AI scientists familiar with current problem-solving techniques, and who can program in the INTERLISP language (Teitelman, 1978) (since AGE is implemented in INTERLISP); and are familiar with production-rule representations of knowledge (Davis and King, 1977). In other words, AGE is initially aimed at people who could conceivably write knowledge-based programs themselves.

For the person in this category, the advantages of using AGE are two-fold:

(1)   The basic system components are already programmed (e.g. rule interpreters and other control mechanisms, traces, explanation modules and other components basic to many systems).

(2)   AGE allows the user to experiment with different problem solving techniques without extensive reprogramming.

Eventually, AGE will be able to help the less knowledgable or less experienced person.

12.1.3 Outline of the chapter

The term **knowledge engineering** is being used more frequently to refer to the process of writing application programs using primarily AI methods. The historical context in which knowledge engineering arose and the nature of the work are described by Feigenbaum (1977). Section 12.2 contains a brief description of the task for the AGE program within the context of knowledge engineers' work. It is followed by an overview of the facilities in the current version. Section 12.4 contains a short description of an organizational method by which frameworks are decomposed to form a basis for a software laboratory. It is followed by a summary.

12.2 Task for the AGE system

Currently there are several projects that aim to provide prepackaged tools for knowledge engineers (UNITS (Stefik, 1978); EMYCIN (van Melle, 1979)) or to provide programming languages (KRL (Bobrow and Winograd, 1978); AIMDS (Sridharan, 1978)). In preprogrammed packages, all or most of the paradigm, system design and implementation choices have been made by the package designers. In languages no decisions, or very few, have been made for the user. Neither approach guides the user in the design and the construction of knowledge-based programs. AGE has been conceived to bridge the gap between these two extremes – to provide some guidance in the what, why and how of programming; plus some preprogrammed problem-solving frameworks.

Ideally, then, AGE is an attempt to define and cumulate knowledge-engineering tools, with rules to guide in the use of these tools. It must itself be a knowledge-based system containing knowledge about building knowledge-based programs, combined with a facility that allows the user to explore and experiment with various concepts and techniques. It must provide the user with a variety of preprogrammed modules, allow her to modify them and to add her own. And, above all, it must be able to produce running programs. How the AGE system itself is organized for modularity will be described in Section 12.4. In the next section we describe a framework currently available to the user to construct a knowledge-based program.

12.3 Profile of the current AGE system

To correspond to the two general research goals described in the Introduction, the AGE program is being developed along two separate fronts. The first of these fronts is the development of tools to help the user build a variety of knowledge-based programs – the *generality* front. The second front is the development of *intelligence* in the interaction between the user and the AGE program; i.e. moving from dialogues on how to use the tools in AGE to what tools to use – the *how-to-what* spectrum described by Feigenbaum (1977).

12.3.1 Currently implemented tools

The building-block components currently available to the users have been carefully selected and modularly programmed to be usable in combinations. The current AGE system aims to provide the user with a framework for incremental hypothesis formation, known as the blackboard model (Figure 12.1) (Erman and Lesser, 1975; Lesser and Erman, 1977). It can be described as follows:

(1)   there is a global database (the blackboard) that is used as a means of communication and interaction among the knowledge sources (KSs);

(2)   there are diverse KSs that are kept separate and independent; and

(3)   the KSs respond to changes in the blackboard.

The paradigm itself does not specify the structure of the database, the representational form of the KSs, or the response mechanisms. When a model is translated into a program, various architectural and implementation decisions are made by the designers, and programs that use the same paradigm may have different organization and behavior. For example, although Hearsay-II (Lesser and Erman, 1977) and CRYSALIS (Engelmore and Nii, 1977) use the blackboard model, the basic architecture, knowledge representation and knowledge utilization tech-

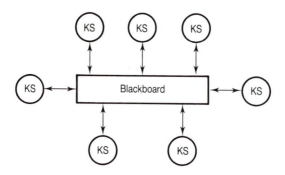

Figure 12.1   The blackboard model.

niques differ. The differences can be attributed to many factors: the nature of the problem (understanding speech signals and interpreting X-ray crystallographic data); implementation language; real-time constraints; noise level of data; quality and amount of available knowledge; and, last but not least, the designers' tastes.

In AGE the blackboard-based program design has been implemented to allow flexibility in representation and in the application of other problem solving methods within the framework. It consists of three major components:

(1) *The blackboard*   The blackboard contains hypotheses in a hierarchical data structure; it represents the task domain in terms of a hierarchy of analysis levels of the task.

(2) *The KSs*   The KSs contain the knowledge of the task domain (which the user must provide) that can perform the analysis. The KSs are represented as sets of production rules.

(3) *The control*   The control component contains mechanisms that allow the user to (a) specify the conditions for the invocation of the KSs and (b) select items on the blackboard for focus of attention (Hayes-Roth and Lesser, 1977).

In the remainder of this section these components will be described in more detail.

The blackboard

The combined process of KS selection and incremental changes to the blackboard is viewed as a general process of hypothesis formation consistent with the following definition. A hypothesis can be generated:

(1) deductively, using *support from above* – this support can be

    (a) *theoretical* support (or model-based support),

    (b) support from more inclusive hypotheses that have independent evidential support; or

(2) inductively, using evidential *support from below* (Hempel, 1966).

This definition suggests that the most natural way to represent hypotheses is in some form of hierarchy. The structure of the hierarchy may be strict. It may be flat consisting possibly of only two levels – input data and its translation – or it may be complex, consisting of many related hierarchies (often referred to as blackboard planes (Engelmore and Nii, 1977)). Currently AGE can represent all of the above forms of hierarchy. A hypothesis is represented as hierarchically organized hypothesis elements integrated by links that represent support from above (called the *expectation-link*) or support from below (called the *reduction-link*) (see Example 1).

Example 1 Hypothesis structure in CRYSALIS (Engelmore and Nii, 1977)

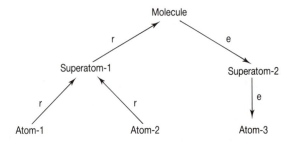

Molecules, superatoms and atoms are hypothesis level names.
r and e represent reduction- and expectation-links.

A *hypothesis element* is a named node in the hypothesis structure that represents an aggregation (summary, interpretation, etc.) of lower-level hypothesis elements. Each element contains information in the form of attribute–value pairs that are meaningful at that particular hypothesis level (see Example 2). The inferred information is generated by the rules in the KSs and can, in turn, be used for further hypothesis formation.

Example 2 A possible hypothesis element in CRYSALIS

```
Hypothesis level: ATOM
Hypothesis element name: ATOM-10
Inferred attribute-value pairs:
    Atom.name  Sulfur
    Location   (12.3 13.6 24.2 +- .02)
    Partof     (OR CYS14 CYS17)
    Bonded to  HEME-1
    Bondtype   Hydrogen
```

In some problems all the hypothesis elements needed to solve the problems are known *a priori*. In other problems the number of hypothesis elements in the solutions are not known in advance. For example, in PUFF (a program to diagnose pulmonary function disorder (Kunz *et al.*, 1978)), all the possible disease states which account for specific patient data are known in advance. On the other hand, in cryptogram problems (see Appendix A) the number of letters, words, parts of sentence, etc., are not known until a specific cryptogram is being solved. To accommodate both types of solution space, AGE allows the user to generate and name hypothesis elements in advance, generate and name them dynamically, or generate them in some combination.

The hypotheses are generated by inference rules in the KSs. What the KSs look like and how they work are described next.

Knowledge representation

Knowledge representation in AGE is based on the premise that there are at least four broad categories of knowledge that are needed to solve problems:

(1)   knowledge of specifics,
(2)   knowledge of ways and means of dealing with the specifics,
(3)   knowledge of universals and abstractions in the task domain (Bloom, 1956), and
(4)   knowledge of problem solving and knowledge utilization methods in the task domain.

Within the framework of incremental hypothesis formation using the blackboard model, an attempt has been made to help the user identify, represent and utilize these diverse types of knowledge.

Domain knowledge in AGE represents the knowledge necessary to accomplish the goals of the user's program. This knowledge reflects the *knowledge of specifics* and the *knowledge of ways and means of dealing with the specifics*. The knowledge is represented as production rules (Davis and King, 1977). These rules are organized into sets called the knowledge sources.

Knowledge sources   A knowledge source is a *mega-chunk of knowledge* consisting of a labeled set of rules that are *a priori* deemed to belong together. How the rules within a KS are organized and what rules are included in a KS depend on the intended role of the KS in the overall problem solving plan. For example, a KS may be organized to represent models, in which case all rules are grouped around some objects or concepts, much like schemata or frames, or a KS may be organized around events, in which case all rules which, for example, process input data, are grouped together. In order to solve problems within the framework of the blackboard model, KSs must place their inferences on the blackboard. In other words, KSs must generate hypotheses using rules that:

(1)   add or modify hypothesis element(s), or

(2)   add or modify relationships between elements by:

    (a)   analyzing data (support from below),

    (b)   specializing or instantiating a more inclusive hypothesis element (support from above), or

    (c)   generating expectation(s) from

- models, or
- more inclusive hypothesis elements that must be verified by data.

Each KS has associated with it: (1) preconditions (a list of events) for its invocation; (2) a list of pairs of hypothesis levels that it spans; (3) a list of links generated by it; (4) a 'single' or 'multiple' hit strategy to be used for the rules, and (5) a facility for variable bindings to set local context, to simplify expressions in the rules, to avoid multiple evaluations of the same expression, and to allow communication between the condition and the conclusion halves of a rule.

AGE allows the use of just one KS in the user's program if desired. Whether a single KS is sufficient to solve a problem or not depends on the characteristics of the problem and on the formulation of the KS. MYCIN (Shortliffe, 1976) is an example of a program that has an equivalent of one KS; all the rules are chained in a goal-directed fashion to represent a line of reasoning meaningful in that domain.

The set of domain-specific KSs may be manipulated in many ways by other higher-level KSs (Davis and Buchanan, 1977; Nii and Feigenbaum, 1978). The higher-level knowledge may reflect both knowledge about ways and means of dealing with the specifics, knowledge of problem-solving methods useful in the task domain, and knowledge about other knowledge in the domain. These higher-level KSs are often integrated into the control component described later.

Rules   A *rule* in AGE is a chunk of knowledge written in a syntax comprehensible to AGE. Each rule consists of a left-hand side (LHS) and a right-hand side (RHS). The LHS specifies a set of conditions or patterns for the applicability of the rule (i.e. premises). The RHS represents the implications or conclusions to be drawn under the situation specified in the LHS.

To be consistent with the various ways in which hypothesis elements can be generated, the current implementation of the RHS can:

(1)   add elements to the hypothesis; or add or modify the values of the attributes of elements or the relationship between elements;

(2)   generate expected elements or values of (or relationship between) elements in the hypothesis;

(3)   generate goals to establish some elements, values, or links within hypothesis elements.

Rule credibility   The domain rules that generate hypotheses are, more often than not, judgmental and uncertain. A *credibility value*, or *weight*, can be associated with the rules to reflect uncertainty. AGE provides means of associating weights (certainty values, probability, etc.) with inferences generated by the RHS of rules. It also provides some preprogrammed procedures for the manipulation of these weights, for example, an algorithm to compute certainty factors (CF) from MYCIN. For users who need different algorithms, AGE provides mechanisms for integrating user-provided algorithms.

Example 3 Integrating weights

Note: The rules used in this example, and some others, are based on PUFF rules (Kunz *et al.*, 1978). From pulmonary function test data, the PUFF program determines if a patient is normal, has obstructive airway disease (OAD), restrictive lung disease (RLD), or other pulmonary function-related diseases; and the severity of the diseases. It further determines if OAD is of type emphysema, asthma, or bronchitis. (RV in the example refers to a measurement – residual volume.)

> *Weight-adjuster:* `$ADJWT (MYCIN algorithm)`
>
> *Rule to be evaluated:*
> ```
> if (TYPE = OAD) & (RV > 220) then (PROPOSE DISEASE
>     (SEVERITY SEVERE .8))
> ```
>
> *Hypothesis element before rule evaluation:*
> ```
> hypo-element name: DISEASE-05
> type: (OAD .8)
> severity: (SEVERE .6)
> ```
>
> *Hypothesis element after rule evaluation:*
> ```
> hypo-element name: DISEASE-05
> type: (OAD .8)
> severity: (SEVERE .92) ←
> ```

Rule evaluators   The applicability of a rule is determined by how the premises in the LHS are evaluated. The term 'applicability' can have a different definition for different problems – it may mean that all or some of the premises in the LHS need be true, or that the premises require more complex evaluation. The user can define this applicability in the form of a function to serve as the 'LHS evaluator'. Some preprogrammed LHS evaluators are available; for example, a type of threshold evaluator used in MYCIN.

Example 4 LHS evaluator: $ANDMIN

This function is similar to the one used in MYCIN where evidence with less than .2 value is ignored.

> *Hypothesis element name:* DISEASE-03
> disease: (OAD .8)
> subtype: (EMPHYSEMA .1)
> severity: (SEVERE .6)

> *Rule 1:* if (isa disease OAD) and
>   (isa subtype EMPHYSEMA) then...

> *Rule 2:* if (isa disease OAD) and
>   (grdeg severity MODERATE) then...

Using $ANDMIN, only Rule 2 is found applicable within the context of the given hypothesis state.

Example 5 shows how the features described thus far are represented within a KS. Note that some relevant features (e.g. credibility computation) reside outside the KS, because they are relevant to all the KSs in the user program.

Example 5 A KS summary (AGE version of PUFF)

> --->Knowledge Source: OAD-SUBTYPERULES
>   Precondition: (OAD-DEGREE)
>   Inference levels: (from . to)
>   (DISEASE . DISEASE)
>   (PATIENT . DISEASE)
>   Links between levels: NONE
>   Hit strategy: (MULTIPLE)
>   Local variable bindings: NONE
> [*other relevant information specified elsewhere*]
>   *LHS-evaluator:* $ANDMIN
>   *Wt-adjuster:* $ADJWT]

```
if
  (GREQDEG ($VALUE OAD DEGREE) MILD)
  (GREQDEG ($VALUE PATIENT DIF-DEF) MILD)
  (GREQ    ($DATA TLC-BB:OBS/PRED) 110)
  (GREQ    ($DATA RV/TLC:OBS/PRED) 10)
then PROPOSE
  change.type MODIFY
  hypo-element OAD
  attr-val/link (SUBTYPE EMPHYSEMA .9)
     (FINDINGS "OAD, diffusion defect, elevated
      TLC and TV together indicate Emphysema")
  event.type OAD-SUBTYPE
  comment (Rule 31 of EMYCIN version)
```

Knowledge utilization and control mechanisms

As mentioned earlier, the invoking of higher-level knowledge about the appropriate use of problem-solving methods and the invoking of other domain-specific knowledge appropriate to the situation are both accomplished in the control component. Until recently, very few attempts had been made to express *control* information explicitly. Davis and Buchanan (1977) addressed the problem of expressing knowledge about other knowledge in production rule form and called it *meta-knowledge*. Nii and Feigenbaum (1978) attempted to distinguish inference-generating KSs and knowledge-utilization KSs by organizing the KSs themselves into a hierarchy. In AGE, we have tried to provide concepts and mechanisms whereby users can express different types of higher-level knowledge. The structure of the control component is described below very briefly (see Appendix B for a more detailed description). Whether the whole structure is sufficiently general to handle a variety of problems is still under study.

There are several system components grouped under the heading of *Control*. The various subcomponents can be individually specified or programmed by the user. In order to simplify the designing process for the user, AGE provides preprogrammed components where appropriate. The control components that need to be specified are:

(1)   input data format,
(2)   initialization function,
(3)   processing method to be applied to each inference step,
(4)   rules or procedure to select the next step to be processed,
(5)   rules to select the relevant KS to process the selected step,
(6)   termination condition, and
(7)   post-processing function.

Components 1 and 2 deal with getting input data and performing

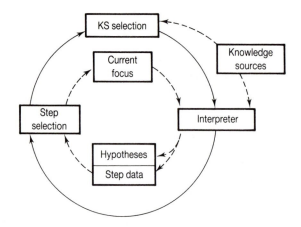

Figure 12.2   Control of the blackboard model in AGE.

setup operations in the user's program. The data can be brought in from a file or typed in from a terminal. The data elements are bound to names prespecified by the user. Within the initialization function the user may preprocess the data or perform other initialization activities – the only requirement for AGE is that the initialization function return a name of the first KS to be invoked.

Components 3–6, called the *control kernel* (Figure 12.2), constitute the core of the blackboard control component. The primary functions of the control kernel are to select and invoke the appropriate KSs and to select the focus of attention within the blackboard. The control in the user's program is a simple loop consisting of:

(1)   *Rule evaluation*   In the invoked KS each rule is evaluated according to the user-specified LHS-evaluator (see Section 12.3.1). When the LHS meets the evaluation criteria, i.e. evaluates to true, the rule is *fired* (i.e. the RHS is executed).

(2)   *Inference generation*   Fired rules either (1) PROPOSE a change in the hypothesis (this change is made in the hypothesis and is also placed on the Event-list), (2) indicate that some change in the hypothesis is EXPECTed to occur (this expectation is placed on the Expectation-list), or (3) indicate that the hypothesis needs to ACHIEVE a particular value or a state (this goal is placed on the Goal-list). Each of these actions is called a *Step*.

(3)   *Focus of attention*   Within the Step-selection module, select a step (an event, an expectation or a goal) and a hypothesis element or data to process next. Within the KS-selection module, choose a KS relevant to the selected step, and invoke that KS. (The KS may

have associated with it a *processing method*; for example, a KS may require a backward-chaining mechanism for the rules to achieve a goal.) [*go to 1*]

Components 5 and 6 deal with terminating the kernel control loop and processing the completed hypotheses. One characteristic of the blackboard model is that there is no prescribed way that the incremental hypothesis formation process terminates short of running out of relevant KSs. Thus, the user needs to specify the conditions under which the processing is to terminate; AGE monitors for the occurrence of these conditions. In the postprocessing function, the user may perform any further processing required; for example, print the current hypothesis.

Control macros   Since the specifications required for the control kernel are quite complex, AGE provides control macros, currently one for event-driven control and one for expectation-driven control.

Event-driven hypothesis formation is characterized by incremental formation of hypothesis elements from evidence found in data or in lower level hypothesis elements. The elements can be processed by rules on the basis of first-in-first-out, first-in-last-out, or best-first. These correspond roughly to breadth-, depth- and best-first processing of the hypothesis space. When an element is chosen to be processed, it is called a *focused element*. The event-type associated with the focused element helps determine which KS is to be invoked in the future.

The control loop for the Event-driven macro is:

(1)   ⟨rule⟩ modifies the hypothesis and causes an event (with associated event-type).

(2)   If ⟨event-type⟩ = ⟨KS-precondition⟩ then invoke the KS.

[Go back to 1]

Within an *expectation-driven* system, expectations in the hypotheses are generated by the rules. These rules are normally grouped around objects and their properties, similar to a schema (frame) organization. They usually form models of objects from which other properties can be inferred or can be expected to occur. For example, a rule of the form:

```
if (isa disease oad) & (isa severity severe)
     then (expect RV >200)
          (expect RV/TLC.RATIO >20)
             etc.
```

has a schema-like flavor and produces expectations that need to be verified.

In order to determine if an expectation has been met, or can be met, the user must provide an *expectation matching function*. AGE always checks to see if the expected situation has occurred either in data or in the hypothesis (i.e. performs a passive match of expectation). In the above example, the expectation would be met for a case in which RV >200 and RV/TLC.RATIO >20.

The control loop for the expectation-driven macro is:

(1)   〈rule〉 generates an expectation.

(2)   If an expectation is met, then modify the hypothesis as specified. This action generates an event.

(3)   If 〈event type〉 = 〈KS precondition〉 then invoke the KS.

[Go back to step 1]

For most problems, both the expectation-driven (or model based) and the event-driven (or data-driven) methods are needed in some combination. For the sake of completeness the control components from which the macros were created are described in Appendix B.

12.3.2 The intelligent front-end in AGE

AGE assumes that the user neither knows nor understands the concepts and implementations of the various program components described above. It is the task of the front-end to guide the user in constructing a program using the component parts. Currently the *intelligence* in the front-end is limited to: (1) a tutor subsystem that allows the user to browse through the textual knowledge base, and (2) a design subsystem that guides the user through each step of program specification. An 'unfamiliar' user is always introduced to AGE by way of the tutor subsystem.

The textual knowledge base contains (1) a general description of the building-block components at the conceptual level, (2) a description of the implementation of these concepts within AGE, (3) a description of how these components are to be used within the user's program, (4) how they can be constructed by the user, and (5) various examples. The information is organized in a network to represent the conceptual hierarchy of the components and to represent the functional relationship among them.

The design subsystem guides the user in *design and construction*. The knowledge necessary for AGE to accomplish this task is represented in a data structure in the form of an AND/OR tree that, on the one hand, represents all the possible structures available in the current AGE system; and, on the other hand, represents the decisions the user must make in order to design a program. Using this schema, the design subsystem can guide the user (in the *guided* design mode) from one design decision point to another. At each decision point, the user has access to the textual knowledge base, to advice on the decisions to be made at that point, and to acquisition functions that aid the user in specifying the appropriate component. The user also has direct access (in the *unguided* design mode) to various acquisition and editing functions.

The reader is referred to Appendix A which contains extensive examples of the various interactions currently possible in AGE.

12.4 Decomposition of frameworks

Although the intention of this paper does not include discussion of the architecture of AGE itself, we briefly describe some of the motivation behind the decomposition of problem-solving frameworks into inter-changeable parts.

Our concept of a software laboratory is a facility in which the users are provided with a variety of *preprogrammed problem-solving frameworks* – similar in spirit to designs of prefabricated houses. The user augments and modifies a framework to develop his or her own programs. In order to provide such a facility, a framework must be built with parts that can be 'unplugged' and replaced. Each framework is decomposed into self-contained modules, creating a hierarchically organized set of component parts. These parts in turn are interpreted or evaluated by 'various' managers. As an example, a part of the decomposed blackboard framework is shown in Figure 12.3.

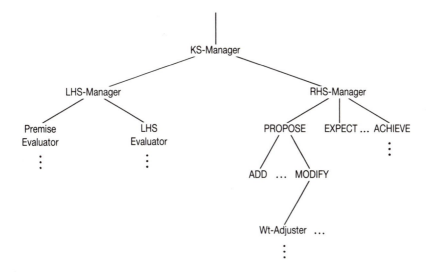

Figure 12.3 Blackboard model decomposition.

Theoretically, then, each module (with all of its subparts) is replaceable. For example, the whole RHS-Manager can be replaced if the user wants a definition of the RHS of rules different from the one we currently provide.

However, complete modularity is not achieved, because some of the modules are not independent. From a practical standpoint the greatest barrier to replacing some of the modules is in their inaccessibility. Nevertheless, as in prefabricated houses, every module can be modified or replaced – some changes are more costly than others in terms of time and detailed knowledge of the implementation needed. In general, those parts nearer the bottom of the hierarchy are more accessible and easier to change. For example, the definition of ADD (add a new hypothesis element) can be changed by simply redefining the ADD function; or another function that makes changes to the hypotheses in a different way can be added. On the other hand, the LHS- and the RHS-Managers are not independent. For those components that are independent, and easily modified or replaced, AGE provides some aids for making changes – acquisition functions and descriptions in the textual knowledge base. For those more difficult to change, we provide less aid, with the intention of discouraging novice users.

In order to have a useful software laboratory, we need to provide the user with diverse tools – some tools need to be flexible in their utility while others need to be fine tuned for specific use; and some tools require substantial skill in their use while others do not. By organizing the program modules by their utility and providing easy access to those that are general and easy to use (but allowing skilled users access to all modules), we hope that the laboratory can be useful to a wide range of users.

12.5 Summary and concluding remarks

AGE is an experimental program currently running on a DEC KI-10 at the SUMEX-AIM Computing Facility at Stanford University. The immediate goal of the project is to provide software tools with which a knowledge engineer can reduce the time it takes to build knowledge-based programs. The longer-range goal is to aid people less knowledgeable in AI methods to build knowledge-based programs. We have taken a small step toward reaching these goals by exploring the various ways in which blackboard-based programs can be built, and by implementing a set of parts from which such a program can be built.

In the process of building AGE, we have used it to write some programs: CRYPTO, a program that solves cryptogram problems; a portion of a bidding strategy problem in bridge games; two different versions of PUFF (Feigenbaum, 1977; Kunz et al., 1978) – one using the

Event-driven control macro and another using the Expectation-driven control macro (Nii and Aiello, 1978). Since the domain-specific knowledge for PUFF already existed and was being used in EMYCIN, the AGE version took about a week to bring up – time to reorganize the existing rules into KSs and to rewrite the rules in AGE rule syntax. Currently, the CRYSALIS program (Engelmore and Nii, 1977) is being rewritten using AGE.

To the extent that we have been able to use AGE to develop some programs, we feel encouraged to continue with further development. However, there are still many issues that need to be explored in the current work – the adequacy of the user interface and debugging facility; generality of the current functional breakdown of the blackboard model; sufficiency of the current rule syntax and semantics to express a wide range of knowledge; adequacy of the production rule representation itself for a variety of tasks; reliability of the system; etc. We have made no progress in providing a facility for explanation within the object program; we need more basic research in this area before such a facility can be implemented.

Postscript (added December 1987)

By 1982, when the AGE project was completed, the following additional capabilities were in the system:

(1) an extensive debugging facility which included the ability to trace various system components;

(2) an ability to generate and update the user reference manual automatically from in-line text in the program code;

(3) an interface to the UNITS Package (Smith and Friedland, 1980) such that AGE rules could access, use and modify information and knowledge represented as frame-based objects in UNITS;

(4) a graphic interface for machines with bit-map displays (e.g. Xerox LISP machines) which replaced the textual interface with menus and block diagrams;

(5) an explanation-generation facility.

Acknowledgments

This research was supported in parts by the Defense Advanced Research Projects Agency under ARPA Contract No. MDA 903-77-C-0322 and the National Institutes of Health Grant No. RR-00785.

Appendix A Building a knowledge-based program with AGE

This appendix shows the AGE system from a user's point of view. We have included an example program with parts of actual protocols to illustrate various facilities. User responses are shown in bold type.

Cryptograms

The problem used as an example is translating cryptograms. The cryptogram solution consists of a four-level hierarchical hypothesis structure. The rules to solve cryptograms were provided by a human expert. The task for CRYPTO is to take a 'newspaper' cryptogram (10–20 words long, about 100 letters) and, using a set of heuristics, translate it into an English sentence. For example, the cryptogram 'GSHSUO CI DXDV BSS CLESVBFGB BS HD NCGU HJB ISLD JGNCGU EDSEYD EVSXD BZFB BZDVD'I IBCYY F RDP SR JI PZS FVD BSS ILFYY.' translates to 'Nobody is ever too important to be kind but some unkind people prove that there's still a few of us who are too small.' The word boundaries and punctuation are given. There is a one-to-one correspondence between the cryptletters and their translation, and no letter translates to itself.

Typical run

An AGE user typically builds a knowledge-based program over a period of time, conducting many hands-on sessions. In the first session the user gets acquainted with the system, learning the different components available and the system conventions, and discovering what information must be provided (i.e. what to think about before the next session). During the next few sessions the user designs and builds a program. Finally, the user iterates on checking out the program, running it and modifying it.

>TUTOR: *The TUTOR subsystem is described in Section 12.3.2. All remarks are in italics.*

>*[After the user logs on, AGE begins by determining if the user needs a tutorial]*

Are you already familiar with this system?: **No**
This and all subsequent sessions will be recorded.
The record will go on your directory as DRIB(name)(date).

Following is a list of AGE conventions which may be useful to you.

[description of AGE user conventions]

[canned text on other topics]

What follows is a tutorial session designed to acquaint you with AGE.

[The following text describes the organization of the AGE on-line manual]

Each topic in the AGE system has one or more modifiers attached to it. A modifier may be a descriptive word (e.g. Hypothesis.element) or it may be one of the following:

ISA: Definition or definitional description.

FORMIS: Representation or structural description.

FORMEDBY: How ⟨topic⟩ is generated or created internally during user program execution.

TOSPECIFY: Description of the acquisition function.

GEN: ..... in general (⟨topic⟩ without any qualifier gives about the same information)

AGE: ..... as interpreted or implemented in AGE.

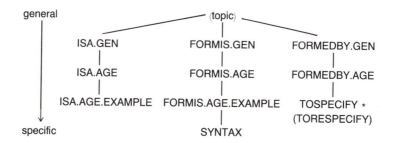

[canned text on further topics]

[The following interaction shows cross-referencing]

---There are some pre-assembled control structures available for convenience. (See CONTROL.MACRO)

References are: HYPOTHESIS.STRUCTURE CONTROL.MACRO
Do you want to see them now?: **y**
HYPOTHESIS.STRUCTURE Y/N:: **y**

The hypothesis structure in AGE is hierarchically organized. There may be more than one hierarchy in the hypothesis (generally known as blackboard planes). Each hierarchy consists of linked hypothesis elements, HYPOTHESIS.ELEMENT, grouped into levels of abstractions.

[Tutorial session is eventually terminated.]

This ends the AGE tutorial session. From this point on you will be given a menu of tasks to select from. To start, I suggest you begin with the DESIGN task.

DESIGN: *Refer to Section 12.3.2 for a description of the Design subsystem.*

What do you want to do next?
Tasks available are: [*These are top-level tasks in* AGE]

name	description
Tutor	System explanation.
Browse	Browse thru the AGE manual.
Design	Create the user program.
Save	Save the user program on a file.
Getsys	Get the user program from a file.
Check	Check syntax of the user program.
Run	Execute the user program.
Sysout	Save everything (i.e. SYSOUT)

:: **design**

Create the user program.
What is the name of your system?:: **CRYPTO**
[New Program]
   [AGE *determines if there already exists a program by that name*]

Bo you want a Guided design session, or Unguided session?
:: **g**
   [*Only a minimal number of consecutive letters that uniquely identifies the prompt is needed.*]

Beginning DESIGN and ACQUISITION: You will need to design and specify three major components of your program: the hypothesis structure, the domain-specific rules, and some control information.

You may begin working on: HYPOTHESIS.STRUCTURE KNOWLEDGE.DOMAIN-RULES CONTROL

During this design session, in addition to specifying or editing components of the system, you may ask for ADVICE, more INFORMATION from the manual, or to QUIT the session.

What do you want to do next?
Your options are: Hypothesis.structure Knowledge.domain-rules Control Advice
   Information Quit
Type H/K/C/A/I/Q: **a** [*asking for advice*]

Specify the hypothesis structure first; it will aid you in structuring your problem. Then enter some domain rules, followed by control information. Within the control specification, choose system-provided control methods to see how your rules work. More rules can be added or more sophisticated control can be specified later.

HYPOTHESIS: *See Section 12.3.1 for a general discussion of the Hypothesis.*

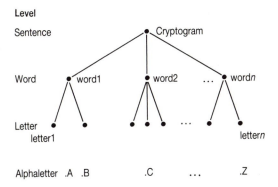

Figure 12.4   CRYPTO hypothesis structure.

CRYPTO uses a four-level structure, as shown in Figure 12.4. At the highest level (SENTENCE) there is one named node CRYPTOGRAM, where information inferred about the whole cryptogram will be stored. At the WORD level, elements WORD1 to WORDn are created dynamically for each word of the cryptogram; and at the LETTER level, elements LETTER1 to LETTERn for each letter.

What follows is an example protocol of the acquisition of the hypothesis structure for CRYPTO.

What do you want to do next?
:: **info** [*ask for information*]
Select a topic
:: **hypothesis.s**
Select from sub-topic
Type Isa/FORMIs/FORMEdby/All/Q: HYPOTHESIS.STRUCTURE.**forme**
   [*choose sub-topics until Hypothesis.Structure.Tospecify is found*]

Function: (HYPO)
The user is asked for the names of levels of hypothesis elements, and for the names of the attributes at each level. The level names must be unique; the attribute names need only be unique within a level. When AGE asks for attributes, only attributes should be given and not the names of the links between two levels. AGE will start from the highest level, LEVEL1.

Do you want to work on Hypothesis.structure?:: **y**
Acquiring HYPOTHESIS.STRUCTURE
Name of LEVEL1?
   A level name can be any literal atom not already used for the
   name of another level. Type Done to quit.
:: **sentence**
Attribute?

Attributes must be unique within a level.
:: **words**
Attribute?
:: **englishwords**
Attribute?
:: **letters**
Attributes?
:: **done**
Name of LEVEL2?
:: **wurd** [*misspelled name – to be corrected later*]
Attributes?
:: **letters**

[*The remainder of hypothesis acquisition and editing deleted.*]

:: **print**   [*print the hypothesis structure*]
LEVEL1 – SENTENCE
      WORDS – NIL
      ENGLISHWORDS – NIL
      LETTERS – NIL
LEVEL2 – WURD   [*misspelled level name*]
      LETTERS – NIL
      ENGLISHWORD – NIL
      ORDREINSENTENCE – NIL   [*misspelled*]
      POSSIBLEWORDS – NIL
LEVEL3 – LETTER
      CRYPTLETTER – NIL
      ORDERINWORD – NIL
      RELFREQ? – NIL

KSs: *Refer to Section 12.3.1 for a general description of the KSs as used in AGE. The protocol shows the partial acquistion of two KSs. The specification of each KS begins with some declarative information needed to evaluate the rules in the KS. Then the user is prompted for parts of the rules. The first KS is a set of rules that look at the whole cryptogram. It is called once after initialization and any time thereafter to find a new part of the cryptogram to focus on. This KS assumes that certain information exists in the hypothesis structure as a result of initialization. The first rule looks for one-letter words which could either be A or I, with A more likely than I.*

You need to specify: Rule.evaluator Knowledge.sources Control
You may modify: Hypothesis.structure
[*AGE keeps track of what has and has not been specified*]

What do you want to do next?
:: **kn**
What is the name of the KS you want to create or add rules to?
:: **wholesentencerules**
[New knowledge source]

What events invoke this knowledge source?

:: **always** [*Always means any event can be a precondition to this knowledge source*]

Between which Hypothesis levels does this KS make inferences?

From?

:: **letter**

To?

:: **alphaletter**

From?

:: **none**

Which links are used to record inferences made by this KS?

:: **possiblevalue** [*Possiblevalue links will connect elements from the letter level to possible values in the alphaletter level*]

Inverse link?

:: **possiblevalue/of**

Link?

:: **assignedvalue** [*Assignedvalue links will connect positively assigned values from the alphaletters to the crypt letters on the letter level*]

Inverse link?

:: **assigned/to**

Link?

:: **none**

Do you want to use multiple or single hit strategy for this KS?

You can specify Onceonly with Single or Multiple.

:: **single onceonly** [*Single to fire only one rule and Onceonly to mark that rule so that it won't be fired again*]

Local variables can be defined as (variable value) or (variable).

Define a local variable.

:: **(wordnodes ($value 'cryptogram part))**

[*Store the node names for the word nodes in WORDNODES. The function $VALUE retrieves those names by following the 'part' link from the CRYPTOGRAM node*]

Define a local variable.

:: **(word)**

Define a local variable.

:: **(lrs)**

Define a local variable.

:: **done**

What is the first condition? Type None when done.

[*This problem involves searches which are awkward with the current rule syntax and requires extensive LISP code. See Example 5 for the more usual use of rules.*]

:: **(setq word (for wd in wordnodes thereis**
        (and (eq (length ($value wd letters)) 1)
            (null ($value wd englishword]

[looking for a word of length 1, not already assigned a value]
Next condition?
:: **none**

Next, you will be prompted for the RHS of the rule.
PROPOSE, EXPECT, GOAL, or LOOP?
::**? propose**   *[ask about PROPOSE]*
PROPOSE is used to change the hypothesis structure.
:: **prop**   *[specification of PROPOSE follows]*
ch.type:: **supersede**   *[replace current value]*
hypo-element:: **word**   *[of word element]*
attr-value:: **(englishword 'a)**   *[with an 'a']*
link-node:: **none**
event.type:: **assignword**   *[name of the event it generates]*
comment:: **(A one letter word is most likely 'a')**

PROPOSE, EXPECT, GOAL, or LOOP?
:: **propose**   *[more than one action allowed in the RHS]*
       [etc., etc.]
link-node:: **(assignedvalue 'a)**   *[change the relational link]*
event.type:: **assignletter**
comment:: **(assign the letter 'a' to the cryptletter)**

PROPOSE, EXPECT, GOAL, or LOOP?
:: **none**
More rules?:: **no**
What is the name of the next KS you want?
:: **fill-inrules**
[New knowledge source]
       [some declarative information deleted]

PROPOSE, EXPECT, GOAL, or LOOP?
::**? loop**   *[ask about LOOP]*

       LOOP is used to indicate an iterative action, either PROPOSE, EXPECT, or GOAL.
If LOOP is used, you will be prompted for the name of an iteration variable and the name of
a list of values on which to repeat the action.
:: **loop**
iteration variable?
:: **ol**
Name of the list to be iterated on?
:: **otherletters**
PROPOSE, EXPECT, or GOAL?
:: **propose**
       [remainder of rule acquisition deleted]

       CONTROL: *Refer to Section 12.4 and Appendix B for discussion of
knowledge utilization and control mechanisms. The overall strategy for
solving cryptograms is to focus on a particular word or a combination of
letters that has 'potential'; work on the focused item and follow through on
all the ramifications, which in turn may generate a new focus.*

:: **control**

Control specification: Currently there are three methods of specifying the control information. Two are macros which require minimal specification, EVENT-DRIVEN-MACRO and EXPECTATION-DRIVEN-MACRO. The third method, DETAILCONTROL, involves detailed specifications of several subcomponents.

New additions to design component: (Detailcontrol Control.macro.event-driven Control.macro.expectation-driven)

[When a design node is chosen, it opens up other lower level nodes that require further specifications]

What do you want to do next?
:: **detail**

Detailed Control Specification: There are several components grouped under the heading of DETAILCONTROL. To simplify the designing process, AGE provides default specification where appropriate. The components that need to be specified are:

(1)   input data format: INPUTFORMAT,
(2)   initialization function: INITIALIZATION,
(3)   processing method to be applied to each step-type: part of KERNEL,
(4)   rules to select a step to be used as the current-focus-of-attention: part of KERNEL,
(5)   rules to select relevant KS (or procedure) to process the selected step: part of KERNEL,
(6)   termination condition: TERMINATION, and
(7)   post processing function: POSTPROCESSING.

New addition to design component: (inputformat initialization Control.Kernel Termination Postprocessing)

What do you want to do next?
:: **inputform**
The input data you use in your system will be stored on an implicit level of the hypothesis structure called INPUTDATA. A function $DATA is available to access the data. At the beginning of each run you will be asked to input (from a file or TTY:) the actual data associated with each data name.
First name?
:: **inputcryptogram**
Next name?
:: **done**

What do you want to do next?
:: **initial**
You must provide a function that will return, as its value, the name of the first KS to be invoked. Within this function you may do any processing you wish.

What would you like to call your initialization function?
:: **crypto-initialization**
[NEW FUNCTION]
Your initialization function must return the name of a KS.
Please define CRYPTO-INITIALIZATION

(CRYPTO-INITIALIZATION (LAMBDA NIL   *[This line provided by AGE]*
    (prog (cg)
    (cg ← ($data inputcryptogram))
    (fill-inlevels)
    (computerelfreqs)
    (return 'wholesentencerules]

What do you want to do next?
:: **terminate**
You must provide a function which will determine when to terminate your program.

What is the name of your termination function?
:: **crypto-quit**
[NEW FUNCTION]
Please define CRYPTO-QUIT
    [define CRYPTO-QUIT function in the same manner as above]

What do you want to do next?
:: **post**
You can provide a function to do postprocessing, e.g. printing the results, translating the results into a more readable form.

Take up this option or bypass it?   *[optional component]*
:: **take**
What would you like to call your postprocessing function?
:: **decodedprint**
    [Define DECODEDPRINT]

What do you want to do next?
:: **control.k**
This function allows the user to specify various options which determine how events, expectations, and goals will be processed.
First we will look at the event processing information.

Do you want to enter kernel information now?:: **y**
Which event selection method would you like to use? LIFO and FIFO are available or you can write your own function. Type LIFO, FIFO, or function name.
:: **?**
The Event-selection is used to decide which event from the event list to process next. LIFO chooses the last event added. FIFO chooses the earliest event. You can provide your own function. For example, best-first might depend on the weights associated with each event.
:: **lifo**

Name an event type to be collected.
:: **fill-in**
:: **done**

The control rules are used to determine what step type to process next. Each control rule consists of a condition and a step type.

STEPTYPE:: **event**
CONDITION:: **expectationlist**

STEPTYPE:: **expectation**
CONDITION:: **none**

USER FUNCTIONS: *The final information the user must provide is the names and definitions of the functions used in the rules or called from other user-defined functions. The user can name and define functions one at a time or load them from files.*

EDITING: *There are two ways to edit: (1) by calling the appropriate editing function from Unguided design session or (2) during the Check-out session. The Check subsystem is described below.*

SYSTEM CHECKOUT: *The Check subsystem does a syntax check on the user-created program. It finds errors in the designed structures and points out missing, but required, information. Check also allows the user to edit the errors as they are found by calling the appropriate editor.*

What do you want to do next?:: **check**
Check syntax of the user program.
checking hypothesis levels – ALPHALETTER LETTER WORD SENTENCE
checking knowledge sources – FILL-INRULES WHOLESENTENCERULES
Warning: 2 events not used as preconditions ASSIGNWORD FILL-IN
[*they will be used by KSs to be defined later*]
1 syntax errors in the user program.
Do you want to edit the errors now?:: **n**

What do you want to do next?:: **Q** [*terminate the session*]

RUNNING: *Once all the information is specified, the user can run the program in two modes, debugging mode or normal mode. In debugging mode, AGE prints a trace of the control flow showing the rules evaluated, the actions taken, and the steps and focuses selected. In normal mode, AGE only prints the input data and the results.*
 A complete run will begin with a request for input data. Next the user's initialization function which returns a KS name is evaluated. That KS is the first to be interpreted and starts the control loop, which will continue until the termination condition is met. Finally, the postprocessing function is called. The following is a sample run of the CRYPTO program. We have deleted a large section of the protocol to save space.

What do you want to do next?:: **run** [*top-level prompt*]
Execute the user program.
Do you want to input data from a file or from a terminal?
(filename or TTY:):: **crypto-data1** [*input from a file*]
((INPUTCRYPTOGRAM (GSHSUO CI DXDV BSS CLESVBFGB BS HD NCGU
HJB ISLD JGNCGU EDSEYD EVSXD BZFB BZDVD'I IBCYY F RDP SR JI PZS FVD
BSS ILFYY)))

Knowledge source invoked – WHOLESENTENCERULES

> *[WHOLESENTENCERULES is the KS name returned by the initialization function.]*

Left-hand side of applicable rule –

((SETQ WORD (for WD in WORDNODES thereis (AND ...

> *[first rule to fire, word17, letter73, is probably 'A'.*
> *Two events result, ASSIGNLETTER and ASSIGNWORD]*

NAME OF NEW EVENT: ASSIGNWORD
NAME OF NEW EVENT: ASSIGNLETTER

****

NEXT STEP: EVENT   *[choose the next step – EVENT]*

FOCUS EVENT-(ASSIGNLETTER(LETTER73) (ASSIGNEDVALUE A)
    WHOLESENTENCERULES EV2 NIL)

> *[Since the ASSIGNLETTER event was added to the EVENTLIST last, it is the next focus event under the depthfirst (LIFO) selection method. When there are no further ramifications of ASSIGNEDLETTER, ASSIGNWORD will become the focus event.]*

Knowledge source invoked – FILL-INRULES

Left hand side of applicable rule –

((SETQ OTHERLETTERS (for L in CRYPTLETTERNODES join ...

> *[find other letters with some cryptvalue as letter73 FILL-IN those letters with value 'A']*

NAME OF NEW EVENT: FILL-IN

****

NEXT STEP: EVENT

FOCUS EVENT – (FILL-IN (LETTER92) (ASSIGNEDVALUE A)
    (ASSIGNEDVALUE A) EV13 NIL)

> *[letter92 was assigned last, thus with a depthfirst selection method, it becomes the new focus.]*
> *[etc.]*
> *[The rest of the protocol continues in the same manner until terminated.]*

Summary

One common question asked about the CRYPTO system is: When CRYPTO makes an incorrect assignment, can CRYPTO back up? The answer is no. There is no back-up or alternative hypothesis capability. In CRYPTO we believe that with enough rules and with the POSSIBLEVALUE attributes and weights, the system will always make the correct assignments. This belief stems from the sessions recorded with the expert newspaper cryptographer, who never needed to back up. The expert never guessed at a value or tried to confirm or contradict a guess by looking at its ramifications. However, we do recognize that the concept of alternative hypotheses is a powerful one, and we expect to add facilities to AGE to allow them in the future.

Appendix B Summary of the control kernel

The control kernel consists of several components (Table 12.1) each of which must be specified by the user. The sequence of actions which are taken within the kernel is described below.

(1) Invoke rules (CONTROLRULES) to select the next step-type to process – EVENT, EXPECTation, or GOAL;

(2) If the selected step-type is EVENT, then

    (a) select an event, (SELECTIONMETHOD provided by the user);

    (b) collapse the EVENTLIST by deleting/merging events referring to identical attributes and values of the events specified by the user (COLLECTIONRULES);

    (c) select a KS (EVENTRULES generated by AGE from the KS preconditions).

(3) If the selected step-type is EXPECT, then

    (a) select an expectation (SELECTIONMETHOD);

Table 12.1 Summary of control kernel components and options.

Step-type	Event	Expectation	Goal
SELECTIONMETHOD	FIFO | LIFO | ⟨fns name⟩	FIFO | LIFO | ⟨fns name⟩	FIFO | LIFO | ⟨fns name⟩
COLLECTIONRULES	⟨KS name⟩ | ()	—	—
MATCHER	[EVENTRULES]*	⟨fn name⟩ | passivematch	⟨fn name⟩ | nil
SEEKMETHOD	—	—	⟨fn name⟩

(1) CONTROLRULES: (⟨condition⟩ ⟨steptype⟩) where step-type is EVENT|EXPECTATION|GOAL
(2) ⟨fns name⟩: name of a function provided by the user that performs a specific component task.
(3) EVENTRULES are made by AGE using KS preconditions.

    (b)   evaluate to determine if the expectation has been met (MATCHER),

    (c)   if so, process the expected event by executing the remainder of the RHS that generated the expectation.

(4)   If the selected step-type is a GOAL, then

    (a)   select a goal (SELECTIONMETHOD);

    (b)   evaluate to determine if the goal has been met (MATCHER);

    (c)   if not, apply a goal-seeking method (SEEKMETHOD);

    (d)   if the goal has been met, execute the remainder of the RHS of the rule that generated the goal.

13

The Design and an Example Use of Hearsay-III

Lee D. Erman, Philip E. London and
Stephen F. Fickas

13.1 Introduction

Hearsay-III is a domain-independent framework for knowledge-based expert systems. That is, rather than addressing the problems in a specific application domain, Hearsay-III provides a 'bare' architecture in which to cast an expert problem solver for a chosen domain. In this sense, it is similar in spirit to EMYCIN (van Melle, 1979) and AGE (Nii and Aiello, 1979) and other 'expert-system-building systems'. However, Hearsay-III differs substantially in the specific representation and control regimes it makes available to the expert-system builder.

Although Hearsay-III is specifically not a speech-understanding system (and we know of no one who expects to use it for building a speech-understanding system), it draws strongly on the architectures of the Hearsay-I (Reddy *et al.*, 1973b) and Hearsay-II (Erman *et al.*, 1980) speech-understanding systems. As was intended by the choice of its name, Hearsay-III can be viewed as an extension along some dimensions of the Hearsay-II architectural style, and as a generalization of it along others. The concepts of large-grained, modular knowledge sources and system-wide communication via a structured global blackboard were attractive to us because they provide a major first step toward achieving our design goals for Hearsay-III.

This chapter presents the motivations behind the design of Hearsay-III, a detailed overview of its architecture and facilities, and illustrations, via examples, of use of its features. Although we concentrate on the novel aspects of Hearsay-III, we do not attempt to classify each feature as being new or from Hearsay-II; Balzer (1980) presents an overview of Hearsay-III with such an orientation.

The overall design goal for Hearsay-III is the development of representation and control facilities with which a user can construct an expert system for his chosen domain. The specific attributes we want our system-building system to embody include:

- Facilities to support codification of diverse sources of knowledge. We have avoided building into Hearsay-III any commitment to a class of application domains (such as medical diagnosis) which might allow some specificity in the language for describing sources of knowledge. Instead, we attempt to provide as much generality as possible in the types of knowledge that might be brought to bear on a problem from the chosen application domain.

- Facilities to support application of these diverse sources of knowledge. Beyond mere application of the knowledge sources, an important design goal is to allow flexible coordination of the knowledge sources in their pursuit of an acceptable solution.

- Facilities to represent and manipulate competing solutions which are *incrementally* constructed. This aspect of the Hearsay-III architecture distinguishes it from the 'diagnosis-system-building systems', such as KAS (Duda *et al.*, 1978), EMYCIN (van Melle, 1979) and EXPERT (Weiss and Kulikowski, 1979).

- Facilities for reasoning about partial solutions. That is, not only does Hearsay-III allow for incremental construction of competing solutions, but it also supports in a straightforward way the ability to reason about and manipulate those solutions during the various stages of their construction.

- Facilities for describing and applying domain-dependent consistency constraints to the competing partial solutions. Thus, the system supports application of knowledge globally so as to aid in reducing the search for a solution.

- Support for long-term, large system development and, in particular, experimentation with varying knowledge for the application domain, and varying schemes for applying that knowledge.

In summary, our goal for Hearsay-III is to develop, debug and experiment with theories of domain expertise. One important area we do not emphasize as a goal for the Hearsay-III design is performance of the application system. It is intended that one use Hearsay-III to gain an understanding of the problem-solving principles of a chosen domain – to study the domain. Later, it may be necessary to use a more efficient formalism to construct a performance system for the domain.

13.2 The architecture of Hearsay-III

13.2.1 The underlying relational database

Hearsay-III is built on a foundation consisting of a relational database system and its corresponding control facilities. The database language is called AP3 (Goldman, 1978) and is embedded in INTERLISP (Teitelman, 1978). As will be seen in subsequent sections, Hearsay-III relies critically on the facilities provided within AP3.

The AP3 database is similar in structure to those available in the PLANNER-like languages (Hewitt, 1972), but it also includes strong typing on assertion, retrieval and parameter passing in function calls. The type facility in AP3 is available to a Hearsay-III user for application domain modeling in addition to being used to advantage within the Hearsay-III system itself. The Hearsay-III blackboard (see Section 13.2.2) and all publicly accessible Hearsay-III data structures are represented in the AP3 database. Additional annotations required by the application knowledge sources may also be placed in the AP3 database. Because knowledge-source triggers are implemented as uniformly represented AP3 demons, modification to the database gives rise to knowledge-source activity (as described in Section 13.2.3).

AP3 also makes available to Hearsay-III applications a context mechanism similar to those found in AI programming languages such as QA4 (Rulifson *et al.*, 1972b) and CONNIVER (McDermott and Sussman, 1974). Hearsay-III supports contexts in such a way as to make them an integrated part of the reasoning mechanisms made available to an application. This feature is somewhat unique among expert-system writing systems. The context mechanism supported in Hearsay-III allows reasoning along independent paths which may arise both from a choice among competing knowledge sources and from a choice among competing partial solutions.

The AP3 database system also provides facilities for inference rules and constraints. These facilities, in addition to being used in the implementation of Hearsay-III itself, are also available to the user for encoding global domain-dependent relationships. The interaction of constraints and contexts is supported by Hearsay-III in that reasoning in a context that produces a constraint violation results in the context being flagged as *poisoned* (see Section 13.2.3).

13.2.2 Blackboard structure

The blackboard is the central communication medium provided by Hearsay-III. It is used by an application program as a repository for a domain model, for representation of partial solutions, and for representation of pending activities. Hearsay-III supports the representation on the blackboard of graph structures consisting of structured nodes called *units* and labeled arcs called *roles*. The blackboard is segmented into two: the *domain blackboard* and the *scheduling blackboard*. The domain blackboard is intended as the site for competence reasoning, while the scheduling blackboard is intended as the site for performance reasoning. The application writer can further subdivide each of these blackboards.

Units

Blackboard units are the fundamental components of the representations built by application programs in Hearsay-III. Units are typed AP3 objects: their types are called *unit-classes*. In fact, the segmentation of the reasoning space into distinct blackboards is accomplished simply as the decomposition of the unit-class *Unit* into several distinct subclasses. Thus, the domain blackboard consists solely of units of class *Domain-Unit* (and its subclasses); the scheduling blackboard consists solely of units of class *Scheduling-Unit*. When desired, access can be restricted to a given blackboard simply by using type-restricted AP3 database retrievals.

Choice sets

Units have structure in addition to their types. One interesting feature of units is that they can be augmented to explicitly represent unresolved decisions. Such units are called *choice sets*. Associated with a choice-set unit is a set of alternatives or a generator of alternatives (or both). A choice set can be viewed as a partial elaboration of a decision point; the alternatives represent still further elaborations (and they themselves might be choice sets). Thus, competing problem solutions may be represented with a single locus. Furthermore, structure common to all alternatives may be factored out and associated with the choice-set unit itself. The choice-set representation allows for the representation of decisions to be data about which the system can reason.

Hearsay-III provides two mechanisms for resolving the ambiguity represented by a choice set. These mechanisms interact in an integrated fashion with the context mechanism of AP3. The first mechanism is called a *deduce-mode Choose* of the choice set. An application program may perform a deduce-mode Choose when it has conclusive evidence that one alternative is the correct solution for the problem represented by the choice set and that there will be no desire to retract that choice based on further evidence. In this case, the choice set is replaced by the alternative (i.e. their properties are merged) in the context in which the choice is made. In this context, all evidence that the choice set ever existed is eliminated and the blackboard structure appears as if this choice was never there.

The second choice mechanism is called an *assume-mode Choose*. An assume-mode Choose also replaces the choice set with a unit which represents a merge of the properties of the choice set and the chosen alternative. However, an assume-mode Choose makes these changes in a newly created context that is a child of the one in which the choice was made. The appearance of the blackboard structure in the new context is identical to that resulting from a deduce-mode Choose. The choice-set unit still exists in the parent context with structure modified only to eliminate the alternative just chosen. Thus, if subsequent reasoning indicates this alternative may not be best, it is possible to return to the original context and select a different alternative.

Acceptance

Units have associated with them a further attribute called *acceptance*. Acceptance can be thought of as the process of assimilating a unit into larger structure and verifying that it is appropriate in that structure. More simply, Hearsay-III allows the application writer to associate with each unit-class a collection of procedurally defined predicates called *Validator*, *Canonicalizer*, *Uniqueness-Determiner*, *Conflict-Determiner* and *Integrator* (the names are merely intended to be suggestive of how they are to be used). Each time a unit is created or is marked unaccepted by a KS, the acceptance routines defined for the unit's class are run. If all succeed, the unit is marked as *accepted*. If any fail, the unit is marked as being *unacceptable*; this usually results in the currently active context being poisoned (see Section 13.2.3). Until a unit has been accepted, Hearsay-III prevents KSs from triggering on it.

Component roles

As mentioned earlier, Hearsay-III supports the construction of labeled graphs on the blackboard. Units are the nodes in those graphs. The labeled arcs are called *component roles* (or simply *roles*), and are represented as typed relations connecting two units. The typing of roles is of significant convenience, because it allows the use of type-restricted AP3 retrievals to simplify searching the structure. Roles, in addition to being typed, are also placed in classes called *role sets*. Role sets are used for two purposes. First, they define distinct component hierarchies in which units are related by the transitive closure of the roles in a given role set. This allows the suppression of detail along the chosen dimensions when examining the blackboard structure. The second use of role sets relates to consumption, discussed next.

Consumption

Hearsay-III supports a facility for describing mutual exclusion of units in an aggregated blackboard structure. This is accomplished by prohibiting any structure in which two units are both components of a third unit (by transitive closure over a role set), while at the same time those two units are declared to *consume* a fourth. This facility allows a convenient form for expressing the undesirability of using the same partial solution or interpretation for different purposes in an overall solution.

13.2.3 Knowledge sources

The domain-specific knowledge for an application built in Hearsay-III is embodied in knowledge sources. Each KS can be thought of as a large-grained production rule: it reacts to blackboard changes produced by other KS executions and in turn produces new changes.

To define a KS, the user provides a *triggering pattern*, *immediate code* and a *body*. Whenever the pattern is matchable on the blackboard, Hearsay-III creates an *activation record* unit for the blackboard and runs the immediate code. At some later time, the activation record may be selected (see Section 13.2.4 about scheduling) and *executed*, i.e. the body, which is arbitrary LISP code, is run. In more detail:

(1)   The triggering pattern is expressed as an AP3 pattern. As such, it is a predicate whose primitives can be AP3 fact templates and arbitrary LISP predicates, composed with AND and OR operators. Whenever the AP3 database (which includes the Hearsay-III blackboard, i.e. the units and roles) is modified such that any of the AP3 templates in the pattern is matched, the entire pattern is evaluated. If the entire pattern matches, an activation record is created and has stored in it the KS's name, the AP3 context in which the pattern matched, called the *triggering context*, and the values of the variables instantiated by the match. (In AP3, the context in which a pattern matches is defined to be the least general context in which each of the pattern parts has matched.)

(2)   At the point the activation record is created, the immediate code of the KS is executed. This code, which is also arbitrary LISP code, may associate information with the activation record that may be of value later in deciding when to select this activation for execution. In addition, the immediate code must return as its value the name of some unit class of the scheduling blackboard. The activation record is then placed on the blackboard as a unit of that class. The immediate code is executed in the triggering context and has available to it the instantiated pattern variables.

(3)   At some subsequent time, the system's base scheduler (see below) may call the Hearsay-III *Execute* action on the activation record. The usual result of this is for the body of the KS to be run in the triggering context and with the pattern variables instantiated. If, however, at the point of execution, the triggering context of the activation is poisoned and the KS has not been marked as a *poison handler*, the body is not run; rather, the activation record is marked as *awaiting unpoisoning*, and will have its status reverted to *ready* if the poison status of the context is ever removed.

Each KS execution is indivisible: it runs to completion and is not interrupted for the execution of any other KS activation. This insulates the KS execution and simplifies the coding of the body: there need be no concern that during a KS execution anything on the blackboard is modified except as effected by the KS itself.

13.2.4 Scheduling

Hearsay-III is intended for use in domains in which scheduling schemes are likely to be complex. Also, the application writer is not expected to have a good *a priori* notion how to accomplish the scheduling, but to need to be able to experiment freely with various schemes. Since we view the scheduling problem itself as having characteristics similar to the domain problem, we feel the Hearsay-III blackboard-oriented knowledge-based approach is appropriate for its solution as well and thus supply the same mechanisms for its solution.

Because of the indivisibility of KS execution, the scheduling problem in Hearsay-III can be stated as follows. At the end of each KS execution, determine, from the state of the system, the KS activation to execute next. To help solve this problem, several concepts, features and mechanisms are useful:

(1)   As described above, the time of execution of a KS body is delayed arbitrarily long from its triggering, with the activation record unit, on the scheduling blackboard, as the mechanism for representing the activation. Also, the immediate code of the KS is run on creation of the activation record, allowing KS-specific scheduling information to be added to the activation record.

(2)   Some knowledge sources, termed *scheduling KSs*, may make additional changes to the scheduling blackboard to facilitate the selection of activation records. Scheduling KSs may respond to changes both on the domain blackboards and on the scheduling blackboard, including the creation of activation records. The actions

they may take include associating information with activation records (e.g. assigning and modifying priorities) and creating new units to represent meta-information about the domain blackboards (e.g. pointers to the current highest-rated units on the domain blackboard). The scheduling blackboard is the database for solving the scheduling problem.

(3)   The application writer provides a *base scheduler* procedure that is called by Hearsay-III after startup and actually calls the primitive Executive operation for executing each selected KS activation. We intend the base scheduler to be very simple; most of the knowledge about scheduling should be embodied in the scheduling KSs. For example, the base scheduler might consist simply of a loop that removes the first element from a queue, maintained by scheduling KSs, and calls for its execution. If the queue is ever empty, the base scheduler simply terminates, marking the end of system execution.

(4)   Hearsay-III provides a default base scheduler. It is composed of two functions, either of which can be replaced by the application writer. The default *outer base scheduler* repeatedly calls the default *inner base scheduler* and expects it to return a list of activation record units. (When the inner base scheduler returns the empty list, the outer base scheduler exits, halting system execution.) The outer base scheduler executes each activation record in turn. If the KS executed is a scheduling KS and its execution returns a list of (non-scheduling) activation records, the outer base scheduler immediately executes each of those activation records in turn. Each time the default inner base scheduler is called it nondeterministically chooses one ready scheduling KS activation record, or, if there are none, one nonscheduling KS activation record. The default inner base scheduler is particularly trivial and is expected to be replaced in any serious application; the default outer base scheduler is likely to be a reasonable skeleton for many applications.

13.3 An example of use

To illustrate the use of Hearsay-III as an implementation language for expert systems, we describe here the implementation of the Jitterer problem-solving system (Fickas, 1980). The problem addressed by the Jitterer is the automatic transformation of program parse trees. The Jitterer maps a given parse tree (initial state) into a new parse tree (the goal state) by the application of a sequence of equivalence-preserving transformations. The initial parse tree and the intermediate and final parse trees generated by the transformation sequence are called *program development states*. The description of the goal state is supplied by the user.

The Jitterer is one component of a *Transformational Implementation* system (Balzer, 1980) which allows a user to semi-automatically refine and optimize a high-level program specification into an efficient implementation. An example of an optimization step a Transformational Implementation user might attempt is the merging of two set enumeration loops. Before actually executing the merge step, the user might call on the Jitterer to reach a (goal) state in which the two loops (1) are adjacent, (2) generate the same sets, and (3) do not rely upon or affect the enumeration order of the set elements. If the Jitterer is successful, the user can execute the merge step and achieve the desired optimization.

Each transformation is composed of (1) a *left-hand-side pattern* (or simply LHS) that must match a portion of the current program development state, (2) zero or more *enabling conditions* that must hold in the LHS match context, and (3) a set of *actions* to perform when 1 and 2 have been satisfied. The application of a transformation generates a new, semantically equivalent, program development state.

The Jittering system faces several interesting problems:

- Many transformations in the catalog may be applicable in a given development state. Further, many transformations have a corresponding inverse transformation, allowing infinite sequences.

- Establishing the enabling conditions of a transformation may be costly, in both machine time and user effort.

- Each Jittering problem has in general more than one solution (sequence of transformation applications leading to the goal state). Metrics must be identified for ordering competing solutions. (One solution metric is how well a solution fits in with the user's more global development strategy. For example, any Jitterer-produced solution which undoes a previous optimization or prevents a future optimization must be given low priority. To compute this metric, the Jitterer must be able to analyze past development steps and predict future development steps, the latter presenting obvious problems.)

13.3.1 Design of the Jitterer

The Jitterer's basic problem-solving mechanism is a backward-chaining, best-first search. This choice helps alleviate the problems associated with the large transformation fan-out, the potentially high cost of establishing enabling conditions, infinite paths and solution ordering.

The Jitterer makes two types of control decisions: a selection from among the competing partial solution paths of the next path to extend, and a selection from among competing transformations of a transformation for continuing the chosen path. In order to limit search, rules are used to guide both kinds of decisions. An example of a path selection rule is 'If a path's length exceeds PathThreshold, suspend it', here PathThreshold has been determined experimentally. An example of a transformation selection rule is, 'If a transformation has side-effect X, lower (raise) its desirability'.

These selection rules reference features extracted from the current state as well as features predicted about the effects of possible selections. Features referenced by the path selection rules include current path cost, predicted cost to solution, number of transformations applied, predicted number of total transformations needed, current status (dead, suspended, alive, complete solution) and solution compatibility. For transformation selection, features of interest include transformation side-effects and predicted transformation cost, as computed in both machine time and user effort. Feature information can be computed on demand or stored and maintained explicitly: the latter approach was chosen because of perceived recomputation costs.

A transformation can be applied to a program development state only after its LHS has been matched and its enabling conditions have been established. A straightforward approach to establishing these conditions for a single transformation application would lump all tests into a single schedulable activity. Given the potentially high cost of establishing enabling conditions, this approach is too inflexible. It may be more efficient to order the establishing of the enabling conditions; an attempt to establish one enabling condition may provide information which will lead to the suspension or abandonment of the transformation application. Thus we require that the establishment of each enabling condition be a separate, schedulable activity.

13.3.2 Hearsay-III implementation of the Jitterer

In this section, we describe how each component of the Jitterer is implemented in Hearsay-III.

State/space representation

The Jitterer design requires two collateral spaces: the program development space, generated by transformation applications and representing various program development states, and the reasoning space, generated by the best-first and backward-chaining search and representing partial solution paths and goal/subgoal relationships. By using Hearsay-III's unit-class mechanism, the class of Domain-Units can be subdivided into *Reasoning-Units* and *Development-Units*, and thus we implement the two spaces as a segmentation of the domain blackboard. Although the reasoning space references units in the development space, the two spaces were essentially independent.

A state in the reasoning space is an AND/OR goal tree. The goal tree is built from Reasoning-Units (*goal-unit*, *transformation-unit*) and component roles (*sub-goal*, *achieves*). An OR node represents the choice among competing transformations. An AND node represents the set of goals (transformation applicability checks) that must be satisfied in order to apply a particular transformation. The Hearsay-III choice-set mechanism (see Section 13.2.2) provides a framework both for structuring the set of competing transformations and for managing child contexts associated with the choice. An assume-mode choose is used, spawning new reasoning states (contexts) when a transformation is chosen.

A state in the program development space represents the entire program parse tree at a particular stage of development. The parse tree is built from Development-Units (e.g. *loop-unit*, *assignment-unit*) and component roles (e.g. *predicate*, *then-clause*, *loop-body*). In the development space there is no notion of a choice set, rather, simply a recording of various program development paths. The application of a transformation generates a new Hearsay-III/AP3 context. Note that there is no need to copy the program development state (i.e. the syntax tree) into the new context; the Jitterer relies on the context inheritance mechanism and thus needs to represent explicitly only those portions of the structure that are new or modified.

Transformation representation

Each transformation is implemented as a domain KS (henceforth, *transformation KS*). Because of the Jitterer's backward-chaining control, the trigger of a transformation KS corresponds to the action portion (translated so to match the goals of the reasoning space) of the corresponding transformation. The immediate code of a transformation KS is responsible for setting up as subgoals the LHS pattern to be matched and the enabling conditions to be established: we describe this further in the next section. The body, when executed, creates a new context (program development state) and makes the appropriate modifications.

Control knowledge

As described in Section 13.3.1, the Jitterer uses rule-based selection knowledge to control search. Each selection rule is implemented as a scheduling KS (see Section 13.2.4). For example, one selection rule treats the desirability of a transformation as a function of the side-effects it produces. Figure 13.1 shows the scheduling KS form for one instance of this rule, namely that a transformation that unfolds a function in-line has

```
(Declare-SKS structural-flattening (Op)
      Trigger: (AND (CompetingOperator OP)
                    (SideEffect Op UnfoldsFunction))
      Immediate Code: Operator-ordering-level
      Body: (DecreaseDesirability OP))
```

Figure 13.1   A transformation selection rule. (The actual AP3/Hearsay-III syntax has been modified here for clarity.)

the deleterious side-effect of flattening the program structure.

Earlier, we mentioned a rule that checks for a path growing beyond a PathThreshold. Figure 13.2 shows the scheduling KS form of this rule. Note that the evaluation of the immediate code of the two scheduling KSs places their corresponding activation records on separate scheduling levels. The Jitterer's base scheduler gives Path-state-change-level priority over Operator-ordering-level, and hence path suspension is attempted before transformation ordering.

As discussed in Section 13.3.1, the Jitterer's selection rules reference certain computed problem-solving features. This information is stored as *auxiliary reasoning structures* attached to the relevant units on the scheduling and domain blackboards. For example, an auxiliary reasoning structure for path selection is attached to each goal-unit in the reasoning space. (Each goal is viewed as the frontier of a path from the root goal.) The scheduling KS in Figure 13.2 makes reference to the path length of Path. Current path length information is stored in and retrieved from the auxiliary structure associated with Path's frontier goal.

To describe the auxiliary reasoning structure used for transformation selection, we must look more closely at the implementation of transformations as KSs. Hearsay-III divides a KS application between triggering and execution. As described in Section 13.2.4, once a KS is triggered, an activation record is created on the scheduling blackboard where it resides until executed by the application's base scheduler. The Jitterer selects from among the set of activation records of triggered transformation KSs. Thus, this set must be ordered. The immediate code of each transformation KS is responsible for attaching an auxiliary reasoning structure to the corresponding activation record. For example, the scheduling KS in Figure 13.1 makes reference to the side-effects of a transformation. These side-effects are among the information stored in the auxiliary reasoning structure attached to the corresponding activation record. The immediate code is also responsible for adding the activation record to the choice set of the appropriate OR goal in the reasoning space.

```
(Declare-SKS lengthy-path (Path)
      Trigger:
            (AND
                (CompetingPath Path)
                (> (CurrentPathLength Path) PathThreshold))
      Immediate Code: Path-state-change-level
      Body: (MarkAsSuspended Path))
```

Figure 13.2 A path selection rule.

The scheduling of enabling conditions

The Jitterer design calls for the separate scheduling of each enabling condition. This is implemented in Hearsay-III in the same manner described for auxiliary reasoning structures in the previous section: the immediate code of a transformation KS augments the activation record with the set of enabling conditions. The scheduling KSs and the base scheduler order the set and determine when to attempt establishment of the individual conditions. In some cases it may be undesirable to execute an activation record even though all enabling conditions have been established. A few scheduling KSs look for these cases and flag the activation record accordingly. In general, the ability to divide problem solving into such fine-grained activities has been helpful for the Jitterer.

The scheduling of scheduling KSs

The Jitterer's selection rules, implemented as scheduling KSs, help order the path and transformation search space. However, we are left with the problem of scheduling the scheduling KSs. The Jitterer's scheduling blackboard is divided into a set of mutually exclusive, prioritized scheduling levels. Each scheduling KS is assigned to a single level by its immediate code. The Jitterer's base scheduler returns, for execution, an activation record from the highest level on which activation records reside.

For many levels, intra-level scheduling consists simply of executing activation records in arbitrary order until none remain on the particular level. Operator-ordering-level, referenced in Figure 13.1, is scheduled in this way. However, some scheduling levels provide structures for ordering their activation records. One example is the level on which the activation records of competing transformations are placed: the transformation selection rules maintain an ordered list. Another level, Report-solution-level, discussed below, provides a queue for recording the order of activation record appearance. When an activation record is placed on this level, a 'queue maintenance' scheduling KS adds it to the end of the queue. Given the best-first search, the final queue will contain spokesmen for all solutions found by the Jitterer in their order of preference.

We have previously seen, in Figures 13.1 and 13.2, two of the defined scheduling levels. Another example is the scheduling black-board's highest priority level, Report-solution-level. (This is actually not quite the highest level; even higher are those used by the scheduling KSs that do intra-level structuring.) Because the KS that detects complete solutions is assigned to this level by its immediate code, its activation records are executed immediately following any KS activation that satisfies its triggering pattern. Thus, the Jitterer reports a solution to the user as soon as it is found. If instead the Jitterer was to find all solutions to a problem before reporting any, Report-solution-level should be made the lowest priority scheduling level.

Use of the acceptance routines

The Jitterer's scheduling KSs normally determine the difficulty of achieving a particular goal, attaching appropriate information to the goal's auxiliary structure. However, detecting Jittering goals that are inherently impossible is performed by a Validator acceptance routine. When a new Jittering goal is posted in the reasoning space, the appropriate Validator determines whether it falls into this special class. If so, the goal is marked as impossible before being considered by the rest of the system. Currently, only easily determined impossible goals are handled by the Validator routines. Thus, more sophisticated tests about impossible goal states are not included in the Validator routines because we want the system to be able to schedule these costly activities. Once a goal unit is created, all Validator routines pertaining to that goal are run.

The Jitterer applies a set of normalization and simplification rules each time a new program development state is generated (i.e. whenever a parse tree is changed). Note that while these rules also make changes to the parse tree, they do not cause the generation of new development states. This clean-up process has been implemented in Hearsay-III through the Canonicalizer acceptors: each node type (unit-class) of a parse tree (e.g. loop-unit, assignment-unit, conditional-unit) has an associated Canonicalizer; each Canonicalizer embodies the set of clean-up rules for its node-type. It is the responsibility of a transformation changing the parse tree to mark the relevant nodes (units) for (re)acceptance (see Section 13.2.2.).

13.4 Conclusion

Hearsay-III was exercised initially on two small test cases: a crypt-arithmetic problem and a cryptogram decoding problem. In addition to the Jitterer, two major implementation efforts are currently underway.

The first of these is the reimplementation of SAFE, a system for constructing formal specifications of programs from informal specifications (Balzer *et al.*, 1978). Second, Hearsay-III is being used as the basis for a system for producing natural language descriptions of expert system data structures (Mann and Moore, 1979).

In some problem domains, the major implementation effort will be the encoding of the competency portion of the problem-solving system in the form of KSs. The performance portion of the system may not require sophisticated scheduling techniques, sufficing on a reasonably tunable set of hard-wired scheduling regimes, such as the AGE system provides. In these cases, the Hearsay-III system may seem less useful since the user will have to build up all but the most primitive control structures from scratch. Although such is currently the case, as more and more projects use Hearsay-III, the stock of different application schedulers will grow. It seems reasonable to assume that with a little work these schedulers can be generalized to provide a new user with a library of Hearsay-III schedulers from which to choose. A new problem domain may be able to use an existing scheduler directly or as the foundation for a more application-specific scheduler.

Our experience to date supports our belief that the Hearsay-III architecture is a helpful one. The separation of competence knowledge from performance knowledge helps in rapidly formulating the expert knowledge required for a solution. The flexibility that the Hearsay-III architecture gives toward developing scheduling algorithms will undoubtedly go a long way toward simplifying this difficult aspect of the overall problem-solving process.

Acknowledgments

This research was supported by Defense Advanced Research Projects Agency contract DAHC-15-72-C-0308. Views and conclusions contained in this document are those of the authors and should not be interpreted as representing the official opinion or policy of DARPA, the US Government, or any other person or agency connected with them.

Hearsay-III was originally designed by Bob Balzer, Lee Erman and Chuck Williams, with contributions by Jeff Barnett, Mark Fox and Bill Mann. Subsequently, Phil London and Neil Goldman contributed significant design modifications. Lee Erman and Phil London implemented and maintain Hearsay-III. AP3 was designed, implemented and maintained by Neil Goldman. Steve Fickas designed and implemented the Jitterer. Neil Goldman, Bill Mann, Jim Moore, and Dave Wile have also served as helpful and patient initial users of the Hearsay-III system.

14

BB1: An Implementation of the Blackboard Control Architecture

Barbara Hayes-Roth and Micheal Hewett

14.1 Introduction

BB1 is a task-independent implementation of the blackboard control architecture (Hayes-Roth, 1985). In this chapter, we review the blackboard control architecture, describe the language and capabilities of BB1 from the point of view of the application builder and characterize the implementation from a software engineering perspective.

14.2 A theory of dynamic control reasoning

14.2.1 The control problem

In attempting to solve a domain problem, an AI system performs a series of problem-solving actions. Each action is triggered by data or previously generated solution elements, applies some knowledge source from the problem domain, and generates or modifies a solution element. At each point in the problem-solving process, several such actions may be possible. The control problem is: Which of its potential actions should an AI system perform at each point in the problem-solving process?

The control problem is fundamental to all cognitive processes and intelligent systems. In solving the control problem, a system decides, either implicitly or explicitly, what problems it will attempt to solve, what knowledge it will bring to bear, and what problem-solving methods and strategies it will apply. It decides how it will evaluate alternative problem solutions, how it will know when specific problems are solved, and under what circumstances it will interrupt its attention to selected problems or subproblems. Thus, in solving the control problem, a system determines its own cognitive behavior.

Despite increasing sophistication in problem-solving knowledge and heuristics, most AI systems employ relatively simple control programs. In contrast, people do not rely on predetermined control programs to guide all of their problem-solving efforts. Instead, they draw upon a repertoire of control knowledge that includes proven control programs and heuristics for dynamically constructing, modifying and executing control programs during efforts to solve particular domain problems.

This adaptability in the control of one's own problem-solving behavior is the hallmark of human intelligence. Because of it, people do not simply solve a problem. They often know something about how they solve the problem, how they have solved similar problems in the past, why they perform one problem-solving action rather than another, what problem-solving actions they are likely to perform in the future, and so forth. They use this knowledge to adapt their behavior to the demands of the problem-solving situation, to explain their behavior, to cope with new problems, to improve their approaches to familiar problems, and to transfer problem-solving knowledge to other people and to computers. Truly intelligent AI systems must do no less.

14.2.2 The semantics of contol

What kinds of control behaviors should an AI system exhibit? This section sets forth eight behavioral goals for an AI architecture. Each goal rests upon assumptions about effective problem solving and the nature of intelligence. Thus, the goals are claimed to be necessary (but not sufficient) behaviors for an intelligent system. Although some readers may disagree with this analysis, at least it exposes the goals and assumptions underlying the blackboard control architecture to examination and criticism. It also provides criteria against which to evaluate the architecture and its alternatives.

An illustrative problem domain: multiple-task planning

The behavioral goals are illustrated with examples from a hypothetical intelligent planner that solves the following problem:

> You have just finished working out at the health club (see Figure 14.1). It is 11:00 and you can plan the rest of the day as you like. However, you must pick up your car from the Maple Street parking garage by 5:30 and then head home. You would also like to see a movie today, if possible. Show times at both movie theaters are 1:00, 3:00 and 5:00. Both movies are on your 'must see' list, but go to whichever one most conveniently fits into your plan. Your other errands are as follows:

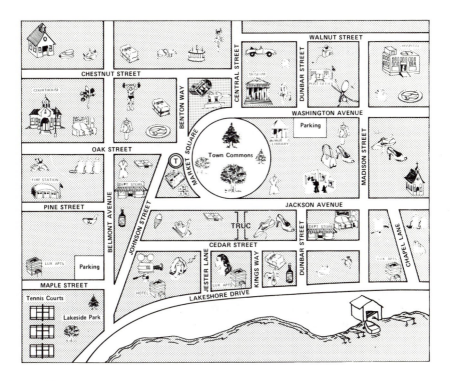

Figure 14.1 Town map used for multiple-task planning.

- Pick up medicine for your dog at the vet.
- Buy a fan belt for your refrigerator at the appliance store.
- Tour two of the three luxury apartments.
- Meet a friend for lunch at the restaurant of your choice.
- Buy a toy for your dog at the pet store.
- Pick up your watch at the watch repair.
- Special-order a book at the bookstore.
- Buy fresh vegetables at the grocery.
- Buy a gardening magazine at the newstand.
- Go to the florist to send flowers to a friend in the hospital.

Develop a plan that:

(1) specifies which tasks to perform, the ordering of tasks, and the routes to travel between successive tasks;

(2) accomplishes as many tasks as possible, accomplishes high-priority tasks rather than low-priority tasks, honors time constraints, and provides efficient routes.

Behavioral goals for intelligent control

(1)   Make explicit control decisions that solve the control problem.

To solve a problem, a system performs a subset of its potential problem-solving actions in a particular order. Intelligent problem solving entails explicitly solving the control problem – deciding which actions to perform and when to perform them – as well as performing selected actions. For example, given several possible next actions, the hypothetical planner explicitly decides to perform the action that locates the vet on the town map.

(2)   Decide what actions to perform by reconciling independent decisions about what actions are desirable and what actions are feasible.

Intelligent control reasoning recognizes both the desirability and the feasibility of potential actions. An intelligent system decides what kinds of actions it should perform, thereby establishing its operative control heuristics. It decides what actions it can perform, thereby identifying its currently executable knowledge sources. The system reconciles these two kinds of decisions in order to decide what actions to perform. For example, the planner might decide that it should perform actions involving high-priority tasks. It might also decide that, in the current problem-solving situation, it can execute several knowledge sources, including one whose action would locate the vet, a high-priority task. Reconciling its task-priority heuristic and its executable knowledge sources, the planner decides to locate the vet.

Although an intelligent system does not allow either the desirability or the feasibility of potential actions to dominate control problem solving, it drives the problem-solving process in either direction under appropriate circumstances.

Suppose the system decides that it should perform actions having a particular attribute, but discovers that it cannot perform any such actions. In other words, the specified actions are desirable, but not feasible. In that situation, an intelligent system performs actions that enable it to perform the desired actions. For example, the planner might decide that it should perform actions that generate abstract partial plans, but discovers that it cannot perform any such actions. In that situation, the planner examines its knowledge sources that produce abstract plans, determines that it needs task-location information in order to apply them, and adopts a control heuristic favoring actions that generate task-location information.

Conversely, suppose the system has decided that it can perform several pending actions that share an 'interesting' attribute, but notices that it has not yet decided that it should perform such actions. In other words, the specified actions are feasible, but not explicitly desirable. In that situation, an intelligent system performs actions that incline it to perform the feasible actions. For example, the planner might decide that it can perform several actions sharing the attribute 'triggered by time constraints', which is interesting because the problem instructions include a requirement to honor time constraints. However, it also might notice that it has not yet decided that it should perform such actions. In that situation, the planner adopts a control heuristic favoring actions triggered by time constraints.

(3)   Adopt variable grain-size control heuristics.

In some problem-solving situations, the most useful control heuristics prescribe classes of actions, while in others the most useful heuristics prescribe specific actions. Similarly, in some situations, the most useful heuristics prescribe actions to be performed at any time during a relatively long problem-solving time interval, while in others the most useful heuristics target actions for specific problem-solving 'cycles'. An intelligent system adopts control heuristics whose grain-size is appropriate for the problem-solving situation.

For example, the planner might generate two credible partial plans, PP–NW and PP–SE (see Figure 14.2). In that situation, any actions that extend either partial plan or connect the two plans would advance the problem-solving process. Therefore, the planner adopts a relatively large-grain control heuristic favoring actions whose triggering information includes an unconnected end-point of either of the plans or whose solution context is the spatial–temporal region between the two plans. The heuristic prescribes performance of such actions during the problem-solving time interval beginning immediately and continuing until the two partial plans are connected.

Once the planner has connected the two partial plans, for example with PP–MID (see Figure 14.2), the only remaining problem-solving objective is to connect the integrated plan with its termination point. In that situation, the planner adopts a smaller-grain control heuristic favoring actions whose knowledge source is Extend-Route and solution interval is '5:15 Lakeshore Apartments, 5:30 Maple Street parking garage'. The heuristic prescribes performance of those actions on the few remaining problem-solving cycles.

(4)   Adopt control heuristics that focus on whatever action attributes are useful in the current problem-solving situation.

Attributes of a problem-solving action's triggering information, knowledge source or solution context may affect its utility in different problem-solving situations. An intelligent system adopts control heuristics

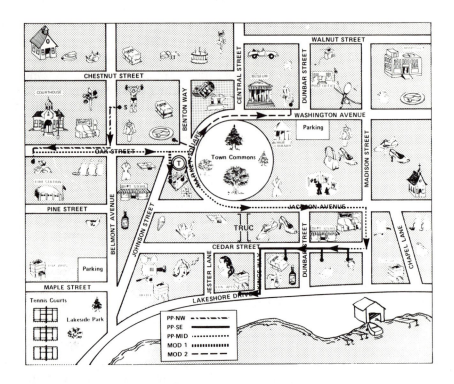

Figure 14.2   Illustration of partial plans.

that focus on whatever attributes are useful in the current problem-solving situation. For example, if a planning problem specifies tasks that vary widely in priority, the planning system adopts a heuristic favoring actions triggered by high-priority tasks. If problem-solving time is at a premium, it adopts a heuristic favoring actions whose knowledge sources are efficient and reliable. If the planning system has already generated two credible partial plans, it adopts a heuristic favoring actions whose solution contexts represent the interval between those plans.

(5)   Adopt, retain and discard individual control heuristics in response to dynamic problem-solving situations.

Different control heuristics are useful in different problem-solving situations and the problem-solving situation can change repeatedly during the problem-solving process. An intelligent system adopts, retains and discards control heuristics in response to dynamic problem-solving situations. For example, the planner might determine early in the problem-solving process that the requested tasks vary widely in priority and that the allowable plan execution time is insufficient for performing all of them. It immediately adopts a heuristic favoring actions triggered by high-priority tasks. Ordinarily it would retain that heuristic for the duration of the problem-solving process. However, if the planner subsequently develops a partial plan that includes all of the high-priority tasks but does not exhaust the allowable execution time, it abandons the heuristic. For another example, sometime in the middle of the problem-solving process, the planner might generate the partial plans, PP–NW and PP–SE (see Figure 14.2). At that point, it adopts a heuristic favoring actions that connect those plans. However, once the planner has completely connected PP–NW and PP–SE (for example, with PP–MID in Figure 14.2), that heuristic is no longer useful and the planner abandons it.

(6)   Decide how to integrate multiple control heuristics of varying importance.

Several operative control heuristics (those the system has adopted and not yet abandoned) may bear simultaneously, but differentially, on a particular problem-solving situation. An intelligent system integrates all operative heuristics in deciding which specific action to perform next. For example, the planner might decide that: (1) it is very important to generate abstract partial plans until there are at least three high-credibility partial plans; (2) it is always moderately important to perform actions whose knowledge sources are reliable; and (3) it is always moderately important to perform actions whose triggering information is credible. Until decision 1's criterion is met, the planner uses all three heuristics to decide which actions to perform. After 1's criterion is met, the planner abandons it and uses only the remaining two heuristics.

On a given problem-solving cycle, several potential actions may have different ratings against different subsets of the operative control heuristics. An intelligent system decides how to integrate each action's ratings and by what rule to choose a single action to perform next. For example, early in the problem-solving process, the planner might decide simply to choose the potential action that has the highest sum of ratings, weighted by importance, against all operative control heuristics. Later, as problem-solving time becomes more precious, it might decide to identify the subset of its potential actions that rate high on knowledge source speed and reliability and to choose from that set the single action that has the highest weighted sum of ratings against the remaining control heuristics.

(7)   Dynamically plan strategic sequences of actions.

Strategic sequences of actions sometimes provide problem-solving power not achievable through independently chosen actions. An intelligent system plans strategic sequences of actions under appropriate circumstances. For example, the successive-refinement strategy reduces the combinatorics of search for multiple-task planning problems that specify a large number of tasks. The hypothetical planner uses that strategy to plan a sequence of: (1) actions that generate abstract partial plans; followed by (2) actions that refine, extend and connect the most credible partial plans.

Strategic plans are complex control heuristics. Rather than prescribing a single kind of action, they prescribe a sequence of different kinds of actions. Therefore, an intelligent system deals with strategic plans just as it deals with simpler heuristics. It adopts variable grain-size strategic plans that focus on whatever action attributes are useful in the current problem-solving situation. It adopts, retains and abandons strategic plans in response to dynamic problem-solving situations. It integrates strategic plans with its other control heuristics in deciding which specific action to perform next.

Dynamic planning also entails a readiness to interrupt, resume or re-plan performance of a strategic sequence of actions in response to dynamic problem-solving situations, as discussed below.

Some actions that do not conform to an adopted plan have other desirable attributes. An intelligent system interrupts its execution of strategic plans to perform such actions. For example, the planner might: (1) adopt the successive-refinement strategy; (2) begin performing a sequence of actions that, if completed, would generate PP–MID, connecting PP–NW with PP–SE (see Figure 14.2); and (3) complete actions plotting the route segments beginning at the vet and ending at the intersection of Oak Street and Johnson Street. At this point, the planner can perform either of two actions, one that would continue the strategic action sequence and one that would interrupt it. The strategic action would plot a route segment from the intersection of Oak Street and Johnson Street to the next intersection on the way to PP–SE. The nonstrategic action would modify PP–NW to include the newsstand, a task previously excluded from consideration for being of low priority, but now worth incorporating in the plan because it is very convenient to the plotted route. In this situation, the planner interrupts its strategic route-plotting actions to perform the action that incorporates the newsstand in the plan (MOD1 in Figure 14.2).

Some interruptions do not affect a strategic plan's utility. On completing noninterfering interruptions, an intelligent system resumes plan execution. For example, inclusion of the newsstand makes only a minor modification to PP–NW. The planner subsequently resumes its strategic route-plotting actions to complete PP–MID.

On the other hand, some interruptions obviate pending strategic actions. On completing interfering interruptions, an intelligent system adapts its execution of the strategic plan to the new problem-solving situation. For example, following incorporation of the newsstand, the planner might perform additional interrupting actions, further extending PP–NW to include lunch at the Oak Street Restaurant followed by a stop at the Washington Avenue Pet Store (MOD2 in Figure 14.2). Given this substantial extension of PP–NW, a route from the vet to the watch repair no longer makes sense. Therefore, the planner does not resume its efforts to plot that route. Instead, it 'backs up' in its strategic plan, first plotting routes within the extended PP–NW and then plotting a route connecting it to PP–SE – this time a route from the pet store to the watch repair.

(8)   Reason about the relative priorities of domain and control actions.

Just as an intelligent system performs domain actions to generate solution elements for a domain problem, it performs control actions to generate solution elements for the control problem, namely control decisions. Because there is no *a priori* reason to presume that either type of action is more productive on any particular problem-solving cycle, the system reasons about the relative priorities of domain and control actions just as it reasons about other control issues. For example, the planner might have two feasible actions: (1) a domain action that would generate an abstract plan encompassing three of the requested tasks: the health club, the florist, and the vet; and (2) a control action that would adopt a heuristic favoring actions whose knowledge sources are reliable. If, for example, the planner has an operative heuristic favoring actions that generate abstract partial plans, it performs the domain action first. Alternatively, if it has an operative heuristic favoring control actions, it performs the control action first. If the planner has both heuristics, it performs the action favored by the heuristic it considers most important.

14.2.3 The blackboard control architecture

The blackboard control architecture was designed to achieve the behavioral goals discussed above. It provides a uniform blackboard mechanism for performing one or more base tasks and for solving their associated control problems. Functionally independent knowledge sources incrementally construct hypothetical solutions to specified problems on solution blackboards. These knowledge sources and blackboards are task specific and defined by the system builder. Similarly, functionally independent control knowledge sources incrementally construct dynamic control plans for the system's own behavior on a control blackboard. Although many control knowledge sources are task specific and defined by the system builder, the control blackboard itself and several generic control knowledge sources are task independent and defined within the architecture. A single, integrated scheduling mechanism invokes, schedules and executes all knowledge sources. The scheduler has no specific control knowledge or heuristics. Instead, it applies whatever scheduling heuristics are recorded in the current control plan on the control blackboard. As a consequence, the blackboard control architecture enables systems to dynamically construct, modify and execute control plans for their own task-oriented behavior.

14.3 A user's view of BB1

BB1 is a particular implementation of the blackboard control architecture. The following sections describe the BB1 blackboard representation, knowledge source functionality, control cycle and user interface.

14.3.1 Blackboard representation

Like other blackboard architectures, BB1 uses data structures called blackboards to record and organize solution elements generated during problem solving. As discussed below, BB1 also uses blackboards to record other kinds of information, such as the problems a system can solve, the knowledge it uses, and the control plan that guides its problem-solving behavior.

A BB1 blackboard organizes objects in two ways:

(1) It can partition its objects into named levels of abstraction, with characteristic attributes and links to other objects.

(2) It can link objects by means of named relations to other objects on the same or different blackboards.

An application system may have multiple blackboards, multiple levels within blackboards, and multiple objects at each level. A given object may be linked to any number of other objects (across levels and blackboards) with any specified links. The user can define application-specific inheritance paths for static and procedurally defined attributes. As discussed below, knowledge sources can retrieve information from objects on blackboards by means of various blackboard access functions and variables. Knowledge sources can modify objects by means of various blackboard modification functions. A typical BB1 system includes instances of the following types of blackboards.

Problem blackboards record the information associated with particular problems a system must solve. They are application-specific and defined by the system builder. For example, the hypothetical planner described above might represent its planning problem on a problem blackboard.

Solution blackboards record hypothetical elements of the solutions

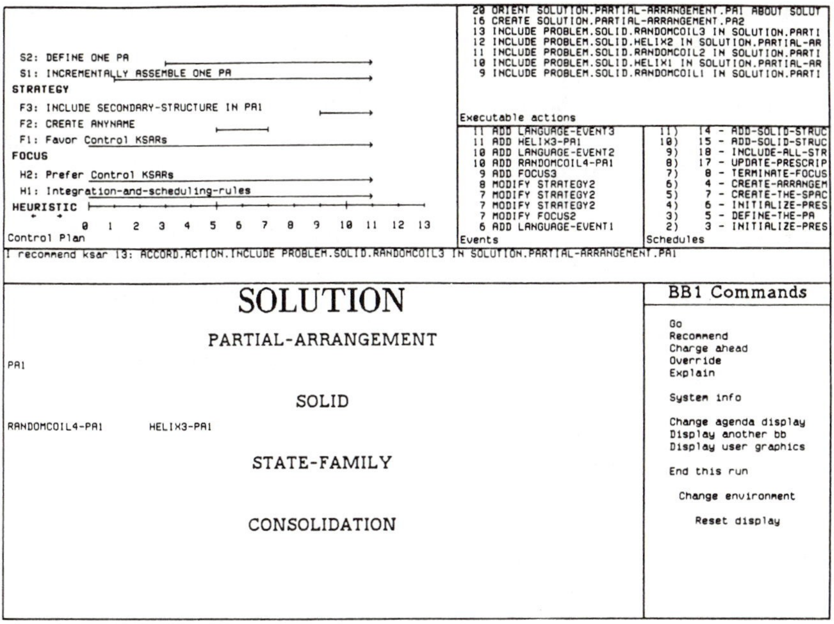

```
                                                    20 ORIENT SOLUTION.PARTIAL-ARRANGEMENT.PA1 ABOUT SOLUT
                                                    16 CREATE SOLUTION.PARTIAL-ARRANGEMENT.PA2
                                                    13 INCLUDE PROBLEM.SOLID.RANDOMCOIL3 IN SOLUTION.PART1
   S2: DEFINE ONE PA                                12 INCLUDE PROBLEM.SOLID.HELIX2 IN SOLUTION.PARTIAL-AR
   S1: INCREMENTALLY ASSEMBLE ONE PA                11 INCLUDE PROBLEM.SOLID.RANDOMCOIL2 IN SOLUTION.PART1
   STRATEGY                                         10 INCLUDE PROBLEM.SOLID.HELIX1 IN SOLUTION.PARTIAL-AR
                                                     9 INCLUDE PROBLEM.SOLID.RANDOMCOIL1 IN SOLUTION.PART1
   F3: INCLUDE SECONDARY-STRUCTURE IN PA1
   F2: CREATE ANYNAME                             Executable actions
   F1: Favor Control KSARs
   FOCUS                                            11 ADD LANGUAGE-EVENT3    11)  14 - ADD-SOLID-STRUC
                                                    11 ADD HELIX3-PA1         10)  15 - ADD-SOLID-STRUC
   H2: Prefer Control KSARs                         10 ADD LANGUAGE-EVENT2     9)  18 - INCLUDE-ALL-STR
   H1: Integration-and-scheduling-rules             10 ADD RANDOMCOIL4-PA1     8)  17 - UPDATE-PRESCRIP
   HEURISTIC                                         9 ADD FOCUS3              7)   8 - TERMINATE-FOCUS
            0  1  2  3  4  5  6  7  8  9 10 11 12 13  8 MODIFY STRATEGY2       6)   4 - CREATE-ARRANGEM
   Control Plan                                      7 MODIFY STRATEGY2       5)   7 - CREATE-THE-SPAC
                                                     7 MODIFY STRATEGY2       4)   6 - INITIALIZE-PRES
                                                     7 MODIFY FOCUS2          3)   5 - DEFINE-THE-PA
                                                     6 ADD LANGUAGE-EVENT1    2)   3 - INITIALIZE-PRES
                                                   Events                   Schedules
   I recommend ksar 13: ACCORD.ACTION.INCLUDE PROBLEM.SOLID.RANDOMCOIL3 IN SOLUTION.PARTIAL-ARRANGEMENT.PA1
```

SOLUTION	BB1 Commands
PARTIAL-ARRANGEMENT	Go
	Recommend
PA1	Charge ahead
	Override
	Explain
SOLID	
	System info
RANDOMCOIL4-PA1 HELIX3-PA1	Change agenda display
	Display another bb
	Display user graphics
STATE-FAMILY	
	End this run
	Change environment
CONSOLIDATION	Reset display

Figure 14.3   The BB1 display – COMMON LISP version.

to particular problems as they are generated by associated knowledge sources. A given system may have any number of solution blackboards corresponding to different perspectives on a single task or to different tasks the system must perform concurrently. Solution blackboards are application-specific and defined by the system builder. For example, Figure 14.3 shows the solution blackboard for the PROTEAN application system (Hayes-Roth *et al.*, 1986a), which distinguishes three levels of abstraction: solid, state-family and consolidation.

Knowledge blackboards record relatively stable information available to a system for solving problems. A given system may have any number of knowledge blackboards corresponding to different useful partitions of the knowledge base. All knowledge sources in a BB1 system are recorded on knowledge blackboards. In addition, knowledge blackboards may explicitly record knowledge in a declarative form for use by multiple knowledge sources. Systems that have learning knowledge sources may modify information on knowledge blackboards.

The control blackboard records information about a system's own actions: actions that are desirable, actions that are feasible, and actions that are executed. Its structure is independent of any particular task or application. The control plan blackboard records the dynamic, multilevel plan of desirable actions constructed by control knowledge sources during problem solving. Each control decision describes a class of actions that are desirable during a particular problem-solving time interval. The control plan is structured along two dimensions. The horizontal dimension represents the sequence of problem-solving cycles. A given control decision is operative during a specified interval of problem-solving cycles. The vertical dimension represents control decisions at different levels of abstraction, where decisions at higher levels of abstraction are typically more general and encompass longer problem-solving time intervals. A BB1 system may have any number of abstract strategy levels and it may create them dynamically at run-time. In addition, it may create multiple parallel strategies. All strategies terminate in focus decisions. For example, Figure 14.3 shows the control plan blackboard during a run of the PROTEAN system. The control data blackboard records the running agenda of executable actions (see Figure 14.3). On each cycle, the scheduler uses the operative focus decisions to select one of the executable actions for execution. That decision also is recorded on the control data blackboard. Like objects on other blackboards, control decisions, agendas and executed actions are available for inspection and modification by knowledge sources.

BB1 provides a graphical tool called BBEdit for defining all blackboards and placing objects and relations on them during system building. Figure 14.4 shows a BBEdit display during development of the PROTEAN system.

BB1's distinct blackboards and levels within blackboards serve a primarily conceptual function, organizing solution elements and control decisions in ways that system builders find meaningful and computationally useful. The distinctions among concurrent tasks, alternative perspectives on a task, and levels of abstraction of a solution are particularly useful in this regard. Earlier versions of BB1 also used the blackboard structure as an index into knowledge sources for triggering efficiency. The current version of BB1 uses a variety of information for this purpose and no longer depends in any significant way on blackboard structure.

14.3.2 Knowledge sources

BB1 knowledge sources are structured descriptions of a system's potential actions and the information required to instantiate those actions. BB1 distinguishes three types of knowledge source. Task knowledge sources describe actions that solve a particular type of problem. When executed, they add or modify information on solution blackboards. Control knowledge sources describe actions that solve the control problem. When executed, they add or modify information on control blackboards. Learning knowledge sources describe actions that affect a system's

BBEDIT Commands			BBEDIT
System information KB information Blackboard information Compile a kb file Save to a file Reset display Refresh display	Edit another blackboard Rename this blackboard Delete this blackboard Edit another knowledge bas Rename this knowledge base Delete this knowledge base Merge with a knowledge bas	Add a level Copy a level to this bb Change link information Change attribute informati Change inheritance informa Change data information Enter hierarchical mode	PROTEAN *CONCEPT*

CONCEPT

MAIN-TYPE

CONCEPT	NATURAL-TYPE	ROLE-TYPE	TYPE	INDIVIDUAL
INSTANCE	CONSTRAINT	CONTEXT	MODIFIER-TYPE	

NATURAL-TYPE

STATE	EVENT	ACTION	OBJECT

OBJECT-TYPE

REGIONAL-OBJECT	PROCEDURAL-OBJECT	PHYSICAL-OBJECT

ROLE-TYPE

ARRANGEMENT-ROLE

CONTEXT-TYPE

SPACE-AND-TIME	TIME	SPACE	TIME-AND-PEOPLE

CONSTRAINT-TYPE

TRANSFORMATION-CONST	STATE-CONSTRAINT	CONSTRAINT-SET	CONTEXT-BASED-CONSTR	OBJECT-BASED-CONSTRA

Figure 14.4   The BBEdit program.

knowledge. When executed, they add or modify information on the knowledge blackboards.

All knowledge sources have the same structure. The trigger describes blackboard events that signal a knowledge source's applicability. The context describes multiple blackboard contexts in which a triggered knowledge source can instantiate its action. The precondition describes additional blackboard states that must obtain at the time of action execution, although not necessarily at the time of triggering. The obviation condition describes blackboard states whose occurrence obviates the instantiated action. Finally, the action describes a parameterized set of blackboard modifications to be instantiated with particular parameter values identified during triggering, context matching and precondition matching. BB1 provides a graphical tool called KSEdit that guides the specification of application-specific knowledge sources. (See Figure 14.5.)

Because of its distinctive approach to control reasoning, BB1 provides a number of generic control knowledge sources for use in combination with application-specific control knowledge sources. For example, the knowledge source Terminate-Prescription is invoked when the goal of a previously posted strategy or focus decision is satisfied. Its action deactivates the identified strategy or focus decision and its

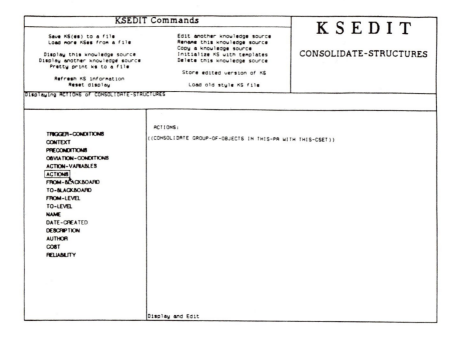

Figure 14.5   The KSEdit program.

subordinates. As a second example, the control knowledge source Generate-Sequence is invoked by strategy decisions that prescribe specified sequences of subordinates. Its action posts each specified subordinate when its predecessor is deactivated.

14.3.3 The execution cycle

A running BB1 system iterates the following basic cycle:

(1)   Execute the scheduled KSAR, producing changes to blackboard objects.

(2)   Update the agenda to include KSARs newly triggered by the recent blackboard changes and to modify the status (triggered/executable/obviated) of KSARs as appropriate given those changes.

(3)   Schedule the executable KSAR that best satisfies the current control plan.

The BB1 cycle differs from other blackboard system cycles in two important ways. First, the scheduler is a simple and general program that has no *a priori* control knowledge. Instead, it chooses KSARs according to criteria posted by control knowledge sources in the control plan. Second, since control knowledge sources are triggered by the dynamic problem-solving situation and, when scheduled, modify the operational control plan, the criteria used by the scheduler change as the problem-solving situation unfolds. As a consequence, a BB1 system adapts its behavior to unanticipated opportunities and demands placed before it by the problem-solving environment.

14.3.4 User interface

BB1 provides a graphical user interface that displays the dynamic contents of solution and control blackboards. Users interact with BB1 via a 'mouse' or a typescript window. Figure 14.3 illustrates the BB1 display during a run of the PROTEAN application system (Hayes-Roth *et al.*, 1986a).

The user can inspect information in the knowledge base or on blackboards by using the mouse to designate objects of interest and potential operations on those objects listed on menus. For example, the user can display a graph of objects by specifying a root node and a set of link names. Similarly, the user can use the mouse to designate a particular object to be displayed in detail.

The user can request any of several different types of explanation of BB1's actions. If the user requests an explanation of KSAR feasibility, BB1 describes how a particular event triggered the KSAR and how particular blackboard states satisfied its preconditions. If the user requests an explanation of the strategic plan underlying an action, BB1 provides a menu of alternative explanation forms, ranging from the local strategic context to the complete plan for solving the larger problem. If the user requests an explanation of a scheduling decision, BB1 describes the current control foci and shows how the scheduled KSAR satisfies them. On request, BB1 describes the comparative desirability of alternative KSARs against current foci. (See Figure 14.6.)

The user can intervene in BB1 operation in three ways. First, the user can override one of BB1's scheduling decisions and instruct it to perform a different action on the agenda. Second, the user can instruct BB1 to adopt a particular control decision and incorporate it into all subsequent scheduling decisions. Third, the user can instruct BB1 to operate autonomously for a specified number of cycles.

14.4 A software engineer's view of BB1

BB1 is a moderately large (about 500 Kbytes of LISP source code) system. Originally implemented in 1983, the current publicly available version of BB1, v2.0 (Garvey *et al.*, 1986), is implemented in COMMON LISP for

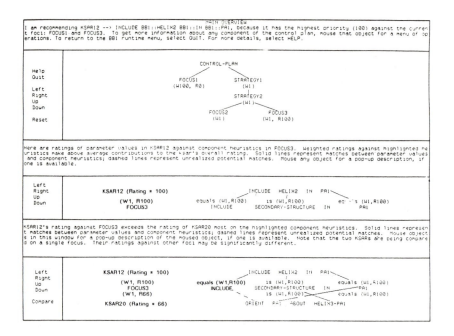

Figure 14.6 A BB1 explanation, illustrating (top) the user-defined control plan, (middle) the ratings for one KSAR, and (bottom) a comparison of ratings for two KSARs.

use on the TI Explorer and in INTERLISP for use on the Xerox 1100-series workstations. BB1 users have ported the COMMON LISP implementation to the Symbolics 3600-series workstations (under Genera 7) and the LMI Lambda workstation. Both implementations use standard programming techniques, but versions v2.5 and v3.0 (currently available only in COMMON LISP and only at Stanford) incorporate object-oriented programming techniques, which provide a more natural representation of blackboard concepts and a more flexible system implementation.

At run-time, BB1's memory requirements depend upon the size of the application. PROTEAN, which is the largest application currently running at Stanford, starts with over 1 Mbyte of data files (knowledge sources, knowledge bases and LISP functions) and consumes at least 7 Mbytes (in addition to the LISP environment) of virtual memory on a Xerox 1100-series workstation during a typical run.

Similarly, BB1's speed varies considerably among applications and even from cycle to cycle within an application. During application development, the main performance factor is cycle time, which depends primarily on the size of the agenda and only slightly on the complexity of the current control plan. In general, cycle time appears to be well within tolerable limits for program development. At run-time, the speed of BB1 *per se* is less important; the main performance factor is number of cycles required to solve the problem. Here, an application's effective use of BB1's control architecture can substantially improve problem-solving efficiency (Garvey *et al.*, 1987).

BB1 differs from other blackboard system implementations in its emphasis on uniform data representation. Because it puts 'everything' on the blackboard, BB1 effectively has no internal data structures. This principle first arose in our efforts to make control reasoning explicit. However, we have found that the uniform representation and associated uniform data access methods enhance clarity and robustness of the implementation and facilitate all aspects of system development.

BB1's control architecture has also proven useful in application development and debugging. Like other blackboard architectures, it allows independent design and debugging of loosely coupled knowledge sources and experimentation with alternative control strategies on a constant set of task knowledge sources. The control architecture provides an added advantage in its modularization of control knowledge, effectively recreating the task-level development advantages at the control level. BB1's explanation module provides useful run-time debugging information regarding how a strategy determines the sequence of problem-solving operations and why individual operations are chosen over others in particular situations.

BB1's considerable generality is both its greatest strength and its greatest weakness. It is a strength because of its great range of potential applicability. In fact, BB1 has been used for a variety of knowledge-based systems at Stanford University (e.g. Brugge and Buchanan, 1987; Johnson and Hayes-Roth, 1988; Hayes-Roth *et al.*, 1986a; Schulman and Hayes-Roth, 1987; Tommelein *et al.*, 1987a) and elsewhere (e.g. Dodhiawala *et al.*, 1986; Jagannathan *et al.*, 1986; Murphy *et al.*, 1987; Pardee and Hayes-Roth, 1987; see also Chapter 21). It has been distributed by Stanford's Office of Technology Licensing to over 40 academic and industrial research groups. BB1's generality is a weakness because it does not constrain the application builder; thus, the design and development of an application system remain challenging tasks requiring technical and domain expertise. To remedy this weakness, we have begun to develop 'higher-level languages' for BB1 that tailor it to particular application classes. One of these, the ACCORD design framework, is discussed elsewhere in this volume.

15

MXA – A Blackboard Expert System Shell

Anita Tailor

15.1 Introduction

MXA was initially developed for the problem of tactical picture compilation, i.e. producing a representation of the environment surrounding a Naval task group, derived from sensor information and displayed as a set of labelled or unlabelled objects. The tactical picture needs to be updated every few seconds and the related processing has to work in close to real time. The sensor information stems from several and diverse sources, e.g. radar, ESM, intelligence, etc., which need to be integrated.

MXA was therefore designed from the outset with facilities to cope with the above problem. Although the examples given in this chapter reflect these origins, MXA has, in fact, a generalized set of facilities which can be used for a much wider range of problems.

The system is able to generate new hypotheses as soon as evidence is made available from sensors. It is also capable of adding evidence in support of hypotheses already in existence. For instance, the existence of a well justified track (hypothesis) leads naturally to the conclusion that there is an as-yet unidentified object associated with it (hypothesis formation). At some later time, more evidence may become available to support the object hypothesis and MXA takes this new evidence into account and recalculates the probability that the object hypothesis is correct (hypothesis reinforcement).

MXA includes both forward-chaining (event driven) and backward-chaining (goal driven) inference mechanisms. This bidirectional reasoning capability, together with the requirement for real-time operation, characterizes the MXA system.

An application of MXA (termed a *Model*) is written in the MXA language, which is an extension of Pascal. The MXA compiler translates

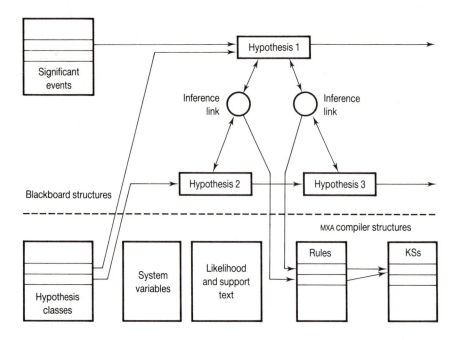

Figure 15.1   MXA data structures.

this into Pascal code which is then compiled by the host computer's Pascal compiler. An MXA application system, therefore, appears as one Pascal program. Several data structures are used within MXA. These are summarized in Figure 15.1, and are examined in more detail later. The dynamic information relating to the activity of the system is held as a global blackboard, controlled through the data structures generated by the MXA compiler.

15.2 Blackboard

15.2.1 Introduction

The fundamental data structure of a multiple knowledge source system is the data shared between these knowledge sources. Without such shared data there can be no communication between the experts these knowledge sources emulate and, consequently, no cooperation either. This shared data is commonly referred to as the blackboard. Examples of other blackboard systems can be found in Hanson and Riseman (1978b), Nii (1980), Nii *et al.* (1982) and Balzer *et al.* (1980).

As the internal means of communication and the repository of all knowledge, the blackboard and all parts of it can be accessed by the rules. This freedom of access is necessary so that the rules can establish whether the preconditions necessary to draw some inference hold. If they do, the rule can invoke its action part which in turn can record the results of this inference on the blackboard. This, in turn, may establish preconditions for other rules to fire. Thus the blackboard serves, on the one hand, as input to the rules, and, on the other, as a record of the outcome of the rules.

Because the blackboard holds all of the information the system has about the world, the system may use knowledge, i.e. rules, to identify a likely subset of this data which the user would want to have displayed. This would be, in effect, a display of the best interpretation of the specific problem at that time.

15.2.2 Contents

As already indicated, the blackboard is a record of the hypotheses reached so far and of the way they interconnect. Hypotheses can arise in a variety of ways. The most obvious and basic way is as a result of input (for example, from sensors). Whenever the system receives a new item of input, it records the details on the blackboard in the form of a hypothesis. It is a hypothesis for good reasons. The mere receipt of an input does not necessarily constitute a fact about the outside world. The input can be distorted, for instance by a sensor malfunctioning. Recording its reading as a hypothesis allows the input to be ascribed some likelihood based on the view of its current reliability.

Second, hypotheses can arise as the result of conclusions reached by rules. On the basis of information recorded in a current set of hypotheses, the rule can postulate a new hypothesis, record its details, and assign a measure of likelihood to it.

Third, rules can create hypotheses not only on what has happened, but also on what they expect to happen. They can record these expectations in the form of hypotheses on the blackboard. Later, other rules may establish some correlation between expectations and actualities and draw suitable conclusions based on whether the latter fulfill the former or not, as the case may be.

The blackboard records not only the hypotheses but also how they are linked. An evidential link from hypothesis A to hypothesis B indicates that A supports B. Additional information attached to the link can record associated information such as the strength of support, explanatory text for the support, and the like. The link is accessible from both ends so as to enable searches for supporting as well as supported hypotheses.

Any one hypothesis on the blackboard is an instance of a class. A

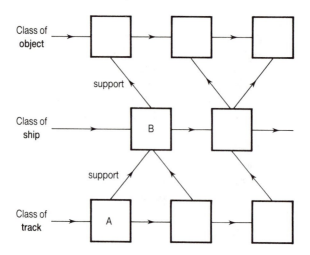

Figure 15.2   Hypothesis classes.

class indicates the nature of the hypothesis, such as to what degree an item is ship-like, target-like, track-like, etc. A class definition gives the information needed to describe a class, i.e. the fields that constitute it. When a new hypothesis is created, a new instance of its parent class is recorded on the blackboard. This new instance is added to the list of existing instances of the class. The members of a class are linked together to enable the system to find all instances of, for example, ship hypotheses, target hypotheses, etc. (see Figure 15.2). The quantifiers which appear in the rules effectively follow these links to find the members of a set.

15.2.3 Expectations

It has been found that one of the most successful methods for achieving combinatorial compression of a search space is to implement a mechanism for allowing expectations to be expressed (Nii *et al.*, 1982).

An expectation is a particular form of hypothesis. Both have the same structure and are linked in similar ways. An expectation differs in that, rather than being part of the bottom-up reasoning structure, it tries to interpret low-level signals in the light of high-level information and thus is an expression of top-down reasoning. The use of expectations is best described with the help of an example.

The diagram in Figure 15.3 illustrates the entry of a flight plan into an MXA system. The plan identifies the vehicle in every particular. It is

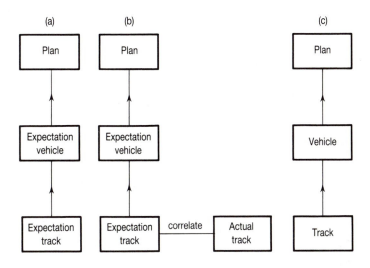

Figure 15.3   Entry and correlation of flight plan to track.

the task of the system to correlate this plan with the track detected by a sensor. Clearly, there is a large conceptual gap between the (low-level) track and the (high-level) plan. Expectations can be used to form a bridge, as follows:

(1)   The plan implies a vehicle; a vehicle hypothesis is posted on the blackboard as an expectation and linked to the plan; some parameters are copied to the vehicle hypothesis, for instance its identification.

(2)   The vehicle hypothesis implies the existence of a track; this too is posted and relevant attributes are copied into it from the plan, e.g. expected bearing at detection, range, heading, etc.

Thus a pseudo-evidential chain, track-vehicle-plan is generated, but without low-level justification for the track (Figure 15.3(a)).

Eventually, a track will be built up and some rule, which does not ignore expectations, will correlate the actual with the expectation (Figure 15.3(b)), then the evidence chain will be substantiated and the plan now tied in to reality (Figure 15.3(c)).

To avoid ambiguity and to speed processing, expectations have an associated timeout field specified at posting. The expectation will only be considered after the timeout has expired.

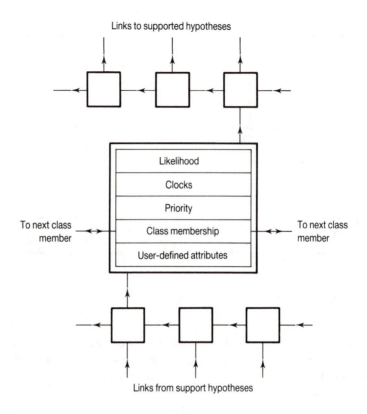

Links to supported hypotheses

Likelihood

Clocks

Priority

To next class member   Class membership   To next class member

User-defined attributes

Links from support hypotheses

Figure 15.4   General form of MXA hypothesis.

15.2.4 Hypothesis structure

Hypotheses in MXA are defined in a similar way to those in the HASP/SIAP system (Nii *et al.*, 1982). A hypothesis is composed of two parts:

- the 'hidden' structures required by the system to maintain control, and
- the 'visible' part holding user-defined attributes.

The general form of a hypothesis is illustrated in Figure 15.4.

Hidden structure

- *Likelihood field*   This field records the 'degree of belief' in the hypothesis, expressed typically as a probability measure. It is automatically maintained by the system, as described in Section 15.5.

- *Clock fields* Time stamping is required for overall control. There are three clock fields:

  (a) time hypothesis created,
  (b) time last updated,
  (c) time to be considered.

  The latter is for use in expectations, i.e. hypotheses due for consideration by the system and after some elapsed time-interval from posting.

- *Link fields* To record the relationship between hypotheses as described in Section 15.2.2, defining:

  (a) class membership,
  (b) evidence structure.

The above items are made accessible in the rule language by function calls or other mechanisms in order to hide implementation details.

Visible structure

This is user defined in the form of data declarations analogous to Pascal data declarations. These represent domain-dependent hypothesis attributes and can be accessed directly by the user, if so desired.

15.3 Rules and the rule language

15.3.1 General principles

Rules in MXA perform two functions. They provide:

(1) the means of representing (encoding) knowledge of the problem domain;
(2) the means of reasoning about the domain, i.e. how the knowledge is applied.

The current state of reasoning is recorded on the blackboard as hypotheses, which are related:

- in classes of similar hypotheses,
- in evidential reasoning chains.

Rules are condition–action pairs. Although the mechanism is different in detail, the general effect on each MXA cycle is to match rule conditions against the state of the blackboard and then to fire a rule, i.e. to execute the action part. The action may then update the blackboard which could later cause further rules to fire.

Successive elemental matching operations in a condition will lead either to a failure to satisfy the whole condition, in which case the system moves on to consider another rule, or else the condition will be satisfied. The result of a successful match is a set of groups of hypotheses (tuples) which then form the context in which the action is obeyed. In practice, the system may find several such tuples which satisfy the condition. In this case the action must decide whether to perform its processing on all, some or none.

15.3.2 Rules

Rule processing is best described with the aid of an example. We start by describing the rule in English. We assume that two classes of hypothesis have been declared: 'ships' and 'tracks'. Both have 'range' and 'bearing' attributes. We wish to encode the rule:

> If there are any ships and tracks in close proximity, associate each ship with its adjacent track, but only if such an association does not already exist.

The rule, formally encoded, will appear as follows:

```
RULE near_ship_and_track: "near ship and track correlation rule" IS    (1)
    S = SET_OF TUPLE (x:track;y:ship)                                   (2)
    SUCH_THAT                                                           (3)
    X DOES_NOT_SUPPORT Y                                                (4)
        AND Near (X,Y)                                                  (5)
    ACTION                                                              (6)
        FOR_ALL a IN S DO                                              (7)
            SUPPORT (a.x,a.y,7,3,10,                                    (8)
            "track is very near the ship")
        END_FOR_ALL OF a
END_RULE                                                               (9)
```

Line by line, this means:

(1)   The rule is named and explanation text specified.

(2)   The condition builds tuples consisting of two hypotheses. This set of tuples will be referred to, in the action, by the name s and each tuple contains two hypotheses, a track called x and a ship called y.

(3)   Filter the tuples with the following constraints.

(4)   Allow through only those tuples (x,y) for which x does not support y.

(5)   For every (X,Y) pair generated by (2), call the user-written predicate 'near' which, on the basis of the attribute fields, decides whether the separation between the objects is sufficiently small as to allow association of the two.

(6)   Pass s, the set of uncorrelated, near (X,Y) tuples to the action.

(7)   Iterate over all members of s giving the tuple the local name a, i.e. do for each (X,Y) tuple the action on the next line.

(8)   Create an evidential link such that the track now provides substantiation for the ship hypothesis. The figures represent the Bayesian weightings which describe to what extent the track affirms and denies the ship hypothesis. The text associated with SUPPORT and the text associated with the rule are attached to the evidential link for use in explanation generation. The system will recalculate the likelihood of the ship hypothesis in the light of the new (track) evidence.

(9)   The rule terminates and the structure s is destroyed (but the hypotheses are not).

In the preceding example, many (X,Y) pairs had to be generated. This is expensive and can commonly be avoided. The following example illustrates other facilities for earlier discrimination of the wanted set of tuples. Our rule is:

> If there are any ships within 5 nautical miles of that one, find the nearest.

We assume that ships have attributes recording the nearest ship field.

```
RULE nearest-ship "rule to find the nearest ship" IS
     S = SET-OF (x,y:ship)                              (1)
     SUCH-THAT
          x # y                                         (2)
     AND Separation (x,y) <5                            (3)
     AND THERE-IS-NO z:ship                             (4)
          SUCH-THAT
          (Separation (x,y) > Separation (x,z)          (5)
          AND x # z)                                    (6)
     ACTION
          FOR-ALL a IN S DO                             (7)
               a.x.nearest-ship:=a.y                    (8)
          END-FOR-ALL OF a
END-RULE
```

Notes:

(1)   Make the set, s, of ships where y is the nearest ship to x.

(2)   x is clearly different from y.

(3)   The distance between x and y is less than 5 nautical miles.

(4)   Deny the existence of another ship . . .

(5)   which is closer to x than y . . .

(6)   . . . and which, of course, is different from x.

(7)   Perform the action for each tuple, a, in the set s.

(8)   Set the user field nearest_ship to the value of the nearest ship, y.

15.3.3 Other language issues

The examples given in Section 15.3.2 illustrate the general principles of rule writing and some of the facilities that the writer has at his or her disposal.

We do not attempt here formally to define the syntax and semantics of the language. However, we present below the major features of it in order that examples can be written directly.

Built-in functions

MXA models make extensive use of built-in functions, which are encoded in Pascal. Section 15.3.5 contains some examples of those that are provided. Their primary purpose is to hide the underlying implementation from the rule writer.

Knowledge sources

These are described in more detail in Section 15.4. The general form of a knowledge source is:

```
KNOWLEDGE_SOURCE track_update "KS for tracking" IS
INITIALLY ON PRIORITY 25
    — followed by list of rules —
END_KNOWLEDGE_SOURCE
```

The string, as always, is available to the run-time system for use in explanation generation.

ON and the priority value are attributes of the knowledge source and may be used and modified to assist in scheduling.

It is most important to note that a knowledge source in the implementation considers each rule in the order of specification and fires any that it finds. However, this is unlikely to be a problem provided that the rule writer can be sure of the order in which actions are performed and take care in the rules to avoid unwanted side-effects.

Class declaration

The class declaration specifies the hypotheses types available to the rules. The general form of the declaration is:

```
CLASS ship "ship hypothesis" IS
       x:integer;
       y:real;
       a:ARRAY [SUBRANGE 1..n] OF integer;
```

The string is for explanation, as usual. The user-defined attributes are as for Pascal. The system creates the additional fields for system-defined attributes (such as likelihood) and the internal mechanisms required to manipulate the hypothesis instance on the blackboard.

15.3.4 Language features

Local variables

The MXA language permits the user to declare local storage for use within knowledge sources, rules or actions. The scope of the variable is limited to that knowledge source, rule or action and the contents of the variable are not preserved from one invocation to the next, e.g.

```
RULE

ACTION
      VAR i:integer;
      VAR a:ARRAY [SUBRANGE 1..n] OF real;
         .

         .

END_RULE
```

Global variables

These are declared at the head of the rule base in standard Pascal format.

User-written procedures and functions

These are either written in MXA and placed within the model itself, or in Pascal and placed in some external module. In the former case, the declaration follows the practice of the underlying dialect of Pascal.

Preamble

A rule base is introduced by a MODEL declaration.

15.3.5 Example

There now follows an example of a simple MXA rule base.

```
MODEL example "A simple MXA model"

CLASS ship "ship hypothesis" IS
     refno:integer

CLASS track "track hypothesis" IS
     x-coord,
     y-coord,
     z-coord:real

VAR some-global-data:integer

FUNCTION is-near (A:ship,B:track):boolean
  .
  .
  .
END-FUNCTION

KNOWLEDGE-SOURCE correlate "Correlate ships and tracks"
IS INITIALLY ON
   PRIORITY 2

RULE Add-support "Make nearby tracks support ships."
IS
     S = SET-OF (sh:ship;tr:track)
     SUCH-THAT
          tr DOES-NOT-SUPPORT sh
     AND is-near (sh,tr)
ACTION
     FOR-ALL x IN S DO
          Support (x.tr,x.sh,9,1,10,"the track is near
          the ship")
     END-FOR-ALL OF x
END-RULE

RULE Make-new-ships "Create ships to explain tracks."
IS
     S = SET-OF (tr:track)
     SUCH-THAT
```

```
        THERE-IS-NO sh:ship
        SUCH-THAT
                tr SUPPORTS sh

ACTION
VAR sh:ship
BEGIN
        FOR-ALL x IN S DO
                sh:= CREATE ship PRIOR 5 (42)
                support (x.tr,sh,5,1,10, "the track suggests a
                ship")
        END-FOR-ALL OF x
END-RULE


END-KNOWLEDGE-SOURCE
    .

    .

    .

more knowledge sources
```

15.3.6 Built-in routines

A wide selection of built-in routines is provided for traversal and manipulation of the blackboard structures. Some examples of these are:

- CREATE which creates a new instance of a hypothesis of the given class with a given prior probability and given values for the user fields;
- SUPPORT which creates a supporting line between two hypotheses;
- LIKELIHOOD which returns the likelihood of a given instance of a hypothesis;
- NEXT which, given an instance of a hypothesis, returns a pointer to the next instance in the same class.

Meta-knowledge sources (see Section 15.4.2) have additional functions available to them, such as:

- KS-PRIORITY which returns the priority of a KS;
- COUNT which returns the number of hypotheses instantiated in the given class.

15.4 Knowledge sources and the system cycle

15.4.1 General

The MXA system executes in a continuous loop, choosing knowledge sources to fire and executing them. These may be turned on or off, or scheduled according to priorities, by some higher level of authority. The higher-level authority is the meta-knowledge source.

15.4.2 Scheduling and meta-knowledge

At any instant, several KSs may be candidates to run. The implementation of MXA ensures that all knowledge sources which contain rules that may now run (consequent to recent updates to the blackboard) are known to the system. The choice of which to run is made by meta-knowledge sources. As befits their supervisory role, meta-KSs have additional access rights, e.g.

- to normally hidden fields on the blackboard,
- to control fields associated with KSs,
- to the internal scheduling mechanisms.

This, of course, raises the question of what schedules these scheduling KSs. This decision is left to the rule writer. A meta-level scheduling scheme is created with the generalized mechanisms most suited to the purpose. In this way alternative techniques may be explored.

It should be noted that the internal operation of the knowledge sources, in particular the decision as to which, if any, rules to fire, is internal to the KS.

15.4.3 Knowledge sources

A KS, whether at the user or meta-level, is simply a group of rules with the following characteristics:

(1) It may be turned on or off, i.e. there is a flag to permit focusing of system resources for greatest benefit, or to select a particular knowledge source from several possibilities for the resolution of a particular problem.

(2) It has a priority, which can be set by meta-rules, once again to assist in the focusing of control.

(3) All the rules in a KS which can fire, will fire.

(4) By convention (analogous to structured programming), a KS should contain rules of a particular type, or dedicated to a particular purpose, dependent on the application.

Knowledge sources can be invoked by meta-knowledge sources or by the user at system run-time. These 'ordinary' knowledge sources are similar in form to those in the HASP/SIAP (Nii *et al.*, 1982) and AGE (Nii, 1980) systems.

15.4.4 Significant events

The MXA executive watches the activity on the blackboard and takes note of some events. Those that are noticed are termed 'significant events'. Examples of significant events include:

- the creation or destruction of a hypothesis,
- the timeout of a hypothesis posted for later consideration,
- the modification of a user-defined hypothesis attribute,
- an update to the likelihood of a hypothesis.

Significant events can therefore be used by the user-written scheduler to determine which knowledge source is best to fire for any particular system cycle.

15.4.5 System cycle

The MXA system operates in a cycle, referred to as the System Cycle. During the system cycle the knowledge defined by the user is invoked. In an ideal world only very small chunks of knowledge, perhaps one rule, would be invoked before the system reappraises the environment and decides what knowledge is best to invoke next. In practice, a number of rules can reasonably be invoked before the system reschedules, though the time taken to do this processing must still be short lest the environment should change so much that the knowledge which is currently being invoked is inappropriate. Therefore, on each system cycle one knowledge source is invoked.

As far as the model writer is concerned, therefore, the system cycle can be split into two logically distinct parts: a scheduling part, in which some useful knowledge is selected by the use of meta-knowledge, and a part in which the knowledge source which contains the selected knowledge is invoked.

15.5 Inference

15.5.1 Probabilities

Each hypothesis on the blackboard has a measure of likelihood. This likelihood indicates the system's strength of conviction about the hypothesis. As time passes and evidence accumulates, the likelihoods of hypotheses change.

The likelihood of a hypothesis is expressed on a scale from -100 to 100. There is a standard function likelihood (x) to retrieve the current value for some hypothesis x.

15.5.2 Reasoning

In order to update probabilities in light of new evidence, the system has to employ some method of reasoning. The method used by MXA is based on Bayes' Rule.

In order to use Bayes' Rule the following items of information are needed:

(1)   the prior probability of the hypothesis whose likelihood we are updating;

(2)   the prior and current probabilities of all supporting hypotheses;

(3)   the weights expressing how strongly a supporting hypothesis would confirm or deny its consequent.

15.5.3 Information sources

Input parameters to Bayes' Rule come from the hypothesis being updated, its supporting hypotheses, and the links between the two. Initially, a likelihood value is given to a hypothesis when it is created.

When Bayes' Rule is applied, this value is taken as the prior probability of the hypothesis. Successive applications of Bayes' Rule will update this value by using the current value as the prior probability.

15.5.4 Updating probabilities

As mentioned before, probabilities are updated by employing Bayes' Rule. This allows two sets of information to be taken into account:

(1)   the probability history of the hypothesis summed up by its current probability;

(2)   the probabilities of all supporting hypotheses, both for and against.

From the supporting hypotheses we need both their prior and their current probabilities. Both are recorded as part of the hypotheses. The prior probability field is filled when the hypothesis is created, the current probability field was filled by the last application of Bayes' Rule. (At the time of creation, current probability is initialized to the same value as prior.)

Affirm and deny strengths and an overall scaling factor are associated with each supporting link. They are specified by the call to support that sets up the link. In this way the system can ensure that information is neither lost nor disregarded.

Changing the likelihood of a hypothesis, as indicated in Section 15.4.4, is a significant event. What this means is that it prompts the system to revise other parts of the blackboard and, through that, to update any supported hypotheses. The way this happens is that, whenever the likelihood of a hypothesis changes, the likelihoods of all other hypotheses that this one supports, whether directly or indirectly, are recalculated. In this way, perturbations to a single hypothesis are propagated to all affected parts of the blackboard. The end result is that all hypotheses are kept both up to date and consistent.

15.6 Explanation generation

15.6.1 Introduction

The ability of knowledge-based systems to explain their actions is of paramount importance in making them reliable and credible in real applications. An explanation of a conclusion in a knowledge-based system ought to furnish:

(1)   the *evidence*, i.e. the data on which the argument is based;

(2)   the *warrant* which supplies the connection between the evidence and the conclusion;

(3)   the *qualifier* which indicates with what degree of confidence the evidence leads to the conclusion; and, possibly,

(4)   the *backing* that supplies support for the warrant.

15.6.2 Explanation in MXA

In the MXA framework, the responsibility for the generation of explanations is left primarily to the model and model writer. The primitives are provided for the construction of specific explanations, thereby allowing an explanation of why a conclusion is reached as well as how, i.e. which rules were accessed.

In MXA, the components of an explanation, corresponding to the items in Section 15.6.1, appear as follows:

(1)   The *evidence* is the data on which the conclusion being explained is based. In this instance these are the parameters that a rule used for supporting a blackboard hypothesis. It is obtainable from the blackboard by examining the fields of the supporting hypotheses (for example, 'current position of object is over land').

(2)   The *warrant* is the description of the reason behind the rule. In this instance it is some explanatory text associated with the rule that produced or updated the hypothesis, which is attached to the supporting link (for example, 'ships do not pass over land').

(3)   The *qualifier* is the weight given to the rule, i.e. by how much it affirms or denies its conclusion. This again is a parameter of the rule and it too is attached to the supporting link (for example, '1.0' meaning 'with absolute certainty').

(4)   The *backing* is the rule invoked to set up or modify the conclusion. In our instance this is an identifier given to the rule which is also attached to the supporting link (for example, the 'over-land' rule).

Given the above items of information, conclusions can be justified to the operator by examining the supporting hypothesis and the support links and by accessing the rule writer's explanation text to give the following for the example given:

'*x* is not a ship'	(*the conclusion the operator asked explanation for*)
'because'	
'current position of *x* is over land'	(*the evidence of the supporting hypothesis*)
'and'	
'with absolute certainty'	(*the qualifier*)
'ships do not pass over land'	(*the warrant*)
'by the'	
'over-land' rule	(*the backing*)

The explanation generator gets the necessary data from text strings which appear in the source rule text in:

- the hypothesis class declaration,
- the rule declaration,
- the calls to SUPPORT.

15.7 Conclusion

The main features of the MXA expert system framework have been presented. The blackboard architecture is applicable to dynamic problems, such as planning and signal interpretation, which require a global outlook and can be defined in terms of levels. The constructs within MXA, which allow such things as forward and backward chaining, expectations, scheduling and explanation generation provide a friendly rule-writing language which allows a knowledge engineer to develop and debug a real-time rule based system. However, as in other expert system frameworks, the onus is very much on the model writer to create a consistent and worthwhile model.

MXA has its drawbacks and omissions, such as nonincremental compilation, a lack of consistency checking of rules and no property inheritance; most of these being due to its being one of the first operational blackboard systems produced in Europe. However, it has served to point the way forward and is still a useful prototyping tool in its own right, being sufficiently powerful and reliable to be used in real application systems.

16

BLOBS – An Object-Oriented Blackboard System Framework for Reasoning in Time

Roberto Zanconato

16.1 Introduction

A common characteristic of many knowledge-based command and control systems is a need for them to reason with continuous streams of data from many disparate sensors and information sources. From such data, interpretations are made and hypotheses generated which attempt to describe, as accurately as possible, the state of the world at any given instance. This world description is used, together with representations of predicted future states, to prepare plans which are executed in order to exert control over the environment, so as to create changes in the world state to the advantage of the controller. These changes, if successful, are themselves recognized through further inferences, thereby providing a measure of effectiveness of active and proposed plans.

Such systems require the supporting framework to support time in a variety of ways (Bell, 1984). It must support the primitive operations necessary for reasoning about time and past, or future, events, and also provide support for examination of the problems of reasoning against time (i.e. support for modeling the dilemma: Do I act now, or do I wait until I have thought some more or until new information becomes available?). This differs markedly from simple consultation systems, which often have no need to take into account the consequences of any advice they provide, are not usually constrained to provide results in limited periods of time and are not required to reason with continually changing input data.

This chapter describes the application of the BLOBS framework to the solution of these problems, using examples taken from the domain of air defense. However, these methods are probably equally applicable to many other real-time command and control domains.

16.2 Problems of reasoning in time

Continuous reasoning implies a continual arrival of information into the reasoning system. If we were to retain all information that arrived and interpretations derived therefrom we would soon find that the storage demands made by the system would eventually outstrip supply. Even if we could find a suitable storage device that provided for all our needs, the processing power required to manage such quantities of information would itself become excessive, considerably reducing the response times of the system (probably to unacceptable levels). Fortunately, as this information ages, much of it will become irrelevant to any subsequent reasoning performed by the system. When this occurs it can be safely discarded. However, deciding which information can be thrown away is a nontrivial task. How should this be done? When should it be done? The framework that supports the application is not the ideal place, since if it is to be free of any domain knowledge (a useful criterion for an experimental framework) the only methods available to it would also be independent of the knowledge that was being represented. It must therefore be embedded in the application. However, the framework must provide features that make this explicit control of deletion of unwanted information controllable, extensible and not over-obtrusive to the developer.

A continuous system operating in real time will also be required to reason against time, since a result, no matter how correct, or a plan, no matter how suited, is of no use if it arrives too late to be used. At first sight the answer here is to provide sufficient resources so that this problem would never occur. This unfortunately does not take into account degradation in performance due to partial system failure, or demands made on the system which were not originally envisaged (perhaps due to improved offensive capability of the enemy during the lifetime of the system). Any system in active service must provide graceful degradation in performance under all failure conditions. An experimental system which is hoped will emulate such behavior should, therefore, provide facilities so that appropriate heuristics for handling such failures can be developed and tested.

16.3 The framework requirement

The important features of this application are that it involves processing a continuous stream of data from radar and reasoning about geometrical and temporal information. Very little work in AI has dealt with this type of problem, and that which has has commonly used a type of software architecture called a blackboard system (Nii, 1980), which is a complex form of production system.

Originally our framework was to support only the expert system, with the simulation being performed by an already existent simulator that provided detailed radar plot reports. We quickly realized that this approach would severely limit the modeling that could be performed by a controller built within the framework. These restrictions included the difficulty of using diverse information sources and, more importantly, the inability of the reasoning system to change the behavior of the simulation as a result of decisions made by the controller.

We therefore began by building frameworks for both. We chose a blackboard system to model the controller (Bell, 1984) and a simple object-oriented message-passing system to model the aircraft and radars (Middleton, 1984). Thus the expert system and simulation were at this stage distinct from one another, although they were supported by a common kernel operating system for scheduling the simulation actors and the blackboard knowledge sources. A successful demonstration was built using this system with the object-oriented method being especially suited to simulations. However, there were a number of problems to this approach, some of which were related to the basic incompatibility of the two frameworks, while others were due to inherent problems that we found arose in attempting to use a classic blackboard design for continuous real-time reasoning.

The problems with the standard blackboard approach included the requirement that all state information, no matter how trivial, had to be kept on the blackboard and that all such data once on the blackboard was updatable by all knowledge sources in the system. This free-for-all meant that there was no formal way of restricting access to data to help ensure that it remained consistent. The lack of responsibility for data on the blackboard also made it difficult to decide when it was no longer required, which had the effect of leaving large quantities of useless information on the blackboard. The blackboard system did, however, have one redeeming feature: that of demon activated knowledge sources. These are blocks of code activated not by direct call but as a result of certain conditions occurring on the blackboard, such as the update of the value of a blackboard item or the creation of a new item.

From these two earlier frameworks came BLOBS (BLackboard OBjectS) which has attempted to amalgamate the best features from both the blackboard and object-oriented systems. The rest of our chapter looks at this integrated framework for simulation and reasoning.

16.4 BLOBS

16.4.1 Structure of BLOBS

Each blob consists of a set of declarations and definitions which describe its generic form from which any number of instances may be created. The main components of the definition include:

- *A set of local variable declarations* Every instance of an object corresponding to the generic form possesses an instance of a set of such variables which totally define the state of the object. Each such variable may be declared as *public* or *private*. If *public*, the variable is visible, as read-only to all other instances, while if *private* it is invisible to all other blobs. In either case the owning blob has both read and write access to the variable.

- *A set of pseudo-variable definitions* These provide nonary operators which are evaluated on each access and return a result, the value of the pseudo-variable. Again each definition may be declared *public* or *private* to provide appropriate scoping.

- *A set of procedure definitions* These are local to the blob definition and help improve the readability of code.

- *A set of behaviors* A behavior is the main processing unit of an object which is a procedure-like block of code activated as a result of an event (see below).

- *An inheritance list* This expands the set of declarations and definitions for the blob by including the corresponding set from each of the generics named in the inheritance list.

16.4.2 Communication within BLOBS

BLOBS supports a variety of methods of communication between objects which can be classified into two groups. First, those that involve imperative actions executed within the body of a behavior:

- interrogation of the *public* variables of other blobs,

- the invocation of *public* nonary operators that provide for the lazy evaluation of pseudo-variables,

- the creation of a new instance of a blob with a given state (the initial values of its *public* variables),

and, secondly, those that cause the activation of a behavior:

- the sending of typed messages to specific instances of a blob;

- the updating by a blob of the value of one of its *public* variables, which in turn triggers demons attached to that variable;

- the triggering of demons monitoring the creation (birth) of new instances of blobs;

- the triggering of demons monitoring the deletion (death) of blob instances;

- execution of an arbitrary sequence of program code (in our case, POP-11 (Hardy, 1984).

There is a small cost associated with the introduction of two methods for disseminating information with regard to the ordering of events in time. A blob can learn of an event in two ways: by reading a *public* variable of another blob or by receiving a message. When a blob reads the *public* variable of another blob it receives the *current* value. Messages, however, are queued. It follows that if a blob receives one item of information from one source via a message and receives from another source via a *public* variable *the ordering in time of the two items of information can not necessarily be determined.* No practical problems with this have yet been encountered, but it is certainly something that should be kept in mind.

Without a notion of time a simple object-oriented framework is by itself inadequate to support time-based reasoning. Support for this in BLOBS is provided by a number of low-level primitives associated with the simulation clock. This clock is a pseudo-real-time clock which can be interrogated by any blob instance, and is also used by the scheduler to implement the sending of messages at or after varying intervals of time.

This clock is the same one used for driving all simulation objects defined in the system. However, the clock is halted during periods in which a simulation blob is running (since the behaviors of these objects will in reality not take any of the processor's time) and is left running during the execution of any reasoning blobs, allowing us to measure the time used in performing reasoning. The clock is further advanced when the system is idle in order to select any deferred messages on the message queue.

Each object can also monitor the demands the system as a whole is placing upon the processor, and use this information as a form of meta-knowledge to modify reasoning threads so as to make best use of the available time.

Behaviors are executed within a priority-based scheduler. The blob with the highest priority and a behavior to run is always run first. Each blob has direct control over its own priority which it can modify as it sees fit, allowing activities to be executed according to importance.

For a more detailed exposition of the BLOBS framework the reader is referred to Dickinson (1985), while a more general overview is provided by Middleton and Zanconato (1985).

16.5 Examples of solutions in BLOBS

How can BLOBS help us with the problems described above? It is beyond the scope of this chapter to describe in detail practical solutions to many of the above problems; however, a few examples can give a flavor of how one would attempt such an exercise. We first look at the problem of reasoning in time, followed by the problem of reasoning against time.

One of the easiest ways of representing events within BLOBS is to create an instance of a blob whose instance variables describe the event. For example, the following blob definition could be used to describe the event of a track being lost from radar.

```
dynamic blob lost_from_radar;
   public vars
   track_id
   LKtime
   LKposition  ;;; Last known position
   LKspeed     ;;; Last known speed
   LKheading;  ;;; Last known heading
endblob;
```

Instances of this object can then be created with statements like:

```
create    lost_from_radar -> > instance_id with
             track_id    = my id,
             LKposition  = my position,
             LKheading   = my heading,
             LKspeed     = my speed;
```

Further, each instance variable of this object can be accessed by statements similar to:

```
the track_id of (instance_id) -> id_of_lost_track;
```

The scoping rules of BLOBS, however, prohibit any external agent directly updating these instance variables (this includes deleting the object instance). Since this object is defined without any behaviors (i.e. code), it is itself incapable of performing any actions. The information within each instance of this object is therefore static, and cannot be removed from a running system.

The purpose of maintaining lost_from_radar events is to carry out track repair activities. If at some future time we discover a new track, our first objective will probably be to check to see if this could be the reappearance of a previous track that had left radar cover. By keeping a separate index to lost tracks we remove the need to search through each track object, many of which will not have been lost (they could still be in radar cover or known to have landed).

Unfortunately it is the fate of all tracks that they will eventually leave radar contact and, unless evidence is acquired to the contrary, will be classified as lost. Also many of these lost tracks may well be remnants of tracks lost during previous engagements. This initial approach is therefore not as useful as may be first thought. What is required is some way of limiting the life of these objects so as to reduce the search still further. A suitable pruning would be to delete all instances of lost_from_radar which were over 30 minutes old, or perhaps some smaller value if the airspace is particularly crowded.

The requirement to limit the life of data, events and hypotheses is found to be such a common activity that it is worth examining the problem in a more general form. The following *mixer* blob attempts to define a suitable set of behaviors which can be included in any blob requiring to be endowed with the property of being mortal (i.e. having a limited life).

```
;;; Define messages to be received by this object
message kill_myself;
message extend_life_time [new_life_time new_end_time];

;;; BLOB definition
mixer blob mortal;

  ;;; Declare instance variables
  public vars
    create_time                 ;;; Time the object was created
    life_time  := '00 00:30:00'  ;;; Defaults to 30 minutes
    end_time   := false          ;;; Absolute time if needed

  on_initialization do
    CURRENT_TIME -> my create_time;
    if my end_time.isnumber then
      my end_time - CURRENT_TIME -> my life_time;
    endif;
    if my life_time.isnumber then
      CURRENT_TIME - my life_time -> my end_time;
      send kill_myself after my life_time to (my id);
    endif;
  enddo;

  on_message extend_life_time do
        with new_life_time -> new_life_time
            new_end_time -> new_end_time do
    ;;; If a new life time specified give translate to an end time
    if new_life_time.isnumber then
      CURRENT_TIME + new_life_time -> new_end_time;
    endif;

    ;;; Is the new end time greater than current end time?
    if new_end_time.isnumber and
       new_end_time > my end_time then
          ;;; Replace its value with the new end time
```

```
            new_end_time -> my end_time;
        endif;
    enddo;


    on_message kill_myself do
        ;;; Test if a new "end_time" has been specified
        if CURRENT_TIME > my end_time then
            ;;; Terminate the BLOB instance
            suicide;
        else
            ;;; Wait for an extended period
            send kill_myself at my end_time to (my id);
        endif;
    enddo;


endblob;
```

The initialization behavior, executed when the object is created, arranges for a message to be sent to itself after a predefined time, which if not specified when the object is created will default to 30 min. A message extend_life_time is also included which can be used by external agents to extend this time if they feel that they may have further use of the information held by the object. The second message, kill_myself, behavior is used to check if the object is to be deleted, in which case it commits suicide, or whether it should live for an extended period of time, in which case a further message is sent to perform an identical test some time in the future.

The definition of the blob lost_from_radar can now be extended to behave in the manner described above by simply inheriting the definition of the object mortal into its own definition.

```
dynamic blob lost_from_radar;

    inherit mortal;   ;;; Inherit properties of mixer blob
                      ;;; defined above
    public vars
        track_id       ;;; Identity of track that disappeared
        LKposition     ;;; Last known position {x,y}
        LKspeed        ;;; Last known speed
        LKheading;     ;;; Last known heading

    ;;; Declare a pseudo-variable (a parameterless procedure)
    public definition predicted_position =
        ;;; Constructs a two dimensional vector whose value
        ;;; represents the current predicted position of the lost track
        {% my LKposition(1) * my LKspeed * sin(my LKheading) *
            (CURRENT_TIME - my create_time),
```

```
    my LKposition(2) * my LKspeed * cos(my LKheading) *
    (CURRENT_TIME - my create_time) %};

;;; Further ways to limit the life of this event
on_message you_have_been_found do
    suicide;
enddo;

on_death_of (my creator) do
    suicide;
enddo;


endblob;
```

As can be seen, the definition has also been extended to give the object a little more 'intelligence'. A pseudo-variable predicted_position is included which evaluates the current estimated position of the lost track each time it is called (assuming, of course, that the track continued with the same heading and speed that it had when it disappeared). The procedure of evaluating the predicted_position could of course be made more sophisticated. If the track had previously been associated with a flight-plan, the details of this flight-plan could be used to provide a more accurate prediction. Further, behaviors have also been added which allow for more specific methods of terminating the object; the first on receiving the message you_have_been_found, and a second on the death of the blob's creator.

Behaviors similar to the following can now be used to collect all lost tracks within a given range of a newly observed track and, provided the lifetime of the object had not been changed, each of the lost tracks would be no longer than 30 minutes old.

```
on_birth_of any track -> > trackid do
  vars lost_track;
  [] -> my possible_tracks;
  ;;; Construct a list of all lost tracks that may match the current
  ;;; Loop through all instances of "lost-radar_tracks"
  for lost_track in all lost_radar_tracks do
    if range( the predicted_position of (lost_track),
              the position of (trackid) ) < my sensible_range then
      ;;; Add track to list of possible tracks
      lost_track :: my possible_tracks -> my possible_tracks;
    endif;
  endfor;
  ;;; < Analyze in greater detail each of the possible tracks >
enddo;
```

As an example of reasoning against time, consider the problem of requiring to interpret or respond to some event. Two methods may be available, the first rough-and-ready and another slow-but-sure. The latter method is our desired response, but we may find that the resources available to us are inadequate to complete the action in the time available. The following BLOBS statement may be used to choose the most appropriate method.

```
target-time − CURRENT_TIME −> time-available
if time-to-complete( slow-but-sure ) <
      time-available * IDLENESS then
   send slow-but-sure to (my id);
elseif time-to-complete( rough-and-ready ) <
      time-available * IDLENESS then
   send rough-and-ready to (my id);
elseif time-to-complete( rough-and-ready ) < time-available
   1000 −> my priority;
   send rough-and-ready to (my id);
else
   1000 −> my priority;
   send panic to (my id);
endif;
```

Use is made of the nonadic operator IDLENESS, which returns an indication of the current load the system is having on the processor, as well as explicit updating of the priority of an object to force the execution of a behavior before other noncritical behaviors.

This example is, however, rather crude and in reality many more conditions must be taken into account. These would not only have to measure the current work load of the system but also provide some measure of the predicted work load; in the air defense domain this may involve using information such as the total number of tracks currently visible to the system.

16.6 Conclusions

We have examined a number of the time-related problems associated with the implementation of continuous real-time knowledge-based systems for command and control applications. These have been primarily related to the finite resources that are expected to exist in all practical systems. A basis for the solution of these problems was then presented and described in the object-oriented framework, BLOBS. However, it must be remembered that BLOBS was not developed solely to provide solutions to these problems, but instead to examine a whole cross-section of temporal and spatial problems found in both simulation and reasoning systems associated with air defense.

Acknowledgments

The BLOBS language was developed under contract to the Royal Signals and Radar Establishment, MOD (PE) by Cambridge Consultants Ltd. Views expressed within this chapter are, however, those of the author.

Part IV

17

Recent Applications (1981–1985)

R.S. Engelmore and A.J. Morgan

In Part III we examined several blackboard frameworks that generalized the problem-solving and architectural concepts from the early blackboard applications. How useful are these frameworks? In this part we present some recent blackboard systems implemented in a blackboard framework such as AGE, BB1 or MXA.

The first of these applications, chronologically, does not use one of the frameworks discussed in Part III, but is based on extensions to Hearsay-II. Over the past decade a group of researchers at the University of Massachusetts, under the direction of Victor Lesser, has been developing a model of cooperative, distributed problem solving. The model entails distributed networks of semi-autonomous nodes that work together to solve a single problem. They tested their ideas with an application in which multiple moving vehicles are monitored over time by multiple agents, each of which has only a partial view of the total situation board. The Distributed Vehicle Monitoring Testbed (DVMT), described in Chapter 18, implements the agents as separate blackboard systems whose architecture is based on Hearsay-II. The DVMT is a flexible and fully instrumented research tool for empirically evaluating these problem solving networks. The testbed simulates a class of distributed knowledge-based problem-solving systems operating on an abstracted version of a vehicle monitoring task.

There are two important aspects to the testbed:

(1) It implements a novel generic architecture for distributed problem-solving networks that exploits the use of sophisticated local node control and meta-level control to improve global coherence in network problem solving.

(2)   It serves as an example of how a testbed can be engineered to permit the empirical exploration of design issues in knowledge-based AI systems.

The testbed is capable of simulating different degrees of sophistication in problem-solving knowledge and different focus-of-attention mechanisms, for varying the distribution and characteristics of error in its (simulated) input data, and for measuring the progress of problem solving. Node configurations and communication channel characteristics can also be independently varied in the simulated network.

AGE was a generalization of the HASP program, so it is natural that other signal-understanding applications would fit well with its architecture. One such application is TRICERO, developed at ESL from 1983 to 1984. TRICERO was actually the second blackboard system developed at ESL, both of which are based on AGE. The first system, called HANNIBAL, was a prototype system for interpreting signals in the radio frequency portion of the electromagnetic spectrum. The data consisted of the location of the signal source, the frequency, modulation type, and other properties of the signal and, in some cases, parts of the communication itself, e.g. keywords in a message. An interpretation consisted of a description of the organization, e.g. a tank battalion, that was producing these communications. A number of sources of knowledge were required, ranging from relatively low-level rules for determining if two separate radio emissions came from the same or different emitters, to high-level knowledge about the relationships between organizational units, their radio equipment and their expected patterns of communication. In military jargon, this activity is called communication intelligence, or COMINT, for short. Similar acronyms are used for the types of signal interpretation, e.g. ELINT for electronic intelligence derived from radar signals.

The HANNIBAL prototype met its design goals, and further development involved expanding the knowledge sources to include classified information. A field prototype was developed and tested in Europe. Its current status is unknown. Soon after the demonstration prototype was completed, a more general problem was formulated. A military commander typically relies on multiple sources of intelligence (of which COMINT and ELINT are two examples), each interpreted by a specialist in that source. The commander's expertise is in correlating the high-level advice of his subordinates and formulating an overall situation assessment. TRICERO was an attempt to model a hierarchy of experts using multiple blackboard systems.

Like DVMT, the TRICERO system represents an extension of the blackboard system into the area of distributed computing. TRICERO was designed by Harold Brown of the Knowledge Systems Laboratory at

Stanford University. It was built by Mark Williams (ESL, now at Delfin Systems) and Terry Barnes (Teknowledge).

DVMT and TRICERO take different approaches to the problem of how one partitions the task. In DVMT the solution space is partitioned into loosely coupled regions, and copies of the same blackboard system are assigned to each region. In TRICERO the problem is partitioned into independent subproblems, and different blackboard systems (in that they use different knowledge sources and different blackboard structure) are assigned to each subproblem. TRICERO is, a prototype system which contains three blackboard systems – ELINT ANALYSIS, COMINT ANALYSIS and ELINT-COMINT correlation. The main body of Chapter 19 has previously been available only as an internal technical report at ESL. The report has been augmented with additional technical details of the structure and behavior of the system. (Sections 19.4.3–19.4.6 and 19.4.11 are from Nii (1986c).)

PROTEAN is a knowledge-based system, still under development, that attempts to determine the three-dimensional structure of a protein molecule. The project differs from CRYSALIS in the type of information with which one starts. Instead of an electron density map, which is a three-dimensional picture of the molecule (albeit fuzzy and inaccurate), PROTEAN uses information derived from magnetic resonance experiments. The magnetic resonance data can be used to derive a set of distances between certain pairs of atoms within the protein. In practice, there are relatively few such atomic separation specifications, so that the problem of determining the complete (tertiary) structure is highly under-constrained. Finding plausible candidate solutions requires a multi-dimensional search. Controlling the order of search and the range of the search space can make orders of magnitude difference in the execution time of a run. Consequently, control knowledge plays a critical role in the PROTEAN system, and the framework provided by BB1 greatly facilitates its representation and utilization. Chapter 20 describes the problem and how BB1 was used to build the system.

The FMC Corporation has used BB1 to develop a mission-planning system for an autonomous vehicle, described in Chapter 21. The input to the system is a mission statement, specified as a set of goals and constraints, and the output is a sequence of tasks that will achieve the goals. The solution method uses an opportunistic strategy, with the planning proceeding either top-down or bottom-up depending on the current solution state. The successful operation of the system is attributed to the flexibility of the blackboard architecture.

The Admiralty Research Establishment (ARE) at Portsdown, England, have a long-term interest in 'intelligent data fusion'. Their work includes experiments in rule-based processing of data within a naval task group. Such a group will typically include several ships and aircraft –

collectively referred to as 'Platforms'. Each platform may carry several different types of sensor, providing information on the surrounding environment. Additional, less structured information may be available, such as intelligence reports. Synthesizing an assessment of the current situation is a difficult task for a human and some form of automated support is clearly valuable. We have seen other systems with broadly similar requirements in HASP (Chapter 6) and TRICERO (Chapter 19) and this class of problem appears to be highly suited to the blackboard model. Although both TRICERO and ARE attempt to fuse data from a variety of sources, neither includes the possibility of partly analyzed data from other intelligent systems of the same type, as does the DVMT discussed in Chapter 18.

Early work at ARE concentrated on fusing the data from multiple sensors on a single platform. More recently, attention has turned to the additional problems of multiple platforms. One pointer to emerge from the ARE work is the value of combining information of the same kind (e.g. all radar data) before combining data from unlike sources. As a practical step, only pairwise correlations are used between sensors to reduce the number of possible interpretations.

The underlying framework used to support the application is MXA, which was described in Chapter 15. In Chapter 22 the operation of the system is illustrated by extracts from a typical scenario. As with the TRICERO system, its use of a graphics display has proved a valuable aid to understanding the operation of the system, in addition to simulating a suitable interface for the end-user. A well thought out graphics interface may prove a better medium for explanation than a purely textual system, particularly where a complex set of hypotheses is being maintained. Chapter 22 was prepared especially for this book.

18

The Distributed Vehicle Monitoring Testbed: A Tool for Investigating Distributed Problem Solving Networks

Victor R. Lesser and Daniel D. Corkill

There are two major themes of this chapter. First, we introduce readers to the emerging subdiscipline of AI called *distributed problem solving*, and more specifically the authors' research on Functionally Accurate, Cooperative systems. Second, we discuss the structure of tools that allow more thorough experimentation than has typically been performed in AI research. An example of such a tool, the Distributed Vehicle Monitoring Testbed, will be presented. The testbed simulates a class of distributed knowledge-based problem solving systems operating on an abstracted version of a vehicle monitoring task. This presentation emphasizes how the testbed is structured to facilitate the study of a wide range of issues faced in the design of distributed problem solving networks.

18.1 Characteristics of distributed problem solving

Distributed problem solving (also called distributed AI) combines the research interests of the fields of AI and distributed processing (Chandrasekaran, 1981; Davis, 1980; Fehling and Erman, 1983). We broadly define distributed problem solving networks as distributed networks of semi-autonomous problem solving *nodes* (processing elements) that are capable of sophisticated problem solving and cooperatively interact with other nodes to solve a *single* problem. Each node can itself be a sophisticated *problem-solving system* that can modify its behavior as circumstances change and plan its own communication and cooperation strategies with other nodes.

Distributed problem solving is an important research area for several reasons. First, hardware technology has advanced to the point where the construction of large distributed problem-solving networks is not only possible, but economically feasible. While the first networks may consist of only a small number of nodes, distributed problem-solving networks may eventually contain hundreds or thousands of individual nodes. We are nearing a situation of exciting hardware possibilities unaccompanied by the problem-solving technology required for their effective utilization. Second, there are AI applications that are inherently spatially distributed. A distributed architecture that matches their spatial distribution offers many advantages over a centralized approach. Third, understanding the process of cooperative problem solving is an important goal in its own right. Whether the underlying system is societal, managerial, biological or mechanical, we seem to understand competition far better than cooperation. It is possible that the development of distributed problem-solving networks may serve the same validating role to theories in sociology, management, organizational theory and biology as the development of AI systems has served to theories of problems solving and intelligence in psychology and philosophy.

Although this new area borrows ideas from both AI and distributed processing, it differs significantly from each in the problems being attacked and the methods used to solve these problems.

18.1.1 Distributed problem solving and distributed processing

Distributed problem-solving networks differ from distributed processing systems in both the style of distribution and the type of problems addressed (Smith and Davis, 1981). These differences are most apparent when we study the interactions among nodes in each of the types of networks. A distributed processing network typically has multiple, disparate tasks executing concurrently in the network. Shared access to physical or informational resources is the main reason for interaction among tasks. The goal is to preserve the illusion that each task is executing alone on a dedicated system by having the network operating system hide the resource sharing interactions and conflicts among tasks in the network. In contrast, the problem solving procedures in distributed problem-solving networks are explicitly aware of the distribution of the network components and can make informed interaction decisions based on that information. This difference in emphasis is, in part, due to the characteristics of the applications being tackled by conventional distributed processing methodologies. These applications have permitted task decompositions in which a node rarely needs the assistance of another node in carrying out its problem-solving function. Thus, most of the research as well as the paradigms of distributed processing do not directly address the issues of cooperative interactions of tasks to solve a single problem. As will be discussed later, highly cooperative task interaction is a requirement for many problems that seem naturally suited to a distributed network.

18.1.2 Distributed problem solving and artificial intelligence

Distributed problem solving also differs from much of the work in AI because of its emphasis on representing problem solving in terms of asynchronous, loosely coupled process networks that operate in parallel with limited interprocess communication. Networks of cooperating nodes are not new to artificial intelligence. However, the relative autonomy and sophistication of the problem solving nodes, a direct consequence of limited communication, sets distributed problem solving networks apart from most others, including Hewitt's work on the actor formalism, Kornfeld's ETHER language, Lenat's BEINGS system, and the augmented Petri nets of Zisman (Hewitt, 1977; Kornfeld, 1979; Lenat, 1975; Zisman, 1978). The requirement for limited communication in a distributed network has also led to the development of problem-solving architectures that can operate with possibly inconsistent and incomplete data and control information. In many applications, communication delay makes it impractical for the network to be structured so that each node has all the relevent information needed for its local computations and control decisions. Another way of viewing this problem is that the spatial decomposition of information among the nodes is ill-suited to a functionally distributed solution. Each node may possess the information necessary to perform a portion of each function, but insufficient information to completely perform any function.

18.1.3 The uses of distributed problem solving

Most initial work in distributed problem solving has focused on three application domains: distributed sensor networks, distributed air traffic control, and distributed robot systems (Davis, 1980, 1982b; Fehling and Erman, 1983). All of these applications need to accomplish distributed interpretation (situation assessment) and distributed planning. Planning here refers not only to planning what actions to take (such as changing the course of an airplane), but also to planning how to use resources of the network to carry out the interpretation and planning task effectively. This latter form of planning encompasses the classic control problem in AI.

In addition to the commonality in terms of the generic tasks being solved, these application domains are characterized by a natural spatial distribution of sensors and effectors, and by the fact that the subproblems of both the local interpretation of sensory data and the planning of

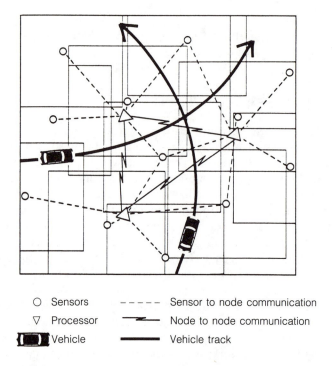

O	Sensors	- - - - -	Sensor to node communication
▽	Processor	▬▬▬	Node to node communication
🚗	Vehicle	▬▬▬	Vehicle track

Figure 18.1   Tracking vehicle movements in a distributed sensor network.

effector actions are interdependent in time and space. For example, in a distributed sensor network tracking vehicle movements, a vehicle detected in one part of the sensed area implies that a vehicle of similar type and velocity will be sensed a short time later in an adjacent area (Figure 18.1). Likewise, a plan for guiding an airplane must be coordinated with the plans of other nearby airplanes in order to avoid collision. Interdependency also arises from redundancy in sensory data. Often different nodes sense the same event due to overlaps in the range of sensors and the use of different types of sensors that sense the same event in different ways. Exploiting these redundant and alternative views and the interdependencies among subproblems require nodes to cooperate in order to interpret and plan effectively. This cooperation leads to viewing network problem solving in terms of a single problem rather than a set of independent subproblems.

It is difficult to develop a distributed problem-solving architecture that can exploit the characteristics of these applications to limit internode communication, to achieve real-time response, and to provide high reliability. Nodes must cooperate to exploit and coordinate their answers to interdependent subproblems, but must do so with limited interprocessor communication. This requires the development of new paradigms that permit the distributed system to deal effectively with environmental uncertainty (not having an accurate view of the number and location of processors, effectors, sensors and communication channels), data uncertainty (not having complete and consistent local data at a node) and control uncertainty (not having a completely accurate model of activities in other nodes).

We see the development of these paradigms as drawing heavily on the work in knowledge-based AI systems and, simultaneously, making contributions to AI. As Nilsson has noted, the challenges posed by distributed Artificial Intelligence will contribute to (and may even be a prerequisite for) progress in 'ordinary' artificial intelligence (Nilsson, 1980). One example of this interaction is the problem of controlling semi-autonomous problem solving agents possessing only a local and possibly errorful view of the global state of problem solving. Solutions being developed for this problem have involved the use of meta-level control, integrated data-directed and goal-directed control, and focus-of-attention strategies based on reasoning about the state of local problem solving (Corkill, 1983). Approaches similar to these are being used to solve the control problems that are faced in the development of a new generation of centralized knowledge-based problem-solving systems, which have significantly larger and more diverse knowledge bases.

In the remainder of this chapter we first describe the functionally accurate, cooperative distributed problem-solving paradigm and pilot experiments that explored the viability of this approach. After describing the issues we wish to explore using the distributed vehicle monitoring testbed, we present the vehicle monitoring task, followed by a detailed discussion of the testbed. Later sections describe how we have quantified system behavior and the use of these measures for simulating and evaluating the performance of various system components, overview the tools that help a user define experiments and analyze their output, review the current status of the testbed implementation, and outline future research directions.

18.2 Functionally accurate, cooperative distributed problem solving

Our research has focused on the design of distributed problem-solving networks for applications in which there is a natural spatial distribution of information and processing requirements, but insufficient information for each processing node to make completely accurate control and processing decisions without extensive internode communication (used to acquire missing information and to determine appropriate node activity). An example of this type of application is distributed vehicle monitoring.

Vehicle monitoring is the task of generating a dynamic, area-wide map of vehicles moving through the monitored area. Distributed vehicle monitoring typically has a number of processing nodes, with associated acoustic sensors (of limited range and accuracy), geographically distributed over the area to be monitored (Lacoss and Walton, 1978; Smith, 1978). Each processing node can communicate with other nearby nodes over a packet radio communication network (Kahn *et al.*, 1978). Each sensor includes the actual acoustic transducer, low-level signal-processing hardware and software, and communication equipment necessary to transmit the processed signals to a high-level (symbolic) processing site.

As a vehicle moves through the monitoring area, it generates characteristic acoustic signals. Some of these signals are recognized by nearby sensors which detect the frequency and approximate location of the source of the signals. An acoustic sensor has a limited range and accuracy, and the raw data it generates contains significant error. Using data from only one sensor can result in 'identification' of nonexistent vehicles and ghosts, missed detection of actual vehicles, and incorrect location and identification of actual vehicles. To reduce these errors, information from various sensors must be correlated over time to produce the answer map. The amount of communication required to redistribute the raw sensory data necessary for correct localized processing makes such an approach infeasible.

One way to reduce the amount of communication and synchronization is to loosen the requirement that nodes always produce complete and accurate results. Instead, each node produces tentative results which may be incomplete, incorrect, or inconsistent with the tentative partial results produced by other nodes. For example, a node may produce a set of alternative partial hypotheses based on reasonable expectations of what the missing data might be. In the vehicle-monitoring task, each node's tentative vehicle identification hypotheses can be used to indicate to other nodes the areas in which vehicles are more likely to be found and the details (vehicle type, rough location, speed, etc.) of probable vehicles. This information helps a node to identify the actual signals in its noisy sensory data. In addition, consistencies between these tentative identification hypotheses serve to reinforce confidence in each node's identifications. Such cooperation is not only appropriate for vehicle identification, but also potentially useful in other stages of processing (identification of raw signals, groups of harmonically related signals, patterns of vehicles, etc.).

This type of node processing requires a distributed problem-solving structure in which the nodes cooperatively converge to acceptable answers in the face of incorrect, inaccurate and inconsistent intermediate results. This is accomplished using an iterative, coroutine type of node interaction in which nodes' tentative partial results are iteratively revised and extended through interaction with other nodes. A network with this problem solving structure is called *functionally accurate, cooperative* (FA/C) (Lesser and Corkill, 1981). 'Functionally accurate' refers to the generation of acceptably accurate solutions without the requirement that all shared intermediate results be correct and consistent (as is the case with conventional distributed processing). 'Cooperative' refers to the iterative, coroutine style of node interaction in the network. The hope of this approach is that much less communication is required to exchange these high-level, tentative results than the communication of raw data and processing results that would be required using a conventional distributed processing approach. In addition, synchronization among nodes can also be reduced or eliminated entirely, resulting in increased node parallelism. Finally, this approach leads to a more robust network since errors resulting from hardware failure are potentially correctable in the same fashion as errors resulting from the use of incomplete and inconsistent local information.

18.2.1 A pilot experiment in distributed interpretation

A set of pilot experiments was performed to investigate the suitability of the FA/C approach using a network of complete Hearsay-II interpretation systems (Lesser and Erman, 1980). The Hearsay-II architecture appeared to be a good structure for each node because it incorporates mechanisms for dealing with uncertainty and error as an integral part of its basic problem solving. Further, the processing can be partitioned or replicated naturally among network nodes because it is already decomposed into independent and self-directed modules called knowledge sources, which interact anonymously and are limited in the scope of the data they need and produce. For further information about the Hearsay-II architecture see Erman *et al.* (1980).

Experiments were performed to determine how the problem-solving behavior of a network of Hearsay-II nodes compared to a centralized system. Each node was completely self-directed in its decisions about what work it should perform and what information it should transmit to other nodes. The aspects of behavior studied included the accuracy of the interpretation, the time required, the amount of internode communication, and network robustness in the face of communication errors. These experiments simulated only the distributed hardware – they used an actual Hearsay-II speech-understanding system analyzing real data. A spatial distribution of sensory data was modelled by having each node of the distributed speech understanding network sample one part (time-contiguous segment) of the overall speech signal.

The experiments showed that a network of three Hearsay-II speech understanding nodes performs well as a cooperative distributed network even though each node has a limited view of the input data and exchanges only high-level (phrasal) partial results with other nodes. In an experiment with errorful communication, network performance degraded gracefully with as much as 50% of the messages lost, indicating that the system can often compensate automatically for the lost messages by performing additional computation.

Although these experiments were extremely positive, they did point out a key issue in the successful application of the FA/C approach. This issue, which we feel is also important for the design of any complex distributed problem-solving network, is that of obtaining a sufficient level of cooperation and coherence among the activities of the semi-autonomous, problem-solving nodes in the network (Davis and Smith, 1981; Corkill et al., 1982). If this coherence is not achieved, the performance (speed and accuracy) of the network can be significantly diminished as a result of lost processing as nodes work at cross-purposes with one another, redundantly applied processing as nodes duplicate efforts, and misallocation of activities so that important portions of the problem are either inaccurately solved or not solved in timely fashion.

In the pilot experiments with the three-node network, we observed that the simple *data-directed* and *self-directed* control regime used in these experiments can lead to noncoherent behavior (Lesser, 1980a). Situations occurred when a node had obtained a good solution in its area of interest and, having no way to redirect its attention to new problems, simply produced alternative but worse solutions. Another problem occurred when a node had noisy data and could not possibly find an accurate solution without help from other nodes. In this situation, the node with noisy data often quickly generated an inaccurate solution which, when transmitted to the nodes working on better data, resulted in the distraction of these nodes. This distracting information in turn caused significant delay in the generation of accurate solutions by nodes with accurate as well as noisy data. We believe that development of appropriate network coordination policies (the lack of which resulted in diminished network performance for even a small network) will be crucial to the effective construction of large distributed problem-solving networks containing tens to hundreds of processing nodes.

18.3 The need for a testbed

Although these experiments provided initial empirical validation for the FA/C approach and pointed out an important set of issues that needed to be solved, they were just a first step. These experiments were not based on a realistic distributed task, and more importantly were limited in the scope of issues that could be addressed. Thus, a more extensive set of empirical investigations was necessary in order to better understand the utility and limitations of the FA/C approach. Empirical performance measures were needed for a wide range of task and problem-solving situations in order to evaluate and analyze the following issues:

(1) *Self-correcting computational structures* What and how much uncertainty and error can be handled using these types of computational structures? What are the costs (and trade-offs) in processing and communication to resolve the various types of error? How does the quality of knowledge used in the network affect the amount of uncertainty and error that can be accommodated?

(2) *Task characteristics and the selection of an appropriate network configuration* What characteristics of a task can be used to select the network configuration appropriate for it? When should problem solving among nodes be organized hierarchically? What type of authority relationship should exist among nodes? Should nodes be completely self-directed or should there be certain nodes that decide explicitly what other nodes should do, or should there be a negotiation structure among nodes (Smith and Davis, 1981)? Similarly, should information be transmitted on a voluntary basis or only when requested or some mixture of these policies?

The candidate task characteristic to evaluate included the size of the network and the communication topology; the type, spatial distribution and degree of uncertainty in information; the quality of knowledge in the network; interdependencies among subproblems; and the size of the search space.

Unfortunately, it was difficult to extend the distributed Hearsay-II speech-understanding system for these studies. There were two major reasons for this difficulty: the computation time needed to run experiments and inflexibilities in the design of the system. We discuss these reasons because they point out why extensive experimentation with large knowledge-based AI systems is very difficult.

The use of an existing knowledge-based system as the basic underlying problem-solving system in the experiments lent credibility to the simulation results and also avoided the extensive knowledge engineering that normally would have been required. The importance of having a concrete framework to explore ideas cannot be underestimated. Not until the problems of getting the Hearsay-II speech-understanding network to work appropriately in a distributed setting were confronted did many of our intuitions about how to design distributed problem solving networks evolve. However, there were major negative implications of using the actual Hearsay-II speech-understanding system. First, it was extremely time consuming to run the multinode simulations since the underlying problem solving system was large and computationally slow.

Second, the speech-understanding system did not naturally extend to larger numbers of nodes and more complex communication topologies without significant changes to the system. In part, this is because the speech task is not a realistic distributed processing task and its sensory data is one-dimensional (the time dimension). Third, efficiency considerations in the design of the speech understanding system led to a tight coupling among knowledge sources and the elimination of data-directed control at lower blackboard levels. This tight coupling precluded the exploration of many interesting network architectures. It was not possible to configure nodes with only a partial set of knowledge sources without significant modifications to the knowledge source interaction patterns. Fourth, the sheer size and complexity of knowledge source code modules made modification a difficult and time consuming process.

Basically, the flexibility of the Hearsay-II speech understanding system (in its final configuration) was sufficient to perform the pilot experiments, but was not appropriate for more extensive experimentation. Getting a large knowledge based system to turn over and perform creditably requires a flexible initial design, but paradoxically, this flexibility is often engineered out as the system is tuned for high performance. Extensive experimentation, if not originally conceived and maintained as a goal of the system design, is a difficult task.

18.4 The distributed vehicle monitoring testbed

This section introduces the distributed vehicle monitoring testbed, a flexible and fully instrumented research environment constructed for the empirical evaluation of alternative designs for functionally accurate, cooperative distributed problem-solving networks. The concept of the testbed evolved from:

- an understanding of both the difficulties and importance of an empirical approach to issues in distributed problem solving;
- the need for a realistic environment for exploring new paradigms for obtaining global coherence.

Here, the motivation for the testbed, its basic structure, and its parameterization and measurement capabilities are described. We had, in fact, earlier embarked on the development of such an environment, based on what we called the Distributed Processing Game (Lesser and Corkill, 1978), but failed. This venture failed because we had chosen an application for which the knowledge engineering was so complex and our understanding of the task was so vague that we could not develop sufficient knowledge for the system to turn over.

18.4.1 Motivation

Our approach to designing the testbed was to:

(1)   take a realistic distributed problem solving task and appropriately abstract it to reduce the problems of knowledge engineering, to speed up problem solving, and to make it a more generic and parameterizable task;

(2)   develop for this abstracted task a distributed problem-solving system that can model (through appropriate parameter settings and pluggable modules of code) a wide class of distributed problem solving architectures;

(3)   create a simulation system that can run this distributed problem-solving system under varying environmental scenarios, different node and communication topologies, and different task data.

We feel that this approach is the only viable way to gain extensive empirical experience with the important issues in the design of distributed problem-solving systems. In short, distributed problem-solving networks are highly complex. They are difficult to analyze formally and can be expensive to construct, to run and to modify for empirical evaluation.

Real distributed problem-solving applications are difficult to construct due to the large knowledge acquisition and engineering effort required, and, once built, they are difficult to instrument and modify for experimentation. Thus, it is difficult and expensive to gain these experiences by developing a 'real' distributed problem-solving application in all its detail.

Likewise, we see the formal modelling route as not viable. The research in distributed problem solving is still in its infancy and formal analytic approaches are not yet available. Underlying the development of analytical approaches are intuitions gained from experiences with actual systems. Without sufficient intuitions for appropriately simplifying and abstracting network problem solving, the development of a model that is both mathematically tractable and accurate is difficult.

Our hope is that the testbed will provide the appropriate environment for acquiring this experience and will eventually be useful in evaluating the accuracy of the analytical models. (The testbed is already beginning to be used in this manner. See Pavlin (1983) on initial attempts at formulating a model for distributed interpretation systems.) Especially important are experiences with large distributed problem-solving networks of tens to hundreds of nodes. It is with networks of this size that we expect to see the problems of cooperation and coherence dominate and where important intuitions about how to design distributed problem-solving networks will arise.

In summary, the empirical approach taken here represents a compromise between the reality of an actual system and simplicity of an analytical model. We have abstracted the task and simplified the knowledge but still are performing a detailed simulation of network problem-solving. It should be mentioned that even with significant simplifications the building of the testbed was a substantial implementation effort. However, in contrast to the construction of a 'real' application, where considerable effort must be spent in knowledge engineering, our efforts have been spent in parameterizing the problem-solving architecture and making the testbed a useful experimental tool.

18.4.2 Why distributed vehicle monitoring?

Distributed vehicle monitoring has four characteristics that make it an ideal problem domain for research on distributed problem solving.

First, distributed vehicle monitoring is a natural task for a distributed problem-solving approach since the acoustic sensors are located throughout a large geographical area. The massive amount of sensory data that must be reduced to a highly abstract, dynamic map seems appropriate for a distributed approach.

Second, distributed vehicle monitoring can be formulated as an interpretation task in which information is incrementally aggregated to generate the answer map. Nilsson (1980) has termed systems with this characteristic commutative.

Commutative systems have the following properties:

(1)   Actions that are possible at a given time remain possible for all future times.

(2)   The system state that results from performing a sequence of actions that are possible at a given time is invariant under permutations of that sequence.

Commutativity allows the distributed vehicle monitoring network to be liberal in making tentative initial vehicle identifications, since generation of incorrect information never precludes the later generation of a correct answer map. Without commutativity, the basic problem-solving task would be much more difficult.

Although the generation of the answer map is commutative, controlling node activity is not. Here we enter the realm of limited time and resources. If a crucial aspect of the answer map is not immediately undertaken by at least one node in the network, the network can fail to generate the map in the required time. In the determination of node activities, mistakes cause the loss of unrecoverable problem solving time and can therefore eliminate the possibility of arriving at a timely answer map. If the nodes and sensors are mobile, their placement adds another noncommutative aspect to the distributed vehicle monitoring task; a misplaced node or sensor can require substantial time to be repositioned. (We are currently limiting our investigations to stationary nodes and sensors.)

Third, the complexity of the distributed vehicle monitoring task can be easily varied. For example:

- Increasing the density of vehicle patterns in the environment increases the computational and communication load on the network.
- Increasing the similarity of the vehicles and patterns known to the network increases the effort required to distinguish them.
- Increasing the amount of error in the sensory data increases the effort required to discriminate noise from reality.

Fourth, the hierarchical task processing levels coupled with the spatial and temporal dimensions of the distributed vehicle monitoring task permit a wide range of spatial, temporal and functional network decompositions. Node responsibilities can be delineated along any combination of these dimensions.

An important decision in the design of the testbed was the level at which the network would be simulated. An abstract modeling level, such as the one used by Fox (1979b), that represents the activities of nodes as average or probabilistic values accumulated over time would not capture the changing intermediate processing states of the nodes. It is precisely those intermediate states that are so important in both building and evaluating in a realistic way different network coordination strategies. Instead, the testbed duplicates (as closely as possible) the data that would be generated in an actual distributed vehicle monitoring network as well as the effect of knowledge and control strategies on that data. This approach also allows users of the testbed to receive concrete feedback about how their algorithms are performing. However, because the purpose of building the testbed is to evaluate alternative distributed problem-solving network designs rather than to construct an actual distributed vehicle monitoring network, a number of simplifications of the vehicle monitoring task were made (Table 18.1). The goal of these simplifications was to reduce the processing complexity and knowledge engineering effort required in the testbed without significantly changing the basic character of the distributed interpretation task.

A second design decision was to instrument the testbed fully. The testbed includes measures that indicate the quality of the developing solution at each node in the network, the quality of the developing solution in the network as a whole, and the potential effect of each

Table 18.1   The simplified vehicle monitoring task.

The major task simplifications in the Distributed Vehicle Monitoring Testbed include:

- The monitoring area is expressed as a two-dimensional square grid, with a maximum spatial resolution of one unit square.

- The environment is not sensed continuously. Instead, it is sampled at discrete time intervals called *time frames*.

- Frequency is represented as a small number of *frequency classes*.

- Communication from sensor to node uses a different channel than internode communication.

- Internode communication is subject to random loss, but if a message is received by a node it is received without error.

- Sensor to node communication errors are treated as sensor errors.

- Signal propagation times from source to sensor are processed by the (simulated) low-level signal processing hardware of the sensor.

- Sensors can make three types of errors: failure to detect a signal; detection of a nonexistent signal; and incorrect determination of the location or frequency of a signal.

- Sensors output signal events, which include the location of the event (resolved to a unit square), time frame, frequency (resolved to a single frequency class), and belief (based on signal strength).

- Incompletely resolved location or frequency of a signal is represented by the generation of multiple signal events rather than a single event with a range of values.

- Nodes, sensors and internode communication channels can temporarily or permanently fail without warning.

---

transmitted message on the solution of the receiving node. This is made possible through the use of an *oracle* containing the structure of the actual problem solution.

A third decision in the design of the testbed was to make it parameterized. Experience with complex artificial intelligence systems demonstrated the difficulty of experimenting with alternative knowledge and control strategies. As a result, potential experimentation with the system is often not performed. Incorporated into the testbed are capabilities for varying:

- the knowledge sources available at each node, permitting the study of different problem solving decompositions;

- the accuracy of individual knowledge sources, permitting the study of how different control and communication policies perform with different levels of system expertise;[†]

[†] The quality of the knowledge used by each node to distinguish between consistent and inconsistent data plays a major role in the success of a functionally accurate, cooperative approach. A network using low quality knowledge is unable to detect subtle

- vehicle and sensor characteristics, permitting control of the spatial distribution of ambiguity and error in the task input data;
- node configurations and communication channel characteristics, permitting experimentation with different network architectures;
- problem solving and communication responsibilities of each node, permitting exploration of different problem solving strategies;
- the authority relationships among nodes, permitting experimentation with different organizational relationships among nodes.

The result is a highly flexible research tool which can be used to explore empirically a large design space of possible network and environmental combinations.

18.5 Testbed node architecture

The Distributed Vehicle Monitoring Testbed simulates a network of Hearsay-II nodes working on the vehicle monitoring task. Each node is an architecturally complete Hearsay-II system (Erman *et al.*, 1980), with knowledge sources appropriate for the task of vehicle monitoring. Each is capable of solving the entire vehicle monitoring problem if it is given all of the sensory data and makes use of all of its knowledge. This permits any subset of the knowledge sources to be used at a node and allows the simulation of a single node (centralized) system to provide a benchmark for various distributed networks monitoring the same environment.

The basic Hearsay-II architecture has been extended in each testbed node to include the capability of communicating hypotheses and goals among nodes, more sophisticated local control, and an interface to meta-level network coordination components (Corkill and Lesser, 1981, 1983; Corkill *et al.*, 1982). In particular, communication knowledge sources, a goal blackboard, a planning module and a meta-level control blackboard have been added (Figure 18.2). The testbed also has several components that are used to measure the performance of each node and the overall network and to vary the 'intelligence' of each node's knowledge sources and scheduler. These components are the *consistency blackboard* and the knowledge source and scheduler *resolvers*.

18.5.1 The structure of the data blackboard

Hypothesized vehicle movements are represented on the *data blackboard*. This blackboard is partitioned into four task abstraction levels: signal,

---

inconsistencies among tentative partial results and may be unable to arrive at an acceptable solution. As the quality of knowledge used in the network is improved, the network should generate an answer with greater accuracy in less time.

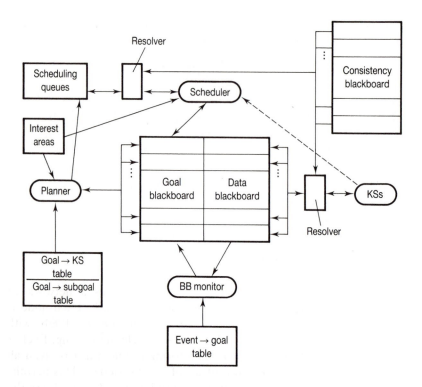

Figure 18.2   Testbed node architecture.

group, vehicle and pattern (Figure 18.3). *Signals* are at the lowest abstraction level and are the output of low-level analysis of sensory data. Each signal includes the frequency, approximate position, time frame of detection, and belief (based partly on signal strength and sensor quality) of the acoustic signal as well as the identity of the detecting sensor. Signals are the basic input to the problem-solving network.

At the next level in the data hierarchy are signal groups. A *group* is a collection of harmonically related signals (emanating from a common source). Each group includes the fundamental frequency of the related signals and its approximate position, time frame and belief (a function of the beliefs and characteristics of the related signals).

Vehicles are the next level in the data hierarchy. A *vehicle* consists of a collection of groups associated with a particular vehicle. Vehicles include the identity of the vehicle and its time frame, approximate position and belief.

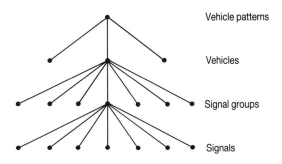

Figure 18.3   Vehicle monitoring task processing levels. Forming a vehicle pattern from sensory signals involves combining harmonically related signals into signal groups. Various signal groups can collectively indicate a particular type of vehicle. Specific vehicle types with a particular spatial relationship among themselves form a vehicle pattern.

At the highest level of processing are vehicle patterns. A *pattern* is a collection of particular vehicle types with a particular spatial relationship among them. Patterns were included in the testbed to investigate the effects of strong constraints between distant nodes. A pattern includes the identity of the pattern and its time frame, approximate position and belief. A single vehicle can be a pattern.

The desired solution, or answer map, is produced from the vehicle patterns based upon their beliefs and continuity over time. There are two types of answer map distribution: one where a complete map is to be located at one or more answer sites within the monitored area and one where a partial (spatially relevant) map is to be located at numerous sites within the area. In distributed vehicle monitoring tasks such as air or ship traffic control, both distributions of the answer map may be required. Each node might use its portion of the distributed map to control nearby vehicles, while the complete map might be produced for external monitoring of the network.

Each of these four abstraction levels is further divided into two levels, one containing location hypotheses and one containing track hypotheses. A *location hypothesis* represents a single event at a particular time frame. A *track hypothesis* represents a connected sequence of events over a number of contiguous time frames.

These orthogonal partitionings result in the eight blackboard levels shown in Figure 18.4. Location hypotheses are formed from location hypotheses at the next lower abstraction level. Track hypotheses can be formed from location hypotheses at the same abstraction level or from

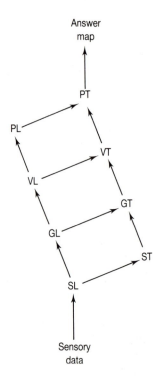

Figure 18.4   Blackboard levels in the testbed. The eight blackboard levels in the testbed are: location (SL), signal track (ST), group location (GL), group track (GT), vehicle location (VL), vehicle track (VT), pattern location (PL) and pattern track (PT). The arrows indicate the four possible synthesis paths from sensory data to generation of the answer map.

track hypotheses at the next lower level. The task processing level most appropriate for shifting from location hypotheses to track hypotheses is dependent on the problem-solving situation.

The relationships among the hypotheses at each level are supplied to the testbed as part of a testbed *grammar*. Changing the grammar automatically varies behavior throughout the testbed. By increasing the size and connectivity of the grammar, the interpretation task can be made more difficult. Another aspect of a testbed grammar that specifies the difficulty of the interpretation task involves tracking vehicle movement. The tracking component of a testbed grammar contains two values: the maximum velocity of a vehicle (and, implicitly, events at all levels) and the maximum acceleration of a vehicle. These values are used in the creation and extension of track hypotheses. By reducing the constraints on vehicle movement, the tracking task becomes more difficult.

18.6 Knowledge source processing

An important consideration in developing the set of knowledge sources for the testbed was to structure processing so that information could be asynchronously transmitted and received at any blackboard level. This permits exploration of a wide range of different processing decompositions based on partially configured nodes (nodes without all knowledge sources) without modifying the knowledge source modules and local control structures.

There are six basic problem solving activities performed by the processing knowledge sources in the testbed. They are:

(1)   *Location synthesis*   Abstracting location hypotheses at one level of the blackboard into a new location hypothesis at the next higher location level.

(2)   *Track synthesis*   Abstracting track hypotheses at one level of the blackboard into a new track hypothesis at the next higher track level.

(3)   *Track formation*   Combining a location hypothesis in one time frame with a 'matching' location hypothesis in an adjacent time frame to form a one-segment track hypothesis.

(4)   *Track extension*   Extending a track hypothesis into an adjacent time frame by combining it with a 'matching' location.

(5)   *Location-to-track joining*   Taking a location hypothesis and combining it with a 'matching' track hypothesis that begins or ends in an adjacent time frame.

(6)   *Track merging*   Merging two overlapping or abutting track hypotheses into a single track hypothesis at the same abstraction level.

18.6.1 Details of goal processing in a node

In order to permit more sophisticated forms of cooperation among nodes in the system, we have integrated goal-directed control into the data-directed control structure of the basic Hearsay-II architecture. This has been accomplished through the addition of a goal blackboard and a planner.

The *goal blackboard* mirrors the structure of the data blackboard. Instead of hypotheses, the basic data units are *goals*, each representing an intention to create or extend a hypothesis with particular attributes on the data blackboard. For example, a simple goal would be a request for the creation of a vehicle location hypothesis above a given belief in a specified area of the data blackboard. An important aspect in the structure of the integrated control architecture is a correspondence between the blackboard area covered by the goal and the blackboard area of the desired hypothesis. This correspondence allows the planner to relate goals and hypotheses quickly.

Goals are created on the goal blackboard by the *blackboard monitor* in response to changes on the data blackboard. These goals explicitly represent the node's intention to abstract or extend particular hypotheses. Goals received from another node may also be placed on the goal blackboard. Placing a high-level goal onto the goal blackboard of a node can effectively bias the node toward developing a solution in a particular way.

The *planner* responds to the insertion of goals on the goal blackboard by developing plans for their achievement and instantiating knowledge sources to carry out those plans. The *scheduler* uses the relationships between the knowledge source instantiations and the goals on the goal blackboard as a basis for deciding how the limited processing and communication resources of the node should be allocated.

18.6.2 Communication knowledge sources

Internode communication is added to the node architecture by the inclusion of *communication knowledge sources*. These knowledge sources allow the exchange of hypotheses and goals among nodes in the same independent and asynchronous style used by the other knowledge sources. There are six types of communication knowledge sources in the testbed:

(1) *Hypothesis send* (HYP-SEND)   Transmits hypotheses created on the blackboard to other nodes based on the level, time frame, location, and belief of the hypothesis.

(2) *Hypothesis receive* (HYP-RECEIVE) Places hypotheses received from other nodes onto the node's blackboard. Incoming hypotheses are filtered according to the characteristics of the received hypothesis to ensure that the node is interested in the information. HYP-RECEIVE uses a simple model of the credibility of the sending node to possibly lower the belief of the received hypothesis before it is placed on the blackboard.

(3) *Goal send* (GOAL-SEND) Transmits goals created on the goal blackboard to other nodes based on the level, time frames, regions, and rating of the goal. GOAL-SEND transmits goals based on meta-level control information – whether or not the node is to attempt to achieve the goal locally.

(4) *Goal help* (GOAL-HELP) Transmits goals that the node's planner has determined cannot be satisfied locally (possibly after executing a number of local problem-solving knowledge sources).

(5) *Goal receive* (GOAL-RECEIVE) Places goals received from other nodes onto the node's goal blackboard. Incoming goals are filtered according to the characteristics of the received goal to ensure that the node is interested in receiving goals of that type. GOAL-RECEIVE uses a simple model of the node's authority relationship with the sending node to possibly lower the rating of the received goal before it is placed on the blackboard.

(6) *Goal reply* (GOAL-REPLY) Transmits hypotheses created on the blackboard in response to a received goal requesting information from the node.

Experimentation with more complex versions of these communication knowledge sources is easily accomplished by simulating a more sophisticated knowledge source by:

- modifying its power (compare Section 18.6.4);
- modifying the code of the knowledge source to use more sophisticated knowledge in its choices (this can be done by adding code that filters the input or output of the knowledge source);
- completely replacing a knowledge source with an alternative module.

18.6.3 Measuring node and network performance

An important aspect of our use of the testbed is measuring the relative performance of various distributed problem-solving configurations and strategies. For example, we conjecture that in a network with accurate knowledge and with input data that has low error, organizing the system hierarchically and using an explicit control and communication strategy would be effective. Likewise, we conjecture that in systems with weaker knowledge sources and with more errorful input data, more cooperative and implicit control/communication strategies are desirable.

In order to understand the reasons for differences in the performance characteristics of alternative systems' organizations, dynamic measures are needed that take into account the intermediate state of system processing and thus permit observations of performance over time. For example, one way of measuring the effectiveness of different communication strategies is to develop measures that evaluate the effect of each transmitted message on the current processing state of the receiving node. The need for measuring the intermediate states of processing have led us to develop a semi-formal model for analyzing how a Hearsay-II-like system constructs an accurate solution and resolves the uncertainty and error in its input data (Lesser *et al.*, 1980). This measure increases as the system becomes more certain of the consistency of 'correct' hypotheses and decreases as the system becomes more certain of the consistency of 'incorrect' hypotheses. The correctness of hypotheses is obtained from a hidden data structure called the consistency blackboard, which is precomputed from the simulation input data. This blackboard holds what the interpretation would be at each information level if the system worked with perfect knowledge. This blackboard is not part of the basic problem-solving architecture of a node but rather is used to measure problem-solving performance from the perspective of the simulation input data. The consistency blackboard is also used to mark consistent and false hypotheses (and the activities associated with them) in system output.

18.6.4 Modifying knowledge source power

One parameter that can have a significant effect on the performance of the network is the problem-solving expertise of the nodes. The ability of a knowledge source to detect local consistencies and inconsistencies among its input hypotheses and to generate appropriate output hypotheses is called the *power* of the knowledge source. Knowledge source power ranges from a perfect knowledge source able to create output hypotheses with beliefs that reflect even the most subtle consistencies among its input hypotheses down to a knowledge source that creates syntactically legitimate output hypotheses without regard to local consistency and with beliefs generated at random. Note that a perfect knowledge source is not the same as an omniscient one. A perfect knowledge source can still generate an incorrect output hypothesis if supplied with incorrect, but completely consistent, input hypotheses.

The testbed can modify the power of a knowledge source to be anywhere along this range. This is achieved by separating each knowledge source into two stages: a candidate generator and a resolver. The *candidate generator* stage produces plausible hypotheses for the output of the knowledge source and assigns each hypothesis a tentative belief value. The candidate generator stage for each knowledge source in the testbed incorporates relatively simple domain knowledge. There are two types of knowledge used in the candidate generator to form possible output hypotheses based on patterns of input hypotheses. One type of knowledge derives patterns from the particular testbed grammar and knowledge of sensor error characteristics. The other type of knowledge is used to compute a belief for each output hypothesis using the beliefs of the input hypotheses and knowledge about the relative consistency of the input pattern. All of the knowledge used by the candidate generator is easily varied through either parameter settings or pluggable code modules.

The next stage, the *resolver*, uses information provided by the consistency blackboard to minimally alter the initial belief values of these plausible hypotheses to achieve, on the average, a knowledge source of the desired power. The hypotheses with the highest altered beliefs are then used by the resolver stage as the actual output hypotheses of the knowledge source.

The alteration of hypothesis belief values by the resolver stage can be used to simulate the detection of more subtle forms of local consistency than is provided by the candidate generator's knowledge (and thereby increase the apparent power of the knowledge source). Hypothesis belief alteration can also be used to degrade the performance of the candidate generator (and thereby reduce the apparent power of the knowledge source).

The work by Paxton (1978) on the SRI speech understanding system comes closest to our approach. He used ground consistency information to simulate statistically the output of the low-level acoustic processor in the SRI speech system. Our approach differs from Paxton's in that it dynamically relates characteristics of the inputs of a knowledge source to the characteristics of its outputs, while Paxton's does not. The output of his model depends on precomputed behavioral statistics which are independent of the belief values and consistency values of its inputs. Because of this difference, we are able to simulate any or all knowledge sources in our system, while Paxton's model is valid only for front-end processing of input data similar to those used to compute the statistics.

Even with the flexibility and detail of our approach, there are limitations:

- Our simulation of knowledge source resolving power is based on a combination of simple knowledge about local consistency and reference to an oracle, while real knowledge sources attempt to infer truth from local consistency alone (and falsehood from local inconsistency).[†]

- The behavior of different simulated knowledge sources sharing similar errors in knowledge will not be correlated due to our statistical approach to knowledge source simulation.

[†] In order to capture more closely the notion of local consistency, we can include on the consistency blackboard false hypotheses that would appear to be consistent by even a perfect knowledge source operating at that blackboard level. The resolver judges the consistency of these false hypotheses (termed 'correlated-false' hypotheses) in the same way as it does true hypotheses.

Given these limitations, we do not expect a simulated knowledge source to behave exactly as a real knowledge source. We feel, however, that the essential behavior of each knowledge source has been captured so that system phenomena are adequately simulated.

18.7 Local node control in the testbed

An important capability of the testbed is the ease with which alternative control and communication strategies can be explored. This exploration has two aspects. The first is the ability to perform experiments comparing the performance of different control strategies (for example, the performance of a hierarchical network versus a laterally organized network). The second aspect is the ability to augment the basic testbed node architecture with additional control components (for example, adding a meta-level control component that varies the organizational relationships among nodes dynamically). Both types of experimentation are possible with the testbed. This section discusses how the local node control architecture has been structured to accomplish both types of experimentation.

18.7.1 Interest areas

A key aspect of the control framework implemented in the testbed is the use of a nonprocedural and dynamically variable specification of the behaviors of each local node's planner, its scheduler, and its communication knowledge sources. Called *interest areas*, these data structures reside on the meta-level control blackboard and are used to implement particular network configurations and coordination policies.

There are six sets of interest areas for each node in the testbed:

(1) *Local processing interest areas*   Influence the local problem-solving activities in the node by modifying the priority ratings of goals and knowledge source instantiations and the behavior of the node's planner and scheduler.

(2) *Hypothesis transmission interest areas*   Influence the behavior of HYP-SEND knowledge sources in the node.

(3) *Hypothesis reception interest areas*   Influence the behavior of HYP-RECEIVE knowledge sources in the node.

(4) *Goal transmission interest areas*   Influence the behavior of GOAL-SEND knowledge sources in the node.

(5) *Goal help transmission interest areas*   Influence the behavior of GOAL-HELP knowledge sources in the node.

(6) *Goal reception interest areas* Influence the behavior of GOAL-RECEIVE knowledge sources in the node.

Each interest area is a list of regions of the data or goal blackboard.

   Each local processing interest area has a single parameter associated with it: a weight specifying the importance of performing local processing within the interest area. Transmission interest areas (hypothesis transmission, goal transmission and goal help transmission) are specified for one or more lists of nodes that are to receive information from the node. Similarly, reception interest areas (hypothesis reception and goal reception) are specified for lists of nodes that are to transmit information to the node. Each transmission interest area has a weight specifying the importance of transmitting hypotheses or goals from that area (to nodes specified in the node-list) and a threshold value specifying the minimum hypothesis belief or goal rating needed to transmit from that area. Each reception interest area has a weight specifying the importance of receiving a hypothesis or goal in that area (from a node specified in the node-list), a minimum hypothesis belief or goal rating needed for the hypothesis or goal to be accepted, and a credibility weight. The credibility weight parameter is used to change the belief of received hypotheses or the rating of received goals. A node can reduce the effect of accepting messages from a node by lowering the belief or rating of messages received from that node. Each hypothesis reception interest area also has a focusing weight parameter that is used to determine how heavily received hypotheses are used in making local problem solving focusing decisions.

18.7.2 Rating goals and subgoaling

Goal ratings specify the importance of creating hypotheses with particular attributes on the data blackboard. They influence the behavior of the planner, the scheduler and the goal communication knowledge sources. The knowledge source instantiation rating calculation is basically a weighted sum of a data-directed and a goal-directed component. The data-directed component captures the expected belief of an output hypothesis (as specified in the knowledge source instantiation's output-set attribute). The goal-directed component measures the ratings of goals that would be satisfied (at least in part) by an output hypothesis. The goal-weighting parameter can be adjusted to change the importance given to producing strongly believed hypotheses versus satisfying highly-rated goals. Gaussian noise is added to the rating calculation to simulate knowledge source precondition procedures with imperfect output hypothesis estimation capabilities.

   In addition to instantiating knowledge sources to achieve a goal, the planner can also create subgoals that reflect the importance of lower-level data in achieving the original goal and that, if satisfied, increase the likelihood of achieving the original goal. Subgoaling is an effective means of focusing low-level synthesis activities based on high-level expectations. There are no prediction knowledge sources in the testbed. Predictive knowledge is used by the planner to generate predictive goals that can be subgoaled to focus activity on lower blackboard levels.

The knowledge needed to perform subgoaling is based on the behavior of the testbed knowledge sources and is parameterized by the grammar. Because subgoaling requires some effort, its use needs to be controlled. In the testbed, subgoaling is controlled in two ways: by restricting subgoaling to particular levels and by a minimum rating threshold for a goal to be subgoaled. The relative settings of these parameters strongly influence the balance between local and external direction. Examples of how specific control and communication relationships are specified in the testbed are presented in Corkill and Lesser (1983).

18.7.3 Knowledge source precondition procedures

The overall performance of each node depends on the ability of its planner and scheduler to estimate correctly which of the potential knowledge source actions is most likely to improve the current problem-solving state as well as the cost of performing that action. In 'real' systems, this estimation is based in part on information provided by each knowledge source to the scheduler about the output the knowledge source is likely to produce given particular input hypotheses (the knowledge source *response frame* (Hayes-Roth and Lesser, 1977)). This estimation is usually fast and approximate – it is made without a detailed analysis of the knowledge source's input data. Increasing uncertainty in this estimation makes it less likely that the planner and scheduler will appropriately decide what knowledge source actions to perform.

In order to investigate the effects of this uncertainty the testbed simulation *pre-executes* the entire knowledge source as the precondition procedure. The knowledge source does not actually create any hypotheses or goals, but instead places an exact specification of their attributes in the *output-set* attribute of the knowledge source instantiation. The output-set provides an exact description of what the knowledge source instantiation will do if executed. (The output-set is updated if the input context of the knowledge source instantiation is modified while it is awaiting execution.) The actual hypotheses or goals are created when the knowledge source instantiation executes.

The information contained in the output-set allows the knowledge source instantiation rating to be made with perfect knowledge of the knowledge source instantiation's behavior. Precondition procedures with less than perfect estimation abilities are simulated by perturbing these perfect ratings. The details are described in the next section.

18.7.4 Rating knowledge source instantiations

The knowledge source instantiation rating calculation is basically a weighted sum of a data-directed and a goal-directed component. The data-directed component captures the expected belief of an output hypothesis (as specified in the knowledge source instantiation's output-set attribute). The goal-directed component measures the ratings of goals that would be satisfied (at least in part) by each output hypothesis. The goal-weighting parameter adjusts the importance given to satisfying highly rated goals versus producing strongly believed hypotheses. The weighted sum of these two components is computed for each output hypothesis in the knowledge source instantiation's output-set attribute and the maximum value (multiplied by the knowledge source efficiency estimate) is used as the base rating for knowledge source instantiation.

Since the testbed precondition procedures precompute the actual output hypotheses of the knowledge source instantiation, the scheduler's base rating calculation uses the exact beliefs of the output hypotheses and the goals that they satisfy. Gaussian noise can be added to this base rating to simulate the effects of knowledge source precondition procedures that are imperfect in their estimation of output hypotheses' beliefs and of goal satisfaction.

The knowledge sources' precondition procedures use information localized to a particular region of the data blackboard in estimating the belief values of output hypotheses. On the other hand, the scheduler is in a position to determine how a knowledge source instantiation's expected output hypotheses fit into the overall developing solution at the node. This difference in viewpoint leads to an interesting engineering issue. Should the scheduler rely solely on the myopic estimations of the precondition functions in rating a knowledge source instantiation or should it be given domain-dependent knowledge of its own to determine consistencies between knowledge source instantiation? To experiment with this issue, an oracle weighting in the data-directed component can be used to introduce the consistency of each output hypothesis (as specified on the consistency blackboard) into the rating calculation. As with the knowledge source instantiations themselves, this consistency information is used to simulate the effects of developing additional knowledge which can better detect the consistencies among hypotheses.

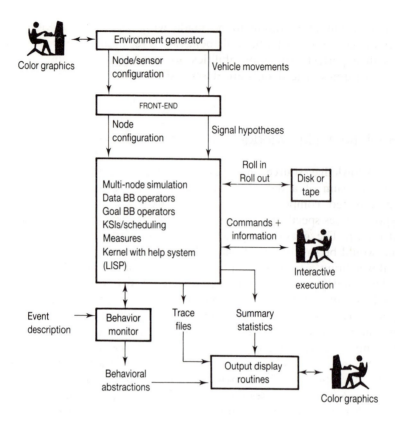

Figure 18.5   Testbed kernel and related subsystems.

18.8 Facilities for experimentation

The testbed kernel is surrounded by a number of other subsystems to facilitate experimentation by making it easy to vary the parameters of an experiment and to analyze the results of an experiment (Figure 18.5).

FRONTEND knowledge source is the special, simulation-level knowledge source used to initialize the testbed network. It is always the first knowledge source executed in an experiment. The FRONTEND reads a complete specification of the run from an input file called the *environment file*. The environment file contains all the input data for the testbed, and consists of system, structural and environmental data. *System data* denotes basic parameters of the simulated vehicle monitoring system: a seed for random number generation, the minimum and maximum location and time ranges, and the numbers of nodes and sensors. *Structural data* denotes the spatial relationships among nodes and the grammar used by knowledge source candidate generators. By varying this grammar, the number of legal patterns of hypotheses can be varied. The most constrained grammar would be one that only allowed the particular scenario for the experiment in question to be recognized. Thus, the nature and the scope of consistency constraints used by knowledge sources to resolve errors can be altered. This ability to modify the grammar combined with the ability to vary the local resolving power of knowledge sources provides a powerful tool for varying the knowledge expertise in the simulated system. *Environmental data* denotes the actual environment for the vehicle monitoring system: locations of patterns and vehicles at various time frames, and information concerning missing and false patterns, vehicles, groups and signals at various time frames. Environmental data is used in conjunction with the structural data by the FRONTEND to create the consistency blackboard.

The environment file has gone through several design iterations as we have recognized the interdependencies among the parameters that must be specified for a testbed experiment and the difficulties of correctly specifying these parameters for networks of more than a few nodes. In its present form, it allows the specification of generic classes of node types, local problem solving capabilities, authority relationships, communication policies and sensor characteristics. These classes are then instantiated to individual nodes and sensors in the network.

The FRONTEND, in its generation of sensor data, can introduce controlled error (noise) to model imperfect sensing. Noise is added to the location and signal class and the distance of the signal from the sensor. FRONTEND processing is also parameterized so that these signals can be introduced into the nodes either all at once or at the time they are sensed. The former provision allows exploration of systems in which there are burst receptions of sensor data.

To facilitate the inclusion of additional control, display and measurement routines into a particular experiment, the testbed has a number of programming 'hooks' available to the experimenter. Each hook consists of a dummy module that can be easily redefined to include calls to the experimenter's procedures. In the testbed, there is a hook at the beginning of the simulation, another hook following the FRONTEND (when all sensory data and the consistency blackboard have been determined), one prior to each knowledge source execution at each node, one when messages are transmitted or received, and one when the simulation is finished. Each hook has sufficient information available (such as the current node that is executing, the type of knowledge source to be executed, the simulation time, etc.) to allow the experimenter's procedures to decide whether or not they are interested in being executed. The experimenter's procedures have complete access to all information in the testbed.

In order to help in the analysis of the results of an experiment, a number of tools have been developed: a selective trace facility, a summary statistics facility, an interactive, menu-driven debugging facility, an event-monitoring facility, and a color-graphics display facility. Each of these tools use the information on the consistency blackboard to highlight its presentations. For example, the trace facility marks knowledge source instantiations based on the correctness (consistency) of their input and output hypotheses. This permits the experimenter quickly to scan a large amount of data for unexpected phenomena.

The trace facility presents a chronological trace of the knowledge sources' creation and execution and the association creation of hypotheses and goals and a run. The user can vary the level of details of the internal operations of the systems that are to be traced.

The summary statistics facility is used at the end of a run to generate a set of measures that indicate the performance of various aspects of the systems. These statistics are both on a node and system basis.

In addition to these fairly common analysis tools, we feel that there is need for tools that permit a more dynamic and high-level view of the distributed and asynchronous activity of the simulated nodes. An event monitoring facility, which has not yet been fully implemented, will permit a user to define and gather statistics on such user-defined events as the average time it takes for a node to receive a hypothesis and incorporate the received information into a message to be transmitted to another node (Bates and Wileden, 1982).

Another facility which is currently operational in a limited form is a color-graphics output facility. The current output display provides dynamic visual representations of the distribution of hypotheses in the x–y space of the distributed sensor network during a simulation. Location and track hypotheses are displayed as symbols and paths connecting symbols, respectively, in the physical x–y space. The level, node, belief and type of event of each hypothesis is encoded in its representation. Through this display, it is possible to get a high-level view of the relationship among the nodes' current interpretations and their relationship to the actual monitored tracks. The hypotheses displayed can be selected according to the characteristics of any of their attributes. For example, it is possible to display only those hypotheses above some belief value or those on a certain level, etc. In addition, an ordering function exists to rank the hypotheses to be displayed according to several attributes (node, level, type of event and end-time) allowing less important hypotheses to be replaced (painted over) by more important ones. We are also working on other display formats that show more abstract measures of system performance such as the transmission rate among nodes, the current reliability of nodes, etc.

18.9 Testbed status, uses and future directions

The testbed, which has been operational since January of 1982, has been a much larger system-building effort than was originally anticipated at the onset of the project. Over the three year development period, between 15 and 20 man-years of effort have gone into the construction of the testbed.

This extensive construction effort has come in part from the large number of major design iterations. The basic concept of the testbed has stayed intact through these iterations but significant modifications to all aspects of the testbed have been required as we came to understand how to better parameterize the various components.

It should also be mentioned that even though the task knowledge was simplified, considerable effort was still required to get the planner and knowledge sources to work effectively together. The testbed uses a very general mechanism for knowledge source interaction, and a number of interaction patterns that would not occur in a centralized system do occur in distributed networks.

The saving grace of all these redesign efforts was that it lead us to a better understanding of how knowledge-based AI systems and, more specifically, knowledge-based distributed problem-solving systems operate. In short, designing a knowledge-based AI system remains an art and requires considerable iteration.

A key concern that we still have about the testbed design, which cannot be answered without extensive use of the testbed, is the range of issues that can be effectively explored in the testbed. So far, only one extensive set of experiments have been run in the testbed. These experiments emphasized the use of the testbed to explore the effects of different network problem-solving strategies (Corkill and Lesser, 1983). Characteristics that were varied included:

- whether communication is *voluntary* (a node transmits hypotheses at its pleasure), *requested* (a node transmits hypotheses only when that information is requested by another node), or a *mixed initiative* combination of voluntary and requested hypotheses (a node volunteers only its highest rated hypotheses and awaits requests before transmitting any other hypotheses);

- whether a node is *self-directed* or *externally directed* in its activities (or a combination of both);

- whether hypotheses, goals, or both hypotheses and goals are used for internode coordination.

The organizational strategies were evaluated using two different network architectures: a laterally organized, four-node network with broadcast communication among nodes and a hierarchically organized,

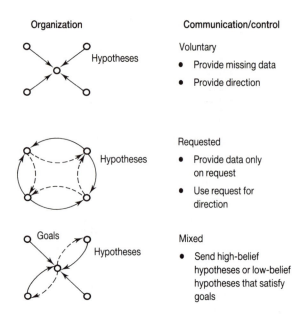

Figure 18.6   Alternative distributed problem solving strategies.

five-node network in which the fifth node acts as an integrating node (Figure 18.6). In both architectures, the network is structured so that the nodes cooperate by exchanging partial and tentative high-level hypotheses.

Although these experiments did not explore all the parameters in the testbed, they do provide evidence of the utility and flexibility of the testbed as a research tool. The different network problem-solving strategies and environmental configurations were easily expressed, and interesting empirical results indicating the performance of the different strategies were obtained. The most interesting of these results was how different organizational and control strategies performed in a noisy input environment that created the potential for the exchange of distracting information among the nodes.

As part of these initial experiments, we had planned to explore larger node configurations (with 10–20 nodes). However, only a few of these larger test cases were run. Between 3 and 5 h of CPU time were required to simulate one of these larger experiments. The efficiency of the simulation is crucial to exploring large node configurations. We are now beginning the process of selectively tuning the testbed but do not have a feel for the potential speedup. We are also beginning work on modifying the testbed to run as a parallel simulation system on a local area network of VAX 11/750s. We had initially hoped to solve the efficiency problem through the use of two different testbeds, one written in LISP as the development system and the other in Pascal as the production system. Unfortunately, with the extensive design iterations that occurred during the building of the testbed, it was impossible to keep the Pascal implementation current and eventually it was dropped.

In setting up larger and more complex configurations, a large number of interrelated parameters needed to be specified. This specification process was both time consuming and error-prone. To remedy this problem, we are now building additional graphical support tools to allow an experimenter to design and view the network configuration. Additionally, we are developing tools allowing complex node topologies to be specified in a generic way, independent of any specific number of nodes (Pattison et al., 1987).

We now firmly believe that no matter how flexible and general a research tool is, if it is not convenient to use, or if the empirical results are not easy to understand, only a small subset of its capabilities will be exploited.

18.10 Conclusion

In this chapter we have described the area of distributed problem solving and discussed some of the important issues that must be addressed. We also introduced the functionally accurate, cooperative approach with its emphasis on dealing with uncertain data and control information as an integral part of network problem solving.

The need for an empirical investigation of distributed problem solving was discussed, especially with regard to network coordination. Such an investigation requires a flexible experimental tool. The distributed vehicle monitoring testbed was presented as an example of such a tool.

The testbed facilitates the exploration of the following factors in distributed problem solving:

- node–node and node–sensor configurations;
- mixes of data- and goal-directed control in the system;
- distributions of uncertainty and error in the input data;
- distributions of problem solving capability in the system;
- types of communication policies used;
- communication channel characteristics;
- the problem-solving and communication responsibilities of each node; and
- the authority relationships among nodes.

The multiple dimensions of independent control and the detailed level of simulation in the testbed provide what we feel is a very useful environment for experimentation.

There is a need for more extensive experimentation with AI systems. All too often getting a large knowledge-based AI system to work at all is the major goal. Extensive experimentation with the system over a range of conditions is rarely done. The testbed is one of the few exceptions. In this presentation we have emphasized what makes the testbed a flexible experimental tool. Many of these techniques are appropriate for any large knowledge-based AI system.

Acknowledgments

A project as large and complex as the distributed vehicle monitoring testbed involved a number of individuals and became itself a distributed problem solving task. The efforts of Richard Brooks, Eva Hudlicka, Larry Lefkowitz, Raam Mukunda, Jasmina Pavlin and Scott Reed contributed to the success of the testbed. We would also like to acknowledge Lee Erman's collaboration on the initial formulation of the functionally accurate, cooperative approach and his work on the pilot experiments. This research was sponsored, in part, by the National Science Foundation under Grant MCS-8006327 and by the Defense Advanced Research Projects Agency (DOD), monitored by the Office of Naval Research under Contract NR049-041.

19

Hierarchical Multi-expert Signal Understanding

Mark A. Williams

19.1 Introduction

Solutions to complex, real-world problems result from the combined and incremental efforts of many experts. These solutions tend to be hierarchical in nature, whereby the lower levels of the hierarchy represent lower-level concepts, and the higher levels of the hierarchy correspond to higher-level concepts. An example of a complex, hierarchical structure is shown in Figure 19.1. In this example, six hierarchical levels (detection, parameter estimation, collection, analysis, correlation and final interpretation) incrementally contribute to the understanding of the identity, activity, location, time and purpose of a series of intercepted signal transmissions. The knowledge of many experts is applied to any one, or more, components of this signal-understanding hierarchy. A typical topology, shown in Figure 19.2, illustrates the distributed and autonomous nature of the various elements of expertise necessary to solve complex problems.

Expert systems technology provides techniques and tools for building computer programs that achieve high levels of performance on problems that require significant human expertise for their solutions. These programs combine factual knowledge and heuristic knowledge (rules of thumb, rules of good practice and judgmental rules) with methods of applying the knowledge to make inferences and decisions. The present state of the art in available tools and techniques for building expert systems requires that all of the reasoning and decision power be centralized in one single expert system. For relatively small prototype systems (up to several hundred expert rules), this is not a limitation. However, as complexity of the problem being solved increases, so does the expert system's size. The increased size of the system results in unacceptable processing times and in unwieldy development and

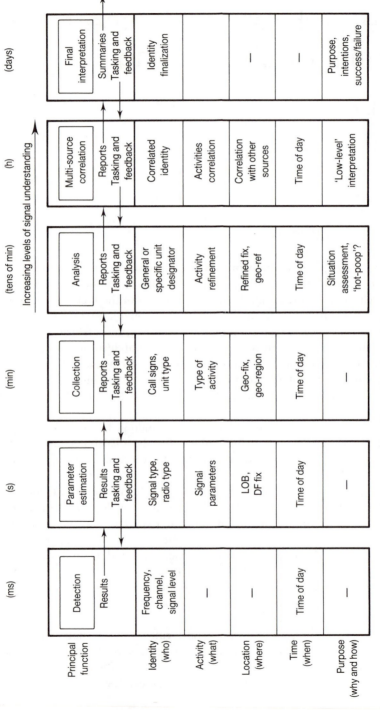

Figure 19.1 A hierarchy for signal understanding.

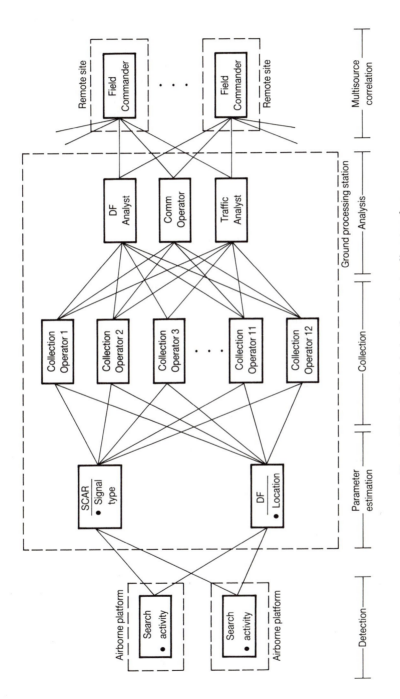

Figure 19.2   A typical signal-understanding topology.

maintenance. Such is the case also with the amount and diversity of expertise necessary for a system to aid in data analyses and decision making in an operational, real-time, tactical application. These limitations are compounded by logistics and communications problems in getting all of the necessary input to a single point. Centralizing the expertise also results in a high degree of vulnerability.

A solution to building very large and complex expert decision aids is to distribute the expertise via an arbitrary interconnection of independent, autonomous and cooperating expert systems. The ability to build multiple interconnected expert systems would allow hierarchical elements to be distributed among any number of sensors, thereby reducing vulnerability to information exploitation and increasing the intelligence level of sensor output.

This chapter documents the results of a research effort to illustrate capability issues in development and implementation of multiple, autonomous and cooperating expert systems.

19.2 A signal-understanding kernel

A long-term goal of this research effort is to design a generalized signal-understanding 'kernel', which when loaded with a specific knowledge base can function as the specific element of the hierarchical level corresponding to that knowledge base. Such a kernel must have a sufficiently general control structure to adapt the behavior of its key elements subject to the loaded knowledge base, to interconnect with, and to cooperate with other expert systems. A set of key functional elements of the kernel is shown in Figure 19.3.

Referring to Figure 19.3, the hierarchical understanding kernel must do the following:

(1) receive and interpret tasking from the next-higher level in the hierarchy;

(2) understand the tasking in light of

    (a)   what it can do,

    (b)   what it cannot do,

    (c)   what lower hierarchies can do to contribute to the task;

(3) generate appropriate tasking to elements of the next-lower level in the hierarchy;

(4) receive results from elements of the next-lower level;

(5) make inferences on the received results to contribute to the local understanding of the problem and solution;

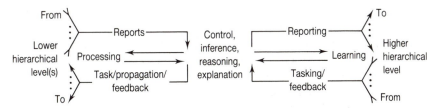

Figure 19.3   The hierarchical-understanding kernel.

(6) repeat steps 3, 4 and 5, as necessary;

(7) report appropriate results to the next-higher level;

(8) modify the local understanding using feedback from higher-level hierarchies;

(9) detect, report and resolve conflicts in the developing understanding between the local understanding and that received through feedback and input from other hierarchical lvels;

(10) be capable of explaining why and how specific decisions, inferences and deductions were made;

(11) modify the local knowledge base to improve performance (learning).

Features of the signal understanding kernel that are necessary at the lower levels of the signal understanding domain may not be evident at the higher levels of the hierarchy, and vice versa. The higher levels emphasize high-level inferencing, whereas the lower levels place more emphasis on knowledge-based signal processing. A key subgoal is determination of the degree of detail to which the theory of a common control structure for signal understanding holds true for more than one hierarchical level. At the least, an abstract control framework can be specified. Implementing expert systems for signal understanding at various hierarchical levels according to this common control framework will greatly simplify the serial and parallel interconnection of multiple expert systems. If the theory of a common inference and control structure holds true to a sufficient level of detail, then a common (military specification) knowledge-engineering tool for hierarchical understanding systems can be specified. With such a tool, multiple expert systems could be more easily implemented along any sequence of hierarchical levels by providing the systems with the applicable knowledge at each level. Such a tool may also be found to be applicable to multidimensional signal understanding, like image understanding.

Unlike conventional software engineering, expert systems cannot be first specified, then designed and, finally, built according to design. Instead, both design and implementation evolve together. Because of this, the only way to develop the details of a signal understanding kernel (and, ultimately, to produce a knowledge-engineering framework or tool for hierarchical understanding systems) is to implement prototype systems. The key elements of the kernel can then be identified and abstracted from the working systems.

During 1984 a prototype multi-expert signal understanding system named TRICERO, consisting of three distributed, interconnected, autonomous and cooperating expert systems, was developed. From this prototype, a number of requirements for the signal understanding kernel have already become evident. A description of these requirements is contained in Sections 19.2.1–19.2.4. Further development of TRICERO, and development of a second lower-hierarchy-prototype system to integrate with TRICERO will help define the other kernel requirements in sufficient detail to allow construction of software for the signal understanding kernel.

19.2.1 Knowledge representation

The question of how to represent knowledge for intelligent use by programs is a major question motivating research in artificial intelligence (Barr and Feigenbaum, 1981). Knowledge representation in an AI program is the choice of conceptual frameworks and computer implementation of those concepts for describing objects, relations, processes and inferential expertise of the application domain. The use of uniform representations, such as production rules, for all of the knowledge in an expert system has simplified the construction of large systems. However, current research is showing a trend toward more complex, heterogeneous representations (Hart, 1982; Patil et al., 1981).

The initial TRICERO prototype clearly identified the need for three different knowledge-representation paradigms to properly capture and make use of the types of knowledge and expertise characteristic of the signal-understanding domain. Static knowledge about known objects and their relationships to other objects is best represented using hierarchical semantic networks or frames with inheritance. Semantic-network representations simplify certain deductions (such as inferences through taxonomic relations) by reflecting them directly in a network structure. Frames generalize this notion, providing structures or frameworks for organizing knowledge. Expert reasoning knowledge is best represented in IF-THEN rules. Rules consist of condition–action pairs where the conditions under which each rule is applicable are made explicit, and the interactions between rules is minimized (one doesn't call another). This modular mechanism for representing reasoning knowledge has proved

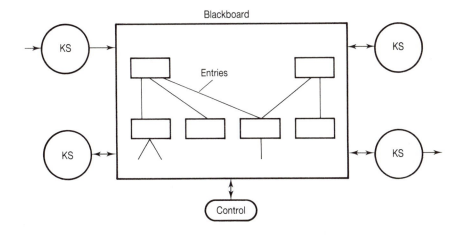

Figure 19.4   The blackboard paradigm.

very successful in building expert systems. Procedural knowledge (knowledge about how to do specific things or how to proceed in well specified situations) is best represented using a formal procedural representation that can be invoked and manipulated through the reasoning knowledge.

Expert systems exhibit 'knowledgeable' behavior by means of mechanisms for retrieving facts from the knowledge base relevant to the problem at hand, inferring new facts about the problem, and reasoning about those facts in search of a solution.

Problems in signal understanding are best solved by inference and reasoning mechanisms that achieve an incremental, opportunistic, event-driven and forward-chained style of problem solving within a blackboard architecture. The blackboard architecture is a problem-solving framework originally developed for the Hearsay-II speech-understanding system (Erman *et al.*, 1980; Hayes-Roth, 1983). The architecture has since been used to structure AI systems in many application areas. The blackboard architecture is particularly useful when knowledge from different levels of detail can be brought to bear on a particular problem. The problem-solving style that results from a blackboard architecture leads to the emergence of partial solution 'islands'. New solution islands appear, disappear and grow in response to input and feedback. Eventually, mutually supportive partial solutions merge to form a complete solution.

The blackboard architecture consists of four main elements: entries, knowledge sources, the blackboard and an intelligent control mechanism. These components are illustrated in Figure 19.4. Entries are intermediate results generated during problem solving. Knowledge sources are independent event-driven processes that produce entries. The knowledge sources contain all of the problem-solving knowledge, and they both respond to changes in and modify the blackboard state. The blackboard is a structured, global database that mediates knowledge-source interactions and organizes entries. It contains the current state-of-the-problem solution. The control mechanism decides if and when particular knowledge sources should generate or modify entries, and it records them on the blackboard.

19.2.3 Match–update–create

An operation common to all elements of the signal understanding hierarchy is the 'match–update–create' cycle. Input entities are first matched against previously reported or known entities according to matching criteria. If a match is found, the matched entity is updated from the input. If no match is found, a new instance of the entity type is created from the input. This match–update–create operation should be an integral part of the signal-understanding kernel, which can then be provided specific matching criteria corresponding to the expertise implemented by a particular element of the hierarchy.

19.2.4 Handling large amounts of data

A practical, fieldable system for signal understanding will need to deal with very large amounts of data. The signal–understanding kernel must therefore provide mechanisms for supporting (storing and retrieving) off-line blackboard entries, 'forgetting' stale information, and removing entries that are no longer supported in the current solution state ('garbage collection').

19.3 TRICERO system

TRICERO consists of three distributed, interconnected and autonomous expert systems for signal understanding in the area of air defense. The three expert systems (ELINT ANALYSIS, COMINT ANALYSIS and ELINT–COMINT CORRELATION) provide situation and threat information from ELINT and COMINT collection data. These three experts span across two levels of signal-understanding hierarchy: analysis and correlation. The functional organization of these three expert systems is shown in Figure 19.5. The choice of the application domain and the three expert systems was based on the availability of in-house experts.

ELINT deduces intelligence data about emitter clusters and platform types from input observations of intercepted radar emissions provided by

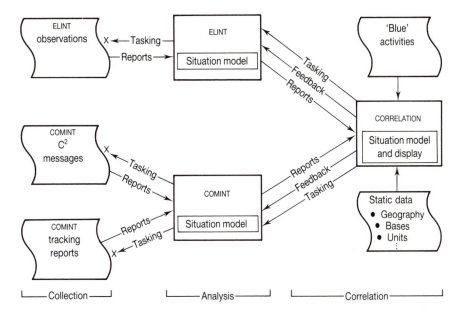

Figure 19.5 TRICERO functional organization.

collection operators in response to ELINT tasks. ELINT reports its results to CORRELATION and modifies its view of the current situation using feedback from CORRELATION.

COMINT receives both intercepted command and control (C^2) messages and intercepted tracking messages, and determines platform activities through C^2 message interpretation and correlation of tracking and C^2 platforms. COMINT provides tasking to COMINT collection and reports its results to CORRELATION. CORRELATION also provides situation-assessment feedback to COMINT.

CORRELATION integrates ELINT and COMINT reports to analyze global activities and recognize threats. It also provides information feedback and tasking to ELINT and COMINT.

TRICERO was implemented as four complete, independent expert systems: ELINT, COMINT, CORRELATION and CONTROL. The control expert, although not one of the three functional problem-solving components, was implemented as a convenient knowledge-based approach to emulate multiple, simultaneously running systems using one machine. Each of the four expert systems of TRICERO is implemented in a blackboard structure using modified versions of the AGE knowledge-engineering tool (Aiello *et al.*, 1981a, b). Each contains its own set of knowledge sources, hypothesis levels and special functions. Multiple machines are emulated on a single machine through context switching of the four experts. Figure 19.6 shows the overall architecture and the

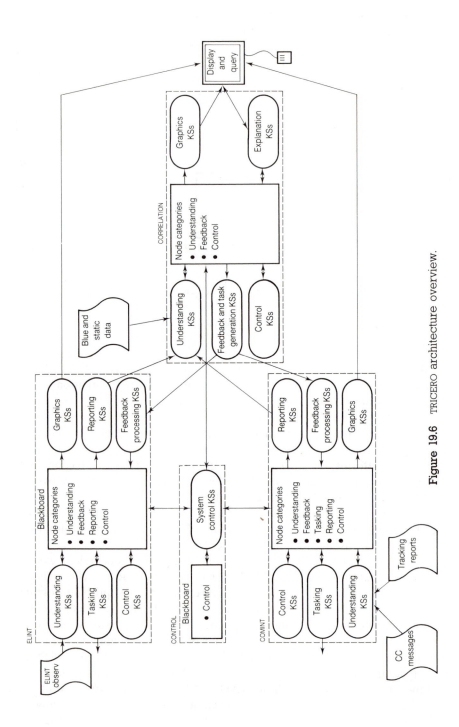

Figure 19.6 TRICERO architecture overview.

Table 19.1   TRICERO features.

ELINT	COMINT	CORRELATION	Feature
√			Processing of input data from a single source
	√	√	Processing of input data from multiple sources (correlation)
√	√	√	Building a model of the scenario
√	√	√	Interpretation of input and model
√	√	√	Decision making
√	√		Revision of model based on feedback
√	√	√	Task generation
√	√		Task interpretation and propagation
		√	Graphics display of model
		√	Interactive knowledge-based explanation
√	√	√	Interactive model-based inspection
√	√	√	Threat evaluation
√	√		Report generation
√	√	√	Conflict detection
		√	Conflict resolution
√	√	√	Confidence assignment, propagation, modification

interconnections of the four expert components. All communication between the experts is handled by expert knowledge sources.

A blackboard architecture was selected as being the best intuitive means of structuring the solution to match the way human experts attack similar signal-understanding problems. Other means were considered and rejected. AGE-1 was chosen as the particular instantiation of the blackboard architecture because of its availability as a software package. Although AGE-1 does not have all of the features necessary in a blackboard structure for signal understanding (as discussed in Section 19.2), it provided for rapid prototyping of the TRICERO system by eliminating the need to implement a blackboard structure from scratch.

Table 19.1 summarizes the main features of each of the three signal-understanding expert components. The overall inference structure of these expert components is shown in Figure 19.7.

Each of the four subsystems was implemented and tested independently on a DEC System-20. All four subsystems were then integrated and run on a Xerox 1108 Dandelion and on a Xerox 1100 Dolphin.

Detailed functional and implementation information is given in Williams (1984a).

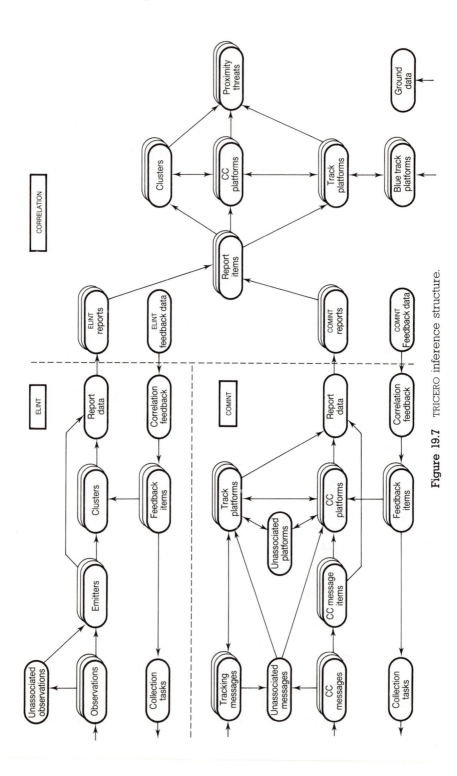

Figure 19.7   TRICERO inference structure.

Table 19.2   Summary of TRICERO size (4/13/84).

	ELINT	COMINT	CORRELATION	CONTROL	Total
Node types	9	14	13	1	37
Knowledge sources	24	33	45	3	105
Rules	49	112	56	21	238
Special functions	48	37	30	17 control 37 graphics	169
Event types	28	39	39	9	115

TRICERO maintains a graphical situation-display of the developing scenario. A user can interact with this display by pointing at displayed objects (platforms, ground stations, collection sites, emitter clusters, etc.) with a 'mouse', to request that more detailed information be presented. Such details include inferred platform activities (e.g. tracking target), platform types (F1 or F2), relationships between platforms (e.g. flight wingman), etc.

The initial TRICERO prototype was built with 1 man-year of effort over an 8 month period. The effort was done in 3 stages. The first 3 months were devoted to design of the basic system architecture and to communications among the expert systems. This was a 3 man-months effort involving the domain experts and an experienced expert-systems builder. The second 3 month period involved a 7 man-month effort of system coding and knowledge acquisition. This 7 man-month effort was made up of 6 man-months of knowledge engineering and programming and 1 man-month of domain-expert time. The final 2 months represented a 2 man-month effort for system integration, testing and documentation. This 1 man-year effort resulted in a system with 238 rules and 169 special functions. In this system, these special functions are, in fact, procedural knowledge, so the total system can be thought of as containing $238 + 169 = 407$ 'knowledge elements'. A summary of the TRICERO system size is shown in Table 19.2. Figure 19.8 shows the growth of the knowledge base during the middle 3 month stage of development.

19.4 Technical issues of TRICERO

In addition to investigating issues of building multiple, interconnected, autonomous expert systems, TRICERO addresses a number of other significant technical issues involved in building expert systems. Sections 19.4.1–19.4.10 describe these issues and the approaches taken to confront them in TRICERO.

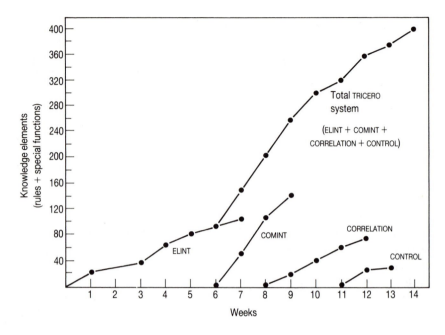

Figure 19.8   TRICERO knowledge growth.

19.4.1 Emulation of multiple blackboards

Since three separate machines were not available for implementing each of the three expert systems of TRICERO in its own machine, multiple blackboard systems were emulated in a single machine. AGE-1 is designed to operate with only one blackboard (one expert system). TRICERO avoids this limitation by setting up a fourth expert system for system control. This control expert sets up various AGE-1 variables so that AGE-1 sees only one (the currently active one) of the four blackboards at any given time. Control knowledge sources cause TRICERO to cycle through the different expert components in order (ELINT, COMINT, CORRELATION) for each increment of time. Time is incremented after the correlation component has completed work on the current time. If an expert component is not present or has run out of scenario input data, it is skipped.

19.4.2 The blackboard structure

The ELINT blackboard consists of three levels: observation, emitter and cluster. The input data arrives at the observation level. These data are tagged with the collection time and the site at which they were collected.

Each node on the emitter level keeps a history of detections from a site having the same identification tag. The history represents radar emissions believed to be emanating from one source. The identification tag could be in error; different sources could have the same identification tag, or one source could have multiple tags. The radar emissions detected at different sites are merged into a hypothetical platform (or a number of platforms 'seen' as one platform) on the cluster level. Each level uses descriptive vocabulary appropriate to that level: the platform types and speed history on the cluster level and the collection site and signal quality on the observation level, for example. The blackboard data structure in the COMINT and correlation subsystems are structured in similar fashions using abstraction levels appropriate to interpreting their data.

19.4.3 The knowledge source structure

The knowledge sources are structured according to the specification in the AGE skeletal system (Nii and Aiello, 1979). Each knowledge source has a precondition part and an action part. The precondition part is a list of tokens, each representing a type of change that could be made on the blackboard. The action part consists of a set of rules. The rules in each knowledge source could be processed as a multiple hit, in which all rules whose condition sides are satisfied are executed, or as a single hit, in which only the first rule whose condition side is satisfied is executed. There is no conflict-resolution process of the type found in OPS-based systems.

19.4.4 Control

Each of the independent subsystems in the TRICERO system uses a subset of control components available in AGE. A globally accessible event list records the changes to the blackboard. At each control cycle, one event on an event list is chosen as a focus of attention. The choice of the event on which to focus is based on a predetermined priority of event types. Once an event (an event type and a node) is selected, it is matched against the event-type tokens in the precondition of the knowledge sources. Those knowledge sources whose preconditions contained the event-type token matching the focused event type are executed according to a predetermined priority of knowledge sources.

The TRICERO system augments the AGE control component to handle the communication among the three subsystems. Each subsystem could send messages to designated subsystems. The receipt of a message by a subsystem is treated as an event focused on a special node on the blackboard. This construct allows the subsystems to treat reports from other subsystems just like any other event.

The basic actions of the control component can be described in two parts:

(1)   Between subsystems:

    (a)   The simulation of the distributed computation consists of round-robin execution of the three subsystems – ELINT, COMINT and CORRELATION.

    (b)   Each subsystem sends report messages to designated subsystems. The receipt of a message is treated as an event with appropriate modification of the recipient's blackboard and event list.

(2)   Within a subsystem:

    (a)   A control module selects a focus event using a list of event priorities. An event contains information about the event type of the change made to the blackboard; that is, the node on which the change is made, the knowledge source and the specific rule that makes the change, and the actual change.

    (b)   Based on the focused event, knowledge sources whose precondition list contained the event are chosen for execution.

    (c)   The rules in the activated knowledge sources are evaluated and executed according to the rule-processing method associated with the knowledge source. Modifications to the blackboard by the rules are events and cause the event to be put on the event list.

19.4.5 Knowledge-application strategy

Most of the knowledge sources engage in bottom-up processing. They combine information on one level to generate a hypothesis on a higher level. The reports from the correlation subsystem to ELINT and COMINT deal primarily with information on the higher level (for example, platform identification) that override the analysis done by the lower-level subsystem. In such cases, the processing in these subsystems becomes top-down. The reports from ELINT and COMINT are treated as input to the higher-level correlation subsystem.

19.4.6 Dealing with time

Continuous variables, such as time, are among the most difficult topics to deal with in AI. This is especially true when temporal information must be represented and used to reason about changes in the world by which some facts cease to be true and others become true. Temporal information is handled in TRICERO by means of time-tagging all data and all decisions and inferences derived from the data. A time quantization of 1 min is used. This quantization was chosen based on the characteristics of the input-collection sensors. Using this time-tagged approach to dealing with time, data and results from any given time increment are readily identifiable, as are data and results from arbitrary time offsets. In TRICERO, past, present and anticipated data/results are all used in reasoning, inferencing and confidence determination.

19.4.7 Dealing with stale data and conclusions

As time progresses and the situation models evolve, blackboard entries that were at one time supported as part of a hypothesis may no longer be valid. Stale entries, which can correspond to either data or conclusions derived from data, arise from either a decrease in an entry's confidence to a level below a predetermined threshold, or from feedback about an entry which is either found (by the expert providing the feedback) to be in error or is part of a no-longer-supported hypothesis or solution. These stale entries are removed from the blackboard, thereby eliminating them from further consideration in the solution path. This garbage collection process is, in effect, a form of belief revision in which stale data and unsupported hypotheses are discarded, resulting in increased efficiency and better accuracy of the situation model.

19.4.8 Textual message interpretation

TRICERO implements a 'context-dependent, keyword-driven, knowledge-guided' approach to textual message interpretation. Expert knowledge is first applied to the message to determine the category of the message from the message sender and/or receiver. The TRICERO COMINT component presently has five different categories: aircraft-to-tower, tower-to-aircraft, aircraft-to-ground-control, ground-control-to-aircraft and aircraft-to-aircraft. Once the message's category (context) is known, the size of the message vocabulary that must be interpreted is drastically reduced. The message is then scanned for known keywords that can occur in the specific message category. When a category-dependent keyword is found, keyword-dependent knowledge tells the following:

Message:　　　　　　BLUE 21 TURN LEFT HEADING 310 DEGREES
↓

(Expert knowledge is applied to determine that message
category is 'ground-control-to-aircraft')

↓

Context:　　　　　　　GROUND-CONTROL-TO-AIRCRAFT

↓

(Message is scanned for known ground-control-to-aircraft
keywords)

Keyword: TURN

↓

(Keyword-dependent knowledge tells to look for a direction
and a number following the keyword TURN and to update
the anticipated turn and course of the receiving aircraft
with these values)

Direction: LEFT
Number: 310

ANTICIPATED TURN　　← DIRECTION
ANTICIPATED COURSE ← NUMBER

Figure 19.9 Example of textual message interpretation in TRICERO.

- where, within the message, to look for associated parameters,
- what attributes of what blackboard entries to update and with what values,
- what reports to generate,
- what threats to report.

Figure 19.9 shows a simple example of how the input message, BLUE 21 TURN LEFT HEADING 310 DEGREES is interpreted and results in the anticipated turn and anticipated course attributes of aircraft BLUE 21 being set to LEFT and 310 respectively.

19.4.9 Confidence

Expert systems must tolerate uncertainty in both input and in results derived from inference and reasoning. Most expert systems that can tolerate uncertainty employ some kind of probability-like measure to weigh and balance conflicting evidence, and to combine supporting evidence. TRICERO takes a completely non-numeric and nonmathematical approach to confidence handling. The initial TRICERO prototype contains five different confidence factors that measure relative amounts of belief in individual pieces of input data, in inferred relationships among entities, and in conclusions or decisions made about entities. Each of these five confidence factors consists of a set of five finite states (Nil, Possible, Probable, Positive and Was Positive) plus a distinct set of special functions which initialize, raise, lower and test each particular type of confidence. These five confidence states were arrived at from careful examination of how the experts deal with uncertainty in signal-analysis problems. In general, transitions from one confidence state to another are determined from past confidence and from the nature and quality of newly input data. Table 19.3 summarizes the five confidence factors used in the initial TRICERO prototype.

19.4.10 Explanation

One of the important features of an expert system is its ability to provide explanations of the program's behavior. TRICERO contains three types of explanation mechanisms, as follows:

- rule-history mechanism;
- blackboard-inspection mechanism,
- knowledge-based explanation mechanism.

The rule history mechanism in TRICERO is that provided by AGE-1. It is a record of the execution of the user program as it progresses. This record contains a list of how AGE-1 did what it did, including what rules fired, what events were posted, and what changes were made to the blackboard. This history mechanism is independent of the application domain and is primarily useful only to the system builder as a means of determining whether or not his system is doing what he thinks it should be doing. Interaction with the history mechanism is through keyboard commands and occurs only after the system is completely finished with an input scenario.

The blackboard-inspection mechanism allows a user to examine the details of any entry on any one of the four dynamic blackboards of TRICERO. The menu-driven situation-dependent mechanism is activated by user interrupt from a button on the mouse during system operation. The desired entry to be displayed is then selected with the mouse from a pop-up menu. All attributes, current values and confidences of the selected blackboard entry are displayed in a formatted window. System operation resumes where it left off when the user is done with blackboard inspection.

The knowledge-based explanation mechanism provides a domain-and-current-situation-dependent explanation of results and decisions made by TRICERO. Expert, domain-specific explanation knowledge is invoked to provide descriptions and supporting evidence for inferences

Table 19.3 Summary of TRICERO confidence factors.

Component	Confidence in	Determined from	States
ELINT	Existence and correctness of each emitter	• Past confidence • History and quality of input observations • Absence of observations for previously observed emitters	Nil Possible Probable Positive Was positive
	Type of each platform associated with a clustering of emitters	• Degree of uniqueness of platform determinations	Possible Probable Positive
COMINT	Existence and correctness of each CC platform	• Past confidence • History and quality of input CC messages	Nil Possible Probable Positive Was positive
	Correctness of each track to CC platform matching	• History of previous matchings • Closeness of matchings • Available matching attributes	Possible Probable Positive
CORRELATION	Correctness of each cluster to CC platform association	• Past confidence • History and closeness of previous matchings • Available matching attributes	Possible Probable Positive Was Positive

and results of items selected by the user. The explanation mechanism is activated through a button on the mouse. Items to be explained are selected from the situation display by the operator's pointing at them with the mouse. A significant accomplishment in TRICERO was the development of a mechanism for 'invoking an expert system within an expert system' in order to produce knowledge-based explanations that made use of domain-dependent explanation knowledge and that took into account the current blackboard state.

19.4.11 Additional notes

(1) The partitioning of the overall task into subsystems in TRICERO is accomplished by assigning the analysis of the abstract information to the CORRELATION subsystem and the analysis of information closer signal data to ELINT and COMINT. As mentioned previously, the knowledge sources that span the various levels of the blackboard hierarchy are logically independent. Thus, the need for coordination among the subsystems is substantially reduced when the problem is partitioned into subsystems along carefully chosen levels of analysis.

(2) As with the other systems described, the TRICERO data is noisy and the knowledge sources uncertain. The radar data, for example, contain 'ghosts', detections of nonexisting objects. The ELINT subsystem handles the existence of this type of error by delaying the analysis until several contiguous detections have occurred. By doing so, it avoids the creation of hypothesis nodes that later need to be deleted.

The issues relating to the deletions of nodes on the blackboard are quite complex. Suppose in TRICERO that a node on the cluster level (an object that represents a platform or a group of platforms) is to be deleted. What does it mean? Has the platform disappeared? Unless it somehow disintegrates, a platform cannot disappear into thin air. Was there an error in interpreting the radar data to begin with? Often, there are 'ghost tracks', a characteristic of which is that the tracks disappear after a short duration. However, suppose the platform disappearance is not due to ghost tracks but to an error in reasoning. Unraveling the reasoning steps that led to the hypothesis (backtracking) and retrying often do not help. The system does not know any more than it did when the erroneous hypothesis was generated. Suppose the platform node is just deleted. What do we do about the network of evidence that supports the existence of the platform? Unfortunately, there is no systematic way of handling node deletions. In HASP the nodes were never deleted. The nodes in error were ignored, and analysis continued ignoring past errors. In TRICERO node creation is delayed until there is strong supporting evidence for the existence of an object represented by the node. When an error occurs, the hypothesis network is restructured according to domain heuristics.

(3)   TRICERO was one of the first blackboard systems implemented on a computer system with a bit-map display (see Appendix). The situation board, symbolically represented on the blackboard of the correlation subsystem, is displayed in terms of objects in an airspace and the objects' past behavior. The graphic-display routines were written as procedural knowledge sources and were executed when certain events (changes on the blackboard) occurred that warranted display updates. There might be some argument about the conceptual consistency of this approach because interfacing is usually not considered a part of problem solving. However, this engineering solution that integrated the display routines with the problem-solving components works very well. An effective display interface requires knowledge about what is appropriate to display when. A knowledge-based control of displays and display updates is easily implemented using the knowledge source organization.

19.5 Topics for further research

The initial TRICERO prototype has elucidated many of the requirements for building multiple, distributed expert systems in the domain of signal understanding. Further research is needed to refine the communications, reasoning and explanation mechanisms of TRICERO and to define a signal-understanding kernel in sufficient detail to allow the construction of a general knowledge-engineering tool for hierarchical signal understanding.

Further work on TRICERO falls into three categories: architecture/implementation, mechanisms and performance. An outline of topics for further work in each of these three categories follows:

(1)   *Architecture/implementation*

   (a)   Add frame-based representation of static knowledge.

   (b)   Split the three expert systems out onto three machines, communicating over the ETHERNET.

(2)   *Mechanisms*

   (a)   Add mechanisms for user inspection of the knowledge base.

   (b)   Add mechanisms for graphic representation of the current inference structure.

   (c)   Improve on mechanisms for tasking, feedback, reporting, blackboard inspection, and knowledge-based explanation.

(d)   Improve display capabilities. (Add message traffic window?)

(3)   *Performance*

(a)   Add knowledge to improve capabilities, robustness and completeness. Suggestions for this are scattered throughout (Williams, 1984a).

(b)   Add more complex and corrupted scenarios. (This may require development of a scenario-generation tool.)

(c)   Increase system speed through compilation. (This will require modification to some global data names.)

Features of the signal-understanding kernel that are necessary at the lower hierarchies of the signal-understanding domain may not be evident from the TRICERO prototype which is implemented at the higher levels of the hierarchy. The higher levels emphasize high-level reasoning, whereas the lower levels place more emphasis on knowledge-based signal processing. An expert-system approach to signal understanding at these lower levels would merge the knowledge-based reasoning techniques of AI with the mathematical tools of signal processing (SP). The power of such an approach lies in its ability to represent the knowledge and judgment of an expert and to subjectively apply the knowledge to otherwise fixed and formal signal-processing algorithms. Computation can be reduced by several orders of magnitude by directing the employment of signal-processing algorithms and by using knowledge-based reasoning. These techniques will also allow the system to 'tune' sensor parameters to expected signals, thereby reducing the required sensor bandwidth and sensitivity. A brief comparison of SP and AI techniques is presented in Table 19.4.

To properly define a signal-understanding kernel, a prototype system at the lower levels of the hierarchy should be developed and later interconnected with TRICERO.

Appendix TRICERO Scenario Number One

TRICERO Scenario Number One is a 30 min scenario in which a zone protected by an airfield is violated by a low-performance transport. Two fighters are scrambled from the airfield located within the zone to intercept the transport, and two additional fighters are scrambled for backup. The interceptors escort the transport out of the zone, and all four fighters return to the airfield. An unrelated distractor is also present in the vicinity. Radar and communications are monitored by two stationary collection sites located outside the zone. A geographic representation of

Table 19.4 Comparison of SP and AI techniques.

	SP	*AI*
Information representation	Abstract mathemetical functions or a sequence of function values represent signals	A symbolic description of signals, describing how each signal was created, is generated
Knowledge representation	All the relevant signal-processing knowledge is identified and applied by the program author as a sequence of operations involved in performing some computation	An explicit representation of the body of knowledge on which the computations are based is generated
Control structures	A detailed, fixed sequence of operations specifies what to do at any given stage of processing	A control strategy specifies how to decide what to do at any given stage of processing
Decision making (with uncertainty)	Is formulated in probabilistic terms using *a priori* probabilities and multivariate conditional probabilities	Is embodied in a subjective concept of uncertainty in which the knowledge and judgment of an expert are substituted for unknown conditional probability functions

the situation is depicted in Figure 19.10. The players in Scenario Number One are described in Table 19.5.

From ELINT's view of the world, the scenario goes through six main phases:

(1)   TIME00–TIME04   BIG EAR collection site is intercepting and tracking radar emissions from the distractor. At TIME04, CORRELATION realizes that the focus of activity is further south and directs BIG EAR to drop what it is tracking and turn its antenna more southerly.

(2)   TIME04–TIME06   No radar intercepts from either collection site.

(3)   TIME07–TIME13   BIG EAR is intercepting and tracking radar emissions from the air patrol leader. GOTCHA is intercepting and tracking radar emissions from the interceptor leader. Both interceptors think they are tracking the same emitters. This leads to the

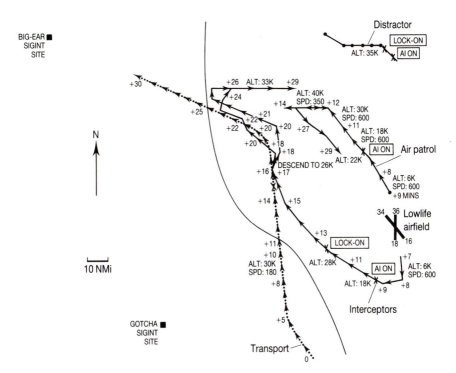

Figure 19.10   TRICERO Scenario Number One.

belief in an emitter cluster well to the east of LOWLIFE airfield. CORRELATION notices the error when this cluster appears to be travelling at speeds in excess of what is known to be realistic. At TIME13, CORRELATION orders BIG EAR to drop its emitters and attempt to re-acquire further south.

(4)   TIME14–TIME17   Both sites tracking interceptor leader.

(5)   TIME18–TIME26   Interceptor wingman becomes active. Both sites track both leader and wingman.

(6)   TIME27–TIME30   Wingman goes silent. Both sites track leader.

From COMINT's view of the world, the scenario goes through four main phases:

(1)   TIME00–TIME06

    (a)   Intercepted command and control messages between LOWLIFE Tower and all four fighters.

Table 19.5   The players in Scenario Number One.

Type of player	Description

Active	• Low-performance transport
	• Airfield tower: MATADOR
	• Point defense interceptors:
	  – BLUE 25 – leader
	  – BLUE 31 – wingman
	  – LIGHTBULB – ground controller
	• Combat air patrol:
	  – GREEN 98 – leader
	  – GREEN 99 – wingman
	  – DOORKNOB – ground controller
	• Distractor

Passive	• Collection Sites:
	  – BIG EAR
	  – GOTCHA

Static	Zone delineations Airfield locations Airfield tower: LOWLIFE

     (b)   No tracking data on the fighters.

     (c)   Tracking data on the distractor and the transport.

(2)   TIME07–TIME17

     (a) C^2 messages between LIGHTBULB and BLUE leader; BLUE wingman silent.

     (b) C^2 messages between DOORKNOB and GREEN leader; GREEN wingman silent.

     (c)   Tracking data on BLUE leader, GREEN leader, transport and distractor.

(3)   TIME18–TIME26   Same as COMINT phase 2 plus:

     (a) C^2 messages between BLUE leader and BLUE wingman.

     (b)   Tracking data on BLUE wingman.

(4)   TIME27–TIME30   Same as phase 2.

Sample graphical situation displays generated by CORRELATION as a result of reasoning about the reports provided by ELINT and COMINT are shown in the screen-bit maps in Figures 19.11–19.16.

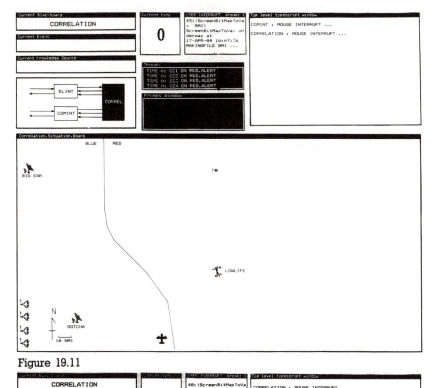

Figure 19.11

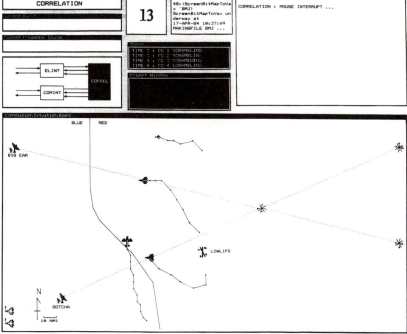

Figure 19.12

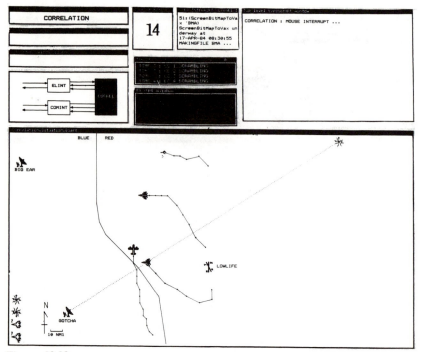

Figure 19.13

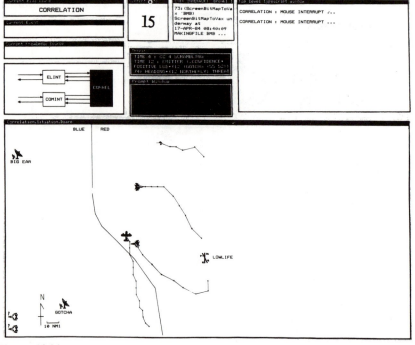

Figure 19.14

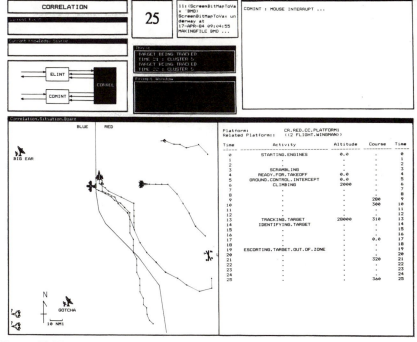

Figure 19.15

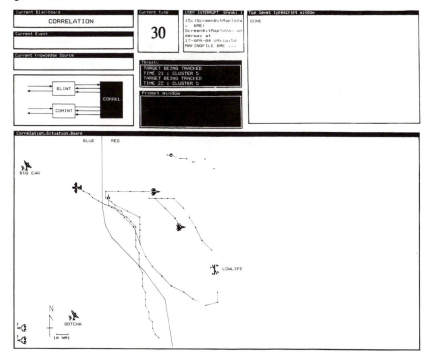

Figure 19.16

20

PROTEAN: Deriving Protein Structure from Constraints

Barbara Hayes-Roth, Bruce Buchanan, Olivier
Lichtarge, Mike Hewett, Russ Altman,
James Brinkley, Craig Cornelius, Bruce Duncan and
Oleg Jardetzky

20.1 Introduction

PROTEAN (Buchanan *et al.*, 1985; Hayes-Roth *et al.*, 1985; Jardetsky *et al.*, 1985) is an evolving knowledge-based system, framed within the blackboard architecture, that is intended to derive the three-dimensional conformations of proteins in solution from empirical constraints. PROTEAN's problem belongs to a subclass of constraint-satisfaction problems in which physical objects must be positioned in *n*-dimensional space so as to satisfy a set of constraints. Accordingly, in designing PROTEAN, we are developing knowledge and methods that apply to arrangement problems generally. We describe the PROTEAN system, as implemented in the BB1 blackboard architecture (Hayes-Roth, 1985), and present a trace of PROTEAN's efforts to solve a small protein fragment, the lac-repressor headpiece. Finally, we discuss PROTEAN's current status.

20.2 Protein structure elucidation

Determining the structures of individual proteins is a fundamental problem in biochemistry. It is the first step toward understanding the physical basic underlying protein functions and, possibly, designing new proteins for medical or industrial use.

Biochemists distinguish the primary, secondary and tertiary structure of a protein. A protein's primary structure is its defining, linear sequence of amino acids. A protein's secondary structure is the sequence of architectural subunits (α-helices, β-sheets and random coils) superimposed on successive subsequences of its primary structure. A protein's tertiary structure is the folding of the primary and secondary

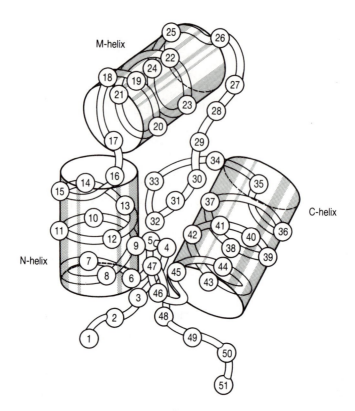

Figure 20.1   The primary, secondary and tertiary structure of the lac-repressor headpiece.

structures in three-dimensional space. Figure 20.1 shows the structure of a protein called the lac-repressor headpiece.

Biochemists have developed reliable methods for determining a protein's primary structure and its secondary structure. In addition, they know the atomic structure of each of the 20 different amino acids that can appear in the primary structure and the radius of each different atom (its *van der Waals' radius*). They know the architectural characteristics of α-helices, β-sheets and random coils. They can determine the overall size, shape and density of the protein molecule with hydrodynamic and light-scattering methods.

Protein crystallography currently is the best method for determining tertiary structure and there has been some success in developing knowledge-based systems for interpreting crystallographic data (Terry, 1983). However, obtaining crystallized samples of proteins is not always possible. Moreover, it is now known whether the identified crystal structures match the structures of proteins in solution. The crystal structures almost certainly deviate from the solution structures in one respect: they conceal the potential mobility of a protein's constituent structures.

High-resolution nuclear magnetic resonance (NMR) offers an alternative method of obtaining structural information about proteins in solution (Roberts and Jardetzky, 1970; Wuthrich, 1976). NMR experiments yield a set of measurements called *nuclear Overhauser effects* (NOEs). Each NOE signifies that two of a molecule's constituent atoms are in close spatial proximity (within a range of 2–5 Å). Other measures reveal the overall size and shape of the protein and identify atoms located near the surface of the molecule. Taken together, these data substantially constrain the space of plausible tertiary structures.

Efforts to develop computer programs for deriving protein structure from NMR data have focused on distance geometry algorithms that minimize the value of some distance error function (Wuthrich, 1976; Wagner and Wuthrich, 1979; Braun *et al.*, 1981; Zuiderweg *et al.*, 1983). These approaches suffer two major limitations. First, since NMR data are sparse, they do not identify a unique solution for a given protein. Existing programs do not thoroughly explore the 'conformational space' of solutions that satisfy a given set of constraints. Instead, they explore a local region of solutions around a plausible starting structure. Second, existing programs treat potential mobility in a very limited fashion. They may hypothesize minor mobility of small substructures (such as amino acid sidechains), while failing to consider major mobility of larger substructures (such as helices).

20.3 Approach

PROTEAN is intended to surmount the limitations of existing methods for elucidating protein structure from NMR data. Thus PROTEAN must: identify the *family* of conformations allowed by available constraints; incorporate all available constraints to restrict the family as much as possible; and characterize the mobility of protein substructures allowed by the constraints. In so doing, it must cope with the large, combinatoric search space entailed in protein-structure analysis.

PROTEAN's fundamental operation is to identify and then refine the family of positions in which a structure satisfies a designated set of constraints. Successively applied constraints successively restrict the family hypothesized for a given structure. We have identified a variety of potentially useful constraints on protein structure (see Table 20.1). Some of these are local constraints, such as NOE data signifying the proximity of a particular pair of atoms. Others are global constraints, such as molecular size. By combining these qualitatively different kinds of constraints, PROTEAN should be able to restrict the space of possible protein conformations.

Table 20.1 Some of the available constraints on protein structure.

Primary structure
Atomic structures of individual amino acids
van der Waals' radii of individual atoms
Peptide bond geometry
Secondary structure
Architectures of α-helices and β-sheets
Molecular size
Molecular shape
Molecular density
NOE measurements
Surface data

PROTEAN must consider two factors in reasoning about structural mobility. First, it must infer mobility whenever it finds that no position for a structural subunit (such as a helix) satisfies a set of applicable constraints. Second, it must incorporate user-specified hypotheses that particular sets of constraints are or are not satisfied simultaneously in a single conformation. In both cases, PROTEAN must reason about alternative families of positions for affected structures under non-simultaneous constraint sets.

To reduce the combinatorics of search, PROTEAN adopts a divide-and-conquer approach. It defines partial solutions that incorporate different subsets of a protein's constituent structures and different subsets of its constraints. It focuses first on satisfying constraints within each partial solution, positioning each structure relative to a single fixed structure. After substantially restricting the positions of structures within two overlapping partial solutions, PROTEAN applies constraints between them.

Also to reduce search combinatorics, PROTEAN reasons bidirectionally across different levels of abstraction (see Figure 20.2). At the *molecule* level, PROTEAN reasons about the overall size, shape and density of the molecule. At the *solid* level, it reasons about the protein's constituent α-helices, β-sheets and random coils, representing these structures as geometric cylinders, prisms and spheres. At the *superatom* level, it reasons about the protein's constituent amino acids, in terms of peptide units (represented as prisms) and sidechains (represented as spheres). Finally, at the *atom* level, PROTEAN reasons about the protein's individual atoms. When PROTEAN reasons top-down, it uses the hypothesized position of a structure at one level to restrict its examination of positions of constituent structures at a lower level. When PROTEAN reasons bottom-up, it uses the hypothesized position of a structure at one level to restrict the position of its superordinate structure. Since most of the current implementation operates at the solid level, we have not yet explored the full power of bidirectional reasoning.

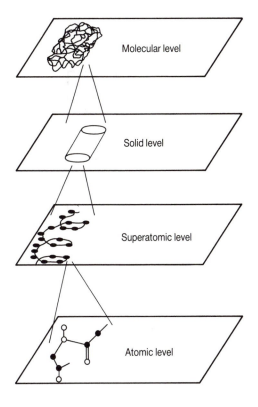

Figure 20.2   PROTEAN's reasoning levels.

We envision a basic successive refinement strategy, with some opportunistic deviation. Thus, PROTEAN should reason top-down through the levels of abstraction, with some bottom-up adjustment of results. It should apply this strategy simultaneously to several overlapping partial solutions, integrating them only after it has applied all or most of their internal constraints. Within this general strategy, PROTEAN still faces an extensive solution space and must reason more specifically about the most efficient order in which to apply individual constraints to individual structures in particular partial solutions. We have implemented a strategy that combines domain-independent computational principles (e.g. choosing partial-solution 'anchors' that have many constraints to many other structures; focusing on structures that have been restricted to small families; and preferring strong constraints) with biochemistry knowledge (e.g. defining the space of potentially useful constraints; and characterizing the constraining power of different constraints). Since intelligent control is a critical component of effective problem solving in PROTEAN, we plan to experiment with these and other control strategies.

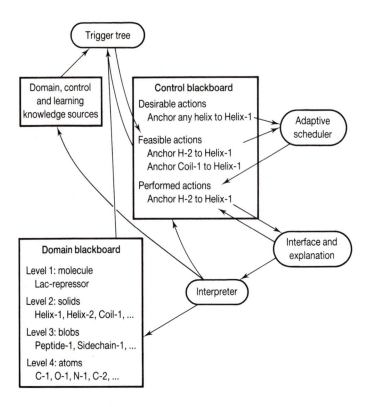

Figure 20.3 The BB1 architecture.

20.4 Current implementation

We are developing PROTEAN within the BB1 blackboard architecture (Hayes-Roth, 1985), which defines: (1) functionally independent *problem-solving knowledge sources* to generate and refine solution elements; (2) a multi-level *solution blackboard* on which these knowledge sources record evolving solutions; (3) *control knowledge sources* to reason about problem-solving strategy; (4) the BB1 *control blackboard* on which control knowledge sources record the evolving control plan; and (5) an adaptive *scheduler* that uses the current control plan to determine which knowledge source should execute its action on each problem-solving cycle.

A BB1 system (see Figure 20.3) iterates the following steps:

(1) An action (called a KSAR or knowledge source activation record) is executed, causing changes to elements on the solution or control blackboard.

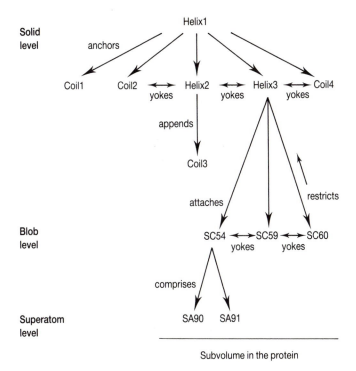

Figure 20.4   A PROTEAN partial solution for the lac-repressor at the solid level.

(2)   These blackboard changes trigger one or more problem-solving or control knowledge sources, placing new KSARs on the agenda. Each KSAR instantiates an action definition from a knowledge source in the context of the current problem-solving state.

(3)   The scheduler chooses the pending KSAR that best satisfies the current control plan.

Thus, BB1 provides a uniform, integrated blackboard mechanism for reasoning about the solution to the problem at hand as well as about the problem-solving process *per se*.

PROTEAN currently uses a four-level solution blackboard, including the levels in Figure 20.2. Figure 20.4 shows a partial solution for the lac-repressor headpiece at the solid level of the blackboard. The example also illustrates PROTEAN's language of partial solutions. All structures within a partial solution are positioned relative to a uniquely-positioned *anchor*. In Figure 20.4, Helix1 is the anchor. When PROTEAN applies constraints between the anchor and another structure, it *anchors* an *anchoree*. In Figure 20.4, Helix1 anchors five anchorees, Coil1, Coil2, Helix2, Helix3 and Coil4. When PROTEAN applies constraints between an

Table 20.2   PROTEAN's problem-solving knowledge sources.

Knowledge source	Behavior
Post-the-Problem	Retrieves the description of a test protein and associated constraints from a data file and posts them on the blackboard in a form that is interpretable by other PROTEAN knowledge sources
Post-Solid-Anchors	Creates objects that represent and describe the details of all of the test-protein's secondary structure (α-helices and random coils). Each one is a potential anchor for a solution
Activate-Anchor-Space	Chooses a particular solid-anchor to be the anchor of a partial solution
Add-Anchoree-to-Anchor-Space	Chooses a particular solid-anchor (representing it as a token object that *copies* the chosen solid-anchor) to be an anchoree in a previously established anchor-space
Express-NOE-Constraint	Identifies the family of positions in which the NOE contact site of a structure can lie while satisfying an NOE with another structure
Express-Covalent-Constraint	Identifies the family of positions in which the site of a covalent bond connecting a structure to another structure can lie
Express-Tether-Constraint	Identifies the family of positions in which the site of a covalent bond connecting a structure to another structure via a short random coil can lie
Anchor-Helix	Identifies the family of positions in which a helix can lie while satisfying one or more constraints with an anchor, along with all constraints previously applied to it
Anchor-Coil	Identifies the family of positions in which a coil anchoree can lie while satisfying one or more tether constraints with an anchor, along with all constraints previously applied to it
Append-Helix	Identifies the family of positions in which a helix appendage can lie while satisfying one or more constraints with an anchoree, along with all constraints previously applied to it
Yoke-Helices	Restricts the established families of positions for two helix anchorees to satisfy one or more constraints between them

anchoree and a structure that has no constraints with the anchor, it *appends* an *appendage*. In Figure 20.4, Helix2 appends an appendage, Coil3. When PROTEAN applies constraints between two anchorees or appendages, it *yokes* them. In Figure 20.4, for example, Helix2 and Helix3 yoke one another.

PROTEAN's current problem-solving knowledge sources (see Table 20.2) define partial solutions at the solid level and position α-helices and random coils relative to one another within those partial solutions. Although the current implementation of PROTEAN has only 11 problem-solving knowledge sources, it instantiates most of them many times for a single protein. For example, the knowledge source Anchor-Helix generates different KSARs for different anchor–anchoree pairs and for different constraints between a given pair.

Three knowledge sources, Anchor-Helix, Anchor-Coil, and Yoke-Structures, rely upon a set of numerical functions called the *geometry system* or GS (Brinkley *et al.*, 1986). The GS represents the position of each structure as a set of six parameters. Three parameters place the structure at a particular location in the three-dimensional coordinate space and three parameters orient the structure about its own axes. The GS explores all values of the parameters at some level of resolution, determining whether a designated structure positioned with those values can satisfy the designated constraints.

PROTEAN currently operates under the following problem-solving strategy:

(1)   Establish the longest, most constraining helix as the anchor.

(2)   Position all other secondary structures in the protein relative to the chosen anchor, giving priority to actions that apply strong constraints to structures that are helices, that are long, that constrain many other structures, and that have many constraints with the anchor.

Working within the BB1 architecture, PROTEAN represents this strategy as a hierarchy of decisions on the control blackboard (see Figure 20.5). At the *strategy* level, PROTEAN records a decision to use this particular strategy, along with the information it needs to generate the prescribed sequence of steps at the appropriate time. PROTEAN records the steps as individual decisions at the *focus* level, encompassing sequential problem-solving time intervals. Each focus decision also records the information PROTEAN needs to generate the associated heuristics, which it records as decisions at the *heuristic* level. Each heuristic encompasses roughly the same time interval as its superordinate focus decision.

PROTEAN generates its strategy incrementally, one decision at a time, with the 16 control knowledge sources described in Table 20.3.

```
STRATEGY
   Develop-PS-of-Best-Anchor
       |----------------------------------------------------------------------------------------- >

FOCUS
   Position-All-Structures-Helix1
                                      |------------------------------------------------------- >

   Create-Best-Anchor-Space
                   |-------------------- |

HEURISTIC
   Prefer-Strong-Constraints
                                                        |  ----------------------------- >

   Prefer-Strongly-Constrained Anchorees
                                                      |  ----------------------------- >

   Prefer-Mutually-Constraining-Anchorees
                                                    |  ----------------------------- >

   ...

   Prefer-PS-Anchor-is-Helix1              |---------------------------------------------- >
   Prefer-Strongly-Constrained-Anchors
                   |----------- |
   Prefer-Long-Anchors
               |-------------- |
   Prefer-A>B>R-Anchors
               |---------------- |

CYCLE     ...........................................................................................
          0        5              10              15              20              25
```

Figure 20.5   A PROTEAN control plan.

Four of these are generic BB1 control knowledge sources: Initialize-Focus, Update-Focus, Terminate-Focus and Terminate-Strategy. The other 12 control knowledge sources are domain-specific. The next section illustrates PROTEAN's use of the knowledge sources to control its efforts to solve a small protein, the lac-repressor headpiece.

20.5 Example: PROTEAN's partial solution of the lac-repressor headpiece

The lac-repressor headpiece is a protein with 51 amino acids. Its true structure is unknown, but NMR data are available for it and several research groups have partially identified its structure (Kaptein *et al.*,

Table 20.3 PROTEAN's control knowledge sources.

Knowledge source	Behavior
Generic BB1 control knowledge sources	
Initialize-Focus	Identifies the initial focus prescribed by a newly recorded strategy
Update-Focus	Identifies each subsequent focus prescribed by a strategy
Terminate-Focus	Changes the status of a focus to 'inoperative' when the focus's goal is satisfied
Terminate-Strategy	Changes the status of a strategy to 'inoperative' when the strategy's goal is satisfied
Domain-specific control knowledge sources	
Develop-PS-of-Best-Anchor	Records the develop-ps-of-best-anchor strategy
Create-Best-Anchor-Space	Records the create-best-anchor-space focus
Position-All-Structures	Records the position-all-structures focus
Prefer-Helix>Sheet>Coil-Anchors	Records a heuristic that gives high ratings to KSARs that operate on helix anchors, intermediate ratings to KSARs that operate on β-sheet anchors, and low ratings to KSARs that operate on random coil anchors
Prefer-Long-Anchors	Records a heuristic that gives higher ratings to KSARs that operate on long anchors
Prefer-Strongly-Constraining-Anchors	Records a heuristic that gives higher ratings to KSARs whose anchors have many constraints with many other structures
Prefer-Strategically-Selected-Anchor	Records a heuristic that gives higher ratings to KSARs that operate on the strategically selected anchor
Prefer-Helix>Sheet>Coil-Anchoree	Records a heuristic that gives high ratings to KSARs that operate on helix anchorees, intermediate ratings to KSARs that operate on β-sheet anchorees, and low ratings to KSARs that operate on random coil anchorees
Prefer-Long-Anchoree	Records a heuristic that gives higher ratings to KSARs that operate on long anchorees
Prefer-Strongly-Constrained-Anchoree	Records a heuristic that gives higher ratings to KSARs that operate on anchorees that have many constraints with the anchor.
Prefer-Mutually-Constraining-Anchoree	Records a heuristic that gives higher ratings to KSARs that operate on anchorees that have many constraints with other anchorees
Prefer-Strong-Constraint	Records a heuristic that gives higher ratings to KSARs that apply strong constraints

Table 20.4   Interpreted data for the lac-repressor headpiece.

Data type	Data value
PROTEIN-NAME	LAC-REPRESSOR-HEADPIECE
PRIMARY-STRUCTURE	(MET1 LYS2 PRO3 VAL4 THR5 LEU6 TYR7 ASP8 VAL9 ALA10 GLU11 TYR12 ALA13 GLY14 VAL15 SER16 TYR17 GLN18 THR19 VAL20 SER21 ARG22 VAL23 VAL24 ASN25 GLN26 ALA27 SER28 HIS29 VAL30 SER31 ALA32 LYS33 THR34 ARG35 GLU36 LYS37 VAL38 GLU39 ALA40 ALA41 MET42 ALA43 GLU44 LEU45 ASN46 TYR47 ILE48 PRO49 ASN50 ARG51)
SECONDARY-STRUCTURE	(Coil1 1 MET1 THR5) (Helix1 1 LEU6 GLY14) (Coil2 2 VAL15 SER16) (Helix2 2 TYR17 ASN25) (Coil3 3 GLN26 ARG35) (Helix3 3 GLU36 LEU45) (Coil4 4 ASN46 ARG51)
NOES	(1 VAL4 3 TYR17 5) (2 VAL4 3 LEU45 4) (3 VAL4 3 TYR47 5) (4 THR5 3 TYR47 5) (5 LEU6 4 TYR17 5) (6 LEU6 4 VAL24 3) (7 LEU6 4 MET42 5) (8 LEU6 4 TYR47 5) (9 TYR7 5 TYR17 5) (10 ASP8 3 LEU45 4) (11 VAL9 3 MET42 5) (12 VAL9 3 LEU45 4) (13 VAL9 3 TYR47 5) (14 ALA10 2 TYR17 5) (15 ALA10 2 VAL20 3) (16 TYR12 5 ALA32 2) (17 TYR12 5 ALA40 2) (18 TYR12 5 ALA41 2) (19 TYR12 5 MET42 5) (20 TYR12 5 GLU44 4) (21 TYR12 5 LEU45 4) (22 ALA13 2 VAL38 3) (23 ALA13 2 ALA41 2) (24 VAL15 3 TYR47 5) (25 TYR17 5 MET42 5) (26 VAL20 3 VAL38 3) (27 VAL24 3 TYR47 5) (28 VAL30 3 MET42 5) (29 MET42 5 TYR47 5)

1985; Jardetzky, 1984). Interpreted data for the lac-repressor are shown in Table 20.4. This section describes the first 25 cycles of a program trace of PROTEAN's efforts to solve the lac-repressor headpiece.

Post-the-Problem initiates PROTEAN activity at the molecular level by recording a new protein-analysis problem and all available constraints. This event triggers two knowledge sources: Post-Solid-Anchors and Develop-PS-of-Best-Anchor.

Since there are no control heuristics on the control blackboard yet, the scheduler uses the default scheduling rule: Prefer-Control-KSs. It schedules and executes Develop-PS-of-Best-Anchor, which records PROTEAN's strategy (see Figure 20.5). This event triggers Terminate-Strategy, which will not be executable until the strategy's *goal* (explained below) is satisfied. It also triggers Initialize-Focus.

The scheduler chooses Initialize-Focus, which uses the strategy's *generator* to identify the first focus it prescribes. It records the name of that focus, Create-Best-Anchor-Space, as the strategy's *current-focus*. This event triggers Create-Best-Anchor-Space.

The scheduler chooses Create-Best-Anchor-Space, which records the corresponding focus (see Figure 20.5). This event triggers three control knowledge sources whose names are listed as the new focus decision's *heuristics*: Prefer-Helix>Sheet>Coil-Anchors, Prefer-Long-Anchors and Prefer-Strongly-Constraining-Anchors. It also triggers Terminate-Focus, which will not become executable until the new focus's goal is satisfied.

On the next three cycles, the scheduler chooses three pending KSARs, each of which records a heuristic (see Figure 20.5). These events do not trigger any new knowledge sources.

The scheduler chooses the only pending KSAR, Post-Solid-Anchors, which creates a potential anchor representing each secondary structure in the protein. Each of these events triggers a corresponding KSAR involving Create-Anchor-Space.

Now the scheduler uses the three heuristics posted on the control blackboard to determine which of the Create-Anchor-Space KSARs to execute. Since Helix1 is the longest, most constraining helix, it chooses the KSAR that creates an anchor space for Helix1 (see Figure 20.4). This event satisfies the goal of the Create-best-Anchor-Space focus (the best anchor space has been created), thereby making the corresponding KSAR for Terminate-Focus executable. The event also triggers the knowledge source Add-Anchoree-to-Anchor-Space once for each other secondary structure in the protein.

The scheduler chooses Terminate-Focus, which changes the *status* of the existing focus and its subordinate heuristics to 'inoperative'. It also records the focus name, Create-Best-Anchor-Space, as the strategy's expired-Focus. This event triggers the control knowledge source Update-Focus.

The scheduler chooses Update-Focus, which uses the strategy's generator to identify the next focus it prescribes and records the name of that focus, Position-All-Structures, as the strategy's current-Focus. This event triggers the knowledge source Position-All-Structures.

The scheduler chooses Position-All-Structures, which records the corresponding focus (see Figure 20.5). This event triggers the knowledge source Terminate-Focus, which will not become executable until its goal is satisfied. The event also triggers the six control knowledge sources named in the new focus decision's heuristics: Prefer-Strategically-Selected-Anchor, Prefer-Helix>Sheet>Coil-Anchorees, Prefer-Long-Anchorees, Prefer-Strongly-Constrained-Anchorees, Prefer-Mutually-Constraining-Anchorees and Prefer-Strong-Constraints.

On the next six cycles the scheduler chooses KSARs that record heuristics for the new focus. These events do not trigger any new knowledge sources.

Now the scheduler uses the six new control heuristics to choose pending KSARs. At this point, the agenda contains only KSARs involving the knowledge source Add-Anchoree-To-Anchor-Space. The scheduler chooses the KSAR that adds Helix3 (see Figure 20.4). This event triggers several KSARs for Express-NOE-Constraint, one for each of the NOEs between Helix1 and Helix3.

The scheduler chooses a series of Express-NOE-Constraint KSARs. Each one records the family of positions in which the NOE contact site on Helix3 can lie, relative to Helix1. Each of these events triggers a corresponding KSAR for the knowledge source Anchor-Helix.

The scheduler continues using the six control heuristics to choose pending problem-solving knowledge sources, including many different triggerings of the knowledge sources: Add-Anchoree-to-Anchor-Space, Express-NOE-Constraint, Express-Tether-Constraint, Anchor-Helix, Anchor-Coil and Yoke-Structures. Each such action triggers new KSARs, which are added to the agenda and compete for scheduling priority. All of these KSARs together position all secondary structures relative to Helix1 with all applicable constraints (see Figure 20.4).

Because the results of these actions satisfy the goal of the Position-All-Structures goal (all structures have been positioned), Terminate-Focus becomes executable and the scheduler chooses it. Terminate-Focus changes the status of the current focus and its associated heuristics to 'inoperative'. It also records the focus name as the strategy's expired-Focus. This event triggers Update-Focus.

The scheduler chooses Update-Focus, which uses the strategy's generator to identify the next focus it prescribes, which in this case is 'None', and records it as the strategy's current-focus. This event satisfies the strategy's goal and makes the pending Terminate-Strategy KSAR executable.

The scheduler chooses Terminate-Strategy, which changes the strategy's status to 'inoperative'.

In performing the actions summarized above, PROTEAN produces a solid-level solution for the lac-repressor headpiece, as illustrated in Plate 8, specifying the positional families within which each of the protein's secondary structures can lie while satisfying the applicable constraints. PROTEAN's solution closely matches the manually identified solution described in Jardetzky (1984).

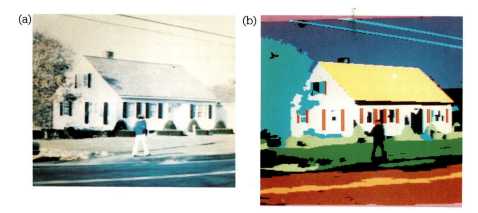

Plate 1   House scene 1: (a) original color image, (b) final interpretation.

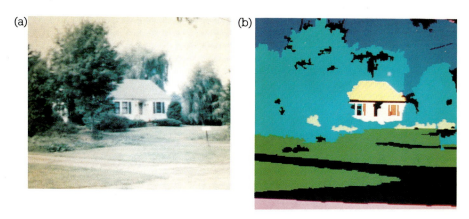

Plate 2   House scene 7: (a) original color image, (b) final interpretation.

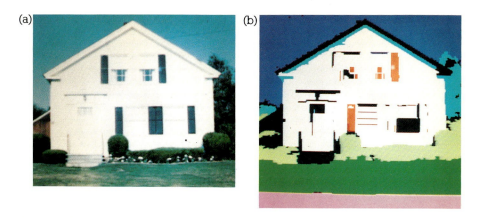

Plate 3   House scene 10: (a) original color image, (b) final interpretation.

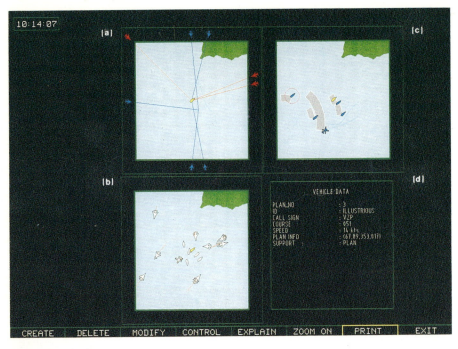

Plate 4 Compiled tactical picture.

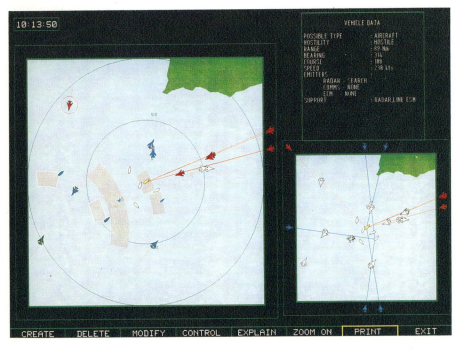

Plate 5 Radar/ESM correlation.

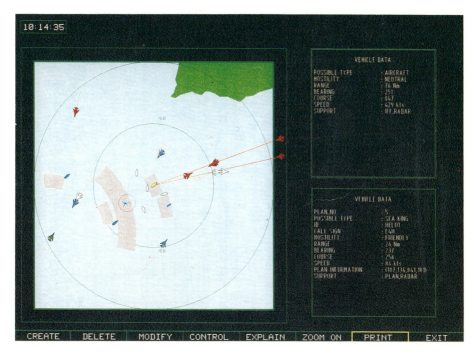

Plate 6 Radar/IFF/plan correlation.

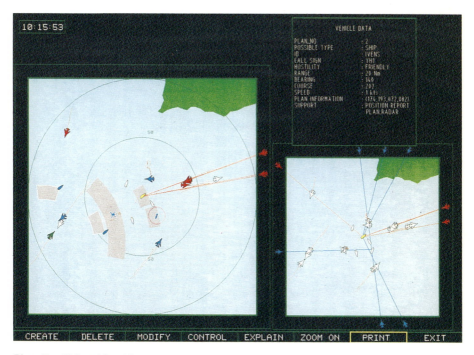

Plate 7 Object identification.

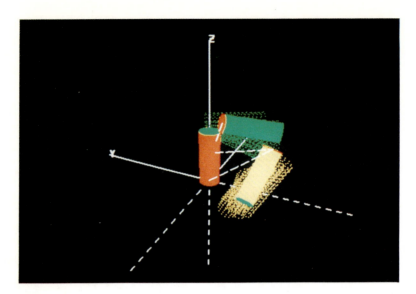

Plate 8   Results of PROTEAN on the lac-repressor headpiece protein. Three helices are represented: the anchor defining the coordinate system along the z-axis (in red); and two helices positioned with respect to the anchor. The clouds of points indicate regions of space in which the helices satisfy all constraints. The yellow and green cylinders each represent one possible position of the corresponding helix within the respective cloud. Dashed lines between the anchor and the cylinders are constraints that were used to determine the clouds.

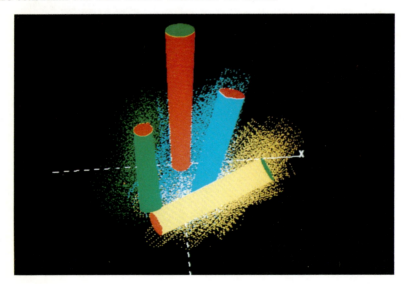

Plate 9   PROTEAN results for four helices of myoglobin. Using data generated from atomic positions in a crystal structure, the clouds reflect possible positions of three helices (green, blue and yellow) as defined by constraints with respect to the anchor helix (red). One instance of each helix is displayed as a solid cylinder.

20.6 Current status of PROTEAN

The current PROTEAN system demonstrates the appropriateness of the blackboard architecture for protein-structure analysis. Although PROTEAN currently reasons only about helices and random coils, we anticipate that its representational conventions and geometric reasoning methods will apply to other protein structures as well. PROTEAN has been tested against the known structure of myoglobin, producing the results shown in Plate 9. The current system incorporates reasoning about a variety of constraints: the known architectures of helices, covalent bonds, NOEs, the known architectures of amino acid sidechains, and van der Waals' radii. However, we anticipate a need to introduce qualitatively different representational conventions and geometric reasoning methods to handle the global constraints on the overall size, shape and density of the molecule. The blackboard architecture easily incorporates different solution representations at different blackboard levels and incorporates different methods in its functionally independent knowledge sources.

The current system also suggests that the BB1 blackboard control architecture will support the critical control reasoning PROTEAN must perform. PROTEAN currently uses a single control strategy that is well captured in control knowledge sources and produces a perspicuous control plan during problem solving. This strategy works well enough for reasoning about the secondary structures of a small protein with a subset of the available constraints. However, when reasoning about all constituent structures in larger proteins with all available constraints, PROTEAN will need a new strategy. It will have to reason about multiple partial solutions and their relationships to one another. It will have to sequence its constraint-satisfaction operations intelligently to avoid a computationally intractable explosion of hypothesized structures. It will have to reason about alternative protein conformations corresponding to constraints that are not satisfied simultaneously. Since we do not know an optimal general control algorithm for this problem, we must experimentally evaluate alternative control strategies. To support this investigation, we are developing learning mechanisms to acquire control knowledge from experts automatically (Hayes-Roth and Hewett, 1985) and to comparatively evaluate different control strategies. We are also developing explanation mechanisms that explicate the relationships between problem-solving actions and the underlying control strategy (Hayes-Roth, 1984).

Acknowledgments

This work was funded in part by: NIH Grant RR-00785; NIH Grant RR-00711; NSF Grant DMB84-2038; NASA/Ames Grant NCC 2-274; Boeing Grant W266875; and DARPA Contract N00039-83-C-0136. We thank Jeff Harvey, Vaughan Johnson and Alan Garvey for their work on BB1.

21

Mission Planning within the Framework of the Blackboard Model[†]

Glen Pearson

21.1 Introduction

Mission planning is the process of generating a sequence of actions to satisfy goals and constraints posed by a military commander. Mission plans are typically constructed at different levels of abstraction, where higher levels represent coarse plan descriptions and lower levels represent more refined plan descriptions. As the plan is developing, human planners may make decisions that refine higher-level decisions or they may make high-level decisions based on constraints or opportunities discovered during low-level planning. Thus, planning proceeds opportunistically, both top-down and bottom-up (Hayes-Roth *et al.*, 1979; Hayes-Roth and Thorndyke, 1980). The blackboard model, described later in this chapter, provides a promising framework in which to build our mission planner.

Previous work in planning uses hierarchical structures for representing their plans. They proceed to plan using a top-down strategy, refining goals from higher levels of abstraction to lower levels of abstraction. Both NOAH (Sacerdoti, 1975b) and MOLGEN (Cohen and Feigenbaum, 1982) use a top-down, least-commitment strategy where planning steps are refined only when there is evidence that a new line of reasoning will not have to be taken. The work of Hayes-Roth and Hayes-Roth uses an opportunistic strategy, planning both top-down and bottom-up. They use a blackboard model to implement their opportunistic planning strategy. We have adopted this blackboard model in the design of our mission planner for both the planning structure (Hayes-Roth *et al.*, 1979) and the control structure (Hayes-Roth, 1985). This model allows for a flexible architecture with diverse knowledge sources cooperating to formulate a plan. Mission planning for an autonomous vehicle is a complex problem that requires a complex system which includes dynamic planning and replanning, plan execution and monitoring, sensor fusion, scene interpretation, and other situation assessment, obstacle avoidance, road following and terrain typing. This chapter focuses on the design of our planning system before execution of the plan by the autonomous vehicle.

Our mission planner creates a sequence of actions executable by an autonomous vehicle. The planner takes as input a mission statement, currently specified as constraints, and produces a sequence of tasks that will accomplish the mission, locations where the tasks will be performed, and routes through the terrain among task locations. For example, the commander specifies goals such as 'perform reconnaissance around the valley between Hill 119 and Hill 91', or 'transport 3rd Company's 1st Platoon to a safe area', or 'resupply 1st Battalion with ammunition'. The planner must also take into consideration conditions that constrain a satisfactory planning solution which the human may identify explicitly or which may be implicit in the planner's knowledge base of planning expertise. For example, the planner must remain on navigable terrain while executing its plan.

21.2 Mission planning

Our approach decomposes the mission statement into constraints and subgoals, which in turn generate either constraints and subgoals or actions. For example, consider the goal to perform reconnaissance and to transmit the results continuously (e.g. video imagery). This goal entails a subgoal of determining various methods for transmitting continuous data. It also entails the constraint to locate areas for reconnaissance that have the property that communication links can be established to the intended receiver of the data. This highly recursive procedure continues until the planner reduces all goals to actions that satisfy all constraints.

Because of its recursive nature, this approach treats each subgoal as a high-level mission statement; it can incorporate the new subgoal into the existing solution or work on it independently. The knowledge engineer decides *a priori* whether subgoals can be achieved in parallel or whether they must be worked on sequentially; when not known, the system defaults to this sequential approach to problem solving. The conservative viewpoint treats all subgoals as sequential lines of reasoning to the final solution. This does not suggest a specific ordering of the subgoals. Instead, the planner chooses opportunistically which subgoals to expand. In the case where subgoals are known to be independent, we can increase the productivity of our system by working on each subgoal in parallel, using the same opportunistic strategy of the sequential planner.

The knowledge engineer decides whether constraints can be satisfied sequentially or in parallel. These decisions are explicit in the structure of the knowledge base. Thus, the control mechanism can recognize the independence of constraints. Constraints (e.g. terrain feature information, resource limitations, vehicle limitations or military doctrine) differ from subgoals (e.g. performing reconnaissance or determining various methods for real-time communication) in that each new constraint does not generate a new problem statement. Instead, constraints propagate to create new constraints that the mission planner incorporates into its problem-solving process. As the constraints are satisfied, a solution develops. This leads to the simple control heuristic, 'try satisfying constraints that limit the search space'.

Although terrain feature information and vehicle properties can be made explicit, they are expressed implicitly in our representations. For example, a Defense Mapping Agency (DMA) database contains terrain feature information and elevation data. Hence, constraints such as 'don't traverse a lake' are satisfied by using algorithms that generate paths bypassing areas with deep water. That constraint is implicit in the functions that access our database. Likewise, vehicle constraints are represented in a model of the autonomous vehicle. The model returns values given the current physical situation of the vehicle. At this level of detail, physical information is encoded in a numeric representation. We are undertaking a major development effort to integrate the mission planner with the digital database.

This model of mission planning supports a design where military expertise defines the resource limitations, terrain feature information, military doctrine and mission subgoals, but where general planning techniques generate actions that satisfy these constraints and subgoals. In this way, military doctrine is encoded into a knowledge base that responds to different situations by decomposing a mission statement into a tightly bound problem of constraints and subgoals. Given this separation of military expertise from planning expertise, we are building our planner as an opportunistic planner that performs constraint satisfaction and goal reduction. We are building the planner within the framework of the blackboard model.

21.3 Blackboard model

In order to solve the Mission Planning problem described above, we have chosen to use a blackboard architecture, BEDS (Blackboard Event Driven System), a version of BB1 (Hayes-Roth, 1984). Using this system, we can represent the mission plan at different levels of abstraction on the blackboard data structure. We can encode diverse knowledge, such as terrain information, physical properties of the vehicle, military doctrine and planning strategies, into knowledge sources which in turn can cooperate to perform mission planning. Finally, we can control the execution of the knowledge sources, and thus the problem solving behavior of the system using the control structure. These three components, the blackboard, knowledge sources and the control structure, interact through a basic control loop.

The blackboard structure (Erman and Lesser, 1975; Hayes-Roth, 1984) is a global, hierarchical data structure partitioned to represent the problem domain as a hierarchy of analysis levels. Each level consists of nodes, objects in the system that contain slots and values, integrated by links, where a node in the hierarchical structure represents an aggregation of lower-level nodes. A link in the hierarchical structure represents a relationship between the nodes. A link can point to any node from any other node. Thus the blackboard can be structured as an undirected graph of nodes; however, one can place nodes without links on the blackboard. During problem solving, partial solutions begin to grow on the blackboard. The higher levels represent abstract decisions made about the general terrain features of the plan, while the lower levels represent decisions made about the specific details of the plan. Thus, knowledge sources can create decisions that refine the plan from the higher levels of the blackboard to the lower levels of the blackboard, growing the plan in a top-down fashion. Alternatively, knowledge sources can create decisions about the specific details of a plan and incorporate those decisions into the general plan, growing the plan in a bottom-up fashion.

Knowledge sources (Erman and Lesser, 1975; Hayes-Roth, 1984) are specialists that access the blackboard by creating nodes, modifying nodes, or modifying links between nodes. This special design of knowledge sources allows them to contribute information without knowing which other knowledge sources will be using their contribution. These knowledge sources post nodes at different levels of the blackboard. Knowledge sources can perform both goal-directed and data-directed inference; i.e. they can trigger when a goal is posted, or they can trigger when data changes.

The knowledge source is defined as a set of preconditions and rules. The preconditions comprise triggering conditions and invoking conditions. A knowledge source becomes active when its triggering conditions are true, and it becomes executable when both its triggering conditions and its invoking conditions are true. This structure of conditionality allows for opportunistic activation of knowledge sources as events occur within the system. As a simple example, consider taking a child to a restaurant. As soon as he sees the dessert tray (triggering condition), his knowledge source 'eat dessert' activates, but (through parental interaction) he cannot execute 'eat dessert' until he finishes his dinner (invoking condition).

Rules are defined in the traditional IF–THEN style. The rules distinguish between different cases when a knowledge source gets executed. Using the previous example, when the 'eat dessert' knowledge source executes, one might have various rules, such as 'if the dessert tray has cake, then choose chocolate', or 'if the dessert tray has ice-cream, then choose vanilla'.

Both the structure of the blackboard and the structure of knowledge sources have been defined as objects in our system using the Flavors package (Symbolics, 1984) on the Symbolics LISP Machine. Using object-oriented programming, we can post nodes on the blackboard by simply sending the message 'create a node' to the appropriate level of the blackboard. A node will be created with the appropriate values in its slots. Likewise, we can execute knowledge sources by sending them the message 'execute'.

The control structure (Hayes-Roth, 1985) consists of a control blackboard and a set of control knowledge sources. The knowledge sources set up strategies for problem solving by posting Policy and Focus decisions on the control blackboard during problem solving. The basic control loop uses these decisions to determine priorities for the executable knowledge sources. This structure of control allows the system to dynamically change its problem solving behavior by modifying its Policy and Focus decisions.

The basic control loop consists of three phases. First, an executable knowledge source is selected by the scheduler. The scheduler selects this knowledge source by looking on its Agenda, a list of all possible executable knowledge sources, and chooses the executable knowledge source with the highest priority. The system checks the knowledge source's preconditions to determine if the knowledge source is still valid. If it is, the knowledge source is executed; otherwise, the scheduler selects another executable knowledge source from the Agenda.

Second, the knowledge source is executed, creating events, changes made to the blackboard. These events are collected in an event list and used to trigger other knowledge sources. Then, for each rule in the knowledge source, if its conditions are true, the rule fires, until all of the rules are exhausted.

Third, the Agenda is updated. Updating the Agenda consists of triggering new knowledge sources based on the events generated by the execution of the last knowledge source. Next, the system checks the invoking conditions of the triggered knowledge sources to determine which ones are executable. The executable knowledge sources are placed on the Agenda. Given this Agenda, the scheduler can choose the next knowledge source for execution.

This model enables the planner to build partial solutions on the blackboard by creating decisions (nodes) at different levels of the blackboard. As nodes on the blackboard are linked, partial solutions grow; partial solutions are linked to form more partial solutions until a final solution is found. The blackboard model produces multiple solutions when they exist; therefore we need critics to evaluate the different solutions. These critics decide when all of the constraints are satisfied, and a solution is found. However, in planning, situations arise where no solution exists that can satisfy all of the constraints. To solve this problem, the blackboard model allows the planner to hypothesize different partial solutions on the blackboard. If one solution fails, we can expand other partial solutions by executing knowledge sources that focus on this particular part of the solution until we reach success.

21.4 Implementation

Our current mission planner uses constraint satisfaction and goal reduction to formulate a solution to the mission-planning problem. These techniques work well because we have reduced the problem to one of finding the best locations to perform tasks that will achieve our goal. Many mission-planning problems can be solved by finding possible locations that satisfy mission constraints. To perform reconnaissance, we need to find locations where we can see the target, yet remain undetected. To transport troops or supplies, we need to find locations where the troops or supplies can be transported. (These locations are not always given, e.g. 'transport troops to a safe place'.) Finally, to locate a command post, we need to find different locations that satisfy requirements for this command post.

To illustrate our approach, consider the following example. We represent the mission statement 'Perform reconnaissance on Garret using triangulation techniques and report the results immediately' (see Figure 21.1) as a problem description or goal and its constraints. The mission statement takes the following internal LISP form:

```
(PROBLEM-DESCRIPTION CONSTRAINT-LIST)
```

where

```
PROBLEM-DESCRIPTION is
    "perform-reconnaissance"
CONSTRAINT-LIST is
((CONCEALMENT
    (UNDETECTABLE-FROM GARRET))
(CONCEALMENT
    (UNDETECTABLE-FROM HILL-9))
(CONCEALMENT
    (UNDETECTABLE-FROM HILL-112))
(RECON (IN-SIGHT GARRET))
(RECON (TRIANGULATION))
(COMMUNICATION (IN-SIGHT HQ))
(COMMUNICATION (REAL-TIME))).
```

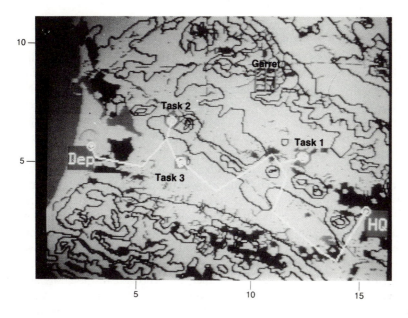

Figure 21.1   Contour map of reconnaissance area. (The route has been enhanced for better reproduction.)

Currently, we read in this LISP representation of the mission statement from a data file. We are headed toward encoding mission planning expertise into knowledge sources that will identify the constraints of the mission statement.

Figure 21.1 depicts an area near Camp Roberts, our test site for the autonomous vehicle. It shows elevation contour lines, the California coast line on the left, water shown in light gray, trees and dense vegetation shown in dark gray. Garret marked by a cross-hatched rectangle, headquarters represented by HQ, and a fuel depot represented by DEP. The vehicle (not shown) is initially located at headquarters.

Here, the solution is two locations that satisfy the following constraints. First, they have concealment from enemy locations; second, they are in sight of Garret; and third, they can transmit continuous data back to HQ. The solution develops on the blackboard as knowledge sources execute and satisfy these constraints. The basic strategy hypothesizes different locations, then either confirms those locations or refutes them. Three different situations best show the flexibility of our mission planner.

First, one should notice that if we try to satisfy the concealment constraints and the recon constraints we would always fail to find a solution. We are trying to find locations that are UNDETECTABLE-FROM Garret and IN-SIGHT of Garret. Without any other constraints, this attempt results in a vacuous solution. However, we have a knowledge source that recognzies this situation and proposes the new constraint, 'stay under cover'. Thus, our cover constraint has been made explicit and not implied by the previous two constraints. We link this new constraint to its predecessors and maintain relationships between the constraints. Now, when we try to find locations as above, we use concealment (trees or dense vegetation) to remain UNDETECTABLE-FROM Garret, yet still IN-SIGHT of Garret. As in MOLGEN (Cohen and Feigenbaum, 1982), we use this technique of constraint propagation.

Second, the communication constraint, REALTIME, generates the subgoal, 'find reconnaissance locations where communications can occur'. Real-time communication, as defined by our scenario, involves having direct line of sight communications (our vehicle uses high-frequency communication channels) from the vehicle to headquarters at the time of reconnaissance activity. To solve this subgoal, one needs to know all possible areas for communication to headquarters and all possible areas for reconnaissance. Only after these facts are known can the subgoal, 'do real-time communication', be achieved. Thus, we have an explicit ordering of the constraints. We cannot begin to solve the subgoal until its preconditions are met. The structure imposed on knowledge sources handles this type of conditionality. We have a knowledge source that can pose the subgoal 'do real-time communication'. This knowledge source triggers when there are communication constraints. However, it does not invoke until communication areas are known and reconnaissance areas are known, so the knowledge source does not generate its subgoal until it is sure that the subgoal can be evaluated. In this way, we have explicitly ordered the constraints.

The last constraint that generates an interesting situation is the recon constraint of TRIANGULATION. Triangulation, as applied to reconnaissance, entails having at least two different locations where the vehicle can view the reconnaissance target. One way to satisfy the triangulation constraint is by using the method mentioned above of constraint propagation to generate new constraints. For example, we could incorporate the new constraint, 'locations must be x meters apart' into our constraints-list. Then, knowledge sources could consider all pairs of locations that satisfied this constraint. However, if we wanted three locations, we would have to consider all triples, etc. In this example, we have increased our search space. An elegant solution is to change the planner's evaluator – the decision maker that provides feedback concerning the planner's progress toward its achieving goals and satisfying constraints – to an evaluator that knows about triangulation techniques. The evaluator, a LISP function, determines whether two different locations have been found for viewing the reconnaissance target. Knowledge sources that satisfy the TRIANGULATION constraint change this function dynamically.

After the mission planner has solved the mission statement, it generates task descriptions and sends them to the Symbolic Path Planner (Kuan *et al.*, 1984; Parodi, 1984). Task descriptions contain the following instance variables (Symbolics, 1984):

- NAME – the name of the task,
- POSITION – the task location,
- CONSTRAINT – ordering constraint.

The Symbolic Path Planner takes this list of tasks and derives a route sequencing them. The path planner takes the starting location of the vehicle and the final destination of the vehicle, and sequences the intermediate subtasks by priority, concluding with the shortest path. It uses the DMA database and its knowledge of the vehicle to generate paths feasible to the autonomous vehicle.

For our example the task list (refer to Figure 21.1 for the task positions) passed to the Symbolic Path Planner would look like:

```
(task1 task2 task3)
```

where

```
task1 — NAME = "recon location"
         POSITION = (12.5 5)
         CONSTRAINT = nil

task2 — NAME = "recon location"
         POSITION = (6.25 7)
         CONSTRAINT = (> task2 task3)

task3 — NAME = "repeater location"
         POSITION = (7 5)
         CONSTRAINT = (< task3 task2).
```

The Symbolic Path Planner takes this list and generates a route that sequences the intermediate tasks at locations (12.5 5), (6.25 7) and (7 5), the starting location of the vehicle, HQ, and the final destination of the vehicle, DEP. The path planner uses the constraint that task3 must occur before task2; i.e. drop off a communication repeater at location (7 5) before performing reconnaissance at location (6.25 7). The final route derived by the Symbolic Path Planner has the vehicle performing reconnaissance at position (12.5 5), dropping off a repeater at position (7 5), and then performing the second reconnaissance at position (6.25 7). Currently, our system makes no distinction between the different tasks – its only concern is the location of each task. We could incorporate a list of commands that make up a task in our task description. For task3, we might have the commands get repeater, place repeater on soil, test repeater, which could be executed when the autonomous vehicle was at position (7 5).

21.5 Conclusion

This approach demonstrates that a class of mission-planning problems, locating areas for performing various tasks, can be solved by using constraint propagation and goal reduction. The mission planner performs spatial reasoning by considering terrain features as it finds the best location to perform a task. It also performs temporal reasoning by ordering the task within the constraints of the problem specification.

The success of this approach lies in the flexibility of the blackboard architecture. This architecture allows us to try different approaches to solving the problem. We can choose a goal-directed line of reasoning, or a data driven-line of reasoning, or both. This allows us to reshape the problem within the blackboard framework when attempts fail, without much loss of previous work.

Although the blackboard model is a generic architecture for building planning systems, there are two inherent problems with our system that must be addressed. First, the blackboard is a memory-consuming data structure – it collects information from the onset of the problem-solving session, rarely discarding anything. This has not been a problem as yet for us, but it may be in the future. Second, the execution of knowledge sources is CPU intensive; therefore, the speed of the system can become an issue when we consider real-time dynamic planning and replanning.

Our research efforts will continue into the areas of dynamic planning and replanning using this design because the blackboard model allows us to build plans using a data-directed strategy. This is important in a dynamically changing environment when one wants the system to be reactive to outside changes.

Acknowledgments

I am indebted to Perry Thorndyke and Darwin Kuan for helpful comments on the content of this paper with special thanks to Barbara Hayes-Roth who was responsible for the BB1 system and made it available to FMC.

22

Intelligent Data Fusion for Naval Command and Control

W.L. Lakin, J.A.H. Miles and C.D. Byrne

22.1 Introduction

22.1.1 Background

The problems of increasing complexity within the naval command and control environment are demanding new technical approaches. Of particular significance is the problem of operator cognitive overload resulting from the steadily increasing volume of incoming information which must be assimilated, interpreted and assessed by the command team of a warship if they are to derive an adequate appreciation of the tactical situation facing them. The problem is compounded by the reduced manning levels imposed by escalating manpower costs. In order to operate effectively in the sophisticated arena of modern naval warfare, the command team requires automated decision aids which will assist with gathering and categorizing available information in a timely manner and, in addition, will provide automated support to the interpretation and assessment of the resulting tactical picture.

22.1.2 Requirement

The work described in this chapter forms part of a research program in progress at the Admiralty Research Establishment into the use of artificial intelligence (AI) techniques to provide automated support to the tasks of situation assessment and resource deployment in naval command and control. The specific problem addressed here is that of generating an appreciation of the tactical situation facing either a single warship or a naval task group. This can be considered in two main stages: the first is the compilation, from the information available, of an objective and coherent 'world picture' in the area of interest; the second is the derivation of an intelligent assessment of what that picture means in tactical terms. We refer to these respectively as 'data fusion' and 'situation assessment'.

In order to build a picture, it is necessary first of all to detect, locate, track and, if possible, classify all objects that might conceivably contribute to the tactical situation. This implies virtually every object within sensor range or within the volume of interest to a single warship or to a group of cooperating maritime units, which may be dispersed over a wide area of ocean. In constructing the picture, it is important to consider not only all the real-time sensor data, but also what might be termed secondary or nonreal-time data so as to provide further evidence for classifying the objects, predicting their intentions and gaining a general appreciation of the tactical situation. Consequently, the information sources include not just radio, acoustic and optical devices, but also human observers providing intelligence data and a background of encyclopedic information and operational plans, all of which set the context for the more dynamic real-time sensor information. The task of combining such disparate data types, having proved well beyond the capabilities of conventional computing methods, has remained the province of the already overloaded human operator, and yet it has to be undertaken in time scales that allow effective response to be taken against today's high-speed missile threat.

This chapter addresses primarily the issue of multiplatform, multisensor data fusion, which forms one of the key stages in the command and control process outlined above. The term 'multisensor' reflects the need to combine data of many different types, both real-time and nonreal-time, arriving through many different channels. The term 'multiplatform' recognizes that ships rarely operate individually, and that the information is normally gathered and assessed by a group of ships, aircraft and possibly submarines operating collectively.

22.2 Data fusion

22.2.1 Correlation ambiguity

The aim of data fusion is to coalesce the information from tracks on the same vehicle from different sensors (using 'track' to mean a set of data over time from any sensor about a single vehicle, and using 'sensor' to embrace both real-time and nonreal-time data channels). It can be viewed as a two-stage problem. First, the evidence must be correlated to find which pieces belong to the same real-world objects; secondly, the evidence must be combined to estimate and infer the required object parameters.

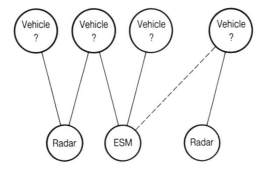

Figure 22.1   Correlation ambiguities.

The problem is not so much in the combination stage, where statistical estimation and expert systems have demonstrated successful solutions. It is in correlation where the most difficulty lies. Because the evidence may be inaccurate, uncertain, false and late arriving, there is ambiguity in the way it fits together. This gives rise to many possible world views, and much of the research effort has been spent finding a general strategy to handle this combinatorially explosive problem.

The problem of correlation ambiguity is illustrated in Figure 22.1. Even if the radar and ESM contacts on the left of the figure are deemed by the correlation rules to be capable of correlation, there are still two possibilities:

- either they are the same object, denoted by the middle vehicle hypothesis,

- or they are two different objects, denoted by the other two vehicle hypotheses.

A single object detected by n sensors will generate $2^n - 1$ hypotheses. As each sensor detects not one but many objects, there is also further ambiguity as to which contacts go together, as illustrated by the radar contact on the right. The inherent inaccuracy of most of the sensor data implies loose correlation rules leading to large numbers of such ambiguities. The need to process several new contacts per second leads to unmanageable combinatorial difficulties with such an approach.

But there is a further problem. Having generated all possible hypotheses to explain the data, it is necessary to decide which ones to output as being the most likely. We attempted to do this by generating every possible consistent output set and then scoring these in some way. For example, suppose the radar track on the right of Figure 22.1 also satisfies the criteria for correlation with the ESM contact. There are then three possible self-consistent output sets or 'views' of the situation. These are:

- left-hand correlation is valid,
- right-hand correlation is valid,
- neither correlation is valid.

By representing all consistent output sets and given a satisfactory scoring system, the 'current best view' is simply the set with the highest score. Unfortunately the enormous number of sets (views) resulting from any realistic scenario renders the approach impractical. For example, even for a single object detected by n sensors, the number of logically consistent views of the situation is given by the so-called Bell number $B(n)$ (Moser and Myman, 1955), where:

$$B(n) = \sum_{i=0}^{i=k} [\binom{k}{i} B(k-i)] \qquad B(0) = 1 \quad k = n-1$$

For example, ten sensors gives $B(10) = 115\ 975$.

22.2.2 Correlation strategy

The choice of a rule-based approach enabled us to adopt a less rigorous but more practical approach than that described above. This approach, illustrated in Figure 22.2, considers only pairwise correlations and involves three distinct rule-driven steps:

(1)   Assume all new contacts are separate and therefore each new contact implies a new vehicle.

(2)   Apply rules that create the possible pairwise correlations between each new track and existing tracks in the system. These correlations must be periodically checked to make sure they are still valid; those that fail the check are deleted.

(3)   Apply rules to confirm strong correlations and to deny others. Where alternatives are of similar strengths, wait for further evidence. Such a rule might require that, in order to confirm a correlation, its likelihood must exceed some absolute threshold and also significantly exceed other possibilities, i.e. be relatively unambiguous. In addition, the correlation must be part of an allowed set. For example, if Track A tentatively correlates with Track B, and Track B with Track C, these can only be confirmed if

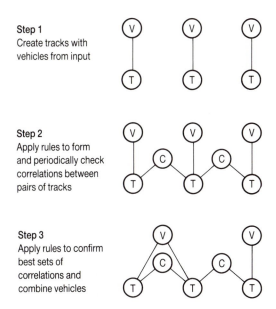

Step 1
Create tracks with
vehicles from input

Step 2
Apply rules to form
and periodically check
correlations between
pairs of tracks

Step 3
Apply rules to confirm
best sets of
correlations and
combine vehicles

Figure 22.2   Data fusion steps.

Track C also correlates with Track A. In other words, all tracks supporting the same vehicle must mutually correlate on a pairwise basis.

22.2.3 Blackboard system

The approach described above has been successfully implemented using a blackboard type of expert system architecture (Nii *et al.*, 1982). The main feature of this architecture (Figure 22.3) is the global data area which hosts a dynamic structure of hypotheses and support links. The hypotheses are organized as a hierarchy, each one representing a possible conclusion from the group of lower level hypotheses that supports it. Input data are posted on the blackboard as new hypotheses. Hypotheses and support links are manipulated by rules which are themselves grouped into knowledge sources. The application of knowledge sources is controlled by a rule-based scheduling system, these rules being contained in meta-KSs. A general-purpose blackboard framework, known as MXA (Rice, 1984), was designed and constructed for this program. As one of its features, MXA provides a language (Stammers, 1983) for encoding rules.

Tracks, correlations and vehicles are represented by hypotheses, and are placed on the blackboard by knowledge sources which deal with

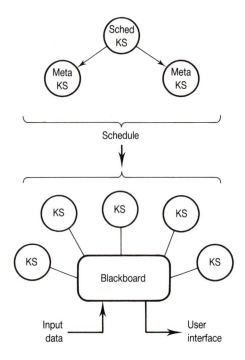

Figure 22.3 Blackboard system.

particular input data types or with specific stages of the processing strategy. Support links are used to create the types of connected structure illustrated in Figure 22.2, and the likelihood mechanism of MXA is used to provide a measure of correlation strength for the purpose of confirming correlations and combining the evidence to form distinct vehicles (Step 3 of Figure 22.2).

22.3 Laboratory demonstrator

22.3.1 Blackboard structure

An initial implementation of the multiplatform, multisensor data-fusion strategy outlined above has been undertaken using the facilities of MXA. It is capable of handling the various types of input data shown in Figure 22.4. The inclusion of datalink information gives the demonstrator its multiplatform, multisensor capability. The blackboard data structure used to perform multiplatform, multisensor data fusion is shown schematically in Figure 22.5. A multitrack level has been included in the data structure to allow for many sensors of the same type, both on own ship and on distributed multiple platforms. The various sets of sensor

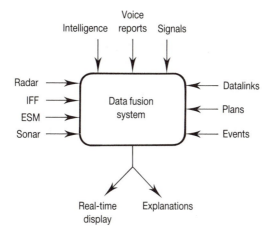

Figure 22.4 Multisensor data fusion experimental system.

data are combined by amalgamating sets of similar sensors first, then sets of dissimilar sensors, thereby producing a hierarchical organization (Lakin and Miles, 1987). The principles adopted in the organization are:

(1) Like sensors on own-ship are combined to form the multitrack level. This applies to active sensors, such as radar and its closely associated IFF systems.

(2) The active sensor pictures from different platforms are combined in order to establish a force-wide picture and, at the same time, to identify and assess any sensor platform position errors.

(3) Like passive sensors, such as ESM and passive sonars, are combined in order to reduce, as far as possible, the position uncertainty of contacts.

(4) Finally, the combined pictures from each type of sensor, along with plans and reports, are fused together to form the vehicle level.

The principle of combining like sensors first has been adopted because like sensors have similar parameters to compare with potentially less ambiguity, whereas dissimilar sensors, in general, only have a few parameters in common. This means that fewer combinations have to be considered during the correlation process.

22.3.2 Experimental system

In order to develop, apply and evaluate the above strategies, it has been necessary to construct an extensive support environment in the laboratory. Its purpose is to provide a steadily increasing degree of realism to

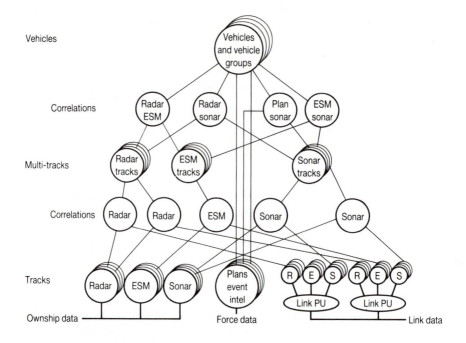

Figure 22.5 Multiplatform data fusion.

the input data provided to test and exercise the data-fusion system. Commencing with scenarios based on a limited set of purely simulated input data, the test environment is gradually being evolved, through the introduction of real data recorded at sea during naval exercises, up to the point of providing a comprehensive set of live data. The fusion system accepts input primarily at the track level, and so plot-level data is preprocessed into tracks.

The components of the multiplatform, multisensor data-fusion system comprise the following items as illustrated in Figure 22.6:

- SDGS Sensor Data Generation System. This software provides offline generation of realistic sensor data down to plot level from a scenario description.

- RATES Radar Automatic Track Extraction System (Shepherd *et al.*, 1986). An offline version of our radar tracking software is used to form radar tracks for input to the data-fusion system. A simplified version is used for ESM data.

- EDP Exercise Data Preparation. This software is used to prepare real data, recorded at sea during naval exercises, for input to the data-fusion system.

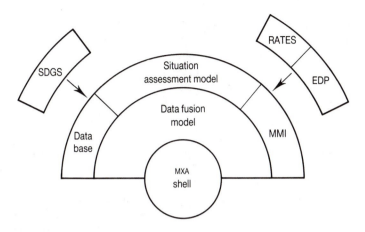

Figure 22.6 Experimental system.

- MMI Man–Machine Interface. In order to demonstrate the data-fusion system in real time, special-purpose graphics software has been developed to drive a high-resolution color graphics terminal using the GKS language.

- MXA the blackboard expert system framework. This runs on a VAX computer under the VMS operating system.

- Data-fusion model This is the data-fusion knowledge coded in the MXA language.

- Situation-assessment model This is the knowledge to derive a higher-level interpretation of the tactical situation, as will be described in a later section.

- Database A database containing geographic and encyclopedic data is required by both the data-fusion and situation-assessment models.

22.3.3 Display capabilities

The compiled tactical picture is displayed using a Sigmex 6264 graphics display system. A hierarchical set of menus controls the degree of complexity of the picture while a set of on-screen windows provides flexibility in the type of information displayed.

Plate 4 shows four windows being viewed simultaneously and introduces some of the symbology used in the compiled tactical picture. Plate 4b shows radar data. The display is centered on own-ship, shown in yellow, but may alternatively be ground stabilized. Radar tracks are denoted by basic vehicle symbols, derived from simple rules which make use of track behavior, such as maximum and minimum speed, in order to establish the set of possible vehicle types to which it may belong. In the event of ambiguity, the platform type representing the highest potential threat is displayed at this stage. These symbols may be displayed with track history. ESM detections, represented by bearing lines with vehicle symbols derived from the emitter characteristics, are shown in Plate 4a. Plans delineating the patrol areas for ships and aircraft are illustrated in Plate 4c. Other inputs such as IFF, events and intelligence reports are not shown in these examples. Allegiance is shown by symbol color: blue – friendly; red – hostile; green – neutral; and white – unknown. The capability is also provided to display range rings and coastlines, as shown in some of the windows.

Selection, using the mouse, of a vehicle on the screen causes it to be encircled (see Plate 4c) and also brings up a text window as shown in Plate 4d. This window provides a readout of the vehicle's attributes, such as range, bearing, course, speed and as much identity information as can be inferred from the available evidence.

22.4 Experimental results

22.4.1 Demonstrator objective

The ultimate objective of data fusion is to combine data from all sources. This will require a very large knowledge base; using the representation chosen in our demonstrators, this implies a very large number of rules. Our more limited aim is therefore to produce an illustrative rather than a comprehensive set of rules across several different areas of correlation types. In order to be operationally acceptable, these basic rules will require considerable enhancement and tuning. The correlation types covered include: radar/radar, radar/IFF, ESM/ESM, ESM/radar, plan/radar and plan/ESM, as well as higher-level correlations, and the use of reports and sightings. The first four correlation types apply to both own-ship and datalink-received sensor information.

The experimental results will be outlined in terms of the action of the system's knowledge, in the form of rules, upon a set of input data. Although the rules for multiplatform, multisensor data fusion were developed using simulated data, in order to test the data-fusion system more rigorously, real data recorded at sea during naval exercises has been acquired. However, because of the difficulties and limitations in recording all the data types, and in view of the desire to incorporate as wide a range as possible, this real data has been augmented by simulated data when necessary. Plates 5 to 7, which include both correlated and uncorrelated displays, will be used to illustrate the actions of these rules upon this composite data.

22.4.2 Exercise scenario

The test scenario chosen consists of a 1 hour sequence from a 4-day NATO maritime exercise. Own-ship, on which the recordings were taken, forms part of a task group comprising four ships (blue force), which was subject to a number of simulated air attacks over the course of the sequence. The group is proceeding in an east-north-east direction with a mean line of advance of 52° at a speed of 15 knots. Other participating units included a number of combat air patrol aircraft (CAP) and helicopters comprising the rest of the blue force, and various attack and surveillance aircraft forming the red force.

To the north (Plates 5 to 7) a geographic coast line is shown, and range rings are scaled in 50 nautical miles. Four ships (blue force) are featured, all operating within their planned sectors. Their patrol boxes are shown with a blue (friendly unit) symbol placed in one corner of the sector to denote the type of unit executing the patrol. The patrol area of a helicopter can also be seen. The ship in the center of the display is referred to as own-ship and is the origin of the recorded data.

22.4.3 Correlation results

Radar/radar correlation

The purpose of the radar/radar correlation rules is to combine track data from radars on a single platform, and to match track data from different platforms. This will eliminate multiple tracks on the same target and provide information for automatically correcting any registration errors between data from remote platforms. This is important for establishing accurate baselines for multiplatform passive sensing such as ESM and passive sonar.

Plate 5 shows an example of radar/radar correlation. On the right is a window with an uncorrelated display showing a double radar track to the south of own-ship, whereas the correlated window on the left shows a single vehicle in which the information from both tracks has been combined.

ESM/ESM correlation

Multiplatform ESM correlation enables targets to be ranged by triangulation, or cross-fixing, provided that the measurements can be correlated and are sufficiently accurate, and a suitable baseline exists. This is important for establishing the positions of vehicles outside radar cover, or in conditions of radio silence.

To the south of own-ship in the uncorrelated window in Plate 5, two bearing lines from two geographically separated ESM receivers are visible: one bearing line emanates from own-ship and the second bearing line from the ship positioned south-south-east of own-ship. The rules have inferred that these detections refer to the same object which, by triangulation, has been represented in the correlated picture as a position error ellipse. This is referred to as a 'point'-ESM track, to distinguish it from the uncorrelated 'line'-ESM. Subsequently, higher-order correlations are assembled, as this point-ESM track goes on to correlate with the multiplatform radar track referred to above.

ESM/radar correlation

The aim here is to combine the good identity information, in terms of platform type and allegiance, derived from the emitter characteristics as picked up by ESM, with the good positional information given by radar. It is first necessary, however, to correlate ESM and radar using whatever common parameters are available. For point-ESM (as defined above), both range and bearing may be compared, but single-platform ESM can only be compared in bearing dimension, thus giving rise to potential ambiguity. These ambiguities can often be resolved over a period of time, and hence the importance of retaining a considerable amount of track and vehicle history. The rules also make use of the behavior characteristics of the radar track, and would not, for example, associate a shipborne emitter with a radar track travelling at say 600 knots.

In Plate 5, a hostile ESM detection on bearing 317° has correlated with a radar track. Thus, on the correlated plot, the ESM bearing line and the radar track marker have been replaced by a single symbol denoting the location, direction of movement, platform type and (by means of color) the allegiance of the object in question, in this case a hostile aircraft. This information is also displayed in the associated text window, along with an indication of the supporting data sources.

Radar/IFF correlation

These rules add allegiance to radar tracks for friendly and neutral vehicles, the association being based largely on position. In Plate 6, the upper text readout indicates that this has occurred for the aircraft to the south-west on a bearing of 246°. The neutral aircraft in question is one of a number of civil airliners using air lanes that cross the exercise area.

Plans

These may be used to show areas where friendly units should be operating. The aim is to correlate plans with sensor contacts in order to identify those contacts and provide an update on the positions of friendly units. There may be considerable ambiguity to be resolved, for example when many ESM tracks cross a plan area, and the sensor may lose contact periodically, requiring recorrelation when detection occurs again. Thus the maintenance of a good picture of friendly units is a continuous process.

In Plate 6, the helicopter, positioned to the south-west of own-ship, has been selected using the mouse. Its precise location is given by radar, and the vehice identity is supplied by plan information. The absence of a white border to the plan denotes that it has been correlated with other information, and its symbol has been moved from the corner to the actual position of the vehicle.

Reports

These refer to all inputs via signals and voice channels, as well as to local events such as aircraft launch and recovery, weapon release, etc. Provided that this type of report information can be correlated with the more timely sensor data, its inclusion can assist the identification process. This can be reasonably straightforward for locally generated reports of aircraft or missile launch, which can be correlated with outgoing tracks from the launch platform. Less timely reports from remote sources are difficult to correlate with elements of the rapidly changing air picture unless some matching identity information is available from the sensors. For the surface and subsurface scenes, such reports are probably the main source of a wider picture which, being slower to change, makes the information more useful.

In Plate 7, the ship lying south-south-east of own-ship illustrates an example of a triple correlation in which radar data, a plan and a position report, received via datalink, have been combined to provide the comprehensive set of object parameters shown in the text window.

22.5 Situation assessment

Although multiplatform data fusion provides a model of the tactical world, this model is essentially low level, and further levels of inferencing are required to provide the information on which tactical decisions must be made. These further levels can be viewed as an extension of data fusion in that they involve bringing together elements of the tactical picture; for example, formations of hostile aircraft to infer the type and strength of a potential threat. In order to distinguish these higher levels of fusion from those associated with the input data, we refer to them as 'situation assessment'. The emphasis in situation assessment is to provide the required output, rather than to merely assemble all of the input data into a consistent model.

Hostile/friendly/neutral groups

Interacting vehicle groups

Functional vehicle groups

Spatial vehicle groups

Vehicles

Possible correlations

Multi-sensor tracks

Possible correlations

Tracks, plans and reports

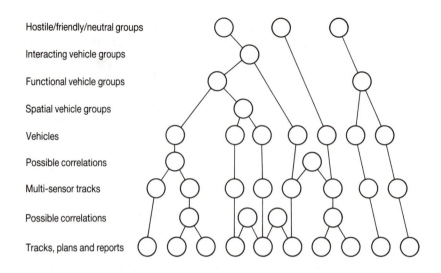

Figure 22.7 Data fusion and situation assessment hierarchy.

Situation assessment is the next stage in our research. It builds on the tactical picture produced by data fusion, and it also feeds back conclusions to the lower levels in order to fill in unknowns. For example, an aircraft may have been assessed as hostile, but others nearby may have no data to support their allegiance. By assessing the group as a formation, the allegiance can be propagated to all members of the group.

At a higher level, some elements of a tactical plan may be identified which may be used to infer the missions of unknown units whose presence was previously unexplained. Thus some parts of situation assessment may be seen as a 'plan recognition' activity. This would normally be organized as a 'backward chaining' task in a knowledge-based structure, in contrast to the forward-chaining nature of the data-fusion activity.

To support situation assessment, a more complex multilevel blackboard-data representation has been designed as depicted schematically in Figure 22.7. The hypothesis structure implemented for multi-platform multisensor data fusion (Figure 22.5) is extended. By forming individual vehicles into groups, further inferences on identity, allegiance, function and mission may be possible. There are three main reasons for forming groups or clusters of vehicles: first, some evidence comes in group form, for example a raid report, or the information has to be dealt with as a group because of sensor resolution limitations; secondly there is a need to group vehicles to infer common attributes and group functions; thirdly, groups form a fundamental component of situation assessment for example, for inferring what tactics the total set of enemy vehicles are employing.

Assuming that a hierarchy of vehicle groups, such as that shown in Figure 22.7, can be formed, the resulting model may be used to produce assessments of particular significance to the user. Possible examples are as follows:

(1) *Threats*   Assessment of potential, possible or actual threats is obviously useful.

(2) *Engagements*   Assessing the outcome of an engagement in real time is important, but it may be difficult to achieve depending on what evidence is available.

(3) *Rules of engagement*   At the build-up stage of a conflict, Command will need to assess whether to take positive action. For guidance, rules of engagement will be in force. An assessment of the threat in the context of such rules might assist in the judgement of when decisions have to be made.

(4) *Sensor and weapon coverage*   In judging the effectiveness of the defence screens, an assessment of sensor and weapon coverage would be of value.

(5) *Plan monitoring*   Given that a number of plans for defensive and offensive actions are in force at any time, this assessment is intended as a check to see how well these plans are proceeding.

(6) *Surveillance*   When active sensors are used, there is a risk that the enemy will be able to detect transmissions and gain information. An assessment of the extent of knowledge on both sides might help suggest which active sensors should be deployed.

Our approach to demonstrating situation assessment, like that for data fusion, is to implement some illustrative examples. However, because the knowledge required is more complex, substantial naval tactical expertise needs to be encapsulated in the rules. Knowledge elicitation is therefore being undertaken based on the so-called 'interview techniques'. Results from this phase of the work will be reported in due course.

22.6 Conclusions and future work

Experience gained from utilizing real exercise data, albeit a limited set, has proved an invaluable aid in constructing the data-fusion knowledge base. The approach has also provided a viable mechanism for evaluating the intelligent data-fusion system. Criteria for evaluating expert systems are, in general, not easily definable; because we are dealing with heuristic knowledge, as opposed to a purely algorithmic model, there may be no formal way to prove that a given outcome is correct.

In our future work program we plan to acquire a more complete set of real data, together with recordings of all nonorganic sources of information for both the benign and the hostile elements of the environment. The tactical picture compiled by the data-fusion system will be evaluated against a reconstruction of that formed during the actual naval exercise.

Although the blackboard problem-solving model is very general, it has proved to be a useful framework for the data-fusion problem described. Consideration is now being given to the more advanced AI toolkits which have since become available, and which offer a choice of problem-solving paradigms, along with a more convenient development environment. However, these toolkits commonly employ the production system technique for forward reasoning. As a result of its implicit control mechanism, a production system may prove too inefficient and inflexible for this demanding real-time problem.

A definitive statement on the applicability of a knowledge-based approach to aspects of naval command and control requires the resolution of many issues in the general areas of hardware engineering, to provide a suitable inferencing capability of sufficient power, software engineering and knowledge engineering. It is in this last area of how to formulate a viable knowledge-engineering discipline for the construction of very large operational systems that many questions remain unanswered. Research aimed at addressing some of these issues has been described in this chapter; others remain as part of our long-term research program.

Acknowledgments

We would like to acknowledge the contributions of the many people who have been involved in the ARE data-fusion program, with special thanks to John Montgomery, Jon Haugh and Rachel Curtis.

Part V

23

Current Directions (1985–1987)

R.S. Engelmore and A.J. Morgan

In this part we examine some of the more recent extensions and refinements to the blackboard architecture. Each of the systems reported here is relatively new and experimental; all have yet to be proven in a significant application. As with the earlier generalizations discussed in Part III, each of these systems emphasizes a different concern on the part of the developers.

Chapters 24 and 25 discuss different approaches to gaining higher performance through parallel execution of knowledge sources in a modified blackboard framework. In Ensor and Gabbe's framework, the problem of maintaining data consistency is addressed by a transaction manager, which controls asynchronous reference to shared data via locks. Knowledge sources, both domain and control, are called agents, and are grouped into nodes which reside on different processors. A knowledge source may perform the usual actions on the blackboard (although only a portion of the blackboard may be visible to it), place an entry on the controller goal queue, or send a message to another knowledge source. The last activity violates one of the basic tenets of the blackboard model, but it facilitates participation by several agents in a common transaction (we should note that Hearsay-II, as actually implemented, did not maintain absolute independence among knowledge sources either).

CAGE and POLIGON represent two other attempts to investigate specific aspects of concurrency in blackboard systems. CAGE (from Concurrent AGE) is a relatively conservative extension of the AGE system (discussed in Chapter 12). POLIGON, on the other hand, is closer to the spirit of the BLOBS system discussed in Chapter 16 than to AGE (although POLIGON was not directly influenced by the design of BLOBS). Both systems are being tested with the same experimental task, and their

461

performance measured by the same tools within an environment that simulates multiple processors. The two systems present an interesting contrast in styles of concurrency. CAGE allows the user to specify parallel execution at three levels of granularity: at the knowledge source level, at the rule level and at the clause-within-a-rule level. CAGE also assumes a shared memory (or, more precisely, a shared address space), as in Ensor and Gabbe's transactional blackboards. POLIGON, on the other hand, attaches knowledge sources to each blackboard node. Whenever a node is created or modified, its attendant KS is activated, which may in turn modify other nodes, etc. The user now must explicitly specify any sequential behavior. Also in contrast to CAGE, POLIGON is designed to run on a distributed address space architecture. While CAGE inherits from AGE the familiar knowledge-source-with-production-rules approach, the POLIGON architecture makes an object-oriented framework a natural choice. At present, it is an open question as to which (if either) of these systems represents the best approach to concurrency.

GBB (General BlackBoard), described in Chapter 26, was developed at the University of Massachusetts. The developers were able to take advantage of their considerable experience in building large blackboard systems (see Chapters 8 and 18). In consolidating this experience, the main emphasis was placed on providing an efficient and well structured blackboard. GBB enforces prior specification of the blackboard structure, and makes its structure available to a 'blackboard administrator'. This strongly parallels the data definition and database administrator aspects of modern database practice. Apart from maintainability, the major benefit of a well structured blackboard is the potential for efficient execution, in terms of insertion and retrieval of blackboard objects. In contrast to BB1, GBB does not emphasize the control of blackboard operations. Control aspects are separated from database aspects, so that the same blackboard structure could be used with different control mechanisms. This includes the possibility for user-defined mechanisms as an alternative to standard system functions.

In contrast to the multiprocessor architectures anticipated by CAGE and POLIGON, MUSE (Chapter 27) takes a conservative view of technology. Typical target hardware in MUSE systems is a 16/32-bit microprocessor system with a (possibly large) semiconductor store, but no disk. Like BLOBS (Chapter 16), MUSE is also aimed at continuous real-time applications. The main system language is an amalgam of the POP-2 language, originally developed at Edinburgh, and Smalltalk. As we have seen, this shift towards object-oriented languages appears in several of the more recent blackboard systems such as BLOBS and POLIGON. In the case of MUSE, it is seen as a way of protecting the user from some of the system complexity. The blackboard in MUSE no longer exists as a single, global database. Instead, it is split into regions (corresponding roughly to the levels of conventional blackboards) through which the knowledge sources communicate. In practice, of course, data on a conventional blackboard is only potentially global; and access to specific areas of a blackboard is limited to a small number of knowledge sources. MUSE simply recognizes this fact at the time the application system is compiled.

MUSE supports two rule languages; one OPS-like for forward production systems, the other backward chaining for goal-directed systems. A MUSE knowledge source can contain any required mix of forward production or backward chaining rules. An efficiency feature is the provision of a 'scratchpad' database within each knowledge source, which we first encountered in the Hearsay-II system. The description of MUSE in Chapter 27 was written especially for this book.

A different approach to building continuous (though not real-time) systems is shown in the Edinburgh PROLOG Blackboard Shell (EPBS), discussed in Chapter 28. Here the main driving force has been to retain PROLOG as the programming language, while providing some of the organizational and control aspects of blackboard systems. Like several of the other generalizations discussed in this part, EPBS has been built with an initial application in mind – in this case, user modeling. The implementation has a number of unusual features. One is that the blackoard system sits 'alongside' the host language rather than being built 'on top' of it. This allows users of the framework – who are expected to be PROLOG programmers – to mix PROLOG code for the application with the blackboard constructs. The blackboard constructs themselves appear to the programmer simply as PROLOG clauses. One consequence of this way of building an application system is that the rules within a knowledge source are grouped together solely for the convenience of the system builder – the system makes no distinction between rules in different knowledge sources. Thus the point of view taken by the EPBS designers is that the blackboard framework is useful primarily for problem conceptualization by humans.

The indexing mechanism on the blackboard is determined by the user, and so is any interpretation of the meaning of the index in terms of a blackboard 'level' or any other dimension. In some ways, this is similar to the use of hypothesis classes which we have seen in other generalizations such as Hearsay-III and MXA. The major difference here is the absence of a prespecified blackboard structure which we see so strongly emphasized in GBB.

The control mechanism of EPBS follows the model proposed in OPM, and in that respect is similar to the BB1 approach which we have already discussed. In EPBS, a choice from pending knowledge source activation records (KSARs) is made on the basis of an estimate of usefulness. The estimate can be an arbitrary PROLOG term, and the default (arithmetic) choice mechanism can also be overridden by a user-supplied predicate.

A further point of interest is the way in which the system maintains consistency of the blackboard. A change to a blackboard item causes the system to update other entries which depended on the absence of a fact in the newly changed item.

The BB1 group at Stanford has been emphasizing a layered approach to the development of more powerful blackboard frameworks. BB∗, discussed in Chapter 29, is a general design for tailoring BB1 to particular classes of applications. One such class is that of arrangement or assembly of objects within a specified set of constraints. PROTEAN (Chapter 20) exemplifies an arrangement task. Generalizing from their experience with PROTEAN, the BB1 group developed a task-specific framework for arrangement-assembly tasks, called ACCORD. (Readers should note that the terminology used in Chapter 29 differs from the conventions used previously in this book. The authors' use of the term 'architecture' corresponds with 'framework', whereas their 'blackboard framework' is what we would call a 'task-specific blackboard framework'.) PROTEAN was reimplemented in ACCORD as a test of ACCORD's representational adequacy. ACCORD was also used in the development of another application system, called SIGHTPLAN (Tommelein *et al.*, 1987a). SIGHTPLAN's task is to arrange pieces of equipment, storage areas and access roads at a construction site so that a variety of constraints are satisfied. ACCORD may also be suitable for temporal arrangement-assembly tasks (e.g. travel planning) and for a more general symbolic arrangement-assembly task; at present these are only speculations offered by the authors. The material in Chapter 29 is based on Hayes-Roth *et al.* (1986c).

24

Transactional Blackboards

J. Robert Ensor and John D. Gabbe

24.1 Introduction

The blackboard architecture is an important structural framework for expert systems. In this architecture, an expert system consists of a shared data region (called the blackboard), a set of knowledge sources, and a control mechanism. The blackboard is a database which is shared by the knowledge sources as their communication medium. Containing rules and hypotheses which express the domain expertise of the system, the knowledge sources respond to each other through observed changes in the blackboard. The control mechanism schedules execution of the knowledge sources according to information from its goal queues and the blackboard.

Several expert systems have been built according to the blackboard architecture. Examples include a speech-understanding system (Erman *et al.*, 1980), a sonar interpretation system (Nii and Feigenbaum, 1978), a vehicular tracking system (Lesser and Corkill, 1978) and a protein crystallography interpretation system (Terry, 1983). Although these systems are founded on the blackboard architecture, they vary significantly within the framework, demonstrating the utility and flexibility of the paradigm. Experience suggests that this architecture is particularly suitable for systems representing multiple areas of expertise and for systems solving problems with complex information interdependences.

Multiprocessor computing environments should be capable of increasing the scope and utility of expert systems and successfully addressing problems beyond the reach of most uniprocessors, such as real-time speech recognition or robot control. The domain and control knowledge of an expert system may be distributed onto several processors. The interactions of modular knowledge sources may simulate their modeled events, with both communication paths and timing of

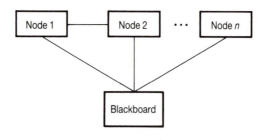

Figure 24.1　Network of processing nodes.

interactions. Thus multiprocessor configurations have the potential to support the construction and execution of expert systems with new and useful properties.

Multiprocessor computers are often difficult to use. While the processors can execute in parallel, the exchange of data, code and results among these processors can often make the overall system slow. Therefore, a balance must be reached among the costs of loading code, accessing data and communicating requests and responses. Two extreme approaches have received most attention by researchers. At one extreme are systems in which processing nodes frequently exchange small sets of data and do small computations with each data set (e.g. Dennis, 1980). At the other extreme are systems that place a large, autonomous program on each processing node. In these systems, the nodes exchange data infrequently and spend most of their time performing 'local' computations (e.g. Lesser and Corkill, 1978). The work described in this chapter focuses on supporting systems closer to the latter extreme. We present mechanisms for constructing expert systems as collections of knowledge sources communicating through a shared data medium. These are systems in which knowledge sources executing on different processors perform moderate to large computations between communications.

The integrity of data that are accessed asynchronously by several clients must be maintained. Providing transactional access to shared databases is a common solution to this problem. A sequence of operations on one or more data elements, beginning with a start-transaction request and ending with either a commit- or an abort-transaction request, a *transaction* is a unit of activity with three properties: atomicity, consistency preservation and permanence. Atomicity means that, in net effect and even when failures occur, either all operations in the unit happen (the transaction commits) or none of them happens (it aborts). Consistency preservation means that a transaction moves data from one consistent state to another. Permanence means that the effect of a committed transaction persists, surviving any non-

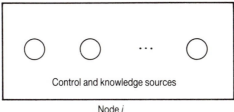

Node *i*

Figure 24.2 Agents within a node.

catastrophic failures, until the next transaction involving that data is committed.

We extend the blackboard architecture to support systems executing in multiprocessor environments by providing transactional access to the blackboard. Our extensions are novel in their ease of use and in the richness of structure that they support. Two mechanisms are provided for safe access to the blackboard data. Knowledge sources can communicate by accessing shared data in separate transactions. Furthermore, several knowledge sources can participate in a common transaction if they need to see a common, consistent view of shared data.

24.2 System structure

Figures 24.1 and 24.2 illustrate a system that we designed to understand the use of the blackboard. We term the control and knowledge sources *agents* because they are both modular units of activity. The agents are distributed on various processors and may execute concurrently. Knowledge source activities on each node are controlled by the control sources on that node. (The collection of control sources is the controller mentioned in the blackboard architecture description.) In our present implementation, the distribution of agents is subject to restrictions. The initial distribution is specified by the system designer, and we provide no mechanism to support agent migration among processors. Although the blackboard resides on a single machine, it could be distributed without changing its interface.

24.2.1 The blackboard

The blackboard is a repository of data; each datum holds an arbitrary LISP s-expression. Because agents may share data and reference them in an interleaved fashion, some mechanism is needed to maintain consistency of the blackboard. We associate a transaction manager with this database, and require that any reference to the blackboard be part of a transaction.

The blackboard transaction manager controls asynchronous references to shared data via locks. There are two types of locks: write and read. The holder of a write-lock has exclusive access to the locked datum and may modify the datum. Holders of read-locks may read the data concurrently. No writer may access data while a read-lock for that data is held. When a client first references data, the transaction manager attempts to obtain the appropriate lock. All locks are held to the end of the transaction in which they were obtained. Thus the transaction manager preserves data consistency by preserving serializability (Eswaran *et al.*, 1976).

When trying to obtain a lock, the transaction manager might find that it is not available. The transaction that needs the unavailable lock is suspended until the lock can be obtained. Sometimes more than one transaction may be waiting to obtain a lock, and this introduces the potential for deadlock among the waiting transactions. For example, transaction A might wait for a lock held by transaction B, while transaction B waits for some other lock held by transaction A. The transaction manager detects deadlocks and resolves them by aborting a suspended transaction. This abortion is simply reported to the agents participating in the transaction; these agents must then decide what action is appropriate.

Data consistency among agents interacting within a transaction is maintained by time stamps. If serializability among agents within a transaction is violated, the blackboard transaction manager aborts the transaction. This abortion is reported to the agents participating in the transaction, as with deadlock detection.

Computation based on the transactional blackboard is not data driven; that is, accessing values in the blackboard does not automatically trigger agent activity. This seems appropriate in a distributed environment because the blackboard might not be able to schedule activities on remote sites. This is in contrast to the centralized case supported in previous proposals (e.g. the Hearsay-III approach of Balzer *et al.*, 1980).

24.2.2 The agents

Each knowledge source contains some of the system's domain specific knowledge. This knowledge is expressed in terms of the data visible to the agent – that portion of the blackboard accessible to the agent plus the data sent as message parameters by other agents. As a knowledge source executes, it examines the visible system state. If the system state matches a condition known to the knowledge source, the agent takes specified actions. These actions include requesting that the controller schedule a knowledge source activity by placing an entry on the controller goal queue, performing some operations on the blackboard, and/or sending a message to another knowledge source.

24.2.3 Inter-agent communication

The multiprocessor environment fosters a richness of system structure. Each processor can support a community of agents – complexes of control sources and groups of knowledge sources working closely together – and these communities can interact with communities on other processors. Agents executing on the same machine can communicate with efficiency and facility, for they may directly access common data and may include arbitrary references as parameters in the messages they send to each other. Since the cost of message transmission between machines is higher than a few memory references on a single one, agents executing on separate machines cannot communicate so cheaply. Further, these agents may include only values in their message parameters, and the conversion of local data to transmittable data values may be expensive. Each node in our system then contains procedures to convert the value of arbitrary s-expressions to transmittable data values. In addition, each communicating agent needs access to procedures to reference these transmitted data values once they have been received.

Agents may also communicate through the blackboard, and two mechanisms are provided for this interaction. Agents can interact by accessing shared data in separate transactions, or several agents can participate in a common transaction. This latter mechanism is often useful; for example, the controller might start a transaction to check the precondition of a goal-queue entry. The knowledge source that the controller then activates might need to access the data mentioned in the goal-queue entry. Because the knowledge source should see this data in the same state as the controller, it continues the same transaction. To include a second agent in a transaction, the first agent merely passes its transaction identifier and status to the second. The transaction status indicates whether the transaction is to be committed, aborted or continued.

24.2.4 Scheduling and transaction protocols

The controller maintains one or more goal queues, each comprising entries generated by knowledge sources. A goal-queue entry has three parts: an expression (called the precondition), an action to be taken if that precondition is true, and a status indicator which may contain a transaction identifier if the action is to continue an ongoing transaction.

Scheduling activity by selecting entries from its goal queue, the controller proceeds down the goal queue evaluating entry preconditions. If the precondition is false, its action can not be selected, and the goal is deferred. If the precondition holds, the corresponding action is executed. In evaluating a precondition, the controller might need to access data in the blackboard. If there is no transaction identifier associated with the queue entry, the controller begins a new transaction. If an identifier is already associated with the queue entry, the controller continues this transaction. At the end of the decision process, the controller aborts the newly started transactions associated with deferred goals. If an agent is activated as a result of the queue entry selection, that agent is given any associated transaction identifier.

In addition to scheduling, the control agents are responsible for the initiation and termination of transactions. These activities are based on the contents of the goal queues. As mentioned above, the controller begins a transaction or continues an existing one when it schedules a knowledge source for activity. When an agent finishes executing, it notifies the controller. The controller now checks the goal queue for entries with the transaction identifier of the knowledge source just completed. If the queue has no entries with this transaction identifier, the controller terminates the transaction according to the transaction status. If other entries contain this identifier, the associated actions will presumably continue this transaction.

24.3 Implementation

Our initial implementation of an expert system using the transactional blackboard is designed to execute on a network of three Symbolics LISP Machines connected via an ETHERNET. ZETALISP flavors (Weinreb and Moon, 1981), the blackboard and knowledge and control sources communicate with each other via messages, the parameterized invocations of flavor methods. The message parameter restrictions discussed above are enforced at run-time by the execution environment. The blackboard transaction manager, which reads or writes objects on behalf of agent requests, and its associated database reside on a single machine.

24.3.1 Data

LISP s-expressions are the unit of storage and retrieval in the blackboard, and blackboard data are indexed by a LISP name. Because the blackboard has no knowledge of the internal structure of the data it stores, the storage and retrieval support functions available to an agent are responsible for constructing transmittable data for storage and reconstructing the representations on retrieval. Generally, these functions need access to the definitions of the data in order to reconstruct their representations.

24.3.2 Transactions

Access to the blackboard data is allowed only within transactions. The transaction manager associated with the blackboard receives requests from agents, executes on their behalf, and packages responses. With each request to the blackboard, an agent presents a unique agent identifier and a transaction identifier. The transaction identifier is returned to an agent when it begins a transaction as a return value of the start-transaction command.

The blackboard transaction manager supports five transaction states and state-changing messages. Figure 24.3 illustrates these states and the messages that cause state transitions. Starting in the ground state, a transaction moves with the start-transaction messages into the active state where read and write messages are handled. Commit-transaction and abort-transaction messages terminate a transaction by moving it to the committed and ground states respectively. The straddle and pre-committed states provide for the implementation of two- and three-phase commit protocols (Skeen, 1981), which are a means of coordinating transactions involving more than one transactional server.

Atomicity

Atomicity ensures that at the end of a transaction all the write actions associated with the transaction have taken place (the transaction committed), or all the data referenced by the transaction is restored to the state that existed when the transaction began (the transaction aborted). In each transaction, existing data is copied before it is first written. (If there is no existing data, the 'copy' so indicates.) This copy

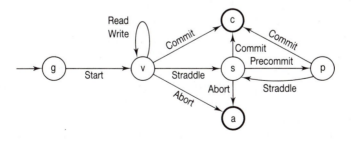

Figure 24.3   Transaction states.

then serves to save the state of the data that existed before the transaction began. If the transaction commits, the copy is discarded; if the transaction aborts, the copy replaces the current version of the data.

Consistency

Our transactional blackboard has two broad consistency tasks: first, to maintain data consistency among several transactions (intertransactional consistency) and, second, to preserve a consistent view of data for those agents within an individual transaction (intratransactional consistency).

Intertransactional consistency of blackboard data is maintained with locks. The write locks are exclusive and guarantee that no activity can interfere with the writer while it is modifying data. Read locks are shared, and many agents may concurrently read the same data. Since the data is not modified during this time, consistency is maintained. All locks are held to the end of the transaction, and requests made to locked data are queued until release of locks.

The transaction manager checks for deadlock whenever it queues a read or write request. In the present implementation, the blackboard retries queued requests referencing particular data in the order in which they are received. If a deadlock exists, the manager calls a deadlock handler to abort one of the transactions. Although the transaction manager contains a default handler, a preferred deadlock handler may be specified by an agent when it initiates a transaction to allow deadlock resolution to be based on domain knowledge.

Intratransactional consistency is maintained through the use of time-stamps. The time-stamps are used to enforce serialization through a basic time-ordered scheduling algorithm (Bernstein and Goodman, 1981). When an agent first participates in a transaction, it is assigned a time-stamp, called the agent time for that agent. The write time-stamp for each blackboard datum is the agent time of the write request being executed on that datum. The read time-stamp for each datum is the later of the datum's current read time-stamp and the agent time of the read request being executed on that datum. A datum maintains a separate read time-stamp for each transaction holding a read-lock. A read request for a datum is rejected if the agent time is earlier than the datum's write time-stamp. A write request is rejected if the agent time is earlier than either the read or write time-stamp of the datum. The establishment of a serializable intratransaction schedule and concomitant coordination of the participating agents is the responsibility of the agent controlling the transaction. The blackboard regards an intratransaction time-order violation as a fatal error and aborts the offending transaction. The blackboard's transaction manager checks for possible time-order violations before queuing a store or retrieve request, so the errors are detected immediately.

Persistence

Persistence ensures that the results of committed (and straddled and precommitted) transactions will survive system crashes. To implement persistence, copies of data are kept on devices with independent failure modes and recovery protocols are supported. We use a straightforward logging and checkpoint scheme to preserve copies on independent devices. The implementation might be expensive in both space and time. It is not practical to encumber all agents with this overhead, and thus logging can be deactivated for any transaction. If a transaction is not logged, crash recovery returns its data to some previous (archived) consistent state, instead of the most recent consistent state. The recovery protocols are not expensive to implement because they are driven by external agents, not the blackboard itself.

24.4 Conclusions

Our transactional blackboard architecture supports the construction of expert systems for multiprocessor environments. The transactional interface allows asynchronous requests to be safely issued to the shared data of the blackboard. Clients of this transactional service must specify the boundaries of each transaction, and they must deal with aborted transactions. We feel that this marginal cost over a serial system is small and should not interfere with the business of building expert systems.

More importantly, we provide mechanisms to make use of this shared data in an intelligent way. Control decisions are based on domain knowledge and communication costs. The controller presumably tries to utilize the processors of the computing facility to effect good system performance or to model some system of interest. The controller remains knowledge based and does not use scheduling to protect shared data. Knowledge sources are not required to provide explicit synchronization or protect the consistency of shared data. If several agents wish, they may participate in common transactions. To do so, they need only to pass transaction identifiers among themselves.

We are using this architecture to build some expert systems. Our experience indicates that this architecture is very helpful for large, multi-author projects, where each designer works rather independently to implement a small area of expertise. In addition to reaffirming the advantages of modularity in program structure, we would like to report on the performance advantages realized by executing our expert systems on multiprocessor computers. Unfortunately, we have not yet performed the necessary experiments.

25

Frameworks for Concurrent Problem Solving: A Report on CAGE and POLIGON

H. Penny Nii, Nelleke Aiello and James Rice

25.1 Background

A *concurrent problem-solving system* is a network of autonomous or semi-autonomous computing agents that solve a single problem. In building concurrent problem solvers, our objectives are two-fold: (1) to evolve or invent models of problem solving in a multi-agent environment and (2) to gain significant performance improvement by the use of multiprocessor machines. Within the community of researchers in artificial intelligence, there is an interest in understanding and building programs that exhibit cooperative problem-solving behavior among many intelligent agents, independent of computational costs (see Corkill and Lesser, 1983; Lesser and Corkill, 1983; Smith, 1981 for some examples). One of the important pragmatics of using many computers in parallel is to gain computational speed-up. (Multiple computers are also used for other reasons besides speed-up – redundancy, mix of specialized hardware, need for physical separation, and so on.) Often, methods useful in a serial (single) problem solver in obtaining a valid solution and coherent problem-solving behavior, usually a centralized control, are not compatible with performance gain in a multi-agent environment. CAGE and POLIGON attempt to find a balance – to achieve adequate coherence with minimal global control *and* to gain performance with the use of multiple processors.

25.1.1 Problem solving and concurrency

Those problems that have been successfully solved in parallel, such as partial differential equations and finite element analysis, share common characteristics: they frequently used vectors and arrays; solutions to the

475

problems are very regular, using well understood algorithms; and the computational demands, for example for matrix inversion, are relatively easy to compute. In contrast, the class of applications we are addressing (and AI problems in general) are ill-structured or ill-defined. There is often more than one possible solution; paths to a solution cannot be predefined and must be dynamically generated and tried; generally data cannot be encoded in a regular manner as in arrays – the data structures are often graph structures that must be dynamically created, precluding static allocation and optimization. These differences indicate that, to run problem-solving programs in parallel, current techniques for parallel programs must be augmented or new ones invented. It is worth reviewing some of the key points to be addressed in building concurrent, problem-solving programs.

Problem-solving issues

Problem solving has traditionally meant a process of searching a tree of alternative solutions to a problem. Within each generate-and-test cycle, alternatives are generated at a node of a tree and promising alternatives selected for further processing. Knowledge is used to prune the tree of alternatives or to select promising paths through the tree. It is an axiom that the more knowledge there is the less generation and testing has to be done. In the extreme, many knowledge-based systems have large knowledge bases containing pieces of knowledge that recognize inter-mediate solutions and solution paths, thereby drastically reducing, or even eliminating, search. These two types of problem-solving techniques have been labeled *search* and *recognition* (McDermott and Newell, 1983). In the search technique the majority of computing time is taken up in generating and testing alternative solutions; in the recognition technique the time is taken up in *matching*, a process of finding the right piece of knowledge to apply. Most applications use a combination of search and recognition techniques. A concurrent problem-solving framework must be able to accommodate both styles of problem solving.

In serial systems meta-knowledge, or control knowledge, is often used to reduce computational costs. One common approach decomposes a problem into hierarchically organized subproblems, and a control module selects an efficient order in which to solve these subproblems. Closely related is the introduction of contextual information, or domain knowledge, to help in the recognition process. Both approaches enhance performance – reduce the number of alternatives to search or the amount of knowledge to match. In concurrent systems meta-knowledge and control modules become fan-in points, or hot-spots. A **hot-spot** is a physical location in the hardware where a shared resource is competed for, forcing an unintended serialization. Does this imply that problem-solving systems that rely heavily on centralized control are doomed to failure in a concurrent environment? Can control be distributed? If so, to what extent? If more knowledge results in less search, can a similar tradeoff be made between knowledge and control? In concurrent systems where control, especially global control, is a serializing process, can knowledge be brought to bear to alleviate the need for control?

Concurrency issues

The biggest problem in concurrent processing was first described by Amdahl (1967). Simply stated, it is as follows: The length of time it takes to complete a run with parallel processes is the length of time it takes to run the longest process plus some overhead associated with running things in parallel. Take a problem that can be decomposed into a collection of independent subproblems that can run concurrently, but which internally must run serially. If all of these components are run concurrently, the run-time for the whole problem will be equal to the run-time for the longest running component, plus any overhead needed to execute the subproblems in parallel. Thus, if the longest process takes 10% of the total run-time that the parallel processes would have taken if run end to end (serially), then the maximum speed-up possible is a factor of 10. Even if only 1% of the processing must be done sequentially this limits the maximum speed-up to 100, however hard one tries and however many processors are used. This is a very depressing result, since it means that many orders of magnitude of speed-up are only available in very special circumstances.

This raises the issue of *granularity*, the size of the components to be run in parallel. Amdahl's argument indicates the need for as small a granularity as possible. For example, is a rule a good candidate grain size for computation? On the other hand, if the process creation and process switching time is expensive, we want to do as much computation as possible once a process is running, that is, favor a larger granularity. In addition, in a multicomputer architecture a balance must be achieved between the load on the communication network and on the processors. It is often the case that, as process granularity decreases, the processes become more tightly coupled – that is, there is a need for more communication between them. The communication cost is of course a function of the hardware-level architecture, including bandwidth, distance, topology, and so on. Finding an optimal grain size at the problem solving level is a multifaceted problem.

Even if one is able to find an optimal granularity, there are forces that inhibit the processes from running arbitrarily fast in parallel. Some of the more common problems are:

(1) *Hot-spots and bottlenecks* It is frequently the case that a piece of data must be shared. In any real machine multiple, simultaneous

requests to access the same piece of data cause *memory contention*. The act of a number of processes competing for a shared resource – memory or processors – causes a degradation in performance. These processor and memory hot-spots cause bottlenecks in the processing of data; they restrict the flow of data and reduce parallelism.

(2) *Communications* Multicomputer machines do not have a shared address space in which to have memory bottlenecks of the kind mentioned above. However, the communications network over which the processing elements communicate still represents a shared resource which can be overloaded. It has a finite bandwidth. Similarly, multiple asynchronous messages to a single processing element will cause that element to become a hot-spot.

(3) *Process creation* Execution of the subproblems mentioned above require that they run as processes. The cost of the creation and management of such processes is nontrivial. There is a process grain size at which it does not pay to run in parallel, because executing it sequentially is faster than executing it in parallel.

Having introduced some issues and constraints associated with parallelizing programs, we now introduce some other concepts that are important in writing concurrent programs, an understanding of which is useful to appreciate the discussions later in this paper fully.

(1) *Atomic operation* This refers to a piece of code which is executed without interruption. In order to have consistent results (data) it is important to have well defined atomic operations. For instance, an update to a slot in a node might be defined to be atomic. Primitive atomic actions are usually defined at the system level.

(2) *Critical sections* Critical sections are usually programmer defined and refers to those parts of the program which are uninterruptible, that is, atomic. The term is usually used to describe large, complex operations that must be performed without interruption.

(3) *Synchronization* This term is used to describe an event that brings asynchronous, parallel processes together synchronously. Synchronization primitives are used to enforce serialization.

(4) *Locks* Locks are mechanisms for the implementation of critical sections. Under some computational models, a process that executes a critical section must acquire a lock. If another process has the lock, it is required to wait until that lock is released.

(5) *Pipeline* A pipeline is a series of distinct operations which can be executed in parallel but which are sequentially dependent; for instance, an automobile assembly line. The speed-up that can be gained from a pipeline is proportional to the number of stages,

assuming that each stage takes the same amount of time, that is, if the pipe is 'well balanced'. Pipeline parallelism is a very important source of parallelism.

25.1.2 Background motivation

In experiments conducted at CMU (Gupta, 1986), Gupta showed that applications written in OPS (Forgy and McDermott, 1977) achieved speed-up in the range of eight to ten, the best case being about a factor of 20. The experiments ran rules in parallel, with pipelining between the condition evaluation, conflict resolution and action execution. The overhead for rule matching was reduced with the use of a parallelized Rete algorithm. (In programs written in OPS, roughly 90% of the time is spent in the match phase.) The speed-up factors seem to reflect the amount of relevant knowledge chunks (rules) available for processing a given problem-solving state; this number appears to be rather small. Although the applications were not written specifically for a parallel architecture, the results are closely tied to the nature of the OPS system itself, which uses a monolithic and homogeneous rule set and an unstructured working memory to represent problem-solving states.

The premise underlying the design of CAGE and POLIGON is that this discouraging result could be overcome by dividing and conquering. It is hoped that by partitioning an application into loosely coupled sub-problems (thus partitioning the rule set into many subsets of rules), and by keeping multiple states (for the different subproblems), multiplicative speed-up, with respect to Gupta's experimental results, can be achieved. If, for example, a factor of seven speed-up could be achieved for each subproblem, the simultaneous execution of rule sets could result in a speed-up of seven times the number of subproblems. We are looking for methods that can provide at least a two orders of magnitude speed-up. The challenge, of course, is to coordinate the resulting asynchronous, concurrent problem-solving processes toward a meaningful solution with minimal overheads.

25.1.3 The blackboard model and concurrency

The foundation for most knowledge-based systems is the problem-solving framework in which an application is formulated. The problem-solving framework implements a computational model of problem solving and provides a language in which an application problem can be expressed. We begin with the blackboard model of problem solving (Nii, 1986b), which is a problem-solving framework for partitioning problems into many loosely coupled subproblems. Both CAGE and POLIGON have their

Figure 25.1 The blackboard metaphor.

roots in the blackboard model of problem solving. The blackboard framework seems, at first glance, to admit the natural exploitation of concurrency. Some of the possible parallelism that can be exploited are:

- *knowledge parallelism* The knowledge sources and rules within each knowledge source can run concurrently.
- *pipeline parallelism* The transfer of information from one level to another allows pipelining.
- *data parallelism* The blackboard can be partitioned into solution components that can be operated on concurrently.

In addition, the dynamic and flexible control structure can be extended to control parallelism.

These characteristics of blackboard systems have prompted investigators (for example, Lesser and Corkill, 1983; Ensor and Gabbe, 1985) to build distributed and/or parallel blackboard systems. The study of parallelism in blackboard systems goes back to Hearsay-II (Fennell and Lesser, 1977).

The blackboard problem-solving metaphor itself is very simple; it entails a collection of intelligent agents gathered around a blackboard, looking at pieces of information written on it, thinking about them and writing their conclusions up as they come to them. This is shown in Figure 25.1.

There are some assumptions made in this model that are so obvious that they might be missed. An understanding of the implications of these

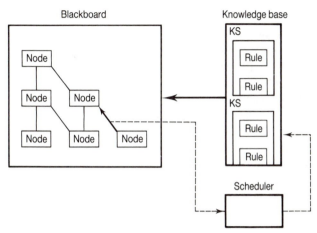

Figure 25.2   The serial blackboard model.

assumptions is vital to an understanding of the problem of achieving parallelism in blackboard systems.

- All of the agents can see all of the blackboard all of the time, and what they see represents the current state of the solution.
- Any agent can write his conclusions on the blackboard at any time, without getting in anyone else's way.
- The act of an agent writing on the blackboard will not confuse any of the other agents as they work.

The implications of these assumptions are that a single problem is being solved asynchronously and in parallel. However, the problem-solving behavior, if it were to be emulated in a computer, would result in very inefficient computation. For example, for every agent to 'see' everything would entail stopping everything until every agent has looked at everything. Existing, serial blackboard systems make a number of modifications to the pure blackboard metaphor in order to make a reasonable implementation on conventional hardware. In effect, they modify the blackboard metaphor so that it *cannot* be executed in parallel. Some of these modifications are shown in Figure 25.2 and are described below.

(1)   Agents are represented as *knowledge sources*. These are schedulable entities and only one can be running at any time. It will be shown later that one of the possible sizes for computational grains is the knowledge source.

(2)   To coordinate the execution of knowledge sources, a scheduling or

control mechanism is implemented. This is, in many ways, an efficiency gaining mechanism, which uses meta-knowledge to select only the most 'valuable' knowledge source at any given moment to work on the problem.

(3) The blackboard is not truly globally visible in the sense prescribed by the blackboard metaphor. Instead, the blackboard is implemented as a data structure, which is sufficiently interconnected that it is possible for a knowledge source to find its way from one data item to a related one easily. Knowledge sources can only work on a limited area of the blackboard – knowledge sources and their context of invocation are, in fact, treated as self-contained subproblems.

(4) An implicit assumption is made that a knowledge source operates within a valid, or consistent, context and that the 'ordered' execution of knowledge sources, even when the ordering is done dynamically, preserves the consistency of the blackboard data.

Trying to directly parallelize serial blackboard systems characterized above have certain limitations. First, only a modest speed-up can be achieved by a central scheduler determining the knowledge sources to be run in parallel. The performance levels off very quickly at a very low number (a gain of less than a factor of three in our experiments) no matter how many knowledge sources are run in parallel and no matter how many processors are used. Second, one of the most difficult problems in parallel computation is to maintain consistent data values. In concurrent blackboard systems, the data consistency problems occur in three different contexts:

(1) on the entire blackboard, maintaining consistent solution states;

(2) in the contents of the nodes, assuring that all slot values are from the same problem solving state; and

(3) in the slots, keeping the value being evaluated from changing before the evaluation is completed.

25.2 The Advanced Architectures Project

CAGE (Aiello, 1986) and POLIGON (Rice, 1986), two frameworks for concurrent problem solving, are being developed within the Advanced Architectures Project (AAP) at the Knowledge Systems Laboratory of Stanford University. The objective of the AAP is the development of broad system architectures that exploit parallelism at different levels of a system's hierarchical construction. To exploit concurrency one must begin by looking for parallelism at the application level and be able to formulate, express and utilize that parallelism within a problem-solving framework, which, in turn, must be supported by an appropriate language and software/hardware system. The system levels chosen and some issues for study are:

(1) *Application level* How can concurrency be recognized and exploited?

(2) *Problem-solving level* Is there a need for a new problem-solving metaphor to deal with concurrency? What is the best process and data granularity? What is the trade-off between knowledge and control?

(3) *Programming language level* What is the best process and data granularity at this level? What are the implications of choices at the language level for the hardware and system architecture?

(4) *System/hardware level* Should the address spaces be common or disjoint? What should the processor and memory characteristics and granularity be? What is the best communication topology and mechanisms? What should the memory-processor organization be?

At each system level one or more specific methods and approaches have been implemented in an attempt to address the problems at that level. These programs are then vertically integrated to form a family of experimental systems – an application is implemented using a problem-solving framework using a particular knowledge representation and retrieval method, all of which use a specific programming language, which in turn runs on a specific system/hardware architecture simulated in detail on the LISP-based CARE simulator (Delagi, 1986). Each family of experiments is designed to evaluate, for example, the system's performance with respect to the number of processors, the effects of different computational granularity on the quality of solution and on execution speed-up, ease of programming, and so on. The results of one such family of experiments have been reported by Brown *et al.* (1986) and Schoen (1986).

Within the context of this AAP organization, CAGE and POLIGON are two systems that are implemented to study the problem-solving level. Both CAGE and POLIGON use frames and condition–action rules to represent knowledge. The target system architecture for CAGE is a shared-memory multiprocessor; the target architecture for POLIGON is a distributed-memory multiprocessor, or multicomputer.

Both CAGE and POLIGON aim to solve a particular, but broad, class of applications: real-time interpretation of continuous streams of errorful data, using many diverse sources of knowledge. Each source of knowledge contributes pieces of a solution which are integrated into a meaningful description of the situation. Applications in this class include a variety of signal understanding, information fusion and situation assessment problems. The utility of blackboard formulations has been successfully demonstrated by programs written to solve problems in our target application class (see Brown *et al.*, 1982; McCune and Drazovich, 1983; Shafer *et al.*, 1986; Spain, 1983; Williams, 1984a).

Most of the systems in this class use the recognition style of problem solving with knowledge bases of facts and heuristics; numerical algorithms are also included as a part of the knowledge. Some search methods are employed but are generally confined to a few of the subproblems.

In designing a concurrent blackboard system for the AAP, two distinct approaches seemed possible – one to extend a serial blackboard system and the other to devise a new architecture to exploit the event-driven nature of blackboard systems. Each has its own problems and its own advantages, which will be described in the following sections.

25.3 Extending the serial system – CAGE

CAGE is a concurrent blackboard framework system, based on the (serial) AGE (Nii and Aiello, 1979) blackboard system. AGE uses a set of rules as a representation for its knowledge sources; it uses a set of event tokens as preconditions (a trigger) for the knowledge sources, and each significant change to the blackboard posts an event in a global data structure. The controller selects an event and executes a knowledge source whose precondition matches the selected event. (There are more elaborate constructs in AGE, but this description suffices for the current purpose.) In addition to the basic functionality found in AGE, CAGE allows user-directed control over the concurrent execution of many of its constructs (see Figure 25.3). Otherwise, the two systems are functionally identical.

25.3.1 The CAGE architecture

The basic components of a system built with CAGE are:

(1) A global data store (the blackboard) on which emerging solutions are posted. Objects on the blackboard are organized into hierarchical levels, and each object is described with a set of attribute–value pairs.

(2) Globally accessible lists on which control information is posted (for example, lists of events, expectations, and so on).

(3) An arbitrary number of knowledge sources, each consisting of an arbitrary number of rules.

(4) Control information that can help to determine (a) which black-

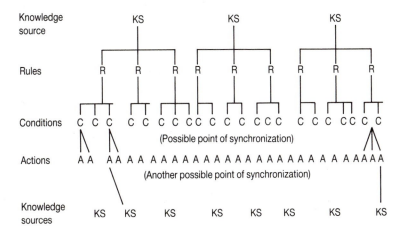

Figure 25.3   Parallel components of CAGE.

board elements are to be the focus of attention and (b) which knowledge sources are to be used at any given point in the problem-solving process.

(5)   Declarations that specify which components are to be executed in parallel (knowledge sources, rules, condition and action parts of rules), and at what points synchronization is to occur.

The user can run CAGE serially (at which point CAGE behavior is identical to that of AGE), or can run with one or more of the components running concurrently. In the serial mode, the basic control cycle begins with the selection and execution of a knowledge source. A resulting change to the blackboard may cause several knowledge sources to become relevant and candidates for execution. CAGE uses a global list structure to record the changes to the blackboard, called events. The controller selects one of the events. The user can specify how the event is to be selected, such as FIFO, LIFO, or any user-defined best-first method. The event in focus is then matched against the knowledge source preconditions. The knowledge sources, whose preconditions match the focus events, are then executed in some predetermined order. The rules within each knowledge source are evaluated, and the action part of the rule is executed for those rules whose condition parts are satisfied. The user may choose to allow only one rule to fire per knowledge source activation or many rules to fire. Each action part may cause one or more changes on the blackboard and a corresponding number of events is recorded on the event list. Figure 25.4 shows the serial CAGE control cycle.

Using the concurrency control specifications, the user can alter the simple, serial control loop of CAGE by requesting the concurrent

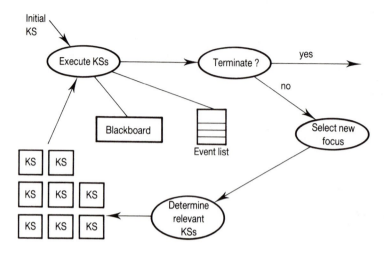

Figure 25.4 CAGE serial control cycle.

execution of application components. CAGE allows for a range of granularity for these concurrent processes; from knowledge sources all the way down to predicates in the condition parts of rules. The various concurrency operations that can be specified, together with the serial version, are summarized below and shown in Figure 25.3.

(1) *Knowledge source control*

   (a) *Serial* Pick an event and execute the associated knowledge sources.

   (b) *Parallel*:
   - As each event is generated execute the associated knowledge sources in parallel, or
   - Wait until all active knowledge sources complete execution, generating a number of events, and then execute the knowledge sources relevant to those events concurrently, or
   - Wait until several events are generated then select a subset and execute the relevant knowledge sources for all the subset events in parallel.

(2) *Within each knowledge source*

   (a) *Serial*:
   - Perform context evaluation.
   - Evaluate the condition parts, then execute the action part of one rule whose condition side matched, or
   - Evaluate all the condition parts then execute all the

actions of those rules whose condition side matched, serially.

(b) *Parallel*:
- Perform context evaluation in parallel.
- Evaluate all condition parts in parallel, then
  - synchronize (that is, wait for all the condition side evaluations to complete) and choose one action part, or
  - synchronize and execute the actions serially (in lexical order), or
  - execute the actions in parallel as the condition parts match.

(3) *Within rules*

(a) *Serial* Evaluate each clause then execute each action.

(b) *Parallel* Evaluate the condition-part clauses in parallel then execute the actions of the action part in parallel.

25.3.2 Discussion of the concurrent components

Each of the potential concurrent components is discussed below.

Knowledge source concurrency

Knowledge sources are logically independent partitions of the domain knowledge. A knowledge source is selected and executed when changes made to the blackboard are relevant to that knowledge source. Theoretically, many different knowledge sources can be executed at the same time as long as the relevant blackboard changes occur close to each other, but the knowledge sources are often serially dependent and some synchronization must be introduced.

In the class of applications under consideration, the solution is built up in a pipeline-like fashion up the blackboard hierarchy. That is, the knowledge source dependencies form a chain from the knowledge sources working on the most detailed level of the blackboard to those working on the most abstract level. (When the program is model driven, this pipeline works in the reverse direction.) Knowledge sources can be running in parallel, processing the data along the pipe.

Thus, there are two potential sources of knowledge source parallelism: (a) knowledge sources working on different regions (partial solutions) of the blackboard asynchronously, that is, 'data parallelism', and (2) knowledge sources working in a pipelined fashion exploiting the flow of information up (or down) the data hierarchy.

Rule concurrency

Each knowledge source is composed of a number of rules. The condition parts of these rules are evaluated for a match with the current state of the solution, and the action parts of those rules that match the state are executed. The condition parts of all the rules in a knowledge source, being side-effect free, can be evaluated concurrently. In cases where all the matched rules are to be executed, the action parts can be executed as soon as the condition part is matched successfully. If only one of the rules is to be selected for execution, the system must wait until all the condition parts are evaluated, and one rule, whose action part is to be executed, must be chosen. Note that this is very similar to the OPS conflict-resolution phase. Refer to Gupta (1986) for the results of running OPS rules in parallel. The situation in which all rules are evaluated and executed concurrently potentially has the most parallelism. However, if the rules access the same blackboard data item, memory contention becomes a hidden point of serialization. At the same time, the integrity of the information on the blackboard cannot be guaranteed. The problem is of two types: timeliness and consistency. First, the state that triggered the rule may be modified by the time the action part is executed. The question is then: Is the action still relevant and correct? Second, if a rule accesses attributes from different blackboard objects, there is no guarantee that the values from the objects are consistent with respect to each other.

(1)   *Condition-part concurrency*   Each condition part of a rule may consist of a number of clauses to be evaluated. These clauses can often be evaluated concurrently. In the chosen class of applications, these clauses frequently involve relatively large numeric computations, making parallel evaluation worthwhile. However, as discussed above, if the clauses refer to the same data item, memory contention would force a serialization.

(2)   *Action-part concurrency*   Often, when a condition part matches, more than one potentially independent action is called for, and these can often be executed in parallel.

This problem of data consistency occurs both in CAGE and POLIGON. It can be partially alleviated by defining an atomic operation that includes both read and write. This ensures that between the time that an item of data is read, processed, and the result stored, there is no change in the state of the node. (In Lamina (Delagi *et al.*, 1986), a programming framework developed for the AAP project, the atomic action is read–process–write.) However, this makes a commitment to a certain level of granularity; for example, read the data for the condition part of a rule and execute the rule. In order to enable experimentation with granularity, atomic actions are kept small and locks, block reads and block writes are provided in CAGE. Although an atomic read/write operation does not solve the problems of timeliness or of global coherence, it does assure that the data within the nodes are consistent. And, although locks have a potential for causing deadlocks, they are provided for the user to construct larger critical sections.

Concurrency control

The action parts of rules generate events, and knowledge sources are activated by the occurrences of these events. In the (serial) AGE system events are posted on a global event-list and, working on these events, a control monitor activates one or more knowledge sources. In order to eliminate the serialization inherent in this control scheme, a mechanism to activate the knowledge source immediately upon event generation is needed. This immediate activation of knowledge sources bypasses the control module and effectively eliminates global control. In some cases, this is acceptable. In other cases, where knowledge sources are serially dependent, some control mechanism is needed. Centralized control mechanisms, such as selecting many events to be processed in parallel, causing many knowledge sources to run concurrently, are also provided.

Some answers to the many questions raised about CAGE's architecture are embedded in the system. However, much of the burden is passed on to the applications programmer. Some useful programming techniques that were discovered are discussed below.

25.3.3 Programming with CAGE

There are a number of problems that crop up during concurrent execution that do not appear during serial execution. The solutions to some of these problems involved reformulating the application problem; some involved the use of programming techniques not commonly used in serial systems. Both CAGE and POLIGON have been used to implement a signal understanding system called ELINT (Brown *et al.*, 1986). It is described briefly below.

The ELINT application

The problem is one of receiving multiple streams of reports from radar systems, abstracting these into hypothetical radar emitting aircrafts and tracking them as they travel through the monitored airspace. These aircraft are themselves abstracted into clusters – perhaps formations – which are themselves tracked. Sometimes the aircraft in a cluster would split off, forcing the splitting of cluster nodes and rationalization of their supporting evidence. The nature of the radar emissions from the aircraft are interpreted in order to determine the intentions and degree of threat of each of the clusters of emitters.

The ELINT application has a number of characteristics which are of significance:

(1)   The system must be able to deal with a continuous data stream. It is not acceptable to wait until all of the data has been read in and then figure out what was going on.

(2)   The application domain is potentially very data parallel. The ability to reason about a large number of aircraft simultaneously is very important.

(3)   The aircraft themselves, as objects in the solution space, are quite loosely coupled.

Pitfalls, problems and solutions

The following programming techniques arose while implementing ELINT in CAGE:

(1)   When the computational grain size is limited to a knowledge source, it is possible to read all the slots of a node that are referenced in the knowledge source by locking the node once and reading all of the slots at once. This is in contrast to locking the node every time a slot is read by the rules. This is equivalent to reading all the blackboard data accessed from a knowledge source before any rules are evaluated. This approach accomplishes two important things: (a) It reduces the number of references to the blackboard, thereby reducing the opportunities for memory contention, and (b) it ensures that all the rules are looking at data from the same point in the evolving solution.

(2)   In a serial blackboard system one precondition may serve to describe several changes to the blackboard adequately. For example, suppose one rule firing causes three changes to be made serially. The last change, or event, is generally a sufficient precondition for the selection of the next knowledge source. In a concurrent system, all three events must be included in a knowledge source's precondition. This is to ensure that all three changes have actually occurred before the knowledge source is executed.

In general, a simple precondition consisting of an event token is not sufficient for CAGE. Either a sophisticated scheduler with detailed specification of the activation requirements of the knowledge sources, or a complex, knowledge-source precondition that contain the same requirements is needed.

(3) It is important when writing the conditions of rules for a CAGE application to keep in mind the feasibility of running the condition clauses concurrently; that is, keeping them independent of each other in the sense of not accessing the same data.

(4) Occasionally two knowledge sources running in parallel may attempt to change a slot at almost the same time. It is possible that the first change would invalidate the firing of the second rule. To overcome this type of race condition, a conditional action – an action that checks the value of a slot before making a change – was added. It allows the action to check the most recent updates before making further changes. The alternative would have been to lock a node for an entire knowledge source execution which would seriously limit parallelism.

A problem with continuous input streams

Since ELINT is a real-time system, it is time dependent. Processing a continuous stream of data can lead to *out-of-order events* caused by delay of one kind or another; an example might be a knowledge source stuck in a memory queue delaying its changes to the blackboard. This means that new data at time t may have to be analyzed before all the ramifications of data from an earlier time $(t - n)$ have been executed – at any point the data can be out of order. The ELINT application had to be reformulated to address this problem. Time tags had to be associated with each event and blackboard value, and the rules had to be rewritten to use the time tags to reason about unordered events.

Experiments with CAGE indicate that it is much more difficult to program a parallel system than a serial one. It lends subjective support to our supposition that an incremental approach to parallelism is easier to program than an all-at-once approach. We began with a serial version of ELINT and turned on clause level concurrency first and debugged it, then experimented with the rule level, and finally knowledge source level concurrency. Only after ELINT was working correctly with each of these concurrent operations were they combined.

As discussed earlier, CAGE can execute multiple sets of rules, in the form of knowledge sources, concurrently. If the rule parallelism within each knowledge source can provide a speed-up in the neighborhood cited by Gupta, and if many knowledge sources can run concurrently without getting in each other's way, we can hope to get a speed-up in the tens. The extra parallelism comes from working on many parts of the blackboard, in other words, by solving many subproblems in parallel. It was found, however, that the use of a central controller to determine which knowledge sources to run in parallel drastically limits speed-up, no matter how many knowledge sources are executed in parallel. Amdahl's limit and synchronization come strongly into play. The implication for

CAGE is that knowledge-source invocation should be distributed, without synchronization. This will eliminate two major bottlenecks – a data hot-spot at the event list, and waiting for the slowest process to finish during synchronization. Still, within a shared-memory multiprocessor system, the interface to the blackboard is the bottleneck. One solution to this is to distribute the blackboard, which is one of the main characteristics of POLIGON.

25.4 Pursuing a demon-driven blackboard system – POLIGON

Control in the blackboard model could be summarized as follows: knowledge sources respond opportunistically to changes in the black-board. As discussed earlier, in reality, and especially in serial systems, the blackboard changes are recorded and a control module decides which change to pursue next. In other words, the knowledge sources do not respond directly to changes on the blackboard. A control module generally dictates the problem-solving behavior. This is a serializing process.

The basic question that led to the design of POLIGON is: What if we attach the knowledge sources to the data elements in the blackboard which, when changed, would result in the activation of those knowledge sources? Instead of waiting until a control module activates a knowledge source, why not immediately execute the knowledge source as the relevant data are changed, and get rid of the control module? A blackboard change would serve as a direct trigger for knowledge source activations. Next, assign a processor–memory pair for each blackboard node, and have the knowledge sources (now on the blackboard processing element) communicate changes to other nodes by passing messages via a communication network (see Figure 25.5.).

Because a knowledge source is activated by a blackboard change, and because a knowledge source is a collection of rules, one can view the rules as being activated (indirectly, to be sure) by a change to some blackboard node. A rule could be activated by a change to a particular slot on a blackboard node. Slots with a property that trigger rules are called *trigger slots*. When the action part of a rule is executed, the changes to the blackboard are communicated to the nodes to be changed. If a change is made to a trigger slot, the condition parts of the *triggered rules* are evaluated; changes to nontrigger slots do not directly cause any processing.

POLIGON was designed from the start to exploit fine-grained parallelism – 'fine' grain here referring to parts of rules. It is generally thought that a shared-memory hardware architecture is not able to deliver

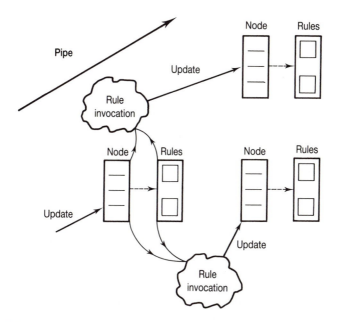

Figure 25.5 Organization of POLIGON.

increasing performance as more processors are added. This is a result of memory contention and of physical limits in the bandwidths of the busses and switches used to connect the processors to the memory. Thus, POLIGON was designed from the start to be run on a form of distributed-memory multiprocessor, the elements of which communicate by sending messages to one another. Its match to the hardware will be seen clearly in the next section where we discuss the structure of POLIGON and what makes it different from existing, serial implementations of blackboard systems.

25.4.1 The structure of POLIGON

In this section we describe the key features of POLIGON. Instead of a detailed description of the implementation, a number of points that are central to POLIGON's computational model are highlighted and contrasted with conventional blackboard implementations.

As has been mentioned above, POLIGON is designed to run on hardware that provides message-passing primitives as the mechanism for communication between processing elements. It is important to note that the way in which information flows on the blackboard can be viewed, at an implementation level, as a message-passing process. This allows a tight coupling between the implementation of a system such as POLIGON and the underlying hardware.

(1) *POLIGON has no centralized scheduler*   This was motivated by a desire to remove any bottlenecks that might be caused by the serial execution of such a scheduler and by multiple, asynchronous processes trying to put events onto the scheduler queue, causing memory contention. (The problem was clearly manifested in CAGE.) This required the definition of a different knowledge invocation mechanism. Not only was a centralized scheduler eliminated but all global synchronization was eliminated as well. This means that it is likely that different parts of a POLIGON program will run at different speeds and will have different views of how the solution is progressing.

(2) Having eliminated the scheduler, there is clearly no need for any – presumably serializing – separation of the knowledge sources from the blackboard. The POLIGON programmer, therefore, specifies at compile-time the classes of blackboard nodes that a particular piece of knowledge is interested in. At compile-time and at system initialization time, knowledge is associated directly with the nodes on the blackboard that might invoke it. This eliminates any communication delay and memory contention that might be caused by having to find a matching rule in a remote knowledge base.

(3) In conventional blackboard systems, knowledge sources are taken to denote both units of knowledge and units of scheduling. If all that a system attempted to execute in parallel was its knowledge sources, a great deal of potential parallelism might be lost by the failure to exploit parallelism at a finer grain. In POLIGON, therefore, *knowledge sources are not scheduling units*, they are simply collections of knowledge. All of the rules in a knowledge source can, in principle, be invoked in parallel and parallelism at a finer grain than this can also be exploited during the execution of rules.

(4) Having eliminated the scheduler a new mechanism was needed that would cause the application's knowledge to be executed. It was decided to go for a very simple mechanism. POLIGON's rules are triggered as demons by updates to slots in nodes. The association between rules and the slots that trigger their invocation is made at compile-time, allowing efficient, concurrent invocation of all eligible rules after an event on the blackboard.

(5) The message-passing metaphor for the implementation and the distribution of the knowledge base over the blackboard mentioned above allowed the development of a computational model which views a blackboard node as a process, responsible for its own housekeeping and for processing messages; for instance, for slot updates and slot read operations.

(6) Serial blackboard systems generally don't have a significant problem with the creation of new blackboard nodes. This is because of the

atomic execution of knowledge sources. Such systems can usually be confident that, when a new node is created, no other node has been created that represents the same object. In parallel systems multiple, asynchronous attempts can be made to create nodes which are really intended to represent the same real-world object. POLIGON provides mechanisms to allow the user to prevent this from happening.

(7)   It was found necessary occasionally to share data between a number of nodes. POLIGON allows no global variables at all so it was necessary to find a suitable way of defining sharable, mutable data, while still trying to reduce the bottlenecks that can be caused by shared data structures. POLIGON, like many frame systems, has a generalized class hierarchy with the classes themselves being represented as blackboard nodes. POLIGON uses class nodes as managers, not only for node creation, as mentioned above, but also to store data to be shared between all of the instances of a class and to support operations that apply to all members of a class.

(8)   Most blackboard systems represent the slots in nodes simply as value lists associated with the name of the slot. The serial operation of such systems allows the programmer to make assumptions about the order of elements in the value list. This assumption allows operations on all of the elements of the value list in the knowledge that no modification will have happened to the value list since it was read, because knowledge source executions are atomic. In POLIGON, because a large number of rules can asynchronously be attempting to perform operations on a slot simultaneously, it was imperative to find mechanisms that would help to keep the operation of the system coherent without slowing down the access to slots too much, causing large critical sections and reducing parallelism. POLIGON, therefore, provides 'smart' slots. They can keep their values in the correct order and know how to index them for flexible and focused data retrieval. They can also have user defined behavior which allows them to make sure that operations performed on them leave them consistent.

25.4.2 Shifting the metaphor

POLIGON's design looks very much like a frame-based program specialized for a particular implementation of the blackboard model. The expected behavior of the system is much closer than the serial systems to the blackboard problem-solving metaphor in one respect – the knowledge sources respond to changes in the blackboard *directly*. Historically, this traces back to Selfridge's Pandemonium (Selfridge, 1959), which influenced Newell's ideas of blackboard-like programs (Newell, 1962). It also has some of the flavor of the actor formalism (Hewitt *et al.*, 1973). As in CAGE there are two major sources of concurrency in this scheme:

(1)   Each blackboard node can be active simultaneously to reflect data parallelism – the more blackboard nodes, the more potential parallelism.

(2)   Rules attached to a node can be running on many different processing elements simultaneously, providing knowledge parallelism.

This demon-driven system with a facility for exploiting both data and knowledge parallelism poses some serious problems, however. First, it is easy to keep the processors and communication network busy, but the trick is to keep them busy converging toward a solution. Second, solutions to a problem will be nondeterministic – that is, each run will most likely produce different answers. Worse, a solution is not guaranteed since the individual nodes cannot determine if the system is on the right path to an overall solution – that is, there is no global control module to steer the problem solving. Within the AI paradigm that looks for satisfying answers, nondeterminism *per se* is not a cause for alarm; however, nonconvergence or an incorrect solution is. One remedy to these problems is to introduce some global control mechanisms. Another solution is to develop a problem-solving scheme that can operate without a global view or global control. We have focused our efforts in POLIGON on the latter approach.

Distributed hierarchical control

A hierarchical control mechanism is introduced that exploits the structure of the blackboard data. The levels, in the AGE sense, of the blackboard are organized as a class hierarchy. Each level is a class and a blackboard node is an instance of that class. Class nodes contain information about their instances (number of instances, their address, and so on), and knowledge sources can be attached to class nodes to control their instance nodes. To minimize confusion, class nodes will be referred to using a more concrete term, *level manager*. Similarly, a super-manager node can control the class nodes.

Within POLIGON, the potential for control is located in three types of places:

(1)   Within each node, where action parts of the rules can be executed serially, for example.

(2)   In the level manager, which can, for example, be used to monitor

the activities of its nodes. Since the level manager is the only agent that knows about the nodes on its level, a message that is to be sent to all the instance nodes must be routed through their manager node. The level manager also controls the creation and garbage collection of the nodes, and attaches the relevant rules to newly created nodes.

(3)   In the super-manager, whose span of control includes the creation of level managers and their activities, and indirectly their offspring.

The introduction of control mechanisms solves some of the difficulties, but it also introduces bottlenecks at points of control; for example, at the level manager nodes. One solution to this type of bottleneck is to replicate the nodes, that is, create many copies of the manager nodes. The CAOS experiments, mentioned earlier, took this approach (Brown *et al.*, 1986). Although POLIGON supports this strategy, our research is leading us to try a different tactic.

A new role for expectation-driven reasoning

It was initially conjectured that model-driven and expectation-driven processing would not play a significant role in concurrent systems – at least not from the standpoint of helping with performance. One view of top-down processing is that it is a means of gaining efficiency in serial systems in the following way: In the class of applications under consideration, the interpretation of data proceeds from the input data up an abstraction hierarchy – the amount of information being processed is reduced as it goes up the hierarchy. Expectations, posted from a higher level to a lower level, indicate data needed to support an existing hypothesis; data expected from predictions; and so on. Thus, when an expected event does occur, the bottom-up analysis need not continue up – the higher-level node is merely notified of the event and it does the necessary processing; for example, increases the confidence in its hypothesis. When the analysis involves a large search space, this expectation-driven approach can save a substantial amount of processing time in serial systems.

In POLIGON hot-spots often occur at a node to which many lower level nodes communicate their results (a fan-in). The upward message traffic can be reduced by posting expectations on the lower level nodes and having them report back only when *unexpected* events occur. This approach, currently under investigation, is one way for a node to distribute parts of the work to lower-level nodes, and hopefully relieve the type of bottlenecks caused by fan-ins at a node without resorting to node replication.

It is generally expected that, within the abstraction hierarchy of the blackboard, information volume is reduced as one goes up the hierarchy.

This translates into the following desiderata for concurrent systems: For an arbitrary node to avoid being a hot-spot, there must be a decrease in the rate of communication proportional to the number of nodes communicating to it. That is, the wider the fan, the less communication is allowable from each node. It was found, while re-implementing the serial ELINT application in POLIGON, that the highest-level nodes had to be updated for almost every new data item. Such a formulation of the problem, while posing no problem in serial systems, reduces parallelism in concurrent problem solvers.

A new form of rules

If, for any given data item, there are many rules that check its state, the system must ensure that this data item does not change until all of those rules have checked it. A typical example is as follows: Suppose there are two rules that are mutually exclusive, one performs some action if a data value is *on* and the other performs some other action if the value is *off*. How can we ensure that, between the time the first rule accesses the data and when the second does so, there is not some other action that changes the data? It was found in POLIGON (and also in CAGE) that these mutually exclusive rules need to be written in the form of case-like conditionals to assure data consistency of the form described above. Since the need for process creation, and subsequent maintenance, is reduced through combining rules, this form of rule also aids in speeding up the overall rule execution. It does mean, however, that the grain size of some of the rules has been made bigger, at least at the source code level.

Agents with objectives

At any given point in the computation, the data at different nodes can be mutually inconsistent or out of date. There are many causes for this, but one cause is that blackboard changes are communicated by messages and the message transit time is unpredictable. In the applications under consideration, where there are one or more streams of continuous input data, the problem appears as scrambled data arrival – the data may be out of temporal sequence or there may be holes in the data. Waiting for earlier data does not help, since there is no way to predict when that data might appear. Instead, the node must do the best it can with the information it has. At the same time, it must avoid propagating changes to other nodes if its confidence in its output data or inferences is low.

Put another way, each node must be able to compute with incomplete or incorrect data, and it must 'know' its objectives to enable it to evaluate the resulting computation. A result is passed on only if it is known to be an improvement on a past result. This represents a change from the problem-solving strategies generally employed in blackboard systems where the control/scheduling module evaluates and directs the problem solving. With no global control module to evaluate the overall solution state, a reasonable alternative is to make each node evaluate its own local state. Of course, there is no guarantee that the sum total of local correctness will yield global correctness. However, the way that blackboard systems are generally organized – each blackboard level representing a class of solution islands, the span of knowledge sources being limited to a few levels, and having functionally independent knowledge sources – appears at this point to provide an appropriate methodology for creating loosely coupled nodes that can be provided with local objectives and a capability for self-evaluation. The 'smart' slots mentioned earlier are used to implement this strategy. It is interesting to note that the need for local goals does not seem to change with process granularity. Although the methods used to generate the goals are very different, Lesser's group has found that each node in its distributed system needs to have local goals (Durfee *et al.*, 1985). In this system each node contains a complete blackboard system; each system (node) monitors the activities in a region of a geographic area which is monitored collectively by the system as a whole.

The design of POLIGON poses an interesting question: Is it still a blackboard system? There is a substantial shift in the problem-solving behavior and in the way the knowledge sources need to be formulated. The structure of the solution is not globally accessible. There is no control module to guide the problem at run-time. The metaphor shifts to one in which each 'blackboard' node is assigned a narrow objective to achieve, doing the best it can with the data passed to it, and passing on information only when the new solution is better than the last one. The collective action of the 'smart' agents results in a satisfying solution to a problem.

In retrospect, these characteristics for concurrent problem solving seem obvious. When a group of humans solve a problem collectively by subdividing a task, we assume each person has the ability to evaluate his or her own performance relative to the assigned task. When there are 'uncaring' people, the overall performance is bad, in terms of both speed and solution quality.

Although there is a substantial shift away from the conventional problem-solving metaphor, POLIGON evolved out of the mechanisms that were present in AGE. Most of the same opportunities for concurrency made available to the user in CAGE are built into the system in POLIGON. The POLIGON language forces the user to think in terms of blackboard levels and knowledge sources. But the underlying system has no global data. Whether such a formulation makes the job of constructing concurrent, knowledge-based systems easier or more difficult for the knowledge engineer still remains to be seen. A difficulty might arise because the semantics of the POLIGON language, that is, the mapping of the blackboard model to the underlying software and hardware architecture, is hidden from the user. For example, there is no notion of message-passing or of a distributed blackboard reflected in the POLIGON language. In contrast, the choice of what, and how, to run concurrently is completely under user control in CAGE.

25.5 Conclusions

In this paper we discussed the relationship between the blackboard model, its existing serial implementations, and the degree to which the intuitively inherent parallelism is really present.

CAGE and POLIGON, two implementations of the blackboard model designed to operate on two different parallel hardware architectures, were described briefly, both in terms of their structure and the motivation behind their design.

Our framework development, application implementations on these frameworks, and initial performance experiments to date have taught us that: (1) it is difficult to write a real-time, data-interpretation program in a multiprocessor environment, and (2) performance gains are sensitive to the ways in which applications are formulated and programmed. In this class of application, performance is also sensitive to data characteristics.

The 'obvious' sources of parallelism in the blackboard model, such as the concurrent processing of knowledge sources, do not provide much gain in speed-up if control remains centralized. On the other hand, decentralizing the control, or removing the control entirely, creates a computational environment in which it is very difficult to control the problem-solving behavior and to obtain a reasonable solution to a problem. As granularity is decreased, to obtain more potential parallel components, the interdependence among the computational units tends to increase, making it more difficult to obtain a coherent solution and to achieve a performance gain at the same time. We described some of the methods employed to overcome these difficulties.

In the application class under investigation, much of the parallelism came from data parallelism – both from the temporal data sequence and from multiple objects (aircraft, for example) – and from pipelining up the blackboard hierarchy. The ELINT application was unfortunately knowledge poor, so that we were unable to explore knowledge parallelism, except as a by-product of data and pipeline parallelism. ELINT has been implemented in both CAGE and POLIGON, and experiments are now being performed. The experiments are designed to measure and to compare performance by varying different parameters: process granularity, number of processors, data rate, data arrival characteristics, and so on.

It is clear that much more research is needed in this area before a combination of a computational and problem-solving model can be developed that is easy to us, that produces valid solutions reliably, and that can increase performance by a significant amount.

Acknowledgments

The authors gratefully acknowledge the support of the following funding agencies for this project; DARPA/RADC, under contract F30602-85-C-0012; NASA, under contract number NCC 2-220; Boeing Computer Services, under contract number W-266875.

26

GBB: A Generic Blackboard Development System

Daniel D. Corkill, Kevin Q. Gallagher and
Kelly E. Murray

26.1 Introduction

Historically, blackboard-based AI systems have been implemented from
scratch, often by layering a blackboard architecture on top of other
support systems. This has fostered a notion that blackboard-based
architectures are difficult to build and slow in execution. Despite this
notion, AI system implementers are increasingly considering blackboard
architectures for their applications. Unlike rule-based and frame-based
AI architectures where a variety of commercial and academic system
development shells are now available, an application developer considering a blackboard approach remains largely unassisted.

A microcosm of this situation existed at the University of
Massachusetts. Several large blackboard-based AI systems had been
implemented (Hanson and Riseman, 1978b; Lesser and Corkill, 1983),
and a number of additional blackboard-based applications were being
considered. We decided to pool our experience in implementing
blackboard systems into a common development system. We felt that by
consolidating our implementation resources we could construct a generic
system that would be more efficient than any of the individual systems, if
they all were constructed from scratch. The goal for the blackboard
development system was to reduce the time required to implement a
specific application and to increase the execution efficiency of the
resulting implementation.

This chapter describes the resulting generic blackboard development
system, termed GBB (Generic BlackBoard). The GBB approach is unique
in several aspects:

(1) A strong emphasis was made on efficient insertion and retrieval
     (pattern matching) of blackboard objects. GBB was designed to

efficiently implement large blackboard systems containing thousands of blackboard objects.

(2)   A nonprocedural specification of the blackboard and blackboard objects is kept separate from a nonprocedural specification of the insertion/retrieval storage structure (Figure 26.1). This allows a 'blackboard administrator' to easily redefine the blackboard database implementation without changing the basic blackboard/object specification or any application code. Such flexibility is not only important during the initial development of the application system, but also to maintain efficient database operation as the scale and characteristics of the application evolve during its use. Both specifications are used by the GBB database code generator to produce an efficient blackboard kernel tailored for the specific application.

(3)   We have defined a general *composite* blackboard object for representing objects composed of discrete elements (such as a phrase of words or a track of vehicle sightings).

(4)   We have defined a pattern language for retrieving simple and composite objects from the blackboard. The application programmer has the ability to insert additional procedural filtering functions into the basic retrieval process. This can be significantly more efficient than applying the filters to the results of the retrieval.

(5)   A clean separation was made between the database support subsystem of GBB and the control level. This allows different control shells to be implemented using the common database supported subsystem. (We feel that it is premature to force a particular control architecture on all blackboard applications.) The interface between the two subsystems is a set of *blackboard events*, signals indicating the creation, modification or deletion of blackboard objects. We are implementing several control shells as part of GBB; however, an application implementer is free to develop a different control shell using the GBB database subsystem.

The emphasis on database efficiency separates GBB from the generic blackboard architectures of Hearsay-III (Erman *et al.*, 1981) and BB1 (Hayes-Roth, 1985). Although both Hearsay-III and BB1 are domain-independent blackboard architectures, their focus is on generalizing control capabilities. The major contribution of GBB is not in any extension of the technology of blackboard architectures, but in the unification of existing blackboard technologies into a development system for high-performance applications.

The remainder of this chapter describes GBB in more detail, focusing on its database support subsystem and pattern matching capabilities. The implementation of control shells will not be described. GBB is implemented in COMMON LISP and is now being tested in a

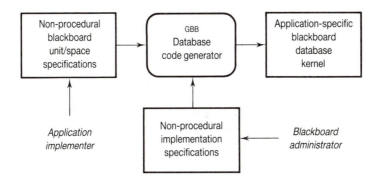

Figure 26.1   The GBB database subsystem.

COMMON LISP reimplementation of the distributed vehicle monitoring testbed (Lesser and Corkill, 1983).

26.2 Specifying the blackboard structure

An application implementer using the GBB system must specify the structure of the blackboard and the objects that will reside on it. In GBB, the blackboard is a hierarchical structure composed of atomic blackboard pieces called spaces. (In designing GBB, we used names that did not evoke preconceived notions from previous blackboard systems. Hence the term 'space' rather than 'level', and the term 'unit' rather than 'hypothesis' or 'object'.) For example, the blackboard abstraction levels (phrase, word, syllable, etc.) of the Hearsay-II speech understanding system would be implemented as spaces in GBB. In addition to being composed of spaces, a blackboard can also be composed of other blackboards (themselves eventually composed of spaces). Finally, blackboards and spaces can be replicated at blackboard initialization time (discussed in Section 26.5).

Spaces are defined first, using **define-spaces**:

define-spaces *spaces [documentation]* &KEY   *[Macro]*
               dimensions

spaces is a list of space names. *dimensions* is a list of specifiers defining the dimensionality of *spaces*. The concept of *space dimensionality* is crucial to efficient insertion/retrieval of blackboard objects, and is best introduced by examples from existing systems.

In addition to having the blackboard subdivided into multiple information levels, the levels of the Hearsay-II speech understanding system (Erman *et al.*, 1980) and the distributed vehicle monitoring testbed (DVMT (Lesser and Corkill, 1983) are *structured*. That is, the blackboard objects are placed onto appropriate areas within each level based on their attributes. In Hearsay-II, each level has one dimension, *time*. In the DVMT, each level has three dimensions: *time* and *x, y* position. In both systems, each level in the system has the same dimensionality. This may not be the case for other application areas, and GBB allows individual spaces to have different dimensionality. (Spaces with differing dimensionality are declared using multiple calls to **define-spaces**.)

An important aspect of the level dimensionality in Hearsay-II and the DVMT is that each dimension is *ordered*. This means that there is a notion of objects being 'nearby' other objects. In Hearsay-II this idea of neighborhood allows retrieval of words to extend a phrase whose begin time is 'close' to the phrase's end time. In the DVMT, a vehicle classification is made from a component frequency track by looking on the blackboard for other component frequency tracks that are positioned close to the original track throughout its length.

In addition to ordered dimensions, GBB supports *enumerated* dimensionality. An enumerated dimension contains a fixed set of labeled categories. For example, in the DVMT, a hypothesis classifying a vehicle could be placed on a space containing a 'classification' dimension, where the dimension's label set consists of vehicle types. GBB allows a space to have both ordered and enumerated dimensions.

The dimensionality of each space is an important part of system design. Although GBB provides flexibility in specifying space dimensionality, the application implementer must determine what is appropriate for the particular application. It should be stressed that specifying the dimensionality of spaces is primarily an issue of representation – not of database efficiency. Efficiency decisions will be discussed in Section 26.4.

Returning to the dimension specification in **define-space**, each dimension is specified as a list where the first element is the name of the dimension and the remainder is a list of keyword/value pairs describing the dimension. The two defined keywords are :RANGE, corresponding to ordered dimensions, and :ENUMERATED, corresponding to dimensions of enumerated classes.

The argument to :RANGE is a list of *(lower-bound upper-bound)* or :INFINITE, indicating a range of $(-\infty, +\infty)$. The argument to :ENUMERATED is the label set for the enumerated dimension. For example:

```
(define-spaces (vehicle-location vehicle-track)
   :DIMENSIONS
     ((time :RANGE (0 30))
      (x    :RANGE (-1000 1000))
      (y    :RANGE (-1000 1000))
```

```
(classification
         :ENUMERATED (chevy porsche toyota
                      vw-beetle unknown))))
```

defines two spaces with identical dimensionality. It is an error to attempt placement of a blackboard object outside the range of an ordered dimension or outside the label set of an enumerated dimension. If *dimensions* is omitted or nil, the space has no dimensionality. Such spaces are *unstructured*.

Once an application's spaces have been defined, the blackboard hierarchy is defined using **define-blackboards**:

define-blackboards *blackboards components*   [*Macro*]
       [*documentation*]

blackboards is a list of blackboard names. *components* is a list of symbols naming those spaces and/or blackboards that will be the children of *blackboards*. For example:

```
(define-blackboards (hyp-bb goal-bb)
    (signal-location vehicle-location vehicle-track))
```

defines two blackboards, each having three spaces.

26.3 Specifying blackboard objects

Once the blackboards and spaces have been specified, the blackboard objects are defined. In GBB, all blackboard objects are termed *units*. Hypotheses, goals and knowledge source activation records are typical examples of units. A unit is an aggregate data type similar to those created using the COMMON LISP **defstruct** macro, but only units can be placed onto blackboard spaces. Units are defined using **define-unit**:

define-unit *name-and-options*   [*Macro*]
       [*documentation*] &KEY *slots links*
       indexes

The *name-and-options* argument is exactly the same as **defstruct** with several extensions. First, a function to generate a name for each unit instance can be specified (using :NAME-FUNCTION). This function is called with the newly created unit instance after all slots in the unit have been initialized, but before the unit is placed onto the blackboard. The function returns a string that is used in a special read-only slot, **name**, that is implicitly defined if the :NAME-FUNCTION option is used. Second, it is often useful when interacting with a blackboard system to retrieve a unit by name rather than through a pattern match on its attributes. GBB provides this capability through a separate hash table of units (indexed by name) that can be dynamically created/destroyed as needed. Code for performing these activities is generated for a unit if the :HASH-UNIT option value is non-nil. Finally, the signaling of blackboard events associated with creating and deleting the unit can be controlled using the :EVENTS option. The :EVENTS argument is a list of :CREATION and/or :DELETION, indicating which events are to be signaled to the control shell for instances of this unit. The :EVENTS argument can also be nil, indicating that no unit events are to be signaled.

The *slots* argument contains a list of slot-descriptions that are also identical to **defstruct** with one addition. Any slot can have a slot option :EVENTS that is a list of *event-name* and *event-predicate–function* pairs. Each event-predicated function is evaluated each time the value of the slot is modified. If the event-predicate–function returns true, the corresponding event-name is signaled.

The *links* argument defines additional slots that hold inter-unit links. The name of the link is used as the new slot name. Note that the slot-names defined by *links* are implicitly defined as slots and are not included in **define-unit**'s *slots* argument. By default, GBB forces all links to be bidirectional; each outgoing unit link must be defined with an accompanying inverse incoming link. GBB generates special modification functions (linkf for adding a single link, linkf-list for adding a list of links, and unlinkf and unlinkf-list for deleting links) that maintain consistent link bidirectionality. For example:

```
(linkf (hyp$creating-ksi this-hyp) current-ksi)
```

adds current-ksi as a new *creating-ksi* of this-hyp.

Each link-description in *links* has the form:

```
(link-name [:SINGULAR]
        {:REFLEXIVE |
        (other-unit other-link [:SINGULAR])}
        [:EVENTS event-descriptions])
```

For example, here is a bidirectional link between hypothesis units:

```
(supported-hyps (hyp supporting-hyps))
(supporting-hyps (hyp supported-hyps))
```

The keyword :SINGULAR is used to implement one-to-one, one-to-many and many-to-one links (the default is many-to-many). The keyword :REFLEXIVE is simply a shorthand for:

```
(link-name (this-unit-name linkname))
```

The optional :EVENTS argument is identical to the event-predicate–function specification discussed for *slots*.

The *indexes* argument specifies how the unit is mapped onto spaces (termed *indexing*). There must be a space dimension corresponding to each unit index (additional space dimensions are acceptable). Slots containing unit indexing information must be described by an index-description of the form:

(*index-name slot-name*)

where *index-name* is an *indexing-structure specification* that describes how to extract the dimensional indexes from *slot-name*. Indexing-structures are defined using **define-index-structure** discussed below.

In its simplest form, an index is just the name of a **define-unit** slot defined in *slots*. For example, if a unit had a slot named *time* containing a numeric value, GBB would have no problem placing that object on the time dimension of a space. Handling a slot value containing a range (such as the time span of a phrasal hypothesis) is also straightforward. Unfortunately, things are not always simple. One problem is that the indexes may be only a portion of a structured slot value, and GBB must be told how to extract the index information from the overall structure. A much more complex situation stems from the need to support composite-units.

A *composite unit* is a unit that has multiple *elements* along one or more of its dimensions. An example of a composite unit is a track of vehicle sightings. Each sighting is an x, y point at a particular moment in time. One way to represent such a track is a *time-location-list*:

```
((time1 (x1 y1))
 (time2 (x2 y2))
    .
    .
    .
 (timeN (xN yN)))
```

Such a unit does not occupy a single large volume of the blackboard, but rather a series of points connected along the time dimension. To indicate this, **time-location-list** must be declared as a composite index-structure.

The information needed to decode a datatype into its dimensional indexes is specified using **define-index-structure**:

define-index-structure *name*   [*Macro*]
        [*documentation*]
        &KEY *type*

> *composite-type*
> *composite-index*
> *element-type indexes*

The *name* argument is a symbol that is defined as a new LISP datatype. *type* is used when the datatype to be decoded is a simple (noncomposite) datatype and simply defines the new datatype *name* as a synonym for the existing datatype *type*. For a composite datatype, *composite-type*, *composite-index* and *element-type* must be specified in place of *type*. The *composite-type* argument specifies the type of sequence that contains the individual index elements. *composite-index* specifies the dimension connecting the composite elements (for example, *time*). *element-type* specifies the datatype of the composed elements. Finally, *index* defines how to extract the dimensional indexes from each element. The format for each index-dimension specifier is:

```
(dimension {:POINT field {(type field)}* |
           :RANGE (:MAX field {(type field)}*)
                  (:MIN field {(type field)}*)})510
```

For example:

```
(define-index-structure TIME-LOCATION-LIST
    :COMPOSITE-TYPE list
    :COMPOSITE-INDEX time
    :ELEMENT-TYPE time-location
    :INDEXES ((time :POINT time)
              (x :POINT location (location x))
              (y :POINT location (location y))))
```

In the above example, GBB would know how to access the *x* index from the first element of the composite datatype **time-location-list** as:

```
(location$x (time-location$location
               (first time-location-list)))
```

Note that all *types* and *fields* must be defined using **defstruct** or **define-units**.

Returning to the *indexes* argument of **define-unit**, *slot-name* is the name of a slot (from the :SLOTS arguments). The slot must have a :TYPE slot-option whose value is the name of an index-structure. *index-name* must be an index in that index-structure.

Here is a highly abridged version of the hypothesis unit specification in the DVMT:

```
(define-unit (HYP (:CONC-NAME "HYP$"
                  (:NAME-FUNCTION generate-hyp-name)
                  (:HASH-UNIT nil))
```

```
"HYP (Hypothesis)"
:SLOTS
((belief 0 :TYPE belief)
 (classification)
 (sensor-id 0 :TYPE sensor-index)
 (time-location-list () :TYPE time-location-list))
:LINKS
((consistency-hyp :SINGULAR (hyp consistent-hyps))
 (consistent-hyps (hyp consistency-hyp :SINGULAR))
 (supported-hyps  (hyp supporting-hyps))
 (supporting-hyps (hyp supported-hyps))
 (creating-ksis   (ksi created-hyps)))
:INDEXES
((time time-location-list)
 (x time-location-list)
 (y time-location-list)
 (classification classification))
```

26.4 Implementing the database

The previous sections presented the blackboard and unit specifications that must be specified by the application implementer. To this point, the specifications defined representational aspects of the application. This section describes how particular implementations of the blackboard database are specified. We concentrate on ordered dimensions – enumerated dimensions are typically implemented as sets or hash tables.

The implementation machinery for storing units on spaces is specified using **define-unit-mapping**:

> **define-unit-mapping** *units spaces*   [*Macro*]
>   [*documentation*] &KEY
>   *indexes index-structure*

    units is a list of unit names, where each unit has identical index dimensions (as defined by the define-unit *indexes* argument). *spaces* is the list of spaces whose implementation machinery is being defined. Note that the same unit type can be stored differently on different spaces, and that different unit types can be stored differently on the same space. *indexes* is the list of indexes whose implementation machinery is being defined. *index-structure* defines the implementation machinery.

Simple hashing techniques do not work for ordered dimensions due to the neighborhood relationship among units. The storage structure must be able to quickly locate units within any specified range of a dimension. A standard solution is to divide the range of the dimension into a series of *buckets*. Each bucket contains those units falling within the bounds of the bucket. The number of buckets and their sizes provide a time/space tradeoff for unit insertion/retrieval. The bucket approach requires that a pattern range be converted into bucket indexes and that units retrieved from the first and last bucket be checked to ensure that they indeed are within the pattern range.

In a three-dimensional blackboard (*x*, *y* and *time*) the bucket approach becomes more complicated. One approach would be to define a three-dimensional array of buckets. A second approach would be to define three one-dimensional bucket vectors and have the retrieval process intersect the result of retrieving in each dimension. To indicate that several dimensions should be stored together in one array, they are grouped together with an extra level of parentheses. For example, ((time x y)) would specify a three-dimensional array, and ((time (x y)) would specify a vector for *time* and a two-dimensional array for (*x*, *y*).

Here is a three one-dimensional vector example:

```
(define-unit-mapping (unit1 unit2) (space1)
  :INDEXES (time x y)
  :INDEX-STRUCTURE
  ((time :SUBRANGES
         (:START 5)
         (5 15 (:WIDTH 5))
         (15 25 (:WIDTH 2))
         (25 :END))
   (x :SUBRANGES (:START :END (:WIDTH 5)))
   (y :SUBRANGES (:START :END (:WIDTH 2)))))
```

26.5 Instantiating the blackboard

Once the structure of the blackboard database has been specified with the functions presented above, it may be instantiated. This creates all the internal structures needed by GBB to actually store unit instances. Sometimes it is useful to be able to create several copies of the entire blackboard database or copies of parts of it. For example, to simulate a multiprocessor blackboard system one could instantiate a copy of the blackboard database for each processor. Instantiation is done via **instantiate-bb-database**:

instantiate-bb-database *replication-desc*   [*Function*]

replication-desc describes the blackboard hierarchy to be created. In the simplest case, it is a symbol that names the root of the tree to be instantiated. This would instantiate one copy of each of the nodes in the tree (all the leaves would be space instances and the interior nodes would be blackboard instances). Note that the root instantiated need not be the root of the entire blackboard hierarchy but can be any node in the tree. This would allow, for example, different parts of the blackboard database to be distributed (and possibly replicated) across a network of processors. The general form of *replication-desc* is:

{*name* | (*name* [*replication-count*] [*description* ...])}

name is the name of a blackboard or a space; *replication-count* is an integer specifying how many copies of the subtree to create; and *description* is a *replication-desc* for one of the components of the specified blackboard (or space). For example:

```
(instantiate-bb-database
    (top-level 3 (goal-bb (level-one 2))
                 (hyp-bb (level-three 3))))
```

would create three copies of the blackboard database rooted at the blackboard top-level. Each copy would have two copies of level-one and three copies of level-three. Any defined blackboards or spaces not mentioned in the *replication-desc* would have one copy created.

26.6 Creating units

A unit is created and placed onto a space using the function **make**-*unit-type*:

make-*unit-type* {*blackboard-path-element*}+   [*Function*]
                    {*slot-keyword slot-value*}*

The unit creation function is automatically generated by define-unit. The *blackboard-path-element* arguments uniquely name the space that is to be searched. The simplest blackboard path is a space name. If a space name is not unique, it must be qualified by its parent blackboards' names until it is unique. In addition, replicated blackboards and/or spaces must be appropriately indexed.

Values for the newly created unit can be specified by *slot-keyword slot-value* pairs. Link slots can also be specified for the newly created unit, and GBB ensures that inverse links are also created.

In addition to creating the unit, **make**-*unit-type* constructs the indexing information needed to retrieve the unit from the blackboard, invokes the name generation function (if specified in define-unit), and inserts the unit into the unit hash table (if unit hashing is enabled).

26.7 Unit retrieval (pattern matching)

Blackboard systems spend a significant amount of time searching the database. Because retrieval is so important we have given the application programmer the means to make it as efficient as possible by eliminating candidate units early in the retrieval process. This is done in two ways. First, the user can specify specialized filter functions that are applied between the initial retrieval of units (such as from a set of buckets) and the subsequent checking of pattern inclusion. Second, the pattern language is rich enough to allow the application programmer to specify complex retrieval patterns that can be analyzed and optimized by GBB. The result is a reduction in retrieval time and, equally important, a reduction in the amount of temporary storage and Consing required for unit retrieval.

The primitive function for retrieving units from spaces is **find-units**:

---

find-units *units {blackboard-path-element}* +   [*Macro*]
      &KEY *pattern filter-before*
      filter-after

The *units* argument identifies which unit types are to be retrieved. The *blackboard-path-element* arguments uniquely name the space that is to be searched. The simplest blackboard path is a space name. If a space name is not unique, it must be qualified by its parent blackboards' names until it is unique. In addition, replicated blackboards and/or spaces must be appropriately indexed.

The two keyword arguments *filter-before* and *filter-after* specify predicates to perform application specific filtering of the candidate units. The *filter-before* predicates are applied to the initially retrieved units before the pattern-matching tests and are intended as a quick first test to shrink the search space. The *filter-after* predicates are run after the pattern-matching tests and can perform additional acceptance testing.

The other keyword argument is the retrieval *pattern* that describes the criteria that must be met by the units retrieved. The simplest pattern is the keyword :ALL that matches all of the specified units on the specified space. A pattern can also be quite complex, represented by a list of pattern specifiers. Much of the richness in the pattern specifier language supports the retrieval of composite units, and many of the options are meaningless unless the pattern's index structure is a composite structure.

A nontrivial pattern is based on a *pattern-object* that may be either an index element, a composite structure or a concatenation of index elements or composite structures. Index structures that are concatenated together need not all be the same nor does the index structure of the pattern need to be the same as the index structure of the unit. GBB is able to efficiently map from one index structure representation to another.

When a pattern needs to be constructed by splicing together components of different index structures GBB decomposes all patterns/objects into sequences of simple dimensional ranges to avoid expensive type conversions.

The *pattern-object* specifies a region of the blackboard in which to look for the units. It is either a list of options or, to concatenate several index structures, a list whose first element is the symbol :CONCATENATE and whose remaining elements are lists of options. The keywords used to specify the *pattern-object* are:

index-object   This is an index structure, for example a time-location-list.

index-type   This is the type of the *index-object*. It is the name of an index structure.

select   This allows extraction of a subsequence of a composite structure based on the *value* of the composite index (for example, *time*).

subseq   This allows extraction of a subsequence of a composite structure based on the *position* in the sequence (the same as selection of a subsequence of a vector).

delta   This expands or contracts a range or expands a point into a range.

displace   This allows the *index-object* to be translated along one or more of its dimensions.

The other pattern specifier keywords are:

element-match   This specifies how each index element from the unit is compared with the index element from the *pattern-object*. It may be one of :EXACT, :OVERLAPS, :INCLUDES or :WITHIN. :EXACT means that the unit's index element must exactly match the pattern's. :INCLUDES means that the unit's index element must include the pattern's. :WITHIN means that the unit's index element must be within the pattern's. :OVERLAPS means that the unit's index element must overlap with the pattern's.

before-extras and *after-extras*   The argument is a range that specifies the minimum and maximum number of index elements that the unit may have before (or after) the index element mentioned in the *pattern-object*. The argument can also be :DONT-CARE that is short for the range (0 MOST-POSITIVE-FIXNUM).

match   This is an inclusive lower bound on the number of index elements that must match. This can either be expressed as a percentage of the length of the *pattern-object*, by saying (:PERCENTAGE 50) or an absolute count by saying (:COUNT 5), or as a difference from the length of the *pattern-object* by saying (:ALL-BUT 2).

mismatch   This is an inclusive upper bound on the number of index elements that are allowed to not match. 'Not matching' means that the unit has an index element for that composite index (for

Pattern:

Unit:

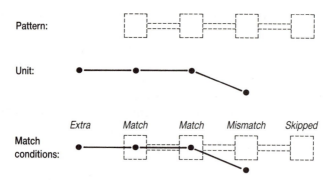

Match
conditions:

Figure 26.2   Composite unit matching conditions.

example, time) that does not match (according to the :ELEMENT-MATCH criterion) with the index element in the *pattern-object*. This does not include index elements that appear in the *pattern-object* but do not have a corresponding index element in the unit (call these *skipped*). (See Figure 26.2.)

contiguous   If this is true, the index elements that match must be contiguous along the composite index dimension.

For example:

```
(find-units '(ghyp hyp) 'goal-bb 'vehicle-track
    :PATTERN
      (:PATTERN-OBJECT
        (:CONCATENATE
            (:INDEX-TYPE      time-region-list
             :INDEX-OBJECT
                (#<TIME-REGION 3 (8 11) (4 6)>
                 #<TIME-REGION 4 (6 10) (6 8)>
                 #<TIME-REGION 5 (5 8)  (8 9)>)
              :DISPLACE      ((x 4) (y 2)))
            (:INDEX-TYPE     time-location
             :INDEX-OBJECT
                #<TIME-LOCATION 6 4 10>
              :DELTA         ((x 2) (y 2))))
          :ELEMENT-MATCH    :INCLUDES
          :MATCH            (:PERCENTAGE 75)
          :MISMATCH         2
          :BEFORE-EXTRAS    (0 5)
          :AFTER-EXTRAS     (0 0)
          :CONTIGUOUS       T)
    :FILTER-BEFORE '(sufficient-belief)).
```

Another useful form of unit retrieval is provided by **map-space**:

map-space*function units*   [*Function*]
           {*blackboard-path-element*}+

function specifies a function that is to be applied to each type of unit (specified in *units*) that resides on the space specified by {*blackboard-path-elements*}+. **map-space** ensures that *function* is not applied more than once to any unit.

26.8 Summary and future developments

High-performance blackboard-based AI systems demand much more than a multilevel shared database. An application's blackboard may have thousands of instances of a few classes of blackboard objects scattered within its database. GBB provides an efficient blackboard development system by exploiting the detailed *structure* of the blackboard in implementing primitives for inserting/retrieving blackboard objects. A *control shell* (implemented using GBB's blackboard database support) is used to generate a complete application system.

We have presented a brief description of the database subsystem of GBB. Length limitations have prevented a thorough discussion of all the details and rationale for particular decisions. We have tried to convey both the capabilities of GBB database support and some of the issues that must be faced in implementing a high-performance blackboard development system.

Although GBB has been implemented and is in use, its development continues. Much effort is being applied to performing compile-time optimizations of insertion/retrieval operations. The next phase of GBB development will be to extend the space specification and initialization aspects of GBB to support a blackboard database that is distributed among a network of processing nodes.

Acknowledgments

This research was sponsored in part by the National Science Foundation under CER Grant DCR-8500332, by the National Science Foundation under Support and Maintenance Grant DCR-8318776, and by the Defense Advanced Research Projects Agency, monitored by the Office of Naval Research under Contract NR049-041.

27

MUSE: A Toolkit for Embedded, Real-time AI

Dave Reynolds

27.1 Introduction

How can one develop embedded, real-time AI applications given current software and hardware technology?

The typical sorts of applications that we have in mind are operator assistance, health monitoring and fault diagnosis on complex electronic and mechanical systems. The prime focus for this work has been support for airborne applications within both fixed wing aircraft and helicopters; however, it can easily be applied to other applications such as flexible manufacturing system (FMS) work cells and process machinery.

These types of application are difficult for a number of reasons. First, we have the fundamental problem of continuous reasoning over time-varying situations which is not yet a well understood area of AI. Secondly, we have practical difficulties of achieving adequate speed of reasoning and response times given the time constraints imposed by the embedded nature of the applications. Finally, we have physical problems of delivering useful AI systems in small enough, and cheap enough, hardware packages to be useful.

The MUSE system which we describe in this chapter is a toolkit designed to support prototype development of experimental AI applications of this sort. (The acronym from which the name MUSE was derived has been lost in antiquity.) Perhaps the key feature of MUSE is that it provides a mechanism for packaging up prototype solutions and delivering them on a small, solid-state target machine which can be used to test and evaluate them *in situ*.

The sort of development cycle we envisage for these applications is a three-stage process:

(1) *Concept development* First refine your problem definition and

tackle the more fundamental problems it involves. The idea is to isolate parts of the problem and tackle them in simplified form using simulations to provide the test data sets.

(2) *Prototype development*   Once you understand what the problem is and have some idea of how to tackle it in abstract terms, then is the time to try to implement a complete solution and test it in more realistic environments. Do not expect to use any of the actual code from the initial experiments for this implementation. Treat the results of the first phase as somewhere between a specification and a set of partial design solutions to particular technical problems. Expect to take a number of iterations at this stage to arrive at a good solution.

(3) *System delivery*   When you have a working prototype you may be half way to a full, delivered solution; you may only be one tenth of the way. In some cases it is possible just to take the prototype, clean up the interfaces, package it and deliver it on the same hardware used for prototype testing. In other cases the prototype is little more than a good system specification which is used to guide the implementation of the final complete solution. This implementation may even be carried out in a completely different language from the initial development.

The MUSE toolkit is aimed primarily at the second stage of this process, at building systems and developing compact implementations that can be physically wired up to the hardware concerned and tested in real time. In some cases, but by no means all, MUSE will also be an appropriate tool to use to deliver the final solution.

27.2 System description

27.2.1 Design goals

The basic design goals of the MUSE system were fairly simple:

(1) It should be as flexible as possible and be suited to a wide range of applications, including problems such as multiple sensor interpretation, which are traditionally tackled with blackboard architectures.

(2) It should be efficient enough to run in real time on a range of applications.

(3) It should be compact enough to run sensibly in a small machine with restricted memory, such as a single board computer.

These goals are mutually antagonistic and we had to make design tradeoffs to achieve a reasonable compromise. The approach adopted was as follows:

(1) *Multiple representation languages* MUSE provides a range of knowledge representation languages (production rules, deductive rules, procedural code and frame structures). This helps us to address the range of required applications. It also helps with the efficiency goal since an application can be constructed using an appropriate combination of representations and does not have to be distorted to fit a single representation approach.

(2) *Object-oriented glue* We manage to cater for this range of representation languages without making the system appear unbearably complex to the user by using an object-centered programming approach.

(3) *Compilation of code* All of the representation languages are compiled into a linear intermediate code. This prevents the system from dynamically modifying its own rule sets on the fly but we do not see this restriction as serious in embedded applications.

(4) *Interpretation of code* The requirement for compact code size on a conventional microprocessor has been met by keeping the compiled code in its intermediate form and interpreting it, not compiling it right down to the underlying machine code. This allows us to tradeoff some of the system performance against the code size.

27.2.2 System structure

The basic structure of a given application is a set of separate reasoning modules which communicate by shared access to particular databases. The number and relations between these modules and databases is not fixed. It is possible to construct an application as small as a single production system firing off a single database. However, most applications are expected to use a blackboard style approach with the separate databases corresponding to the separate layers in a multilevel blackboard and the reasoning modules corresponding to the rule packages which work between the blackboard layers. For this reason the reasoning modules are actually termed knowledge sources (irrespective of how the application is actually constructed).

The system is built using the object-oriented approach to programming. Each knowledge source, rule set, rule, database and database entry in the system is an object in the Smalltalk (Goldberg and Robson, 1983) sense of the term. This allows us to add new rule types or database indexing mechanisms for specialized purposes without having to modify

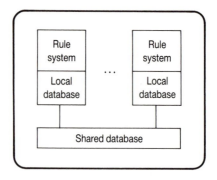

Figure 27.1   Typical knowledge source.

the existing system.

The standard knowledge source structure is shown in Figure 27.1. This consists of a single knowledge source database and one or more rule systems consisting of a set of compiled rules and a database local to the rule set. The rule set databases act as a fast-working memory during reasoning and are not visible, either to other rule sets within the knowledge source or outside the knowledge source. The knowledge source database is accessible to all rule sets within the knowledge source and to any outside objects that have a handle on the knowledge source itself.

Typically, interesting events result in an object being placed in a knowledge source database. The object may, for example, be a useful piece of input data or a goal specification. Its appearance triggers the appropriate rule system which runs, using its local database as a scratch pad, and results in either a result or a reduced set of goals being placed back into the knowledge source database. This may trigger further rule systems from the same knowledge source or other knowledge sources.

An agenda scheduling system, based on simple priority ordering, is used to control the execution of competing knowledge sources. This agenda requires only that knowledge sources be able to respond to a 'run' message of some form and makes very few assumptions about the contents of a knowledge source. This allows us to build procedural knowledge sources consisting of a single function in the underlying PopTalk language and schedule this in the same manner as the more normal multiple rule base knowledge sources.

Another way in which the more general knowledge source structure can be collapsed is to construct a knowledge source containing just a database. Such a knowledge source is, by convention, called a noticeboard and is very useful as a communications channel since the production rules are able to monitor all such global databases for

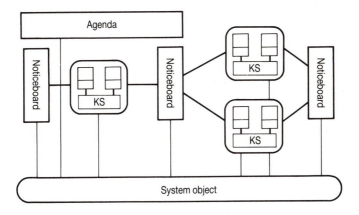

Figure 27.2   Typical application structure.

interesting changes. This allows the construction of blackboard-type systems with noticeboards acting as the blackboard layers. The knowledge sources are then *really* knowledge sources and are fired initially by production rules monitoring the blackboard levels. It is possible to choose between the alternatives of processing any blackboard update and only processing important changes by providing a separate knowledge source rule system as the monitor which, when fired, decides if the rest of the knowledge source should be scheduled.

This approach leads to the typical example system layout shown in Figure 27.2. In this abstract example we place interesting events and goals in the left-hand noticeboard; they are preprocessed by a knowledge source to filter the data and plan any responses. The processed information is then posted on the central noticeboard which triggers a set of knowledge sources who share access to both this database and the final output noticeboard. The 'system object' shown in the figure is simply a top-level handle onto all the knowledge sources and databases in any given application system. It is useful as an access channel for all housekeeping and development operations.

27.2.3 PopTalk

PopTalk is the base language used to implement the bulk of the system structuring (other than the rule languages themselves) and available to the application builder for constructing all procedural code and for directly accessing the object system. It is an object-oriented programming language which is based on the POP-2 language (Burstall *et al.*, 1977) and uses the Smalltalk style of object programming (Goldberg and Robson, 1983), hence the name PopTalk.

PopTalk is implemented in C and compiles functions to an intermediate code for a virtual machine which is then interpreted. The message-based invocation of object behaviors is implemented as part of the virtual machine language, rather than being layered on top of the POP language, thus giving it acceptable efficiency. In any POP-style language implemented on a conventional processor the underlying code has to carry out run-time datatype checking for many operations. In PopTalk the message dispatcher is in effect carrying out this datatype check to determine which behavior code to run. This means that the behavior functions themselves have to carry out less datatype checking which offsets much of the overhead of message lookup.

In PopTalk, objects are defined by other objects called 'schemas' which are linked together into a multiple inheritance hierarchy, thus allowing the use of mixins. These schemas correspond to Smalltalk classes and there is a single 'generic schema' provided by the system as the schema for schemas. All objects are then 'instances' of a given schema and have a set of local storage areas ('slots') and respond to a set of 'messages'. The POP system of updater and selector doublet functions which allows functions to act as data structures is preserved in PopTalk. It is possible to send updater messages as well as selector messages using the same syntax used for placing values in object slots.

As usual in an object-centered system the schema definitions are built out of objects and can be customized to some extent by the user. The definition of slots and behaviors and the combination of inherited definitions for the same slot can be modified by the user. In the base PopTalk system this facility has been used to provide cached and procedural slots which evaluate procedural code to return a slot value and then optionally cache the result to satisfy future lookups. There are also the usual demon facilities which allow arbitrary code to be attached to objects to fire on object creation and on slot updating. Demons are themselves objects which, when created, patch the system message tables to implement the required demon.

Apart from the object system itself most of the procedural functions and facilities of PopTalk are direct equivalents of the POP-2 function set and so will not be described here. One additional system which is important for the current discussions is the data capture facility. A series of data channels is provided which acts as the interface between the PopTalk system and the raw data sources. These channels appear at the PopTalk level as objects which can be attached to physical data sources and which deliver current values of parameter or streams of parameters. Low-level interfacing code then carries out the data capture and stuffs values into these channel interface objects. This low-level code provides a set of monitor functions to directly test incoming numeric data values for significant changes and fire demons when such changes occur. This allows us to filter the data and reduce the number of unnecessary rule system firings to manageable proportions.

27.2.4 The forward production system

The first of the rule languages used in MUSE is a forward production system. This implements an OPS (Forgy and McDermott, 1977) type of match, resolve, fire production cycle. The production rules match against arbitrary objects in PopTalk databases and the matches can be qualified by arbitrary procedural code. The actions carried out by a fired production rule can include arbitrary procedural code (which can thus include processing or scheduling of other rule systems) as well as creating and modifying the structured objects in the accessible databases.

The forward production system is implemented using a heavily modified RETE (Forgy, 1982) net approach. We make use of the strong data typing afforded by the object-oriented databases and filter out unmatched object types at the top of the recognition network. This recognition network approach is very important for the forward production system's use in real-time situations. It means that new data items are processed incrementally and greatly reduces the system's response time to new data.

The forward production system plays a key role in the overall knowledge source architecture by its ability to monitor multiple databases. By default the objects matched and updated by a forward production system are in its local rule set database. However, any production system rule set can be given an 'interest set' of global databases which it should also match against. It is by use of this mechanism that the production rules can be used to monitor the noticeboard databases. They can thus be used to detect patterns in a global problem state and implement the blackboard style of opportunistic problem solving.

27.2.5 The backward chaining system

The other rule language used within MUSE is a backward chaining rule system. Again this rule system matches structured objects in PopTalk databases, which provides a communication path between this rule system and both the forward production system and PopTalk itself. The back chaining rules bind rule variables by unification, rather than by match and are controlled by a depth-first backward-chaining search over both rules and database objects. The rules can invoke arbitrary PopTalk code for use in building predicates and communicating with the rest of the system.

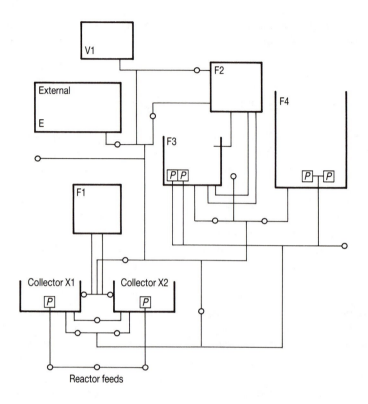

Figure 27.3   Sample storage tank network.

27.3 An example

MUSE is generally being applied to areas such as condition monitoring, fault diagnosis and knowledge-based control. Such applications vary in complexity from a single rule set to complex multi-KS processes. It is a strength of the MUSE shared-database approach that a single toolkit can be used to support such a diversity of architectures.

We can illustrate the types of architecture commonly developed under MUSE with an example. (The details are hypothetical but are derived from three separate successful development projects in the monitoring and control area.) We are required to provide a control system for a network of fluid storage tanks which provide a continuous (variable rate) feed to a reactor plant. See Figure 27.3 for a typical tank layout. The essential job of the controller is to set pumping rates and control valves to drain the storage tanks in a suitable order. The drainage order is constrained to meet a number of objectives concerning balanced drainage and ease of refilling. In addition the network is subject to a

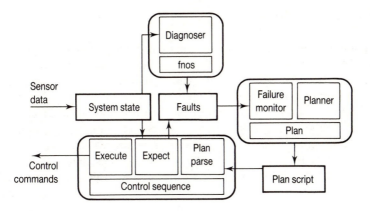

Figure 27.4   Controller architecture.

number of failure modes such as pumping failures, pipe breaks and sticky valves. It is the job of the controller to monitor the performance of the network to detect such problems and to adjust its drainage plan to overcome them.

The MUSE-based architecture for such a controller is illustrated in Figure 27.4. It consists of three main knowledge sources which provide the functions:

- Generation of pumping plans
- Execution and monitoring of pumping plans
- Diagnosis of failures

These knowledge sources communicate by shared access to three noticeboards:

- System state board
- Current failures board
- Current plan board

At any time there is a current pumping plan to be used to control the network. The execution KS has the task of implementing this plan and checking that the network is responding correctly. Data gathered from monitoring points in the pumping network is condensed and fed into the system state noticeboard which the execution KS uses to check on the progress of the plan. The state is also monitored by a fault diagnosis KS which looks for discrepancies which indicate a network failure. Any such failures are diagnosed and the resulting failure indications are posted into the failure noticeboard. The planner KS responds to such failure indications by modifying the current pumping plan.

27.3.1 Planner KS

The planner KS has the job of creating a pumping plan given the current state of the network. The plan is represented as a collection of parallel and serial drainage actions. The planner consists of two different rule sets: the monitor and the plan generator.

The monitor is a data-driven production system which checks the failure noticeboard for changes and triggers a re-planning operation when a significant failure occurs. The monitor is set up to have the failure noticeboard as part of its 'interest set'. This means that any changes to the noticeboard will be broadcast to the monitor rule set for processing. The MUSE scheduler will automatically schedule the planner KS whenever there is data queued up for the monitor rule set to process. It is the job of the monitor to check failure indications against the current plan to determine if they are significant. If they are, it calls the planner rule set.

The planner rule set is implemented as a backward-chaining rule system which is called explicitly by the monitor. The different failure modes (pipe break, valve failing to close, pump failure, etc.) each trigger different predicates in the backward-chaining system which modify the current pumping plan to circumvent the failure. Often this modification involves only changes to drainage routes and rates without distorting the overall drainage sequence. However, serious failures may require a new drainage sequence to be chosen. The overall consistency of the plan with respect to the main constraints is checked by a critic predicate within the same rule set which vets each plan. The modifications to the plan are posted in the plan noticeboard for use by the controller system.

27.3.2 Execution KS

The execution KS uses the pumping plan shown on the plan noticeboard to control the valve and pump settings in the network. It consists of three rule sets: the plan parser, the executer and the expectation monitor.

The plan is specified as a set of drainage actions and routes, some of which can be executed in parallel. The plan parser breaks the drainage plan down into an internal sequence of low-level control actions which are stored in the KS-wide database of the execution KS. The plan parser is a forward production system which includes the plan noticeboard in its interest set so that it will automatically be invoked if the plan changes.

The execution rule set itself takes the next action from the KS database and implements it. This implementation consists of three steps. First, the primitive control action is sent to the machine controller (e.g. 'close pump P3'). For each such action a sequence of sensor reports can be expected which confirm that the action has been correctly carried out. An explicit note is made of which reports to expect. Finally, the execution rule set is explicitly scheduled on the agenda at a time when the action confirmation reports should have arrived.

The expectation rule set is not data driven but is explicitly scheduled by the execution rule set. It checks that the new system status is in agreement with the expectations set up by the last execution cycle. If so, it simply reschedules the execution rule set to be run at a time determined by the detailed pumping plan. If a discrepancy is detected, the nature of the discrepancy is posted in the fault noticeboard.

27.3.3 Diagnoser KS

The diagnoser consists of a single data-driven rule set which is triggered by fault indications appearing in the fault noticeboard. It creates a set of 'fault hypothesis objects' which represent possible explanations of the fault. A set of production rules then match these hypothesis objects against the current system status to determine a minimal set of faults which can explain the symptoms. This set is then posted back into the fault noticeboard as a firm fault indication which will automatically trigger the planner.

27.3.4 Discussion

This architecture is only one of many possibilities but it does illustrate a number of features of the way in which MUSE is used.

First, we tend to approach design by laying out a data flow for the application and then mapping that data flow onto a collection of noticeboards and knowledge sources. All of the different forms of state, failure and plan information could have been stored in a single large database for use by all knowledge sources. The chosen design has the advantages of making the flow of data more explicit and separating the more static plan data from the faster-changing state data.

Secondly, it indicates the range of scheduling approaches that can be used. The normal control action is implemented by the execution KS which explicitly reschedules itself on the agenda with different time delays according to the current plan. The response to a discrepancy between expectations from the plan and sensor data is handled by data-driven invocation of knowledge sources (first the diagnoser and then the planner). Within complex knowledge sources like the planner a simple data-driven rule set is used to detect the significant events and to call the appropriate group of rules directly (i.e. predicate in the planner backward-chaining system rule set) to handle the event.

27.4 The support system

To be useful, a toolkit of this complexity requires a good supporting framework for code development. The MUSE support system exploits the object structure of MUSE. For example, the system editor is a structured editor which can display and manipulate collections of objects at varying levels of detail by opening and closing 'folds' (Inmos, 1985) on objects and slots. This variable resolution display combines nicely with the object structure and reduces the common problem with object editors of not being able to see the wood (objects and overall structure) for the trees (the slots).

The debugging system (called MUDDLE, for MUSE Dynamic Debugging Environment) provides type checking based on the object structure, as well as the usual function call traps and breakpoints. For each slot definition the user can supply a type specification and a restriction. Each is defined using a predicate calculus language in which the names of the object schemas correspond to datatype names. The type specification defines the legal range of datatypes which may be placed in the slot. The restriction specification is a similar but more precise definition of the legal range of values which the slots can take. For example, in the definition of a 'person' datatype we might use:

```
schema person;
  slot sex: { -defaultfemale,
                -typeoneof [male, female] }

  slot age: {   -default 25,
                -typeisinteger,
                -restriction1 =<ˆage and ˆage < 200}

    .

    .

    .

  endschema;
```

These specifications form a useful documentation tool as well as a debugging aid. The type and restriction specifications on slots can be selectively enabled as run-time demons which verify each slot update and trap into the debugging system when a violation is detected.

Tools such as these are useful in helping to detect inconsistencies at run-time and helping to track down their root cause. However, in rule-based programming it is difficult to exhaustively test all rule combinations by test runs, and some form of static consistency checking is required. Our efforts in this direction have concentrated on the forward production system. Given the ability to include arbitrary POP expressions in the forward production rules it is very difficult to check rule consistency at any deep level. Even superficial datatype consistency checks are hard (though not impossible, see Ramsay, 1984). In the current system we restrict ourselves to checking that the structured constants in separate forward production rule match clauses are consistent with the datatype specification given by the object schemas. In the future we hope to extend this work to detect cases such as matches which are provably impossible on datatype grounds by propagating type specifications through simulated variable matches.

27.5 The delivery system

The whole point behind the development of MUSE is the delivery of usable knowledge-based systems (KBSs) onto embedded hardware. The target machine currently used for applications delivery is a small solid-state 68000-based machine, custom built using standard commercial cards. It provides a range of parallel and serial interfaces with an interrupt drive I/O executive for data capture. The KBS code is held in a bank of nonvolatile memory which can be easily loaded from the host machines used for code development. The nonvolatile memory is also used to record events in a log during trials for later post-mortem examination. The same system for specifying static trap points during debugging can be used to define log points which can record events such as rule firings in the nonvolatile memory log.

The particular target machine used is not in itself important. What is important is the ability to deliver KBS code on small, robust hardware which can be used in industrial environments.

27.6 Conclusions

We have discussed a toolkit aimed at delivering real-time knowledge-based systems. The elements of the toolkit are not in themselves revolutionary; they borrow heavily from current AI software technology. The smooth integration of these elements using the object-oriented programming approach is interesting but not unique. What is unique is the successful attempt to build the toolkit in such a way as to be able to deliver working applications on small solid-state hardware (i.e. without disk drives).

We see systems such as MUSE as being vital in the future application of embedded AI in industrial and military situations. It is all too easy to build a very impressive system which only works on benign simulated data using a large processor. Toolkits such as MUSE are needed to enable engineers to test AI applications easily on 'dirty' data, *in situ*; and to be able to do so before going to the trouble and expense of constructing the final dedicated software and hardware that will be needed when it becomes time to deploy the application.

Acknowledgments

This work was sponsored by the Human Engineering Department of the Royal Aircraft Establishment at Farnborough, England.

28

A Blackboard Shell in PROLOG

John Jones, Mark Millington and Peter Ross

28.1 The blackboard architecture

The blackboard architecture is a problem-solving framework developed for the Hearsay-II speech recognition system (Erman and Lesser, 1975). It has since been used in a range of other domains including planning (Hayes-Roth, 1985), plan recognition (Carver *et al.*, 1984), signal and data interpretation (Engelmore and Terry, 1979; Nii *et al.*, 1982) and vision (Williams *et al.*, 1977) and considered as a general problem-solving framework (Hayes-Roth, 1983). Elsewhere (Ross *et al.*, 1985) we have proposed the blackboard architecture for user modelling in command-driven systems, where consistent subsets (see Section 28.3.4) of the blackboard form candidate user models.

The blackboard architecture allows the use of diverse, independent, potentially inaccurate sources of knowledge. In the presence of uncertainty, in the KSs and the data, a solution is found (if at all) by converging on the highest rated candidate explanation. A key feature of this convergence is the incremental emergence of 'islands' in the solution space, regions of the blackboard where a coherent part of the problem has been solved. As the problem-solving continues, these islands grow and merge to form an overall solution.

Key control aspects of this solution process are provided by an intelligent scheduling mechanism (possibly user defined). Each task on the agenda has associated with it various user-defined measures of the reliability, usefulness and correctness of the task to be performed. The scheduler uses this information to select the best task to perform at the moment by applying some criteria, typically fixed. In more sophisticated systems (Hayes-Roth, 1985), these criteria themselves are amenable to reasoning in the blackboard.

An early hope for the blackboard architecture, not yet fully realized (an initial design is described in Ensor and Gabbe (1985)) was that it could be implemented on a parallel processor. Several aspects of the basic control cycle seem amenable to parallel computation (the evaluation of conditions of KSs, for example), although there seems to be a need to maintain some serial aspects. This mix of serial and parallel processing is one of the claims for the psychological validity of the architecture. Others include its production-like nature and the overall style of reasoning. Some evidence to support these claims and further discussion of them is given in Hayes-Roth (1985).

28.2 Implementing the blackboard architecture

Our overriding design aim was that of simplicity in terms of both ease of description and ease of use. To achieve this aim we tried to keep the system very close to PROLOG and make full use of its pattern-matching facilities. Since this is an experimental tool, the question of efficiency is not considered.

28.2.1 Implementing the principal features

The principal blackboard features are implemented in the shell as follows:
 Entries are PROLOG unit clauses of the form:

```
bb(Tag,Status,Index,Fact,Cf)
```

related by an explicit support relation of unit clauses

```
supports(Supporting_Tag,Supported_Tag)
```

The components of an entry may be summarized by:

- Tag is an integer supplied by the system to uniquely identify this entry.

- Status is one of the atoms in, inout or amended and denotes the current status of this entry. The basic status is in, which is given to all entries as they are inserted into the blackboard: knowledge sources can be triggered only on in entries. The status amended is only given to user's entries that have been amended by user's rules and are to be regarded as defunct. Entries of status inout belong to the system, though all status components are created and maintained by the system.

- Index is a PROLOG term representing the 'position' of this entry in the blackboard; if the term is nonground, this entry can be regarded as occurring at all indices it matches. This component is supplied by the user and a judicious choice can provide the desired dimensional structure to the blackboard. It should be noted that at no time does the system need to be told what the possible indices are; the dimensional structure of the board is completely determined by the user's use of indices and patterns by which the entries are retrieved in the conditions of rules.

- Fact is an arbitrary PROLOG term representing the 'content' of the entry as defined by the user.

- Cf is a PROLOG term representing the 'degree of belief' in this entry. These certainty factors are definable by the user (in which case a total ordering must be supplied, usually in procedural form) though a default integer scheme is provided.

Knowledge sources are rules of the form:

```
if Condition then Body to Effect est Est
```

where:

- Condition is some test of the entries present in (or absent from) the blackboard. Tests are constructed as boolean combinations of 'atomic' tests for the presence (absence) of certain [Index,Fact,Cf] combinations. Tags, status and support relationships cannot be tested for. Further details follow in Section 28.3.

- Body is the computation, a PROLOG goal, to determine the desired effect. It is intended that the Body, Condition and Effect all share variables so that the exact conditions of this invocation are bound in the Body by the Condition before it is called, and the action of the Body is to instantiate variables present in the Effect. For example, a mechanism for calculating the certainty factor of an entry from the certainties of its supports must be supplied by the user in the Body if required.

- Effect is the intended effect of the rule to either create a new entry (Effect ='add [Index,Fact,Cf]'), amend an old one (Effect = 'amend [Index,Fact,Cf]') or call some PROLOG goal (Effect = 'action Goal').

- Est arises because during a cycle of the system there will usually be a choice of KSARs to execute: the estimate Est is used to resolve the conflict. The user may supply his or her own total ordering of estimates or adopt the integer scheme as provided by the system.

The independent event-driven nature of knowledge sources is captured in the way that they are activated solely by the scheduler on the basis of changes to the blackboard entries.

Blackboard   In this shell the blackboard does not exist as an explicit data structure *per se* but rather is defined implicitly by the user's use of indices. The system makes use of its own blackboard entries. In particular it constructs a 'shadow' board from the user's rules to record, for each index employed, which rules are interested in changes at that index. Further, the current agenda is kept in the blackboard, each KSAR being an entry of the form:

```
bb(Tag,in,agenda,ksar(body(Body,Effect,_),Evaluated_Est),sure)
```

supported by those entries from which it was constructed. Unlike the most general possible blackboard scheme (where any form of task may be on the agenda) the agenda is composed solely of KSARs; this is merely a simplification which assumes that KSARs are relatively cheap to build and could easily be changed to the more general scheme. It should be noted that because the agenda is composed of ordinary entries the consistency mechanism (see Section 28.3.3) will remove any newly invalid KSARs automatically.

Scheduler   The basic shell is equipped with a simple scheduling scheme wherein changes in the board are used in conjunction with the shadow board to create new entries on the agenda. By putting the agenda and shadow board in the blackboard we have made it possible for users to write their own 'smart' schedulers as ordinary knowledge sources which manipulate the agenda. Presumably such schemes would make use of the definability of KSAR estimates.

28.2.2 An example KS

Before going into further detail on some aspects of the shell we finish this brief description with an example KS taken from our existing application in user modelling.

We are investigating methods of modelling users of command-driven systems, in particular of UNIX (Ross *et al.*, 1985) and it seems that a blackboard architecture is an appropriate framework in which to do this. The example KS proposes corrections for typing errors and comes from the initial analysis of the most recent user's command. Other KSs have been implemented which carry out lexical, syntactic and some semantic analysis of the input.

We present the KS both in its form in the blackboard system and paraphrased in English. In indices we use the PROLOG operator / as a separator. We use a Strips-like representation for UNIX commands, including incorrect usages and commands which simply provide information to the user.

```
if      [strips/A/version(X),[pre:Errors,_,_,_,stderr:unpaged([_])],Cf>0]
    and [parse/full/A/version(X),Parse,Cf1>0]
    and [parse/partial/A/version(X),Partial_parse,Cf2>0]
    and [input/full/A/version(X),problems(_,[]),Cf3>0]
then    (do_correction(Partial_parse,Parse,Errors,Answer,Rating),
        confidence(Cf,Cf1,Cf2,Cf3,Rating,Certainty),
        Y is X+1)
to  add [input/partial/A/version(Y),Answer,Certainty]
est     25.
```

In our user modeling system we interpret this to mean:

```
if      the representation for version X of line A of the user's input produces
        an error message with preconditions Errors
    and the parse of version X of line A in terms of full UNIX path names is
        Parse
    and the parse of version X of line A in terms of the path names the user
        employed is Partial_parse
    and all the fragments of the path names in version X of line A of the user's
        input refer to existing directories
then    use Parse, Partial_parse, Errors, knowledge about the user's file store
        and UNIX commands to select the best correction for the incorrect
        element in the input with rating Rating and calculate the confidence in
        the hypothesis
to add  an entry recording version X+1 of the user's input on line A
est     and rate this KS at 25.
```

28.3 The interface between KSs and the blackboard

An important consideration in designing the shell, which has significant implications for both the user and the implementation, is the exact nature of the interface between KSs and the blackboard. Exactly what kinds of tests can a KS apply to the blackboard, and what can it propose to do to the blackboard should those tests succeed? On the whole, the blackboard literature is unhelpful on this point in that KSs are often paraphrased in English to avoid presenting code. We have made several decisions in this area, and in this section we describe them and their implications in some detail.

28.3.1 Applying conditions

In Section 28.2.1 we indicated that a KS can test for the presence or absence of entries. To test for the presence of a certain kind of entry requires the user to specify a pattern for the index, a pattern for the fact and a test to apply to the certainty of the entry (of the form `Cf < X`, `Cf > Y` or `X < Cf < Y`, where < is globally user definable or, by default, arithmetic comparison). This is achieved in a KS by the atomic test `[Index_pattern, Fact_pattern, Cf_test]`. Such a test succeeds for each entry in the blackboard that matches the patterns and has an appropriate certainty. Consideration has to be given to how a KS should interpret the success of an atomic test in its condition. Due to the nature of unification, a general test may succeed on a specific entry or a specific test on a general entry, for example. The interpretation of this is left to the user through the usual PROLOG notion of sharing variables.

There are two methods of testing for the absence of entries. A test of the form `not Atomic_test` succeeds if no entry in the blackboard passes the test. Further, the entry made by a KS applying such a test is considered to depend on this absence. If in the future such an entry appears in the blackboard, the supported entry is invalidated, and is removed (see Section 28.3.3). In effect, such a KS makes a default assumption. The second absence test is of the form `notnow Atomic_test`. The distinction between this and the previous test is that the dependency described for `not` does not apply. The motivation for this was initially pragmatic, as a means of getting data into the blackboard. However, this is a simple (if naive) way of avoiding the need for a temporal or topological logic with which to reason about such dependencies in support structures. In line with the PROLOG operator `not`, no bindings are made by any test for the absence of entries.

There is also provision to attach arbitrary PROLOG goals to the condition of a KS, for whatever purposes the user requires, in the form `holds Goal`. As far as the logic of the blackboard goes, such goals are considered to simply qualify the success of the remainder of the condition.

28.3.2 Making amendments

As observed in Section 28.2.1, a KS can add an entry or amend an entry already present. Problems posed to the system in doing these two effects and our solution will be discussed in Section 28.3.3. In this section we concentrate on a restriction placed on KSs which amend an entry.

The restriction is motivated by our interpretation of an entry being amended to mean that in the proceeding inference process the amended version should be used in preference to the original. (This touches on the notion of contexts; see Sections 28.3.3 and 28.3.4.) The problem is in determining under what conditions it is appropriate for the new entry to supplant the old entry.

In general, an atomic test succeeding selects an entry in the blackboard. When a KS proposes to make an amendment, since its condition may select several entries in the blackboard, the user must indicate which is to be amended, by prefixing the appropriate part of the condition by the symbol @. As observed in Section 28.3.1, atomic tests can match entries in a variety of ways, some of which would be problematical when making an amendment. For the purposes of illustration, we consider the particular case of a ground atomic test matching a nonground entry to be amended.

We interpret a nonground entry to embody some generality or indefiniteness in the partial solution generated so far. A ground test selects this entry simply on the basis of a particular subcase. If amendment were allowed, how could we carry it out faithfully? We would wish to exclude from further consideration the particular subcase, but leave the remainder of the nonground entry intact. Sometimes the subcase to be excluded may be entirely describable as a particular combination of bindings to variables in the nonground entry and it would be sufficient to redefine unification for that entry to exclude that combination of bindings as a success. However, typically the condition of the KS will contain other tests and arbitrary PROLOG goals which form part of the definition of the subcase so that this naive fix is inadequate.

Hence, if we are to be able to faithfully make an amendment as proposed, we must invalidate the whole entry selected. To ensure that this is a reasonable action, the test selecting the entry must embody at least the generality of the entry it selects. Fortunately, this concept is readily definable in PROLOG as subsumption. In PROLOG, a term t1 subsumes a term t2 if t1 and t2 unify without instantiating any variables in t2.

Thus, the restriction on amendments is that the test that selects an entry in the blackboard to be amended must subsume that entry.

28.3.3 Maintaining consistency

We have seen that the user may have KSs which make default assumptions or amend other entries. Both of these possibilities mean that some effort is required to extract a logically consistent solution to a problem from the blackboard. One approach is the contexts mechanism of Hearsay-III (Erman *et al.*, 1981).

Hearsay-III allows KSs that conclude entries documenting explicit choice points in the solution and KSs that make such choices. In Hearsay-III, all entries are interpreted in one of a hierarchy of 'contexts' parameterized on which such choice points have been temporarily resolved in the inference process up to that point. Further, Hearsay-III allows KSs that make such choices in two ways. One form replaces the choice entry with one of the choices creating a new context which is a subcontext of the present one. Should pursuing this choice turn out to be undesirable, reasoning returns to the parent context and a new choice can be made. The second form makes the choice permanently in the current context. In Hearsay-III the effort required to select logically consistent sets of hypotheses is expended in managing the creation of contexts.

We do not have entries which document explicit choices, but we do have KSs that make default assumptions as the basis for further reasoning. This suggests that some form of contexts mechanism may be appropriate, so that, if some other KS creates an entry that invalidates this default, consequences of these two entries could be pursued in distinct contexts. Similarly with amendments, the original entry and its amended version could be pursued in distinct contexts.

At present the blackboard system does not support contexts although we shall describe in Section 28.3.4 a scheme that introduces similar capabilities. In effect, the present system has only one context and the work required to obtain logically consistent solutions is expended in maintaining the consistency of this context. In this section we elaborate on how this is performed. This and the mechanism of Section 28.3.4 are conceptually similar to those described by McDermott (1983).

In order to clarify the presentation, we introduce some definitions. An entry c in the blackboard (written $c:c$) is said to follow from a set of justifications c, where c is defined inductively on the form of the condition of the KS which concluded c. While considering the following definition bear in mind that, if an atomic test selects an entry in the blackboard, that entry will already have a well defined set of justifications.

The simplest conditions are those that do not select an entry at all or select precisely one entry, in which case the justifications are:

condition	justifications
notnow A	{}
not A	{not(A)}
A	{A*:a}
@A	{amends(A*):a}

where A is an atomic test, A* is the entry it selected (where appropriate) and a its justifications.

For complex conditions involving conjunctions the justifications are defined as the set union of the justifications of the conjuncts. For these purposes, KSs with conditions of the form 'A and B or D' ('A and @ B or D') are rewritten as two KSs with conditions 'A and B', 'A and C' ('A and @ B', 'A and @ D').

We next introduce a nonsymmetric relation between two entries and their justifications as follows. U:u is incompatible with V:v if:

(1)   not(X) is a member of u, where V passes the atomic test X,

(2)   amends(U):u is a member of v,

(3)   there is a member W:w of u such that W:w is incompatible with V:v.

This definition of incompatibility does not preclude the possibility that an entry is incompatible with itself (because of loops in the supports relationship).

Finally, the blackboard is consistent if no pair of in entries are incompatible.

Now, maintaining the consistency of the blackboard is implemented as follows. View each cycle as the application of a KS to generate an entry to be put into the blackboard. Prior to adding the new entry, every entry that would be incompatible with it is removed from the blackboard. In the case of self-incompatibility, detected by a simple nondestructive loop check, the entry is not made.

Maintaining consistency in the present system may result in entries being removed from the blackboard. Such entries are never reinstated, although, should the user's scheduling not exclude it, such entries may possibly be reinferred. There is nothing in the blackboard achitecture which dictates this approach, so it would also be possible to use a reasoning maintenance system which 'unouted' such entries (see Brown (1985) for a formal method of defining the behavior of such systems). In blackboard systems with multiple contexts, reasoning maintenance is subsumed by the handling of contexts.

28.3.4 Implementing multiple contexts

The current consistency scheme may be simply extended to multiple contexts by defining contexts relative to the incompatibility relation as follows:

U is incompatible with V if and only if U and V are in different contexts.

This implicitly involves treating incompatibility as a symmetric relationship and would be reflected in the implementation by regarding all entries incompatible with a new entry as being in an equally good but distinct context rather than as inferior 'old' versions to be removed.

As we saw earlier the generators of incompatibility are not-tests and amendments so we will have no explicit choice entries as in the Hearsay-

III scheme. If, however, we allow the user to define a domain-specific notion of incompatibility between entries (for example by defining two entries of the same index but nonunifiable facts to be inconsistent) then a choice-points mechanism will implicitly be provided by the system. This mechanism differs from that of Hearsay-III by never adopting or retracting contexts: all contexts have equal status in the eyes of the (basic) system. If for the user's particular application it is required that some contexts be favored over others, it is up to users to reflect this in their 'intelligent' scheduling of tasks that favor the 'current' context.

A simple mechanism to implement the scheme described is to maintain the incompatibility relationship explicitly in the same way as the supports relationship. Though this means there are potentially n^2 incompatibilities between n entries we feel that in many applications the choice points are 'isolated' enough that the incompatibilities will interact very little and many fewer than n^2 will be generated. Maintaining an explicit incompatibility relation makes it easy to implement a scheme whereby KSARs can only be constructed on the basis of a set of compatible supports, i.e. entries in the same context.

Acknowledgment

The research described here is funded by SERC grant GR/C/35967.

29

Building Systems in the BB* Environment

Barbara Hayes-Roth, M. Vaughan Johnson,
Alan Garvey, Micheal Hewett

29.1 Overview of BB*

BB* is a modular and layered system-building environment comprising:
(1) a uniform knowledge representation language; (2) basic knowledge-
processing procedures; and (3) a growing hierarchy of compatible
knowledge modules developed within the BB* representation.

The BB* representation language is a conceptual network of frame-
like objects connected by semantic links (Sowa, 1984). It prescribes
fundamental distinctions among concept *types*, which intensionally define
generic concepts by means of is-a links, concept *individuals*, which
exemplify particular concept types, and concept *instances*, which instantiate particular individuals in particular symbolic contexts. It prescribes a
number of particular concept types (*actions*, *events*, *states*) and associated
linguistic templates for instantiating them.

BB* provides a variety of knowledge-processing procedures. It
provides a *knowledge base editor* for constructing and modifying
knowledge modules. It provides a *knowledge base loader* for composing
previously constructed knowledge modules in a seamless conceptual
network. It provides *knowledge access functions*, such as: retrieving
described objects or the values of their attributes; predicate evaluation;
programmable inheritance with optional caching of values; procedural
attachment; and logical relations on multiple links. It provides *interpretation procedures*, such as: parsing an instantiated pattern; matching two
patterns; quantifying the match between two patterns; generating an
instance of a pattern; and translating a pattern into a lower-level
architectural language.

Although BB* knowledge modules potentially exist on an abstraction
continuum, current modules exist at four discrete abstraction levels. At
the most general level lies the overarching BB* conceptual network. At

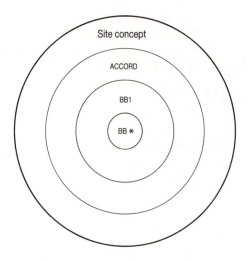

Figure 29.1   An illustrative BB∗ system: SIGHTPLAN.

the next level, *architectures* provide basic knowledge structures for representing all actions, events, states and facts in a system and a mechanism for instantiating, choosing and executing actions. For example, the BB1 architecture provides the knowledge structures and mechanism of the blackboard control architecture (see Chapter 14). At the next level, *frameworks* provide more specific knowledge structures for performing particular *tasks*. For example, the ACCORD framework provides knowledge relevant to an *arrangement-assembly task*, in which the problem solver applies an *assembly method* to solve an *arrangement problem*. At the most specific level, *applications* provide still more specific knowledge relevant for performing particular tasks in particular domains. For example, the PROTEAN and SIGHTPLAN systems require knowledge for performing the arrangement-assembly task in the domains of protein-structure modeling and construction-site layout, respectively.

Within BB∗, systems are built in a layered fashion, with application knowledge layered upon an appropriate task-specific framework, which is layered in turn upon the BB1 architecture (see Figure 29.1). Moreover, BB∗ permits *open systems integration* of modules within a level (see Figure 29.2). As a consequence, system builders can configure existing and new modules in any appropriate organizational scheme. The resulting systems are well structured, perspicuous, modifiable and extensible.

In this chapter, we illustrate the use of BB∗ (see also Hayes-Roth *et al.*, 1986b) in arrangement-assembly systems. Sections 29.2 and 29.3 discuss the arrangement-assembly task and an associated BB∗ framework: ACCORD. Section 29.4 shows how ACCORD supports reasoning for a hypothetical furniture-arrangement task. Section 29.5 discusses applica-

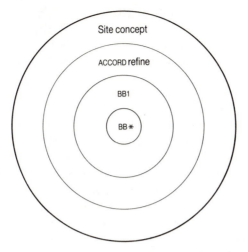

Figure 29.2   Open systems integration: an integrated system for construction-site design and planning.

tions of BB1-ACCORD, including the PROTEAN system for modeling protein structures (Buchanan *et al.*, 1985; Hayes-Roth *et al.*, 1986a) and the SIGHTPLAN system for designing construction site layouts (Tommelein *et al.*, 1987a, b). Section 29.6 summarizes the advantages of building systems within BB*.

29.2 The arrangement – assembly task

In this chapter, we focus on a class of design problems called arrangement problems, in which the problem-solver must arrange a set of objects in some context to satisfy a set of constraints. Arrangement problems occur in a variety of domains, ranging from instrument design to site layout to project planning. As these examples illustrate, arrangement domains may involve: physical, procedural or other symbolic objects; spatial, temporal or other symbolic contexts; and many different kinds of constraints.

In principle, a problem solver could use any of several different methods to solve a given arrangement problem:

(1)   *select* an arrangement that satisfies the constraints from a pre-enumerated set of alternatives;
(2)   *refine* a prototypical arrangement so as to satisfy the constraints;
(3)   *modify* an almost-correct arrangement to satisfy the constraints;
(4)   *generate* a complete arrangement that satisfies the constraints;
(5)   *construct* an arrangement that satisfies the constraints.

In practice, however, the problem solver may not have the knowledge necessary to apply particular methods to particular problems. For example, a problem solver cannot apply the selection, refinement, modification or refinement methods unless it has knowledge of alternative arrangements, a prototypical arrangement, several almost-correct arrangements, or an algorithm for generating complete arrangements.

In the absence of such special knowledge, the problem solver must construct an arrangement. In particular, we have developed an assembly method by which the problem solver incrementally constructs and refines partial arrangements and recursively combines them with one another to construct a complete arrangement. Unlike the other methods discussed above, the assembly method can be applied to any arrangement problem. We refer to any task in which the assembly method is applied to arrangement problems as an arrangement-assembly task.

A problem solver begins to assemble an arrangement by defining one or more *partial arrangements*. Each partial arrangement comprises a subset of the objects and constraints specified in a problem and a subregion of the specified context. One object within the partial arrangement occupies an arbitrary fixed position and defines the local context. All other objects are positioned relative to that one.

The problem solver positions objects within the partial arrangement by applying constraints between them. In so doing, it determines the region in which one object can lie, given: (1) its current hypothesized position; (2) its constraints with the other object; and (3) the current hypothesized position of the other object. The problem solver may use different application-specific procedures for applying constraints and identifying associated legal positions. Later, the problem solver applies constraints to position partial arrangements, relative to one another.

For problems involving a large number of objects, the problem solver may reason at multiple levels of abstraction. By reasoning at a high level of abstraction first, it can reduce the number of positions it must consider for constituent objects at a lower level of abstraction. Conversely, it can use the details of reasoning at a low level of abstraction to restrict the positions it hypothesizes at a higher level of abstraction.

Because arrangement assembly entails a combinatoric space of potential arrangements and the process of applying constraints to search that space is computationally expensive, intelligent control is a key feature of successful problem solving. The problem solver must reason about: how to group objects in partial arrangements; which object to fix in the local context; when to apply particular constraints between particular objects; when to refine partial arrangements at different levels of abstraction; and when to combine related partial arrangements. This reasoning must incorporate general computational principles, such as: reasoning about objects that have many constraints to many other objects; positioning objects relative to those that have been positioned reliably; and preferring constraints that maximally restrict an object's position. It must also incorporate domain-specific knowledge such as defining the space of potentially useful constraints and characterizing the constraining power of different constraints. It may also incorporate knowledge about the particular constraint-satisfaction algorithms being used; for example, that positioning an object relative to a fixed object is computationally less expensive than positioning an object relative to an object whose position is uncertain. Since we know of no optimal general-purpose strategy for assembling arrangements, the problem solver must have strategic flexibility and capabilities for learning and evaluating new control strategies.

29.3 ACCORD: a framework for arrangement – assembly systems

We have formalized the domain-independent knowledge underlying performance of the arrangement-assembly task in a BB* knowledge base called ACCORD. ACCORD provides a framework for building arrangement-assembly systems in particular domains and for empowering those systems to control, explain and learn about their own actions more effectively than they could otherwise. The following sections describe the different kinds of knowledge embodied in ACCORD.

29.3.1 Skeletal concept network

ACCORD provides a domain-independent skeletal concept network (illustrated in Figure 29.3) in which to represent the domain-specific knowledge needed to instantiate actions, events and states for arrangement-assembly problems.

The network distinguishes between concept *types* (including both *natural* types and *role* types), *individuals* that exemplify particular types, and *instances* of particular individuals in particular contexts. Associated relational links indicate that: (1) an instance *instantiates* an individual or *plays* a role; (2) an individual *exemplifies* a type; and (3) a type *is-a* super-type. These distinctions correspond roughly to the distinctions among the generic concepts of a domain, the specific objects involved in a particular problem, and instances of those objects involved in a particular hypothetical solution to the problem. For example, in the domain of furniture arrangement table is-a piece-of-furniture; table-1 is an individual table involved in a particular problem; table-1-1 instantiates table-1 in the context of partial arrangement pa1; and table-1-1 plays the role of anchor in partial arrangement pa1. An implicit $is-a relation holds between any two concepts related by a chain of instantiates, exemplifies, and is-a links.

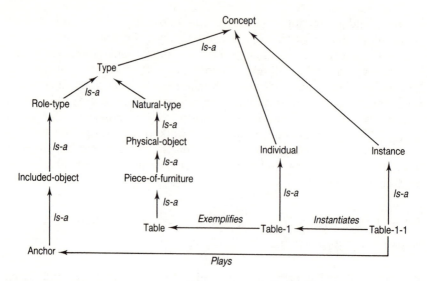

Figure 29.3 Illustrative excerpt from ACCORD's conceptual network.

Thus, for example, table-1-1 $is-a piece-of-furniture. Similarly, an implicit $includes relation holds between any two concepts related by a chain of instantiates, exemplifies, is-a and includes links. Similarly, an implicit $plays relation holds between any two concepts related by a chain of exemplified-by, instantiated-by, and plays links.

The natural-type hierarchy has major branches representing concept types that figure in arrangement problems – object, constraint and context. For example, table is-a piece-of-furniture and piece-of-furniture is-a physical-object. The framework acknowledges the possibility that arrangement problems in other domains might involve different subtypes of objects, constraints and contexts, for example procedural-objects. In addition, natural types may have part–whole relations whereby one concept type *includes* another concept type. For example, table-and-chairs includes table.

Concepts in the network may have attributes whose values are static (e.g. table-1 has the attribute height, whose value is 36 inches) or procedural (e.g. table has the attribute long, whose value is a rating, on a scale 0–100, that is proportional to its length). They can inherit these attributes along connecting links.

29.3.2 A vocabulary of partial arrangements

ACCORD provides a vocabulary to describe the elements of partial arrangements and the relationships among them. A partial arrangement (or pa) includes a number of included-objects. One of these, the anchor,

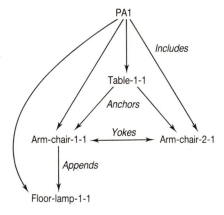

Figure 29.4   Illustrative partial arrangement.

has a fixed position and defines the local context. Objects that have constraints with the anchor are anchorees. Applying such constraints to position anchorees creates corresponding anchors links between those objects. Objects that have constraints with anchorees are appendages. Applying constraints between those objects creates appends links. Applying constraints between anchorees and appendages to further restrict their positions creates yokes links between them. Each included object has a position attribute that specifies its legal position in the context, given the constraints that have been applied at any point in time. Figure 29.4 shows an illustrative partial arrangement in the domain of furniture arrangement.

29.3.3 Types of actions, events and states

ACCORD provides a type hierarchy that intensionally defines the actions, events and states involved in arrangement assembly by means of is-a relations (see Figure 29.5). It also specifies the actions, events and states that certain other ones *entail*. For brevity, we describe this knowledge for actions only. The knowledge for events and states closely parallels the action knowledge.

ACCORD provides a type hierarchy of arrangement-assembly actions. The top-level action type, Assemble, means 'solve an arrangement problem by means of the assembly method'. Assemble has four subtypes. Define means 'construct a partial arrangement that includes particular objects in particular roles'. Position means 'identify the positions in which particular objects can lie within a particular partial arrangement while satisfying particular constraints'. Coordinate means 'identify the positions in which particular objects can lie within a partial

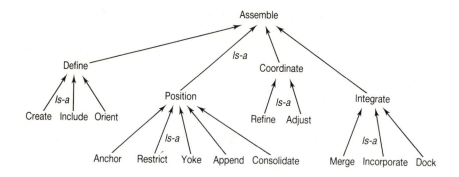

Figure 29.5   The type hierarchy of arrangement-assembly actions.

arrangement while satisfying their part–whole relations with previously positioned superordinate or subordinate objects'. Integrate means 'combine two partial arrangements to form a single, larger partial arrangement'.

Each of the four main action types – define, position, coordinate and integrate – has two or more subordinate subtypes. These terminal action types are the only executable action types in the hierarchy.

Define has three subtypes. Create means 'record a blackboard object representing a new partial arrangement'. Include means 'create instances of particular objects or constraints within a particular partial arrangement'. Orient means 'declare that a particular object in a partial arrangement is the anchor and assign the roles anchoree and appendage to other included objects depending upon whether or not they have constraints with the anchor'.

Position has five subtypes. Anchor means 'identify the position in which an anchoree satisfies particular constraints with the anchor'. Append means 'identify the position in which an appendage satisfies constraints with an anchoree or appendage that has already been positioned'. Yoke means 'prune the positions of two included-objects that have already been positioned so that they include only locations in which the two objects satisfy constraints with one another'. Restrict means 'prune the position identified for an anchoree or appendage to include only those that satisfy additional constraints'. Consolidate means 'prune the positions of three or more objects to include only those that satisfy all constraints among the objects simultaneously'.

Coordinate has two subtypes. Refine means 'identify positions for a previously positioned object's constituent objects so as to satisfy their part–whole relationship'. Adjust means 'identify an object's position to satisfy its part–whole relationship with a previously positioned constituent object'.

Integrate has three subtypes. Merge means 'combine two partial arrangements that have the same anchor'. Incorporate means 'combine two partial arrangements that include anchorees or appendages'. Dock means 'combine two partial arrangements that have no common objects, but include objects that constrain one another'.

Each action type in the hierarchy can *entail* other action types. For example, the anchor action entails the generate action, which means 'generate a family for an included-object'. Similarly, the position action entails the apply action, which means 'apply a constraint to an included-object within a partial arrangement'. Given the inheritance properties of the type hierarchy, every specific type of position action (e.g. anchor, yoke, append) also entails the apply action.

As mentioned above, the type hierarchies for events and states parallel the type hierarachy for actions. They are distinguished by the tenses of the keywords. Thus, the anchor action corresponds to the did-anchor event and the is-anchored state. Similarly, the did-anchor event entails the did-generate event and the is-anchored state entails the is-generated state. In addition, other state types indicate that objects have particular attributes and that objects have particular relations. Given these additional implicit state types and the many possible realizations of them, the number of actual state types in an application greatly exceeds the number of action and event types.

ACCORD also specifies several types of relations among particular types of actions, events and states. Events of a particular type can *trigger* an action of a particular type; that is, they can indicate that an instance of the action may be feasible in a particular problem-solving context. For example, did-generate events trigger yoke actions. States of a particular type can *enable* triggered actions of a certain type; that is, they can ensure that the triggered actions are feasible. For example, has-family states enable triggered yoke actions. Actions of a particular type can *cause* events of a particular type. For example, yoke actions cause did-yoke events. Finally, events of a particular type can *promote* states of a particular-type. For example, did-yoke events promote is-fixed states.

29.3.4 Interpretable representations of actions, events and states

ACCORD provides parameterized templates for instantiating particular action, event and state types. Each template comprises a *keyword*, followed by a specified sequence of *formal parameters*, interspersed with optional *conjunctions*. Particular actions, events, or states are represented as *patterns* that instantiate the formal parameters of the corresponding templates with concepts from a particular domain. Each keyword and formal parameters value in a pattern may be preceded by any number of *modifiers* and followed by a local variable name in parenthesis. For brevity, we discuss this knowledge for actions only. The knowledge for events and states closely parallels the action knowledge.

For example, the anchor-action template is:

Anchor anchoree to anchor in pa with constraint.

Here, the action keyword, anchor, is followed by the sequence of formal parameters: anchoree, anchor, pa (partial arrangement), constraint, with some parameters preceded by the declared noise words: to, in, with. A furniture-arrangement system might instantiate the anchor template as:

Anchor arm-chair-1-1 to table-1-1 in pa1 with neighbor-constraint-6.

It might represent a larger class of actions with this pattern:

Anchor chair to table in pa1 with constraint.

As mentioned above, the templates for events and states parallel the type hierarchy for actions. They are distinguished by the tenses of the keywords. Thus, the did-anchor event template is:

Did-Anchor anchoree to anchor in pa with constraint.

The is-anchored state template is:

Is-Anchored anchoree to anchor in pa with constraint.

They are instantiated as illustrated above for the anchor action template.

29.3.5 Partial match knowledge

ACCORD defines the potential partial matches among different types of actions, events and states by identifying *semantic correspondences* among the formal parameters of their templates. Here are some examples of semantic correspondences from the templates of the arrangement-assembly framework: (1) formal parameters representing objects to be positioned in an action; (2) formal parameters representing the partial arrangement in which an event occurs; and (3) formal parameters representing constraints that have been applied in a state. Sometimes it is convenient to refer to corresponding formal parameters with the same name in all templates. For example, it is convenient always to refer to the partial arrangement as pa. In other cases, there is no universally appropriate name. For example, different templates refer to objects to be positioned as anchorees, appendages or included-objects, reflecting distinctive restrictions on the legal values of those parameters. In addition, there can be one-to-many or many-to-one correspondences among parameters in particular templates. For example, the anchor action template contains one parameter representing an object to be positioned, while the yoke action template contains two corresponding parameters. For these reasons, a framework explicitly declares the partial matches among templates.

Consider, for example, the position and anchor templates:

Position included-object in pa with constraint.
Anchor anchoree to anchor in pa with constraint.

By definition, the two action keywords, position and anchor, correspond. The formal parameters, included-object and anchoree, correspond because they both represent objects being positioned. The two formal parameters called pa correspond because they both represent the partial arrangement in which the actions occur. The two formal parameters called constraints correspond because they both represent constraints that the actions apply. The anchor template's formal parameter called anchor does not correspond to anything in the position template because the position template does not specify the object that lies at the center of the designated local coordinate system.

Given the partial matches among templates, a system can assess the partial matches among instantiated patterns. For example, the pattern:

Anchor arm-chair-1-1 to table-1-1 in pa1 with neighbor-constraint-6.

perfectly matches the pattern:

Anchor chair to table in pa1 with constraint.

because armchair-1-1 is a chair, table-1-1 is a table, pa1 is pa1, and neighbor-constraint-6 is a constraint. The pattern:

Anchor arm-chair-1-1 to table-1-1 in pa1 with neighbor-constraint-6.

partially matches the pattern:

Position important piece-of-furniture in pa1 with constraint.

because anchor is a position action, arm-chair-1-1 is a moderately important piece of furniture, pa1 is pa1 and neighbor-constraint-6 is a constraint.

29.3.6 Architectural translations of framework knowledge structures

Since ACCORD exists in the context of the BB1 architecture, it provides the information needed for translation of its knowledge structures into BB1 knowledge structures and vice versa. Specifically, it provides a parameterized BB1 template for each terminal action, event and state type in the type hierarchy. Like ACCORD templates, these BB1 templates can be instantiated as particular patterns by having their parameters instantiated. Since ACCORD and BB1 templates for a given occurrence type refer to the same formal parameters, any terminal ACCORD pattern can be translated into the corresponding BB1 pattern, or vice versa, by a variable-substitution procedure. Nonterminal patterns can be translated by combining this procedure with procedures for inferring nonterminal patterns from terminal patterns.

29.3.7 Implementation of ACCORD in BB1

ACCORD is implemented as a modular knowledge base within the context of the BB1 architecture. BB1 has the following procedures for operating on the knowledge in ACCORD:

The BB1 *matcher assesses whether a test pattern* matches a *target pattern*. Using the partial matches between templates, it identifies each parameter in the test pattern that corresponds to some parameter in the target pattern. The matcher declares a match for each such parameter in the test pattern whose value has a $is-a, $includes or $plays relation with the value of the corresponding parameter in the target pattern. A *perfect match* is one in which all corresponding parameter values in the two patterns match.

The BB1 *quantifier* records a numerical assessment of the match between each parameter value in a test pattern and: (1) its corresponding parameter value in a target pattern; and (2) each modifier of the corresponding parameter value in the target pattern. It records 0 for each nonmatching parameter value and 100 for each matching parameter. For nonmatching parameters, the quantifier also records 0 for each modifier of the parameter value in the target pattern. For matching parameter values, it records for each modifier a number between 0 and 100, which it determines by evaluating the procedural attachment of the modifier for the matching parameter value in the test pattern. A *perfect quantified match* is one in which the test pattern receives a value of 100 for all matching parameters and their associated modifiers.

The BB1 *generator* uses information in the knowledge base to generate instances of a parameter pattern class. If more than one instance is requested, it generates them 'best first', according to their quantified matches to the pattern class.

The BB1 *translator* uses the framework and BB1 templates specified for each terminal occurrence type and a variable-substitution procedure to translate framework and BB1 patterns for terminal occurrence types into one another.

29.4 Reasoning within a framework

Building an arrangement-assembly system for a particular domain consists of:

(1)   instantiating the skeletal concept network in the domain of interest;

(2)   instantiating particular combinations of occurrence patterns as domain knowledge sources; and

(3)   instantiating particular combinations of occurrence patterns as control knowledge sources.

Given these components, the application system is prepared to perform the actions necessary to solve the class of problems addressed in the domain of interest and to control, explain and learn about its problem-solving actions.

For example, one knowledge source in the domain of furniture arrangement might specify:

```
Trigger:       Did-restrict piece-of-furniture (that-piece) in any-pa (the pa).
Context:       For partner in:
                   Includes the-pa partner.
               For constraint in:
                   Involves constraint that-piece.
                   Involves constraint partner.
Precondition:  Is-positioned partner.
Action:        Yoke that-piece with partner in the-pa with constraint.
```

This knowledge source specifies that whenever a piece of furniture has its position restricted, it *can* be yoked to each other piece of furniture in the same partial arrangement that has already been positioned and has constraints with it. Whenever the knowledge source's trigger is satisfied, it places a uniquely instantiated yoke action on the agenda, as in:

```
Yoke chair-1-1 with chair-2-1 in pa1 with neighbor-constraint-8.
```

BB1 chooses one such action from the agenda on each problem-solving cycle.

Control knowledge sources cooperate to develop a dynamic control plan to guide the scheduling of actions on the agenda. For example one control knowledge source might post the following decision:

Position important piece-of-furniture in pa1 with constraint.

indicating that the system *should* perform actions that position important pieces of furniture in partial arrangement pa1 with whatever constraints are available. BB1 uses such heuristics to decide which action to choose from the agenda on each problem-solving cycle. In this case, it might choose the above yoking action because: (1) Yoke is a position action; (2) chair-1-1 and chair-2-1 are moderately important; (3) pa1 is pa1; and (4) neighbor-constraint-8 is a constraint. After executing all of the pending actions that rate highly against this focus, the system might execute control knowledge source and post this decision:

Position highly-constrained piece-of-furniture in pa1 with constraint.

indicating that the system *should* perform actions that position any remaining pieces of furniture that are highly constrained within the current partial arrangement. Now the system would use this new heuristic to choose actions from the agenda.

Similarly, BB1 also uses its explicit control plan to explain its decisions to perform particular actions and to perform a variety of learning functions.

29.5 Applications of BB1-ACCORD

In collaboration with colleagues here at Stanford, we have used BB1/ACCORD to develop two application systems: the PROTEAN system for protein-structure modeling and the SIGHTPLAN system for designing construction-site layouts. Each application is described briefly below.

29.5.1 PROTEAN: protein-structure modeling

PROTEAN's task is to identify the three-dimensional conformations of proteins. It begins with knowledge of a test protein's primary and secondary structures, along with a variety of local and global constraints. The test protein's primary structure is its defining sequence of amino acids. In addition, PROTEAN knows the atomic architecture of each individal amino acid. The protein's secondary structure is the sequence of higher-order subunits (e.g. α-helices, β-sheets and random coils) defined by the pattern of turns in its primary structure. PROTEAN may also know about a number of constraints on the test protein's conformation. For example, it may know about 50–60 NOEs (nuclear Overhauser effects), each of which indicates that two particular atoms in the protein are within 3–10 Å of one another. PROTEAN may know that certain atoms are accessible to solvent, indicating that they lie near the molecular surface of the protein. It may have knowledge of the overall size, shape and density of the protein molecule. Based on these different kinds of knowledge, PROTEAN must identify the test protein's tertiary structure – the folding of its primary and secondary structure in three-dimensional space. Moreover, given that the tertiary structure is underconstrained, PROTEAN must identify the entire family of such structures consistent with the available constraints.

The current PROTEAN system has approximately eight domain knowledge sources and 20 control knowledge sources. The domain knowledge sources rely upon a geometric constraint satisfaction system that performs an exhaustive generate-and-test of the solution space at a specified level of abstraction. PROTEAN follows a simple strategy: (1) define a single partial arrangement anchored by the largest, most constraining, most rigid secondary structure in the test protein; (2) position all other secondary structures relative to the anchor, giving preference to: anchor and yoke actions; large, constrained, constraining, rigid anchorees and appendages; and strong constraints. PROTEAN has been used to model proteins containing between seven and fifteen secondary structures. We are currently exploring more powerful control knowledge sources to enable PROTEAN to combat the combinatorics entailed in larger proteins. (See Buchanan *et al.* (1985) and Chapter 20 for a more detailed description of the protein-modeling problem and the PROTEAN system.)

29.5.2 SIGHTPLAN: designing construction-site layouts

SIGHTPLAN must arrange pieces of construction equipment (e.g. cranes and trailers) and construction areas (e.g. access roads and lay-down areas) in a two-dimensional construction site to satisfy a variety of constraints. Part–whole relations exist among some of these objects (e.g. the employee-facilities include some trailers and a rest area). Part–whole relations also exist among subregions of the construction site (e.g. the building zone includes the building site and all of its borders). Available constraints include object-based constraints (e.g. the rest area must be within a short distance of the trailers) and context-based constraints (e.g. the access road must intersect the perimeter of the construction site on two sides). Finally, since construction projects proceed in identifiable stages, the layout design must include sub-layouts for different stages. Further, there are transitional constraints between the stages (e.g. the crane must move from the north-west corner of the building site to the south-east corner of the building site between stages 1 and 2).

The current SIGHTPLAN implementation parallels the PROTEAN implementation. Its knowledge sources are nearly identical, except for the substitution of construction-related terms in SIGHTPLAN for the biochemistry terms in PROTEAN. However, its underlying constraint-satisfaction system is much simpler, relying upon a two-dimensional grid to perform analog analyses of objects and contextual positions. We also anticipate that SIGHTPLAN's mature strategies will differ from PROTEAN's for two reasons: (1) the combinatorics of SIGHTPLAN's problem are much smaller; and (2) while PROTEAN must identify all legal arrangements, SIGHTPLAN must identify only a few satisfactory arrangements. (See Tommelein *et al.*, 1978a for a more detailed description of SIGHTPLAN.)

29.5.3 Other applications

We are currently exploring ACCORD's applicability to domains involving other kinds of objects and other kinds of contexts.

For example, we believe that ACCORD applies to tasks involving the arrangement of procedural objects in a temporal context. Consider the task of travel planning: arrange a set of destinations in a designated time interval. We can define each destination as a temporal-object in the ACCORD knowledge base and the time interval as a context. We can define part–whole relationships among sets of destinations (e.g. the India destination includes destinations in Kashmir, Rajasthan, Benares and Darjeeling). We can define part–whole relationships among subintervals of the designated time interval (e.g. the spring interval includes May and June). We can define object-based constraints on the relative times targetted for particular destinations (e.g. go to India after Japan). We can define context-based constraints on the absolute times targetted for particular destinations (e.g. go to Japan in time for the cherry blossoms). Given this representation of the knowledge, we probably could use the ACCORD actions to develop partial itineraries, to order destinations within partial itineraries, to refine high-level destinations into more detailed itineraries for their constituent destinations, and to integrate different partial itineraries to form a complete itinerary. We are exploring applications of BB1-ACCORD involving procedural objects in temporal contexts in order to gain empirical evidence of its applicability to this important subclass of arrangement problems.

Expanding the potential scope of ACCORD even further, it may be possible to apply it to tasks involving the arrangement of general symbolic objects in general symbolic contexts. In particular, it may apply to objects and contexts that are not metric in character. Consider a simplified project-management task: assign a set of project tasks among a designated set of individuals. We can define each task as a task-object in the ACCORD knowledge base and the set of individuals as a context. We can define part–whole relationships among task groups (e.g. the task of designing knowledge sources includes tasks for designing domain knowledge sources and designing control knowledge sources). We can define part–whole relationships among subsets of the individuals (e.g. the expert C programmers are Jim, Craig and Bruce). We can define object-based constraints between different tasks (e.g. the tasks of defining domain and control action languages must be performed by the same individual). We can define context-based constraints on the assignments of particular tasks to individuals (e.g. the geometry system must be implemented by expert C programmers). Given this representation, we might be able to use the ACCORD actions to develop partial project plans, to assign tasks to individuals within partial plans, to refine the assignment of high-level tasks into assignments of their component tasks, and to integrate different partial plans to form a complete project plan.

Of course, most project planning tasks also have a temporal dimension with associated constraints. Assuming that ACCORD applies to tasks involving the arrangement of procedural objects in a temporal context, it might be possible to apply it to the complete project-planning task: assign a set of project tasks to a designated set of individuals for completion at particular times.

29.6 Advantages of building systems in BB*

BB* offers the generally recognized advantages of *modular and layered design* (Goos and Hartmanis, 1981; Green, 1982; Tanenbaum, 1981). First, each abstraction level offers computational services to higher levels, while protecting them from implementation details. Second, people can understand complex systems in terms of their components. Third, modules at one level can be tested and modified independently of modules at other levels. Fourth, we can eliminate unnecessary levels as appropriate. Fifth, levels can produce efficiency improvements. Sixth, high-level knowledge can be shared among several applications.

In addition, BB* has the advantages of open systems integration. First, we can define new systems by reconfiguring modules within a level. Second, we can eliminate redundancy among modules. Third, we can integrate the computations of modules. Fourth, we can apply architectural capabilities for control, explanation and learning on any configuration of modules.

Finally, BB* offers specific advantages for systems that reason about action. First and most important, BB* supports control reasoning. It provides a concise, perspicuous, uniform, modular, interpretable representation for control knowledge sources, KSARs, events and decisions. It provides powerful framework-interpretation procedures for all operations performed on these structures. It explicitly and unambiguously articulates task-specific control parameters and the relationships between them, thereby enforcing a semantically correct mapping between the attributes of potential actions and operative control plans. Second, BB* supports explanation. Its explicit control plans provide databases from which to construct explanations. Its frameworks provide a uniform language of machine-interpretable control reasoning and human-interpretable explanations. Third, BB* supports learning. It limits the number of action parameters a learning system must consider and enforces correct semantics interpretations of those parameters. It provides a natural English-like language for analyzing control decisions, actions and results and for programming new control knowledge.

In sum, BB* is a layered computing environment. BB1 is a general-purpose virtual computer for systems that reason about action. Frameworks such as ACCORD provide the power of higher-level programming languages. Applications such as PROTEAN are specific programs written in either the machine language of BB1 or the higher-level language of an appropriate framework. Like conventional computing environments, BB* is designed to help system builders write better programs more easily. BB* differs from conventional computing environments in its orientation toward intelligent systems: programs that solve problems and reason about their own problem-solving behavior.

Acknowledgments

The PROTEAN project is directed by Bruce Buchanan and Oleg Jardetzky. Other project staff include Barbara Hayes-Roth, Olivier Lichtarge, Micheal Hewett, Russ Altman, James Brinkley, Craig Cornelius, Bruce Duncan, Alan Garvey and John Brugge.

Ray Levitt and Iris Tommelein are the SIGHTPLAN project director and principal designer, respectively. Vaughan Johnson and Barbara Hayes-Roth collaborated on the development of the current SIGHTPLAN prototype.

The research was supported by the following grants: NIH Grant RR-00785, NIH Grant RR-00711, NSF Grant MSM-86-13126, NASA/Ames Grant NCC 2-274, Boeing Grant W266875, DARPA Contract N00039-83-C-0136. We thank Jeff Harvey, Bob Schulman, Reed Hastings and Craig Cornelius for their work on BB1 and BB*. We thank Bruce Buchanan and Ed Feigenbaum for sponsoring the work within the Knowledge Systems Laboratory.

30

Conclusion

R.S. Engelmore and A.J. Morgan

In this chapter we attempt to pull together some of the strands which have emerged in the preceding parts, to generalize some of the concepts, and to identify some of the current trends.

We can first summarize the style of problem solving which has recurred throughout the systems described in this book. The basic approach is to divide the problem into loosely coupled subtasks. These subtasks roughly correspond to areas of specialization within the task (for example, there are human subspecialists for the subtasks). For a particular application, the designer defines a solution space and the knowledge needed to find the solution. The solution space is divided into regions (e.g. levels within the blackboard) containing partial or intermediate solutions. These regions are generally designed to hold data needed by or produced by the subtasks; thus there are syllable and word levels in Hearsay-II because there are procedures for inferring words from syllables, or generating syllables from words. The knowledge is divided into specialized knowledge sources that perform the subtasks. The information in each region is globally accessible on the blackboard, making it a medium of interaction between the knowledge sources. Generally, a knowledge source receives information from one region as its input and sends output information to another region. The decision to employ a particular knowledge source is made dynamically using the current solution state (the latest information contained in the blackboard structure). This particular approach to problem decomposition and knowledge application is very flexible and works well in diverse application domains. One caveat, however: how the problem is partitioned into subproblems makes a great deal of difference to the clarity of the approach, the speed with which the solutions are found, the resources required, and even the ability to solve the problem at all.

30.1 Why use a blackboard framework?

A blackboard framework is only one of several possible alternatives for automatic problem solving. For example, over the last ten years we have seen widespread use of expert system shells based on the MYCIN model. We believe that there are several reasons why a blackboard framework may be preferred to other alternatives:

(1) *Modularity*   Because the architecture is inherently modular (knowledge sources, blackboard levels, control structures, . . .) the design, testing and maintenance of the system can be eased.

(2) *Dynamic control*   The architecture provides a wide range of capabilities for controlling the problem-solving behavior of the system.

(3) *Efficiency*   Careful design of system modules and a control policy that selects the most efficacious knowledge to apply and/or focuses effort on the most profitable regions of the blackboard can give considerable gains in efficiency over, say, a straightforward production system.

(4) *Concurrency*   It is conjectured that the modularity and flexible control structure of blackboard systems may allow different parts of a problem to be processed in parallel.

Of course, these are capabilities rather than features of a framework. The implementer has the responsibility of translating the potential advantages into reality for any particular problem-solving system.

30.2 What kinds of applications are appropriate?

Looking through a list of blackboard applications, one cannot help being struck by the similarities among the problems tackled. There appears to be a range of problem attributes which point to a blackboard solution as being particularly appropriate, and within a specific blackboard application problem (such as signal processing) we can find one or more of the following attributes:

(1) *Many specialized and distinct kinds of knowledge*   The modular knowledge source structure allows the incorporation and integration of varied knowledge types and structures in a fairly straightforward way.

(2) *Integration of disparate information*   The blackboard provides an organizational framework to hold information of fundamentally different 'kinds'; for example, raw time-stamped data from sensors

may appear at a low level and a representation of an abstract concept at a high level within the same blackboard.

(3) *A natural domain hierarchy (or hierarchies)* A key step in the implementation of a blackboard problem-solving system is the recognition of a hierarchical representation of domain concepts. The more obvious and natural the hierarchical representation, the more attractive the blackboard approach becomes.

(4) *Continuous data problems* Many problems, such as those typically addressed by the MYCIN model, produce an end-solution (for example, a diagnosis of an illness based on observations of symptoms). In the MYCIN model, there is no notion of an intermediate result. Blackboard systems, on the other hand, are characterized by building solutions incrementally. Thus, there is always a current best hypothesis. Such a model is particularly appropriate for continuous data problems, where there is no final answer – the system continually tracks input data and (typically) synthesizes an interpretation of the data. The control capabilities of a blackboard framework (for example, the ability to determine when and how to 'forget' outdated information) are also appropriate for such problems.

(5) *Applications with sparse knowledge/data* In cases where uncertain knowledge or limited available data make absolute determination of a solution impossible, the incremental problem solving nature of blackboard systems will still allow progress to be made; for example, by maintaining logically consistent alternative partial solutions on the blackboard.

30.3 Degrees of freedom

Although we have been able to provide only a sampling of the available blackboard literature within the confines of this book, the preceding chapters show a wide diversity of features within the blackboard model. At this point it is worth briefly reviewing some of the alternatives, or 'degrees of freedom', facing the designer of a blackboard system.

30.3.1 The blackboard

(1) *Single or multiple blackboard panels* CRYSALIS and OPM pioneered the use of multiple domain panels, and BB1 has emphasized the use of a separate panel for control of the blackboard.

(2) *Global or dispersed blackboard* In some recent work (such as MUSE) we have seen facilities for partitioning the system's data

storage into regions that are only accessible to a subset of the knowledge sources.

(3) *Single or competing blackboard entries*   The concept of maintaining on the blackboard alternative entries which are competitors (i.e. mutually exclusive) was pioneered in Hearsay-II. Subsequent systems have paid less attention to this aspect, although recent research into Truth Maintenance Systems is likely to become incorporated into future blackboard work.

30.3.2 Knowledge sources

(1) *Homogeneous or heterogeneous knowledge source structure*   In principle, each knowledge source in a system could have a totally individual internal structure, provided that each knowledge source adheres to the common blackboard access protocol. Whereas Hearsay-II used procedures to implement knowledge sources, subsequent systems (e.g. CRYSALIS) have commonly used knowledge sources based on IF–THEN rules. BB1 and AGE permit both rule-based and procedure-based knowledge sources.

(2) *Organization of rules*   In most systems with rule-based knowledge sources the 'condition' and 'action' parts of the knowledge source are a single unit, whereas in some systems, such as Hearsay-II, the condition and action parts of a knowledge source are treated (and scheduled) as separate entities.

(3) *Knowledge source condition structure*   No matter what representation is used, knowledge sources generally contain a set of conditions that must be satisfied before they are executable; but the form of this test (procedures, rules, . . .) and possible ancillary functions (preconditions, local variable bindings, . . .) vary greatly.

30.3.3 Control

(1) *Knowledge-based or blackboard-based scheduling*   The two extremes in controlling the problem-solving behavior of the system are to choose which knowledge source to actuate next, or to choose an area of the blackboard on which to work next.

(2) *Control program flexibility*   The systems described in this book have ranged from those that integrate the control procedures directly into the framework to systems like BB1 in which control has become an expert system in its own right.

(3) *Triggering methods*   Various schemes for selecting knowledge sources must balance the computational cost of optimizing the

selection against the cost of unnecessary computations in irrelevant knowledge sources. Triggering methods can range from very simple, context-independent criteria, such as are used in AGE-based systems, to very sophisticated, multilevel control decisions as in BB1-based systems.

30.3.4 System philosophy

(1) *The goals of the system* The systems discussed in this book show great variation partly because they were designed to meet different goals, such as: solve specific problems (see Parts I and IV), investigate concurrency (CAGE/POLIGON), support knowledge engineering (AGE), experiment with control aspects (BB1), solve real-time problems (MXA), support simulation (BLOBS), and so on.

(2) *Efficient operational or additional development features* To some extent there is a trade-off between the efficiency of the system in solving a problem and the provision of additional features to aid development work (which may slow down system operation). Systems such as GBB and MUSE place emphasis on operational efficiency, as compared with, say, BB1 and BLOBS which are primarily concerned with supporting experimental work.

(3) *Alternative approaches* It is rare for a requirement to point unambiguously toward a specific solution. There are normally several possibilities which the designer must identify and evaluate – possibly to the extent of building throw-away prototypes. See, for example, the discussions on the alternatives considered during the design of the Hearsay-II and HASP systems (Chapters 4 and 6). Every blackboard framework imposes some degree of structure on the organization of the problem-solving process, ranging from the highly structured database-management style of GBB to the relatively unstructured approach of EPBS which leaves organization of rules and blackboard structure largely to the user.

30.3.5 System interfaces

(1) *External interfaces* The external interfaces to the system may vary in number and location. For example, the system may operate from low-level data fed only into the least abstract level of the blackboard (as in Hearsay-II) or may have external information fed into multiple levels (for example, low-level sensor data and high-level intelligence reports in HASP). It is worth noting here that the blackboard architecture is well suited to applications that use

multiple types of data, since all can be treated uniformly as 'events'.

(2) *User interfaces*   Two relevant dimensions here are presentation and emphasis. In common with other areas of computing the last few years have seen a shift toward a more graphical presentation compared with earlier examples. Compare, for example, the original AGE system in Chapter 12 with the TRICERO system (which was based on AGE) in Chapter 19. Designers of different systems can also emphasize different aspects. Roughly speaking, a development which is driven as an application (such as the ARE Data Fusion system) will be oriented toward the results of computations, much more than a system which is primarily a generalization (BB1, for example), which will place more emphasis on the display and control of the system's problem-solving behavior.

30.3.6 Auxiliary data structures

In addition to the major hypothesis structures (which are universally located on the blackboard), there can also be a need for storage of other items, such as intermediate results, focus of control information, and derived data structures. There is some degree of tradeoff between run-time efficiency (for example, the 'private' data held within KSs in Hearsay-II – see McCracken, 1979), and ease of development, which we have seen in the increased use of the blackboard as the only data structure in BB∗.

30.4 Current perspectives

We have seen evidence in the preceding chapters that some classes of complex problems become manageable when they are formulated along the lines of the blackboard model. Moreover, interesting problem-solving behavior can be programmed using the blackboard framework as a foundation. The robustness of the blackboard model is also evident; the systems described in Parts IV and V show that new constructs can be added to blackboard frameworks as the application problems demand, without violating the guidelines of the model.

Another characteristic of the blackboard model is that it lends itself to a variety of perspectives. The blackboard model has been viewed as a model of general problem solving (Hayes-Roth, 1983). It has been used to structure cognitive models (McClelland and Rumelhart, 1981; Rumelhart and McClelland, 1982); the OPM system (Chapter 10) simulates the human planning process. Sometimes the blackboard model is used as an organizing principle for large, complex systems built by many programmers. The ALV project (Stentz and Schafer, 1985), the CMU OPIS project (Smith *et al.*, 1986) and the Edinburgh OPLAN planning system (Currie and Tate, 1985) all take this approach.

An interesting sidelight on this development of virtually all of the blackboard systems in this book has been the need for an application to drive and stress the development. This clearly has to be the case for the applications reported in Parts I, II and IV, but is also generally true of the domain-independent frameworks in Parts III and V; the relationship between PROTEAN and BB1 is a clear example.

Looking back over the ways in which ideas have developed in the first 15 years of blackboard systems, we can see a number of trends.

One trend has been a gradual generalization of blackboard concepts. An example is the evolution of the concept of a hierarchy of levels on the blackboard (as in HASP) toward more general notions such as the spaces of GBB. Another example is the evolution of the BB* architecture, which incorporates alternative reasoning frameworks within a uniform structure.

A second trend has been the incorporation of object-oriented programming techniques – which can be argued to be already part-way toward a blackboard framework. Many systems developed from the mid-1980s, such as BLOBS, take an object-oriented approach as a natural component of the system.

A third trend is the emergence of some strain on the concept of a global blackboard. We can trace two influences at work here. One is the move in modern programming techniques toward functional (stateless) programming and away from the use of global variables. How does one reconcile this style with a model that stores the solution state at all times? The other influence is the interest in concurrency. Although the global blackboard is a software concept rather than a hardware imperative, care must be taken in mapping the concept onto physically realizable hardware without creating memory contention problems. The use of a partitioned blackboard, as in MUSE, points to possible ways of retaining the basic blackboard concepts while avoiding some of the contention problems.

A final trend which is worthy of comment is the growing emphasis on applying software engineering techniques to develop blackboard systems. Some early blackboard work (such as OPM) was considered to be as much experimental psychology as computer science. Now we are seeing systems (such as GBB) which consolidate previous experience into a stable framework for further experimental work. A result of this new-found maturity is the first emergence of commercial blackboard shells intended to be programmed by systems engineers, such as the ESHELL system sold in Japan by Fujitsu.

30.5 Where is more work required?

In spite of the progress that has been made in several areas, there are still many topics requiring additional research. This section summarizes the research topics which we feel are especially important in blackboard systems. Of course, research in areas which are of general relevance to practitioners in AI (such as ways of representing temporal relationships) will also be relevant. However, the special characteristics of blackboard systems point to a need for more work in particular directions.

30.5.1 Explanation

A straightforward approach in many expert systems is to use a history of activations (for example, rule firings) and data bindings as a basis for explanation. Text templates can be used to handle a wide range of user queries; empty slots in a template are filled with extracts from the historical data for a specific query. There are two reasons why this approach is of limited value in many blackboard applications:

(1) The 'answer' the system produces will often be a complex data structure, different parts of which may have been built by different lines of reasoning. In a system that produces a relatively simple final output, like:

'The patient has disease x, with certainty y'

it may be reasonable for the user to query

'How do you know that?'

However, in a system that produces a complex structure as its final output (like most of the systems in Part IV of this book), such a question is difficult to define. Given the incremental, opportunistic style of problem solving, a trace of the system's execution history is unlikely to be very illuminating to the end-user. The research requirement here is to find ways in which users (possibly computer-naive) can make meaningful queries on complex structures and be provided with coherent explanations of the system's reasoning. Just as control of blackboard systems was elevated to the status of a knowledge-based problem in the BB1 architecture, explanation should also be viewed as a knowledge-based task requiring its own special constructs.

(2) A second difficulty in providing explanations lies in dealing with continuous data problems. In such systems, there is never a final

solution to the problem; the system constantly adapts, trying to synthesize an internal representation which models the external world as closely as possible against some predetermined criteria. We have seen examples of such systems in HASP (Chapter 6), TRICERO (Chapter 19), and the Admiralty Research Establishment's Data Fusion System (Chapter 22). Since the system's output will change dynamically as it tracks the changing inputs, explaining results to a user takes on a temporal dimension, in addition to the complexity problems referred to above.

30.5.2 Concurrency

One of the attractions of a blackboard architecture is the apparent potential for concurrency. Most of the systems described in this book, including Hearsay-II, have, at least conceptually, concurrent knowledge sources. In practice, the benefit of this conceptual view has been to facilitate development from the standpoint of system modularity, rather than to improve run-time performance. Virtually all of the blackboard systems (on which documentation is publicly available) use serial invocations of knowledge sources on a single processor. Although the blackboard *model* is inherently parallel, actually translating the potential into a practical concurrent system has proved nontrivial for a variety of reasons. A major reason is that most AI applications are inherently ill-structured problems. In contrast with well structured algorithmic solutions to numeric problems, one cannot predict in advance the flow of control, or the size or frequency of creation of data structures, for example. Another reason is related to the notion of a global blackboard. One can implement the blackboard as either a centralized or distributed data structure. In the case of a centralized blackboard, the cost of access to memory can no longer be ignored. For a distributed blackboard, management of access to its contents can become quite expensive when dealing with interdependent data. Similar problems arise when considering how to 'parallelize' the execution of knowledge sources, which are often not independent with respect to the data accessed or their order of execution. Finally, centralized control is inherent in the blackboard model, and hence is always a potential bottleneck. Thus, although the blackboard model might seem ideally suited to parallel execution on multiprocessors, one encounters basically the same difficulties in achieving enhanced performance as would be found with many other models of serial computation.

The basic blackboard approach seems to be well suited to a coarse-grained style of parallelism, e.g. at the level of knowledge source execution. However, until recently, much of the work on parallelism in AI has concentrated on a finer-grained approach, in particular parallelism at the rule level; examples include the various applications implemented on the DADO machine (Stolfo and Shaw, 1982), including production systems (Gupta, 1984) and AND/OR parallelism in PROLOG programs (Taylor *et al.*, 1983). The recent arrival of commercial products such as the INMOS Transputer, which are designed for use in coarse-grained parallel systems, should give new impetus to research in concurrent blackboards.

There are two obvious ways of adding concurrency in a blackboard environment:

(1)   Divide the problem into several independent subproblems and operate several autonomous blackboard systems, with communication between the systems. This approach has been discussed in DVMT (Chapter 18) and TRICERO (Chapter 19).

(2)   Introduce concurrency into operations within the same system; for example, by running several knowledge sources in parallel. The experimental CAGE and POLIGON systems discussed in Chapter 25 are examples of internal concurrency.

Of course, both these types of concurrency could (in principle) be used in the same application. In practice, introducing concurrency within a single blackboard system appears to pose the greatest technical challenge. The arrival of commercial multiprocessor systems and components has given new impetus to the research. Possibly the key problems lie in finding ways of mapping the global memory of the blackboard model into a concurrent framework, without introducing problems of consistency and/or memory contention.

One approach to these problems, currently under investigation at Stanford, is to design the system in terms of knowledge sources as agents that communicate with each other via communication buffers (Schoen, 1986), thereby resulting in a blackboard system without a blackboard! The blackboard model is retained at a conceptual level only.

30.5.3 Dealing with uncertainty

One of the motivations for choosing a blackboard architecture is the need to deal with uncertain knowledge as well as uncertain data. Yet every application system to date has dealt with the issue of uncertainty in an *ad hoc* manner. Systems that use a standard problem-solving strategy, such as backward chaining, generally deal with uncertainty in a uniform and predictable way. On the other hand, the use of opportunistic reasoning, a hallmark of blackboard systems, complicates the computation of uncertainty, and no uniform method has been developed to date to handle this mode of reasoning. Moreover, the standard methods are inapplicable to continuous data problems. How does one compare, for example, the certainty of very low probability data that recurs over a period of time with high probability data that is observed only once (but expected continually)? Finally, some applications must deal with uncertain knowledge whose degree of uncertainty is dependent on the validity of the data (e.g. much of the predictive knowledge in CRYSALIS was dependent on the resolution of the electron density map). Dealing with uncertainty in the context of blackboard systems is an area wide open for further research.

30.5.4 Validating the blackboard approach

The systems described in this book illustrate the range and scope of blackboard systems. There is now sufficient evidence to reinforce the view expressed by Professor Edward Feigenbaum in the foreword to this book, in which he describes the blackboard approach as '. . . the most general and flexible knowledge system architecture for building expert systems'. We would suggest that the time is now ripe for consolidation of the experience gained so far. Three particular topics are worth exploring:

(1) *The relationship with existing software engineering practices*   Many of the aims and claims of blackboard systems are matched in developments outside AI; for example, the control aspects of a blackboard have much in common with operating systems design. We would like to see such relationships explored, to the mutual benefit of AI and conventional software engineering.

(2) *The range of application types*   We have seen that certain classes of application (such as signal understanding and data fusion) appear to be well matched to the blackboard approach. We feel that more work is required to establish the characteristics that would point to a blackboard solution as being appropriate (or inappropriate) for a particular problem.

(3) *The range of architectural alternatives*   A wide variety of frameworks can be built within the blackboard model because of the options available to the designer at various stages. Section 30.3 lists some of the degrees of freedom that we have encountered in this review. We feel that the properties associated with particular design choices deserve a closer look to determine the part that each plays in the problem-solving behavior of the system.

30.6 Isn't X a blackboard system?

Over the past 15 years blackboard systems have become more widely known and accepted within the AI community. However, in fields outside AI we find many of the same concepts and techniques employed in large software projects, such as modern operating systems. Designers of such systems have often questioned the uniqueness of the blackboard systems or the blackboard model of problem solving. By making some simple analogies, can't we call many 'non-AI' systems blackboard systems?

To illustrate the correspondence of ideas we can take as an example MASCOT (MASCOT, 1987). MASCOT is a design methodology for real-time applications, originally developed for military use (and mandatory on some contracts issued by the UK Ministry of Defence). MASCOT is also widely used (in Europe) in industrial real-time applications.

MASCOT supports the design of a real-time system in terms of a small number of primitive elements. These are principally activities, which contain the processing components of the system, and inter-communication data areas (IDAs) which link the activities together. All of the information flow between activities passes through an IDA. There are two types of IDA: channels, which are queue-like FIFO structures; and pools, which are random-access structures. The execution of activities is controlled by a small run-time kernel.

We can cast the top-level design of Hearsay-II (see Figure 3.3) into a MASCOT form. Each of the levels in Hearsay-II contains a consistent type of data object, and supports random access to these objects by knowledge sources. We can therefore interpret each level of Hearsay-II as a MASCOT pool. The active parts of Hearsay-II which can be individually scheduled are the knowledge sources, which can be interpreted as MASCOT activities. The resulting system is shown in Figure 30.1. Although the knowledge sources are still recognizable from Hearsay-II, the blackboard is fragmented into a number of pools (intercommunication areas), and no longer exists as a single entity. This is rather similar to the MUSE approach which is described in Chapter 27.

We can now ask: Is Figure 30.1 a blackboard system? On balance, we would answer no. A component that is conspicuously absent is intelligent control over the operation of the system (see Chapter 14 for a discussion of the importance of control). We could arrange for the MASCOT system to resemble the demon-driven approach of POLIGON, triggering an activity whenever a new data object arrives in a pool that it can read. It could be argued that Figure 30.1 is rather like a coarse-grained version of POLIGON, but the definition of POLIGON as a blackboard system is itself controversial.

Although we would say that an approach like the MASCOT–Hearsay example does not give us a blackboard system, we could imagine a similar framework with the addition of an intelligent control component, which

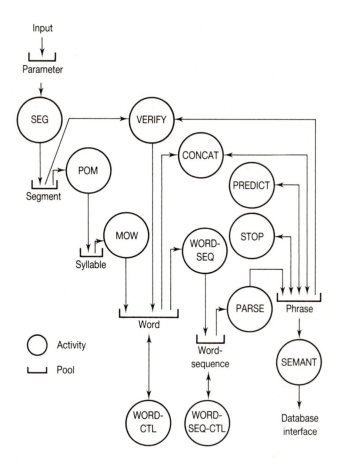

Figure 30.1 MASCOT-Hearsay.

would support the opportunistic problem-solving which is so characteristic of blackboard systems. But that is just saying that the potential is there. To quote Penny Nii:

> What about statements such as: 'FORTRAN COMMON is a blackboard' or 'Object-oriented systems are blackboard systems'? All I can say is: the potential for a thing is not that thing itself. With some effort, one can design and build a blackboard system in FORTRAN, and the COMMON area is a good candidate for storing blackboard data. However, one also needs to design knowledge sources that are self-selecting and self-contained, and control modules that determine the focus of attention and manage knowledge source application. The blackboard framework is a problem-solving framework. It is not a programming language,

although an instance of the framework can have a blackboard language associated with it. It is not a knowledge representation language, although one can use any knowledge representation language for the knowledge sources and the blackboard. Why can't I get away with placing a hunk of ground beef, a can of tomato sauce, a box of spaghetti, and bottles of seasoning in a pile and call the pile a spaghetti dinner or, better yet, linguine a la pesta rosa? It would certainly simplify my life.

We hope that this book has clarified some of the common misconceptions about blackboard systems.

Bibliography

Editors' note: References from all the chapters of this book are collected together here. We have also taken the opportunity of including many additional references, covering the majority of papers on blackboard systems available at the time of writing (late 1987). Those papers mainly concerned with blackboard systems are marked *; other references relate to areas of more general interest in Computer Science. Papers reproduced in this book are marked appropriately in the text of the bibliography.

* Aiello, N. (1983) A comparative study of control strategies for expert systems: AGE implementation of three variations of PUFF. In: *Proceedings of the Third National Conference on Artificial Intelligence* (AAAI-83), pp. 1–4.
* Aiello, N. (1986) *User-Directed Control of Parallelism: The CAGE System.* Technical Report KSL-86-31, Stanford University.
* Aiello, N. and Nii, H.P. (1979) Building a knowledge-based system with AGE. In: *Proceedings of the Sixth International Joint Conference on Artificial Intelligence* (IJCAI-79), pp. 645–55.
* Aiello, N. and Nii, H.P. (1981a) *AGEPUFF: A Simple Event-Drive Program.* Technical Report HPP-81-26, Stanford University.
* Aiello, N. and Nii, H.P. (1981b) *BOWL: A Beginner's Program Using AGE.* Technical Report HPP-81-26, Stanford University.
* Aiello, N., Bock, C., Nii, H.P. and White, W.C. (1981a) *Joy of AGE-ing: An Introduction to the AGE-1 System.* Technical Report HPP-81-23, Stanford University.
* Aiello, N., Bock, C., Nii, H.P. and White, W.C. (1981b) *AGE Reference Manual: AGE-1.* Technical Report HPP-81-24, Stanford University.
  Allen, J.F. (1984) Towards a general theory of action and time. *Artificial Intelligence* **23**, 123–54.

Amdahl, G.M. (1967) Validity of a single processor approach to achieving large scale computing capabilities. In: *Proceedings of AFIPS Computing Conference 30*, 1967.

Arbib, M.A. (1978) Segmentation, schemas, and cooperative computation. In: *Studies in Mathematical Biology*, Part 1, Levin, S. (ed.), MAA Studies in Mathematics, Vol. 15: 118–55.

Arbib, M.A. and Caplan, D. (1979) Neurolinguistics must be computational. *Behavioural and Brain Sciences* **2(3)**, 449–483.

Arbib, M.A. and Hanson, A.R. (eds) (1987) *Vision, Brain, and Cooperative Computing*. MIT Press, Cambridge, MA.

Bahl, L.R., Baker, J.K., Cohen, P.S., Dixon, N.R., Jelinek, F., Mercer, R.L. and Silverman, H.F. (1976) Preliminary results on the performance of a system for the automatic recognition of continuous speech. In: *Proceedings of the IEEE International Conference on Acoustics, Speech, and Signal Processing*, pp. 425–33, Philadelphia, PA.

Bahl, L.R., Baker, J.K., Cohen, P.S., Cole, A.G., Jelinek, F., Lewis, B.L. and Mercer, R.L. (1978) Automatic recognition of continuously spoken sentences from a finite state grammar. In: *Proceedings of the IEEE International Conference on Acoustics, Speech, and Signal Processing*, pp. 418–21, Tulsa, OK.

Ballard, D.A. (1978) Model-directed detection of ribs in chest radiographs. In: *Proceedings of the Fourth International Joint Conference on Pattern Recognition* (IJCPR-78), Kyoto, Japan.

Balzer, R. (1980) Transformational implementation: an example. *IEEE Transactions on Software Engineering*, Nov. 1980 (also Technical Report RR-79-79, USC/Information Sciences Institute).

* Balzer, R., Erman, L.D., London, P. and Williams, C. (1980) Hearsay-III: a domain-independent framework for expert systems. In: *Proceedings of the First National Conference on Artificial Intelligence* (AAAI-80), pp. 108–10.

Balzer, R., Goldman, N. and Wile, D. (1978) Informality in program specifications. *IEEE Transactions on Software Engineering*, **SE-4(2)**, 94–103.

Barnett, J.A. and Bernstein, M.I. (1977) *Knowledge-Based Systems: A Tutorial*. Technical Report TM(L)-5903/000/00 (NTIS: AD/A-044-883), System Development Corporation, Santa Monica, CA.

Barr, A. and Feigenbaum, E.A. (1981) *The Handbook of Artificial Intelligence*, Vol. 1, pp. 141–222. W. Kaufman, Los Altos, CA.

Barrow, H.G. and Tenenbaum, J.M. (1976) *MYSYS: A System for Reasoning about Scenes*. Technical Report 121, AI Center, SRI, Menlo Park, CA.

Barrow, H.G., Garvey, T.D., Kremers, J., Tenenbaum, J.M. and Wolf, H.C. (1978) Interactive aids for cartography and photo interpretation: Progress report, October 1977. In: *Proceedings of Workshop on Image Understanding*, 1978, pp. 111–17 (also Technical Note 137, SRI AI Center, 1977).

Bates, P.C. and Wileden, J.C. (1982) Event Definition Language: An Aid to Monitoring and Debugging of Complex Software Systems. In: *Proceedings of the Fifteenth Hawaii International Conference on System Science*, 1982, pp. 86–93.

Baudet, G.M. (1976) *Asynchronous Iterative Methods for Multiprocessors*. Technical Report, Carnegie-Mellon University.

Belknap, R., Hanson, A. and Riseman, E. (1986) The information fusion problem and rule-based hypotheses applied to complex aggregations of image events. In: *Proceedings of the IEEE Computer Society Conference on Computer Vision and Pattern Recognition*, Miami, FL.

* Bell, M. (1984) The ADX – an expert system framework for experimentation in air defence. In: *Proceedings of the IKBS in Defence Seminar*, Malvern, UK.

Bennett, J., Creary, L., Engelmore, R. and Melosh, R. (1978) *SACON: A Knowledge-Based Consultant for Structural Analysis*. Technical Report HPP-78-23, Stanford University.

Bernstein, M.I. (1976) *Interactive Systems Research: Final Report to the Director, Advanced Research Projects Agency*. Technical Report TM-5243/006/00, System Development Corporation, Santa Monica, CA.

Bernstein, P.A. and Goodman, N. (1981) Concurrency control in distributed database systems. *ACM Computing Surveys* **13(2)**, 185–221.

Beveridge, J.R., Griffith, J., Kohler, R., Hanson, A.R. and Riseman, E. (1987) *Segmenting Images Using Localized Histograms and Region Merging*. COINS Technical Report, University of Massachusetts at Amherst.

Bloom, B.S. (1956) *Taxonomy of Educational Objectives*. McKay, New York.

Bobrow, D.G. and Winograd, T. (1977) An overview of KRL, a knowledge representation language. *Cognitive Science* **1(1)**, 3–46.

* Boyle, C. (1985) *Ten Years of the Blackboard Model*. Technical Report, Department of Computer Science, Queen Mary College, University of London, UK.

Braun, W., Bosch, C., Brown, L.R., Go, N. and Wuthrich, K. (1981) Combined use of proton–proton Overhauser enhancements and a distance geometry algorithm for determination of polypeptide conformations: application to mycelle-bound glucagon. *Biochimica et Biophysica Acta* **667**, 377.

* Braunstein, D.M. (1985) *The Blackboard Model in Expert Systems*. MS thesis, University of Texas at Austin.

Brinkley, J., Cornelius, C., Altman, R., Hayes-Roth, B., Lichtarge, O., Buchanan, B. and Jardetzky, O. (1986) *Application of Constraint Satisfaction Techniques to the Determination of Protein Tertiary Structure*. Technical Report KSL-86-28, Stanford University.

Brooks, R. (1981) Symbolic reasoning among 3-D models and 2-D images. *Artificial Intelligence* **17**, 285–348.

Brown, A.L. (1985) Modal propositional semantics for reasoning maintenance systems. In: *Proceedings of the Ninth International Joint Conference on Artificial Intelligence* (IJCAI-85), pp. 178–84.

* Brown, H. *et al.* (1982) *Final Report on HANNIBAL*. Technical Report, ESL Inc, Sunnyvale, CA.

* Brown, H., Schoen, E. and Delagi, B. (1986) *An Experiment in Knowledge-Based Signal Understanding Using Parallel Architectures*. Technical Report KSL-86-69, Knowledge Systems Laboratory, Stanford University.

Brugge, J. and Buchanan, B. (1987) *Evolution of a Knowledge-Based System for Determining Structural Components of Proteins*. Technical Report KSL-87-62, Stanford University.

Buchanan, B.G., Hayes-Roth, B., Lichtarge, O., Altman, R., Brinkley, J., Hewett, M., Cornelius, C., Duncan, B. and Jardetzky, O. (1985) *The Heuristic Refinement Method for Deriving Solution Structures of Proteins*. Technical Report KSL-85-41 (also STAN-CS-86-1115), Stanford University.

Burns, J.B. and Kitchen, L.J. (1987) Recognition in 2D images of 3D objects from large model bases using prediction hierarchies. In: *Proceedings of the Tenth International Joint Conference on Artificial Intelligence* (IJCAI-87), pp. 763–6.

Burns, J.B., Hanson, A.R. and Riseman, E. (1986) Extracting straight lines. *IEEE Transactions on Pattern Analysis and Machine Intelligence* **PAMI-8(4)**, 425–55, 1986.

Burrill, J.H. (1987) *Low Level Vision System*. COINS Technical Report 87-14, University of Massachusetts at Amherst.

Burstall, R., Collins, J. and Popplestone, R. (1977) *Programming in POP-11*. Edinburgh University Press.

Burton, R.R. (1976) *Semantic Grammar: An Engineering Technique for Constructing Natural Language Understanding Systems*. Technical Report No. 3453, Bolt, Beranek and Newman, Cambridge, MA.

Carver, N.F., Lesser, V.R. and McCue, D.L. (1984) Focusing in plan recognition. In: *Proceedings of the Third National Conference on Artificial Intelligence* (AAAI-84), pp. 42–8.

Chandrasekaran, B. (1981) Natural and social system metaphors for distributed problem solving: introduction to the issue. *IEEE Transactions on Systems, Man, and Cybernetics* **SMC-11(1)**, 1–5.

Chandrasekaran, B. (1985) Generic tasks in knowledge-based reasoning: characterizing and designing expert systems at the right level of abstraction. In: *Proceedings of the Second IEEE International Conference on Artificial Intelligence Applications*, 1985.

Christophides, N. (1975) *Graph Theory: An Algorithmic Approach*. Academic Press, New York.

Clancey, W.J. (1984) *Acquiring, Representing, and Evaluating a Competence Model of a Diagnostic Strategy*. Technical Report HPP-84-2, Stanford University.

Clancey, W.J. (1985) Heuristic classification. *Artificial Intelligence* **27(3)**, 289–350.

CMU Computer Science Speech Group (1976) *Working Papers in Speech Recognition IV: The Hearsay-II System*. Technical Report, Carnegie-Mellon University.

CMU Computer Science Speech Group (1977) *Summary of the CMU Five-Year ARPA Effort in Speech Understanding Research*. Technical Report, Carnegie-Mellon University.

Cohen, P.R. (1985) *Numeric and Symbolic Reasoning about Uncertainty in Expert Systems*. Technical Report 85-25, Department of Computer and Information Science, University of Massachusetts.

Cohen, P.R. and Feigenbaum, E.A. (1982) *Molgen*. William Kaufman, Los Altos, CA, pp. 551–62.

* Corby, O. (1986) Blackboard architectures in computer aided engineering. *Artificial Intelligence in Engineering* **1(2)**, 95–8.

Corkill, D.D. (1980) *CLisp Reference Manual (an interactive help facility)*. Department of Computer and Information Science, University of Massachusetts at Amherst.

Corkill, D.D. (1983) *A Framework for Organizational Self-Design in Distributed Problem Solving Networks*. PhD thesis, Technical Report 82-33, Department of Computer and Information Science, University of Massachusetts at Amherst.

* Corkill, D.D. and Lesser, V.R. (1981) *A Goal-Directed Hearsay-II Architecture: Unifying Data and Goal-Directed Control.* COINS Technical Report 81-15, University of Massachusetts at Amherst.

Corkill, D.D. and Lesser, V.R. (1983) The use of meta-level control for coordination in a distributed problem solving network. In: *Proceedings of the Eighth International Joint Conference on Artificial Intelligence* (IJCAI-83), pp. 748–56. Also appeared in *Computer Architectures for Artificial Intelligence Applications*, Wah, B.W. and Li, G.J. (eds), IEEE Computer Society Press, 1986, pp. 507–15.

* Corkill, D.D., Lesser, V.R. and Hudlicka, E. (1982) Unifying data-directed and goal-directed control: an example and experiments. In: *Proceedings of the Second National Conference on Artificial Intelligence* (AAAI-82), pp. 143–7.

Corkill, D.D., Gallagher, K.Q. and Johnson, P.M. (1987) Achieving flexibility, efficiency, and generality in blackboard architectures. In: *Proceedings of the Sixth National Conference on Artificial Intelligence* (AAAI-87), pp. 18–23.

* Corkill, D.D., Gallagher, K.Q. and Murray, K.E. (1986) GBB: a generic blackboard development system. In: *Proceedings of the Fifth National Conference on Artificial Intelligence* (AAAI-86), pp. 1008–14 (reproduced in Chapter 26 of this book).

* Craig, I.D. (1987) *A Distributed Blackboard Architecture.* Technical Report, Department of Computer Science, University of Warwick.

Cronk, R. (1977) Word pair adjacency acceptance procedure in Hearsay-II. In CMU (1977), pp. 15–16.

Cronk, R. and Erman, L.D. (1976) *Word Verification in the Hearsay-II Speech Understanding System.* Technical Report, Carnegie-Mellon University.

Currie, K. and Tate, A. (1985) O-PLAN – Control in the Open Planning environment. In: *Proceedings of the Fifth Technical Conference of the British Computer Society Specialist Group on Expert Systems* (EXPERT-SYSTEMS 85), pp. 225–40, Warwick, UK.

Davis, R. (1976) *Applications of Meta-level Knowledge to the Construction, Maintenance, and Use of Large Knowledge Bases.* Memo AIM-283, Artificial Intelligence Laboratory, Stanford University.

Davis, R. (1980) Report on the workshop on distributed artificial intelligence. *SIGART Newsletter* **73**, 43–52.

Davis, R. (1982a) Expert systems: where are we? and where do we go from here? *AI Magazine* **3(2)**, 3–22.

Davis, R. (1982b) Report on the Second Workshop on Distributed Artificial Intelligence. *SIGART Newsletter* **80**, 13–23.

Davis, R. and Buchanan, B.G. (1977) Meta-level knowledge: overview and applications. In: *Proceedings of the Fifth International Joint Conference on Artificial Intelligence* (IJCAI-77), pp. 920–7.

Davis, R. and King, J. (1977) An overview of production systems. In: *Machine Intelligence 8: Machine Representation of Knowledge*, Elcock, E.W. and Michie, D. (eds), John Wiley, New York.

Davis, R. and Smith, R.G. (1981) *Negotiation as a Metaphor for Distributed Problem Solving.* AI Memo 624, Artificial Intelligence Laboratory, Massachusetts Institute of Technology.

Delagi, B. *CARE Users Manual.* Technical Report KSL-86-36, Stanford University.

Delagi, B.A., Saraiya, N.P. and Byrd, G.T. (1986) *LAMINA: CARE Applications*

Interface. Technical Report KSL-86-76, Knowledge Systems Laboratory, Stanford University.

* Delaney, J.R. (1986) *Multi-System Report Integration Using Blackboards*. Technical Report KSL-86-20, Stanford University.

Dennis, J.B. (1980) Data-flow supercomputers. *Computer* **13**(11), 48–56.

* Dickinson, I.J. (1985) BLOBS *User Manual*. Cambridge Consultants, Cambridge, England.

Dodhiawala, R., Jagannathan, V. and Baum, L.S. (1986) Integrating architectures for complex systems design. In: *Proceedings of ROBEXS-86*, Houston, TX, June 1986.

Draper, B.A., Collins, R.T., Brolio, J., Griffith, J., Hanson, A.R. and Riseman, E.M. (1987) Tools and experiments in the knowledge-directed interpretation of road scenes. In: *Proceedings of the DARPA Image Understanding Workshop*, Los Angeles, CA, pp. 178–93.

Duda, R.O., Hart, P.E., Nilsson, N.J. and Southerland, G.L. (1978) Semantic network representation in rule-based inference systems. In Waterman and Hayes-Roth (1978), pp. 203–22.

* Durfee, E.H., Lesser, V.R. and Corkill, D.D. (1985a) Increasing coherence in a distributed problem solving network. In: *Proceedings of the Ninth International Joint Conference on Artificial Intelligence* (IJCAI-85), pp. 1025–30.

* Durfee, E.H., Lesser, V.R. and Corkill, D.D. (1985b) *Coherent Cooperation among Communicating Problem Solvers*. Technical Report, Department of Computer and Information Sciences, University of Massachusetts.

Elfes, A. (1986) A distributed control architecture for an autonomous mobile robot. *Artificial Intelligence in Engineering* **1**(2), 99–108.

* Engelmore, R.S. and Nii, H.P. (1977) *A Knowledge-Based System for the Interpretation of Protein X-ray Crytallographic Data*. Technical Report HPP-77-2 (also Stan-CS-77-589), Stanford University.

* Engelmore, R. and Terry, A. (1979) Structure and function of the CRYSALIS system. In: *Proceedings of the Sixth International Joint Conference on Artificial Intelligence* (IJCAI-79), pp. 250–6.

* Ensor, J.R. and Gabbe, J.D. (1985) Transactional blackboards. In: *Proceedings of the Ninth International Joint Conference on Artificial Intelligence* (IJCAI-85), pp. 340–4 (reproduced in Chapter 24 of this book).

Erman, L.D. (1974) *An Environment and System for Machine Understanding of Connected Speech*. PhD thesis, Stanford University.

* Erman, L.D. and Lesser, V.R. (1975) A multi-level organization for problem-solving using many diverse cooperating sources of knowledge. In: *Proceedings of the Fourth International Joint Conference on Artificial Intelligence* (IJCAI-75), pp. 483–90.

* Erman, L.D. and Lesser, V.R. (1978a) *Hearsay-II: Tutorial Introduction and Retrospective View*. Technical Report CMU-CS-78-117, Department of Computer Science, Carnegie-Mellon University.

Erman, L.D. and Lesser, V.R. (1978b) System engineering techniques for artificial intelligence systems. In: Hanson and Riseman (1978a), pp. 37–45.

* Erman, L.D., Hayes-Roth, F., Lesser, V.R. and Reddy, D.R. (1980) The Hearsay-II speech understanding system: integrating knowledge to resolve uncertainty. *ACM Computing Surveys* **12**(2), pp. 213–53 (reproduced in Chapter 3 of this book).

* Erman, L.D., London, P.E. and Fickas, S.F. (1981) The design and an example use of Hearsay-III. In: *Proceedings of the Seventh International Joint Conference on Artificial Intelligence* (IJCAI-81), pp. 409–15 (reproduced in Chapter 13 of this book).

Ernst, G. and Newell, A. (1969) *GPS: A Case Study in Generality and Problem Solving*. Academic Press, New York.

Eswaran, K.P., Gray, J.N., Lorie, R.A. and Traiger, I.L. (1976) The notions of consistency and predicate locks in a database system. *Communications of the ACM* **19(11)**, 624–33.

Fehling, M. and Erman, L. (1983) Report on the third annual workshop on distributed artificial intelligence. *SIGART Newsletter* **84**, 3–12.

Feigenbaum, E.A. (1977) The art of artificial intelligence: themes and case studies of knowledge engineering. In: *Proceedings of the Fifth International Joint Conference on Artificial Intelligence* (IJCAI-77), pp. 1014–29.

Feigenbaum, E.A. (1980) *Knowledge Engineering: The Applied Side of Artificial Intelligence*. Technical Report STAN-CS-80-812, Computer Science Department, Stanford University.

Feigenbaum, E.A. and Feldman, J. (eds) (1963) *Computers and Thought*. McGraw-Hill, New York.

Feigenbaum, E.A., Buchanan, B.G. and Lederberg, J. (1971) On generality and problem solving: a case study using the DENDRAL program. In: *Machine Intelligence 6*, Michie D. (ed.), Edinburgh University Press.

Feitelson, J. and Stefik, M. (1977) *A Case Study of the Reasoning in a Genetics Experiment*. Working Paper HPP-77-18, Stanford University.

Fennel, R.D. (1975) *Multiprocess Software Architecture for AI Problem Solving*. PhD thesis, Carnegie-Mellon University.

* Fennel, R.D. and Lesser, V.R. (1977) Parallelism in AI problem-solving: a case study of Hearsay-II. *IEEE Transactions on Computers* **C-26**, 98–111.

Fickas, S. (1980) Automatic goal-directed program transformation. In: *Proceedings of the First National Conference on Artificial Intelligence* (AAAI-80), pp. 68–70.

Forgy, C. (1982) RETE: a fast algorithm for the many pattern/many object pattern match problem. *Artificial Intelligence* **19**, 17–37.

Forgy, C. and McDermott, J. (1977) OPS: a domain-independent production system language. In: *Proceedings of the Fifth International Joint Conference on Artificial Intelligence* (IJCAI-77), pp. 933–9.

Fox, M.S. (1979a) An organizational view of distributed systems. In: *Proceedings of the International Conference on Systems and Cybernetics*, Denver, CO, 1979.

Fox, M.S. (1979b) *Organization Structuring: Designing Large, Complex Software*. Technical Report CMU-CS-79-155, Carnegie-Mellon University.

Fox, M.S. and Mostow, D.J. (1977) Maximal consistent interpretations of errorful data in hierarchically modelled domains. In: *Proceedings of the Fifth International Joint Conference on Artificial Intelligence* (IJCAI-77), pp. 165–71 (also Technical Report, Carnegie-Mellon University, 1977).

Gabriel, R.P. and McCarthy, J. (1984) Queue-based multi-processing LISP. In: *Proceedings of the 1984 Symposium on Lisp and Functional Programming*.

Garvey, A. and Hayes-Roth, B. (1987) *Implementing Diverse Forms of Control Knowledge in Multiple Control Architectures*. Technical Report KSL-87-40, Stanford University.

Garvey, A., Hewett, M., Johnson M.V., Schulman, R. and Hayes-Roth, B. (1986) *BB1 User Manual* – COMMON LISP *Version*. Technical Report KSL-88-61, Stanford University.

* Garvey, A., Cornelius, C. and Hayes-Roth, B. (1987) Computational costs and benefits of control reasoning. In: *Proceedings of the Sixth National Conference on Artificial Intelligence* (AAAI-87), pp. 110–15.

Genesereth, M.R. and Smith, D.E. (1982) *Meta-level Architecture*. Technical Report HPP-81-6, Stanford University.

Gill, G., Goldberg, H., Reddy, R. and Yegnanarayana, B. (1978) *A Recursive Segmentation Procedure for Continuous Speech*. Technical Report CMU-CS-78-134, Carnegie-Mellon University.

Glicksman, J. (1982) *A Cooperative Scheme for Image Understanding Using Multiple Sources of Information*. Technical Report TN 82-13 (PhD Thesis), Department of Computer Science, University of British Columbia.

Goldberg, H.G. (1976) Segmentation and labeling of connected speech. In: CMU (1976).

Goldberg, A. and Robson, D. (1983) *Smalltalk-80: The Language and its Implementation*. Addison-Wesley, Reading, MA.

Goldberg, H., Reddy, R. and Gill, G. (1977) The ZAPDASH parameters, feature extraction, segmentation, and labeling for speech understanding systems. In: CMU (1977), pp. 10–11.

Goldman, N. (1978) *AP3 User's Guide*. Unpublished Memorandum, USC/Information Sciences Institute.

Goodman, G. (1976) *Analysis of Languages for Man-Machine Voice Communication*. Technical Report, Carnegie-Mellon University.

Goos, G. and Hartmanis, J. (eds) (1981) *Distributed Systems – Architecture and Implementation*. Springer-Verlag, New York.

Green, P.E. (ed.) (1982) *Computer Network Architectures and Protocols*. Plenum Press, New York.

Greer, J. (1974) Three-dimensional pattern recognition: an approach to automated interpretation of electron-density maps of proteins. *Journal of Molecular Biology* **82(3)**, 279–301.

Gupta, A. (1984) Implementing OPS5 production systems on DADO. In: *Proceedings of the 1984 International Conference on Parallel Processing*.

Gupta, A. (1986) *Parallelism in Production Systems*. PhD Thesis, Department of Computer Science, Carnegie-Mellon University.

Hanson, A.R. and Riseman, E.M. (eds) (1978a) *Computer Vision Systems*. Academic Press, New York.

* Hanson, A.R. and Riseman, E.M. (1978b) VISIONS: a computer system for interpreting scenes. In: Hanson and Riseman (1978a), pp. 303–33.

Hanson, A.R. and Riseman, E.M. (1987) The VISIONS image understanding system – 1986. In: *Advances in Computer Vision*, Brown, C. (ed.), L. Erlbaum.

Hardy, S. (1984) A new software environment for list processing and logic programming. In: *Artificial Intelligence: Tools, Techniques and Applications*, O'Shea, T. and Eisenstadt, M. (eds), Harper and Row, New York.

Harris, L.R. (1974) The heuristic search under conditions of error. *Artificial Intelligence* **5(3)**, 217–34.

Hart, P.E. (1982) Directions for AI in the eighties. *SIGART Newsletter* **79**, 11–16.

Hasling, D.W., Clancey, W.J. and Rennels, G. (1983) *Strategic Explanations for a Diagnostic Consultation System*. Technical Report STAN-CS-83-996, Stanford University, 1983.

Hayes-Roth, F. (1978) The role of partial and best matches in knowledge systems. In: Waterman and Hayes-Roth (1978).

Hayes-Roth, F. (1980) Syntax, semantics, and pragmatics in speech understanding. In: Lea (1980).

* Hayes-Roth, B. (1983) *The Blackboard Architecture: A General Framework for Problem Solving?* Technical Report HPP-83-30, Stanford University.

* Hayes-Roth, B. (1984) *BB1: An Architecture for Blackboard Systems that Control, Explain, and Learn about their own Behavior*. Technical Report HPP-84-16 (also STAN-CS-84-1034), Stanford University.

* Hayes-Roth, B. (1985) A blackboard architecture for control. *Artificial Intelligence* **26(2)**, 251–321 (previous version in Technical Report HPP-83-38, Stanford University).

* Hayes-Roth, B. (1987) *A Multi-Processor Interrupt-Driven Architecture for Adaptive Intelligent Systems*. Technical Report KSL-87-31, Stanford University.

Hayes-Roth, B and Hayes-Roth, F. (1979a) *Cognitive Processes in Planning*. Technical Report R-2366-ONR, The Rand Corporation, Santa Monica, CA.

Hayes-Roth, B. and Hayes-Roth, F. (1979b) A cognitive model of planning. *Cognitive Science* **3**, 275–310.

* Hayes-Roth, B. and Hewitt, M. (1985) *Learning Control Heuristics in BB1*. Technical Report STAN-CS-85-1036 (also HPP-85-2), Stanford University.

* Hayes-Roth, F. and Lesser, V.R. (1977) Focus of attention in the Hearsay-II speech understanding system. In: *Proceedings of the Fifth International Joint Conference on Artificial Intelligence* (IJCAI-77), pp. 27–35.

Hayes-Roth, F. and Mostow, D.J. (1975) An automatically compilable recognition network for structured patterns. In: *Proceedings of the Fourth International Joint Conference on Artificial Intelligence* (IJCAI-75), pp. 246–52.

Hayes-Roth, F. and Mostow, D.J. (1976) Syntax and semantics in a distributed speech understanding system. In: *Proceedings of the IEEE International Conference on Acoustics, Speech, and Signal Processing*, Philadelphia, PA, 1977, pp. 421–4 (also in CMU (1976)).

Hayes-Roth, B. and Thorndyke, P. (1980) *Decision Making during the Planning Process*. Technical Report N-1213-ONR, The Rand Corporation, Santa Monica, CA.

* Hayes-Roth, F., Erman, L.D. and Lesser, V.R. (1976) Hypothesis validity ratings in the Hearsay-II speech understanding system. In: CMU (1976).

Hayes-Roth, F., Erman, L.D., Fox, M. and Mostow, D.J. (1977a) Syntactic processing in Hearsay-II. In: CMU (1977), pp. 16–18.

Hayes-Roth, F., Gill, G. and Mostow, D.J. (1977b) Discourse analysis and task performance in the Hearsay-II speech understanding system. In: CMU (1977), pp. 24–8.

* Hayes-Roth, F., Lesser, V.R., Mostow, D.J. and Erman, L.D. (1977c) Policies for rating hypotheses, halting, and selecting a solution in Hearsay-II. In: CMU (1977), pp. 19–24.

Hayes-Roth, F., Mostow, D.J. and Fox, M.S. (1978a) Understanding speech in the Hearsay-II system. In: *Natural Language Communication with Computers*, Bloc, L. (ed.), Springer-Verlag, Berlin.

Hayes-Roth, F., Waterman, D.A. and Lenat, D.B. (1978b) Principles of pattern-directed inference systems. In: Waterman and Hayes-Roth (1978).

* Hayes-Roth, B., Hayes-Roth, F., Rosenschein, S. and Cammarata, S. (1979) Modeling planning as an incremental, opportunistic process. In: *Proceedings of the Sixth International Joint Conference on Artificial Intelligence* (IJCAI-79), pp. 375–83 (reproduced in Chapter 10 of this book).

* Hayes-Roth, B., Buchanan, B., Lichtarge, O., Hewett, M., Altman, R., Brinkley, J., Cornelius, C., Duncan, B. and Jardetzky, O. (1985) *Elucidating Protein Structure from Constraints in PROTEAN*. Technical Report KSL-85-35, Knowledge Systems Laboratory, Stanford University.

* Hayes-Roth, B., Buchanan, B.G., Lichtarge, O., Hewett, M., Altman, R., Brinkley, J., Cornelius, C., Duncan, B. and Jardetzky, O. (1986a) PROTEAN: deriving protein structures from constraints. In: *Proceedings of the Fifth National Conference on Artificial Intelligence* (AAAI-86), pp. 904–9 (reproduced in Chapter 20 of this book).

* Hayes-Roth, B., Garvey, A., Johnson, M. and Hewett, M. (1986b) *A Layered Environment for Reasoning about Action*. Technical Report KSL-86-38 (November 1986 version), Stanford University (edited version included in Chapter 29 of this book).

* Hayes-Roth, B., Johnson, M.V., Garvey, A. and Hewett, M. (1986c) Application of the BB1 blackboard control architecture to arrangement assembly tasks. *Artificial Intellignce in Engineering* **1(2)**, 85–94.

Hempel, C.G. (1966) *Philosophy of Natural Science*. Foundations of Philosophy series, Prentice-Hall, Englewood Cliffs, NJ.

Hendrix, G.G. (1975) Expanding the utility of semantic networks through partitioning. In: *Proceedings of the Fourth International Joint Conference on Artificial Intelligence* (IJCAI-75), pp. 115–21.

* Hewett, M. and Hayes-Roth, B. (1987) *The BB1 Architecture: A Software Engineering View*. Technical Report KSL-87-10, Stanford University.

Hewitt, C. (1972) *Description and Theoretical Analysis (Using Schemata) of Planner: A Language for Proving Theorems and Manipulating Models in a Robot*. Technical Report TR-258, Artificial Intelligence Laboratory, Massachusetts Institute of Technology.

Hewitt, C. (1977) Viewing control structures as patterns of passing messages. *Artificial Intelligence* **8(3)**, 323–64.

Hewitt, C., Bishop, P. and Steiger, R. (1973) A universal modular actor formalism for artificial intelligence. In: *Proceedings of the Third International Joint Conference on Artificial Intelligence* (IJCAI-73), pp. 235–45.

Hummel, R.A. and Landy, M. (1985) *A Statistical Viewpoint on the Theory of Evidence*. Technical Report No. 194, New York University, Courant Institute of Mathematical Sciences.

Hwang, S.S.V. (1984) *Evidence Accumulation for Spatial Reasoning in Aerial Image Understanding*. PhD Thesis, Department of Computer Science, University of Maryland.

Ikeuchi, K. (1987) Precompiling a geometrical model into an interpretation tree for object recognition in bin-picking tasks. In: *Proceedings of the DARPA*

Image Understanding Workshop, Los Angeles, CA, 1987, pp. 321–39.

Inmos (1985) *Occam Programming System: Editor Interface*, Inmos Ltd, Bristol, UK.

Itakura, F. (1975) Minimum prediction residual principle applied to speech recognition. *IEEE Transactions on Acoustics, Speech, and Signal Processing* **ASSP-23**, 67–72.

Jagannathan, V., Baum, L. and Dodhiawala, R. (1986) *Constraint Satisfaction in the Boeing Blackboard Framework*. Technical Report BCS-G2010-32, Boeing Computer Services.

Jagannathan, V., Baum, L. and Dodhiawala, R. (1987) ERASMUS: reconfigurable object-oriented blackboard system. In: *Proceedings of the Second International Symposium on Methodologies for Intelligent Systems*, Charlotte, NC.

Jardetzky, O (1984) A method for the definition of the solution structure of proteins from NMR and other physical measurements: the lac-repressor headpiece. In: *Progress in Bio-organic Chemistry*, Ovchinnikov, Y.A. (ed.), Elsevier, Amsterdam.

Jardetzky, O., Lane, A., Lefevre, J.F., Lichtarge, O., Hayes-Roth, B. and Buchanan, B. (1985) Determination of macromolecular structure and dynamics by NMR. In: *Proceedings of the NATO Advanced Study Institute: NMR in the Life Sciences*, 1985.

* Johnson, M.V. Jr and Hayes-Roth, B. (1986) *Integrating Diverse Reasoning Methods in the BB1 Blackboard Control Architecture*. Technical Report KSL-86-76, Stanford University.

Johnson, M.V. and Hayes-Roth, B. (1988) TRANALOGY: *Learning to Solve Problems by Analogy*. Technical Report KSL-88-01, Stanford University (forthcoming).

* Johnson, P.M., Corkill, D.D. and Gallagher, K.Q. (1987) Integrating BB1-style control into the generic blackboard system. Presented at *AAAI-87 Workshop on Blackboard Systems*, Seattle, WA, 1987.

* Jones, J., Millington, M. and Ross, P. (1986) *A Blackboard Shell in PROLOG*. Department of Artificial Intelligence Research Report 277, University of Edinburgh (reproduced in Chapter 28 of this book).

Kahn, R.E., Gronemeyer, S.A., Burchfiel, J. and Kunzelman, R.C. (1978) Advances in packet radio technology. *Proceedings of the IEEE* **66(11)**, 1468–96.

Kaptein, R., Zuiderweg, E.R.P., Scheek, R.M. and Boelens, R. (1985) A protein structure from nuclear magnetic resonance data: lac-repressor headpiece. *Journal of Molecular Biology* **182**, 179–82.

Klahr, D., Langley, P. and Neches, R. (1983) *Self-modifying Production System Models of Learning and Development*. Bradford Books, Cambridge, MA.

Klatt, D.H. (1977) Review of the ARPA speech understanding project. *Journal of the Acoustic Society of America* **62**, 1345–66.

Kohl, C.A. (1987) GOLDIE: *A Goal-Directed Intermediate-level Executive for Image Interpretation*. PhD Thesis, University of Massachusetts at Amherst.

Kohl, C.A., Hanson, A. and Riseman, E. (1987) A Goal-directed Intermediate-level Executive for Image Interpretation. In: *Proceedings of the Tenth International Joint Conference on Artificial Intelligence* (IJCAI-87), pp. 811–14.

Kornfeld, W.A. (1979) ETHER: a parallel problem solving system. In: *Proceedings of the Sixth International Joint Conference on Artificial Intelligence* (IJCAI-79), pp. 490–2.

Kuan, D., Brooks, R., Zamiska, C. and Das, M. (1984) Automatic path planning for a mobile robot using a mixed representation of free space. In: *Proceedings of the First Conference on Artificial Intelligence Applications*, Denver, CO, 1984, pp. 70–4.

Kunz, J.C., Fallat, R.J., McLung, D.H., Osborn, J.J., Votteri, B.A., Nii, H.P., Aikins, J.S., Fagan, L.M. and Feigenbaum, E.A. (1978) *A Physiological Rule Based System for Interpreting Pulmonary Function Test Results*. Technical Report HPP-78-20, Stanford University.

Lacoss, R. and Walton, R. (1978) Strawman design of a DSN to detect and track low flying aircraft. *Proceedings of the Distributed Sensor Nets Workshop*, Carnegie-Mellon University, 1978, pp. 41–52.

* Lakin, W.L. and Miles, J.A.H. (1987) An AI approach to data fusion and situation assessment. In: *Advances in Command, Control, and Communications Systems*, Harris, C.J. and White, I. (eds), Peter Peregrinus, pp. 339–77.

* Lane, D. (1986) *The Application of a Modular KBS Architecture to Object and Shadow Detection in Sector Scan Sonar Imagery*. Technical Report, Department of Electrical and Electronic Engineering, Heriot-Watt University.

Lea, W.A. (ed.) (1980) *Trends in Speech Recognition*. Prentice-Hall, Englewood Cliffs, NJ.

Lea, W.A. and Shoup, J.E. (1979) *Review of the ARPA SUR Project and Survey of Current Technology in Speech Understanding*. Final Report, Office of Naval Research Contract No. N00014-77-C-0570, Speech Communications Research Laboratory, Los Angeles, CA.

* Leao, L.V. and Talukdar, S.N. (1986) An environment for rule-based blackboards and distributed problem solving. *Artificial Intelligence in Engineering* **1(2)**, 70–9.

Lenat, D.B. (1975) Beings: knowledge as interacting experts. In: *Proceedings of the Fourth International Joint Conference on Artificial Intelligence* (IJCAI-75), pp. 126–33.

Lenat, D.B. (1983) EURISKO: A program that learns new heuristics and domain concepts. *Artificial Intelligence* **21**, 61–98.

Lesser, V.R. (1975) Parallel processing in speech understanding systems: a survey of design problems. In: Reddy (1975), pp. 481–99.

Lesser, V.R. (1980a) Cooperative distributed problem solving and organizational self-design. In: Reports on the MIT Distributed AI Workshop, *SIGART Newsletter* **73**, 46.

Lesser, V.R. (1980b) Models of problem solving. In: Reports on the MIT Distributed AI workshop, *SIGART Newsletter* **73**, 51.

* Lesser, V.R. and Corkill, D.D. (1978) *Cooperative Distributed Problem Solving: A New Approach for Structuring Distributed Systems*. Technical Report 78-7, Department of Computer and Information Science, University of Massachusetts at Amherst.

* Lesser, V.R. and Corkill, D.D. (1981) Functionally accurate cooperative distributed systems. *IEEE Transactions on Systems, Man, and Cybernetics* **SMC-11(1)**, 81–96.

* Lesser, V.R. and Corkill, D.D. (1983) The Distributed Vehicle Monitoring Testbed: a tool for investigating distributed problem solving networks. *AI Magazine* **4(3)**, 15–33 (reproduced in Chapter 18 of this book).
* Lesser, V.R. and Erman, L.D. (1977) A retrospective view of the Hearsay-II architecture. In: *Proceedings of the Fifth International Joint Conference on Artificial Intelligence* (IJCAI-77), pp. 790–800.
Lesser, V.R. and Erman, L.D. (1979) An experiment in distributed interpretation. In: *Proceedings of the First International Conference on Distributed Computing Systems*, Huntsville, AL, 1979, pp. 553–71.
* Lesser, V.R. and Erman, L.D. (1980) Distributed Interpretation: a model and experiment. *IEEE Transactions on Computers* **C-29(12)**, 1144–63.
* Lesser, V.R., Fennell, R.D., Erman, L.D. and Reddy, D.R. (1975) Organization of the Hearsay-II speech understanding system. *IEEE Transactions on Acoustics, Speech, and Signal Processing* **ASSP-23**, 11–24.
* Lesser, V.R., Hayes-Roth, F., Birnbaum, M. and Cronk, R. (1977) Selection of word islands in the Hearsay-II speech understanding system. In: *Proceedings of the IEEE International Conference on Acoustics, Speech, and Signal Processing*, Hartford, CT, pp. 791–4.
Lesser, V.R., Pavlin, J. and Reed, S. (1980) Quantifying and simulating the behavior of knowledge-based interpretation systems. In: *Proceedings of the First National Conference on Artificial Intelligence* (AAAI-80), pp. 111–15 (also Technical Report, Department of Computer and Information Sciences, University of Massachusetts at Amherst, 1980).
* Lesser, V.R., Corkill, D.D., Pavlin, J., Lefkowitz, L., Hudlicka, E., Brooks, R. and Reed, S. (1981) *A High-Level Simulation Testbed for Cooperative Distributed Problem-Solving*. COINS Technical Report 81-16, University of Massachusetts at Amherst.
Levine, M.D. (1978) A knowledge-based computer vision system. In: Hanson and Riseman (1978a), pp. 335–52.
Lindsay, R., Buchanan, B.G., Feigenbaum, E.A. and Lederberg, J. (1980) *Applications of Artificial Intelligence for Organic Chemistry: The DENDRAL Project*. McGraw-Hill, New York.
* Lippolt, B., Velthuijsen, H. and Vonk, J.C. (1986) *BLONDIE: a Blackboard Shell*. Memorandum 1404, Dr. Neher Laboratories, Netherlands PTT.
Lowerre, B.T. (1976) *The HARPY Speech Recognition System*. PhD thesis, Carnegie-Mellon University.
Lowerre, B.T. and Reddy, R. (1980) The HARPY speech understanding system. In: Lea (1980), Chapter 15.
Lowrance, J. (1980) *Dependence-Graph Models of Evidential Support*. PhD thesis, Department of Computer and Information Sciences, University of Massachusetts at Amherst.
* McArthur, D. (1987) *An Object-Centred Interpretation of the Blackboard Architecture for Knowledge-Based Programming*. PhD Thesis: Technical Report TR 42, Department of Computer Science, University of Stirling.
McCarthy, J. (1968) The advice taker. In: *Semantic Information Processing*, Minsky, M. (ed.), MIT Press, Cambridge, MA.
McClelland, J.L. and Rumelhart, D.E. (1981) An interactive activation model of context effects in letter perception: Part 1, an account of basic findings. *Psychological Review* **88**, 375–407.
* McCracken, D.L. (1979) Representation and efficiency in a production system for

speech understanding. In: *Proceedings of the Sixth International Joint Conference on Artificial Intelligence* (IJCAI-79), pp. 556–61.

McCune, B.P. and Drazovich, R.J. (1983) Radar with sight and knowledge. *Defense Electronics*, August 1983.

McDermott, D. (1982) A temporal logic for reasoning about processes and plans. *Cognitive Science* **6**.

McDermott, D. (1983) Contexts and data dependencies. *IEEE Transactions on Pattern Analysis and Machine Intelligence* **5**, 237–46.

McDermott, J. (1982) R1: a rule-based configurer of computer systems. *Artificial Intelligence* **19**, 39–88.

McDermott, J. and Newell, A. (1983) *Estimating the Computational Requirements for Future Expert Systems*. Technical Report, Computer Science Department, Carnegie-Mellon University.

McDermott, D. and Sussman, G.J. (1974) *The CONNIVER Reference Manual*. MIT Memo 259a, Massachusetts Institute of Technology.

McKeown, D.M. (1977) Word verification in the Hearsay-II speech understanding system. In: *Proceedings of the IEEE International Conference on Acoustics, Speech, and Signal Processing*. Hartford, CT, 1977, pp. 795–8.

McKeown, D.M., Harvey, W.A. Jr. and McDermott, J. (1985) Rule-based interpretation of aerial imagery. *IEEE Transactions on Pattern Analysis and Machine Intelligence* **PAMI-7(5)**, 570–85.

Mann, W.C. (1979) Design for dialogue comprehension. In: *Proceedings of the 17th Annual Meeting of the Association for Computational Linguistics*, La Jolla, CA, 1979.

Mann, W.C. and Moore, J.A. (1979) *Computer as Author – Results and Prospects*. Technical Report RR-79-82, USC/Information Sciences Institute.

MASCOT (1987) *The Official Handbook of MASCOT*. Defence Research Information Centre, Glasgow, UK.

Medress, M.F., Cooper, F.S., Forgie, J.W., Green, C.C., Klatt, D.H., O'Malley, M.H., Neuberg, E.P., Newell, A., Reddy, D.R., Ritea, B., Shoup- Hummel, J.E., Walker, D.E. and Woods, W.A. (1978) Speech understanding systems: report of a steering committee. *Artificial Intelligence* **9**, 307–16.

Middleton, S. (1984) Actor-based simulation of air defence scenarios in POPLOG. In: *Proceedings of the IKBS in Defence Seminar*, Malvern, UK, 1984.

Middleton, S. (1985) An air defence simulator in the object-oriented language BLOBS. In: *Proceedings of MILCOMP '85*, London.

Middleton, S. and Zanconato, R. (1985) BLOBS: an object-oriented language for simulation and reasoning. In: *Proceedings of AI in Simulation*, Ghent, 1985.

Minsky, M. (1975) A framework for representing knowledge. In: *The Psychology of Computer Vision*, Winston, P. (ed.), pp. 211–77, McGraw-Hill.

Minsky, M. (1979) The society theory of thinking. In: *Artificial Intelligence: An MIT Perspective*, Winston, P.H. and Brown, R.H. (eds), pp. 423–50, MIT Press, Cambridge, MA.

Mitchell, T., Utgoff, P.E., Nudel, B. and Banerji, R.B. (1981) Learning problem-solving heuristics through practice. In: *Proceedings of the Seventh International Joint Conference on Artificial Intelligence* (IJCAI-81), pp. 127–34.

* Mizoguchi, R. and Kakusho, O. (1979) Hierarchical production system. In:

Proceedings of the Sixth International Joint Conference on Artificial Intelligence (IJCAI-79), pp. 586–8.

Moser, L. and Myman, M. (1955) An asymptotic formula for the Bell numbers. *Transactions of the Royal Society of Canada* **XLIX(3)**, 49–54.

Mostow, D.J. (1977) A halting condition and related pruning heuristic for combinatorial search. In: CMU (1977), pp. 158–66.

Mostow, D.J. and Hayes-Roth, F. (1979) Operationalizing heuristics: some AI methods for assisted AI programming. In: *Proceedings of the Sixth International Joint Conference on Artificial Intelligence* (IJCAI-79), pp. 601–9.

* Murphy, A., Jagannathan, V. and Goodrum, S. (1987) A blackboard approach to process planning problems. In: *Proceedings of the Applications of Artificial Intelligence in Engineering Conference*, Boston, 1987.

Nagao, M. and Matsuyama, T. (1980) *A Structural Analysis of Complex Aerial Photographs*. Plenum Press, New York.

Nagao, M., Matsuyama, T. and Ikeda, Y. (1978) Region extraction and shape analysis of aerial photographs. In: *Proceedings of the International Joint Conference on Pattern Recognition* (IJCPR-78), pp. 620–28.

* Nagao, M., Matsuyama, T. and Mori, H. (1979) Structured analysis of complex aerial photographs. In: *Proceedings of the Sixth International Joint Conference on Artificial Intelligence* (IJCAI-79), pp. 610–16 (reproduced in Chapter 9 of this book).

Nevatia, R. and Price, K. (1978) Locating structures in aerial images. In: *Proceedings of the International Joint Conference on Pattern Recognition* (IJCPR-78), pp. 686–90.

Newell, A. (1962) Some problems of the basic organization in problem-solving programs. In: *Proceedings of the Second Conference on Self-Organizing Systems*, Yovits, M.C., Jacobi, G.T. and Goldstein, G.D. (eds), pp. 393–423, Spartan Books.

Newell, A. (1969) Heuristic programming: ill-structured problems. In: *Progress in Operations Research*, Aronsky, J. (ed.), pp. 360–414, John Wiley, New York.

Newell, A. (1975) A tutorial on speech understanding systems. In: *Speech recognition: Invited papers of the IEEE symposium*, Reddy, D.R. (ed.), Academic Press, New York, pp. 3–54.

Newell, A. (1980) HARPY, production systems and human cognition. In: *Perception and Production of Fluent Speech*, Cole, R. (ed.), L. Erlbaum, Hillsdale, NJ, Chapter 11.

Newell, A. and Simon, H.A. (1972) *Human Problem Solving*, Prentice-Hall, Englewood Cliffs, NJ.

Newell, A. and Simon, H.A. (1976) Computer science as empirical enquiry: symbols and search. *Communications of the ACM* **19**, 113–26.

Newell, A., Barnett, J., Forgie, J., Green, C., Klatt, D., Licklider, J.C.R., Munson, J., Reddy, R. and Woods, W. (1973) *Speech Understanding Systems: Final Report of a Study Group*. North-Holland (originally appeared in 1971).

Newell, A., McDermott, J. and Forgy, C.L. (1977) *Artificial Intelligence: A Self-paced Introductory Course*. Computer Science Department, Carnegie-Mellon University.

* Nii, H.P. (1980) *An Introduction to Knowledge Engineering, Blackboard Model, and AGE*. Technical Report HPP 80–29, Stanford University.
* Nii, H.P. (1986a) *CAGE and POLIGON: Two Frameworks for Blackboard-Based Concurrent Problem Solving*. Technical Report KSL-86-41, Stanford University.
* Nii, H.P. (1986b) Blackboard systems (Part 1), *AI Magazine* **7(2)**, 38–53.
* Nii, H.P. (1986c) Blackboard systems (Part 2). *AI Magazine* **7(3)**, 82–106.
* Nii, H.P. and Feigenbaum, E.A. (1978) Rule-based understanding of signals. In: Waterman and Hayes-Roth (1978).
* Nii, H.P. and Aiello, N. (1978) *AGE (Attempt to GEneralize): Profile of the AGE-0 System*. Technical Report HPP-78-5, Stanford University.
* Nii, H.P. and Aiello, N. (1979) AGE (Attempt to GEneralize): a knowledge-based program for building knowledge-based programs. In: *Proceedings of the Sixth International Joint Conference on Artificial Intelligence* (IJCAI-79), pp. 645–55.
* Nii, H.P., Feigenbaum, E.A., Anton, J.J. and Rockmore, A.J. (1982) Signal-to-symbol transformation: HASP/SIAP case study. *AI Magazine* 3, 23–35 (reproduced in Chapter 6 of this book).
Nilsson, N.J. (1971) *Problem-Solving Methods in Artificial Intelligence*. McGraw-Hill, New York.
Nilsson, N.J. (1980) Two heads are better than one. *SIGART Newsletter* 73, 43.
Norman, D.A. (1980) Copycat science, or does the mind really work by table look-up? In: *Perception and Production of Fluent Speech*, Cole, R. (ed.), L. Erlbaum, Hillsdale, NJ, Chapter 12.
Ohta, Y. (1980) *A Region-Oriented Image-Analysis System by Computer*. PhD Thesis, Department of Information Science, Kyoto University.
Pardee, W. and Hayes-Roth, B. (1987) *Intelligent Real Time Control of Material Processing*. Techical Report No. 1, Rockwell International Science Center, Palo Alto Laboratory, CA.
Parodi, A. (1984) A route planning system for an autonomous vehicle. In: *Proceedings of the First Conference on Artificial Intelligence Applications*, Denver, CO, 1984, pp. 51–6.
Patil, R.S., Szulovitz, P. and Schwartz, W.B. (1981) Causal understanding of patient illness in medical diagnosis. In: *Proceedings of the Seventh International Joint Conference on Artificial Intelligence* (IJCAI-81), pp. 893–9.
Pattison, H.E., Corkill, D.D. and Lesser, V.R. (1987) Instantiating Descriptions of Organizational Structures. In: *Distributed Artificial Intelligence*, Huhns, M.N. (ed), Pitman.
Pavlin, J. (1983) Predicting the Performance of Distributed Knowledge-Based Systems: A Modeling Approach. In: *Proceedings of the Third National Conference on Artificial Intelligence* (AAAI-83), pp. 314–19.
Paxton, W.H. (1978) The executive system. In: *Understanding Spoken Language*, Walker, D.E. (ed.), Elsevier, Amsterdam.
Pearson, G. (1985) Mission Planning within the Framework of the Blackboard Model. In: *Proceedings of IEEE Expert Systems in Government Symposium*, pp. 50–55 (reproduced in Chapter 21 of this book).
Pentland, A.P. and Fischler, M.A. (1983) A more rational view of logic. *AI Magazine* **4(4)**, 15–18.

Pohl, I. (1970) First results on the effects of error in heuristic search. In: *Machine Intelligence 5*, Meltzer, B. and Michie, D. (eds), Edinburgh University Press.

Pohl, I. (1977) Practical and theoretical considerations in heuristic search algorithms. In: *Machine Intelligence 8*, Elcock, E. and Michie, D. (eds), Ellis Horwood, Chichester, England.

* Prager, J., Nagin, P., Kohler, R., Hanson, A. and Riseman, E. (1977) Segmentation processes in the VISIONS system. In: *Proceedings of the Fifth International Joint Conference on Artificial Intelligence* (IJCAI-77), 642–3.

Quam, L.J. (1978) Road tracking and anomaly detection in aerial imagery. In: *Proceedings of the Workshop on Image Understanding*, May 1978, pp. 51–5.

Ramsay, A. (1984) Type-checking in an untyped language. *International Journal of Man–Machine Studies* **20**, 157–67.

Reddy, D.R. (ed.) (1975) *Speech Recognition: Invited Papers Presented at the 1974 IEEE Symposium*. Academic Press, New York.

Reddy, D.R. (1976) Speech recognition by machine: a review. *Proceedings of the IEEE* **64**, 501–31.

Reddy, R. and Newell, A. (1977) Multiplicative speedup of systems. In: *Perspectives on Computer Science*, Jones, A. (ed.), Academic Press, New York.

Reddy, D.R., Erman, L.D. and Neely, R.B. (1973a) A model and a system for machine recognition of speech. *IEEE Transactions on Audio and Electro-acoustics* **AU-21**, 229–38.

Reddy, D.R., Erman, L.D., Fennel, R.D. and Neely, R.B. (1973b) The Hearsay speech understanding system: an example of the recognition process. In: *Proceedings of the Third International Joint Conference on Artificial Intelligence* (IJCAI-73), pp. 185–93.

Reiser, J.F. (1976) *SAIL*. Stanford Artificial Intelligence Laboratory Memo AIM-289, Stanford University.

Reynolds, G. and Beveridge, J.R. (1987) Searching for geometric structure in images of natural scenes. In: *Proceedings of the DARPA Image Understanding Workshop*, Los Angeles, CA, 1987, pp. 257–71.

* Rice, J.P. (1984) MXA – a framework for the development of blackboard systems. In: *Proceedings of the Third IKBS in Defence Seminar*, Malvern, UK, 1984.

* Rice, J. (1986) *POLIGON: A System for Parallel Problem Solving*. Technical Report KSL-86-19, Stanford University.

Riseman, E.M. and Hanson, A.R. (1984) A methodology for the development of knowledge-based vision systems. In: *Proceedings of the IEEE Workshop on Principles of Knowledge-Based Systems*, Denver, CO, 1984.

Roberts, G.C.K. and Jardetzky, O. (1970) Nuclear magnetic resonance spectroscopy of amino acids, peptides and proteins. *Advances in Protein Chemistry* **24**, 447–545, Academic Press, New York.

Rosenbloom, P.S. and Newell, A. (1982) Learning by chunking: summary of a task and a model. In: *Proceedings of the Second National Conference on Artificial Intelligence* (AAAI-82), pp. 255–8.

Rosenfeld, A., Hummel, R.A. and Zucker, S.W. (1976) Scene labeling by relaxation operations. *IEEE Transactions on Systems, Man, and Cybernetics* **SMC-6**, 420–33.

Rosenfeld, A. (1986) 'Expert' vision systems: some issues. *Graphics and Image Processing* **34**, 99–102.

Ross, P., Jones, J. and Millington, M. (1985) *User Modelling in Command-Driven Systems*. Research Report 264, Department of Artificial Intelligence, University of Edinburgh.

Rubin, S. (1978) *The ARGOS Image Understanding System*. PhD Thesis, Computer Science Department, Carnegie-Mellon University.

Rubin, S.M. and Reddy, D.R. (1977) The LOCUS model of search and its use in image interpretation. In: *Proceedings of the Fifth International Joint Conference on Artificial Intelligence* (IJCAI-77).

Rulifson, J.F., Dersken, J.A. and Waldinger, R.J. (1972a) *QA4: A Procedural Calculus for Intuitive Reasoning*. Technical Note 73, AI Center, SRI, Menlo Park, CA.

Rulifson, J.F., Waldinger, R.J. and Dersken, J.A. (1972b) A language for writing problem-solving programs. *IFIP* **71**, 201–5, North-Holland, Amsterdam.

Rumelhart, D.E. (1976) *Toward an Interactive Model of Reading*. Technical Report 56, Center for Human Information Processing, University of California at San Diego.

Rumelhart, D.E. and McClelland, J.L. (1982) An interactive model of context effects in letter perception: Part 2, the enhancement effect and some tests and extensions to the model. *Psychological Review* **89**, 60–94.

* Rychener, M.D. and Subrahmanian, E. (1985) A rule-based blackboard system. *SIGART Newsletter* **92**: 101–2.

Sacerdoti, E.E. (1974) Planning in a hierarchy of abstraction spaces. *Artificial Intelligence* **5**, 115–35.

Sacerdoti, E.D. (1975a) The non-linear nature of plans. In: *Proceedings of the Fourth International Joint Conference on Artificial Intelligence* (IJCAI-75), pp. 206–14.

Sacerdoti, E.D. (1975b) *A Structure for Plans and Behavior*. Technical Report 109, SRI AI Center.

Schoen, E. (1986) *The CAOS System*. Technical Report KSL-86-22, Stanford University.

* Schulman, R. and Hayes-Roth, B. (1987) *ExAct: A Module for Explaining Actions*. Technical Report KSL-87-8, Stanford University.

Selfridge, O. (1959) Pandemonium: a paradigm for learning. In: *Proceedings of Symposium on the Mechanisation of Thought Processes*, pp. 511–29, HMSO, London.

Shafer, S.A., Stentz, A. and Thorpe, C.E. (1986) An architecture for sensor fusion in a mobile robot. In: *Proceedings of the IEEE International Conference on Robotics and Automation*, San Francisco, CA, pp. 2002–11.

Shepherd, A.M., White, I. and Miles, J.A.H. (1982) *RATES: Radar Automatic Track Extraction System – A Functional Description*. ARE Memo XCC82003, Admiralty Research Establishment, Portsmouth, UK.

Shockey, L. and Adam, C. (1976) The phonetic component of the Hearsay-II speech understanding system. In: CMU (1976).

Shortliffe, E.H. (1976) *Computer-Based Medical Consultation: MYCIN*. American Elsevier, New York.

Shortliffe, E.H. and Buchanan, B.G. (1975) A model of inexact reasoning in medicine. *Mathematical Biosciences* **23**, 351–79 (an edited version of this paper appears in *Rule Based Expert Systems*, Buchanan, B. and Shortliffe, E. (eds), Addison-Wesley, Reading, MA, 1984).

Simon, H.A. (1969) *The Sciences of the Artificial*. MIT Press, Cambridge, MA.

Simon, H.A. (1977) Scientific discovery and the psychology of problem solving. In: *Models of Discovery*, Reidel, Boston, MA.

Skeen, D. (1981) Nonblocking commit protocols. In: *Proceedings of ACM-SIGMOD International Conference on Management of Data*, pp. 133–42.

Smith, A.R. (1976) Word hypothesization in the Hearsay-II speech system. In: *Proceedings of the IEEE International Conference on Acoustics, Speech, and Signal Processing*, Philadelphia, PA, 1976. pp. 549–52.

Smith, A.R. (1977) *Word Hypothesization for Large-Vocabulary Speech Understanding Systems*. PhD thesis, Computer Science Department, Carnegie-Mellon University.

Smith, R.G. (1978) *A Framework for Problem Solving in a Distributed Processing Environment*. PhD thesis, Technical Report STAN-CS-78-800, Stanford University.

* Smith, R.G. (1979) A framework for distributed problem solving. In: *Proceedings of the Sixth International Joint Conference on Artificial Intelligence* (IJCAI-79), pp. 836–41.

Smith, B.J. (1981) Architecture and applications of the HEP multiprocessor computer system. In: *Proceedings of the International Society for Optical Engineering*, San Diego, CA.

Smith, R.G. and Davis, R. (1981) Frameworks for cooperation in distributed problem solving. *IEEE Transactions on Systems, Man, and Cybernetics* **SMC-11(1)**, 61–70.

Smith, A.R. and Erman, L.D. (1981) NOAH: A bottom-up word hypothesizer for large-vocabulary speech-understanding systems. *IEEE Transactions on Pattern Analysis and Machine Intelligence* **3(1)**, 41–51.

Smith, R. and Friedland, P. (1980) *UNIT Package User Guide*. Technical Report HPP-80-28, Computer Science Department, Stanford University.

Smith, S.F., Fox, M.S. and Ow, P.S. (1986) Constructing and maintaining detailed production plans: Investigations into the development of knowledge-based factory scheduling systems. *AI Magazine* **7(4)**, 45–61.

Sohndi, M.M. and Levinson, S.E. (1978) Computing relative redundancy to measure grammatical constraint in speech recognition tasks. In: *Proceedings of the IEEE International Conference on Acoustics, Speech, and Signal Processing*, Tulsa, OK, 1978.

Soloway, E.M. and Riseman, E.M. (1977a) Levels of pattern description in learning. In: *Proceedings of the Fifth International Joint Conference on Artificial Intelligence* (IJCAI-77), pp. 801–11.

Soloway, E.M. and Riseman, E.M. (1977b) Knowledge-directed learning. In: *Proceedings of the Workshop on Pattern-Directed Inference Systems*, Hawaii, 1977, pp. 49–55 (see special edition of *SIGART Newsletter*, June 1977).

Soloway, E., Bachant, J. and Jensen, K. (1987) Assessing the maintainability of XCON-in-RIME: coping with the problems of a *very* large rule base. In: *Proceedings of the Sixth National Conference on Artificial Intelligence* (AAAI-87), pp. 824–9.

Sowa, J.F. (1984) *Conceptual Structures: Information Processing in Mind and Machine*. Addison-Wesley, Reading, MA.

Spain, D.S. (1983) Application of artificial intelligence to tactical situation assessment. In: *Proceedings of the 16th EASCON*, 1983, pp. 457–64.

Sridharan, N.S. (1978) *AIMDS User Manual*. Technical Report CBM-TR-89, Department of Computer Science, Rutgers University.

* Sriram, D. (1986) DESTINY: A model for integrated structural design. *Artificial Intelligence in Engineering* **1(2)**, 109–16.

* Stammers, R.A. (1983) *MXA Language Manual*. SPL International (now part of Systems Designers plc, Camberley, England).

* Stammers, R.A. (1985) The MXA shell. In: *Research and Development in Expert Systems*, Bramer, M. (ed.), Cambridge University Press.

Stefik, M. (1978) *An Examination of a Frame-Structure Representation System*. Technical Report HPP-78-13, Stanford University.

Stefik, M. (1980) *Planning with Constraints*. PhD thesis, Computer Science Department, Stanford University.

Stentz, A. and Shafer, S. (1985) *Module Programmer's Guide to the Local Map Builder for ALVAN*. Technical Report, Computer Science Department, Carnegie-Mellon University.

Stolfo, S. and Shaw, D. (1982) DADO: a tree-structured machine architecture for production systems. In: *Proceedings of the Second National Conference on Artificial Intelligence* (AAAI-82), pp. 242–6.

Symbolics (1984) *Symbolics Reference Manual*. Symbolics Inc, Cambridge, MA.

Tanenbaum, A.S. (1981) *Computer Networks*. Prentice-Hall, Englewood Cliffs, NJ.

Taylor, S., Maio, C., Stolfo, S. and Shaw, D. (1983) *PROLOG on the DADO Machine: A Parallel System for High-Speed Logic Programming*. Technical Report, Computer Science Department, Columbia University, New York.

Teitelman, W. (1978) *INTERLISP Reference Manual*. Xerox Palo Alto Research Center, Computer Science Laboratory.

* Terry, A. (1983) *The CRYSALIS Project: Hierarchical Control of Production Systems*. Technical Report HPP-83-19, Stanford University.

* Terry, A. and Engelmore, R.S. (1978) *The Design and Evaluation of the First CRYSALIS System*. Technical Report HPP 78-12, Stanford University.

Tommelein, I.D., Johnson, M.V., Hayes-Roth, B. and Levitt, R.E. (1987a) SIGHTPLAN – a blackboard expert system for the layout of temporary facilities on a construction site. In: *Proceedings of the IFIP WG5.2 Working Conference on Expert Systems in Computer-Aided Design*, Sydney, Australia, 1987.

Tommelein, I.D., Levitt, R.E. and Hayes-Roth, B. (1987b) Using expert systems for the layout of temporary facilities on construction sites. In: *Proceedings of CIB (International Council of Building) W-65 Symposium on Organisation and Management of Construction*, London, 1987.

Tsotsos, J.K. (1985) Knowledge organization and its role in representation and interpretation for time-varying data: the ALVEN system. *Computational Intelligence* **1**, 16–32.

Tucker, L.W. (1984) *Computer Vision Using Quadtree Refinement*. PhD Thesis, Polytechnic Institute of New York.

* Tynor, S.D., Roth, S.P. and Gilmore, J.F. (1987) GEST: the anatomy of a blackboard expert system tool. In: *Proceedings of the Seventh International Workshop on Expert Systems and their Applications* (AVIGNON-87), pp. 794–803.

van Melle, W. (1979) A domain-independent production-rule system for consultation programs. In: *Proceedings of the Sixth International Joint Conference on Artificial Intelligence* (IJCAI-79), pp. 942–7.

* Venkatasubramanian, V. and Chen, C.-F. (1986) A blackboard architecture for plastics design. *Artificial Intelligence in Engineering* **1(2)**, 117–22.

* Wagner, G. and Wuthrich, K. (1979) Truncated driven Nuclear Overhauser effect (TOE): a new technique for studies of selective H–H Overhauser effects in the presence of spin diffusion. *Journal of Magnetic Resonance* **33**, 675–9.

Walker, D.E., Paxton, W.H., Grosz, B.J., Hendrix, G.G., Robinson, A.E., Robinson, J.J. and Slocum, J. (1977) Procedures for integrating knowledge in a speech understanding system. In: *Proceedings of the Fifth International Joint Conference on Artificial Intelligence* (IJCAI-77), pp. 36–42.

Walker, D.E. (ed.) (1978) *Understanding Spoken Language*. Elsevier, New York.

Walker, D.E. (1980) SRI research on speech understanding. In: Lea (1980), Chapter 14.

Waterman, D.A. and Hayes-Roth, F. (eds) (1978) *Pattern-Directed Inference Systems*. Academic Press, New York.

Weems, C.C., Levitan, S.P., Hanson, A.R., Riseman, E.M., Nash, J.G. and Shu, D.B. (1987) *The Image Understanding Architecture*. COINS Technical Report 87-76, University of Massachusetts at Amherst.

Weinreb, D. and Moon, D. (1981) *LISP Machine Manual*. Symbolics Inc, Cambridge, MA.

Weiss, S.M. and Kulikowski, C.A. (1979) EXPERT: A system for developing consultation models. *Proceedings of the Sixth International Joint Conference on Artificial Intelligence* (IJCAI-79), pp. 942–7.

Weiss, R. and Boldt, M. .(1986) Geometric grouping applied to straight lines. In: *Proceedings of the IEEE Computer Society Conference on Computer Vision and Pattern Recognition*, Miami, FL, 1986.

Wesley, L. and Hanson, A.R. (1982) The use of an evidential-based model for representing knowledge and reasoning about images in the VISION system. In: *Proceedings of the Workshop on Computer Vision*, Rindge, NH.

Wesley, L., Lowrance, J. and Garvey, T. (1984) *Reasoning about Control: An Evidential Approach*. SRI Technical Note No. 324, Artificial Intelligence Center, SRI International, Menlo Park, CA.

Weymouth, T.E. (1986) *Using Object Descriptions in a Schema Network for Machine Vision*. PhD Thesis, Department of Computer and Information Science, University of Massachusetts.

* Williams, M.A. (1984a) TRICERO *Design Description*. Technical Report ESL-NS539, ESL Inc, Sunnyvale, CA.

* Williams, M.A. (1984b) *Hierarchical Multiexpert Signal Understanding*. Technical Report ESL-IR201, ESL Inc, Sunnyvale, CA (reproduced in Chapter 19 of this book).

* Williams, T., Lowrance, J., Hanson, A. and Riseman, E. (1977) Model-building in the VISIONS system. In: *Proceedings of the Fifth International Joint Conference on Artificial Intelligence* (IJCAI-77), pp. 644–5 (extended version in COINS Technical Report 77-1, University of Massachusetts, Amherst, 1977).

Wolf, J.J and Woods, W.A. (1980) The HWIM speech understanding system. In: Lea (1980).

Woods, W.A. (1970) Transition network grammars for natural language analysis.

Communications of the ACM **13(10)**, 591–606.

Woods, W.A. (1975) What's in a link? Foundations for semantic networks. In: *Representation and Understanding Studies in Cognitive Science*, Bobrow, D.G. and Collins, A.M. (eds), Academic Press, New York, pp. 35–82.

Woods, W.A. (1977) Shortfall and density scoring strategies for speech understanding control. In: *Proceedings of the Fifth International Joint Conference on Artificial Intelligence* (IJCAI-77), pp. 13–26.

Woods, W.A. and Makhoul, J. (1973) Mechanical inference problems in continuous speech understanding. In: *Proceedings of the Third International Joint Conference on Artificial Intelligence* (IJCAI-73), pp. 73–91.

Woods, W.A., Bates, M., Brown, G., Bruce, B., Cook, C., Klovstad, J., Makhoul, J., Nash-Webber, B., Schwartz, R., Wolf, J. and Zue, V. (1976) *Speech Understanding Systems: Final Technical Progress Report*. Technical Report 3438, Bolt, Beranek and Newman, Cambridge, MA.

Wuthrich, K. (1976) *NMR in Biological Research: Peptides and Proteins*. North Holland, Amsterdam.

Zadeh, L.A. (1983) The role of fuzzy logic in the management of uncertainty in expert systems. *Fuzzy Sets and Systems* **11**, 199–227.

Zimmerman, H. (1982) A standard layer model. In: *Computer Network Architecture and Protocols*, Green, P.E. (ed.), Plenum Press, New York.

Zisman, M.D. (1978) Use of production systems for modeling asynchronous, concurrent processes. In: Waterman and Hayes-Roth (1978), pp. 53–68.

Zuiderweg, E.R.P., Kaptein, R. and Wuthrich, K. (1983) Secondary structure of the lac-repressor DNA-binding domain by two-dimensional H nuclear magnetic resonance in solution. *Proceedings of the National Academy of Sciences* **80**, 5837–41.

Index

(In the interests of clarity, certain common terms such as 'blackboard' and 'hypothesis' have been omitted from this index.)